A History of the American Medium Tank

by

R. P. Hunnicutt

Line Drawings
by
D. P. Dyer

Color Drawing
by
Uwe Feist

Foreword
by
General I. D. White, USA-Retired

Published by Echo Point Books & Media
Brattleboro, Vermont
www.EchoPointBooks.com

ISBN: 978-1-62654-861-9

Cover image by Uwe Feist

Cover design by Adrienne Núñez,
Echo Point Books & Media

Editorial and proofreading assistance by Christine Schultz,
Echo Point Books & Media

Printed and bound in the United States of America

CONTENTS

ACKNOWLEDGEMENTS

A book such as this draws material from so many sources that it is virtually impossible to properly identify and thank them all. However, some contributions were so outstanding that they are easily remembered. My friend, Colonel Robert J. Icks, not only supplied many of the photographs, he also encouraged me to start the project in the first place. I would also like to thank General I.D. White who kindly agreed to write the Foreword for this book. As a user of the Sherman in two wars, no officer is better qualified to judge its virtues as well as its weaknesses.

Much of the technical research was performed, necessarily, at various military installations and I am greatly indebted to their personnel. At the U.S. Army Tank Automotive Command in Detroit, Leon Burg provided invaluable help in the Technical Library. In fact, without his work several sections would be missing from the book. Joseph Avesian, Charles Beabes, Carl Rasmussen, Daniel Smith, and Joseph Williams also located valuable photographs and information. John Campbell, Philip Cavanaugh, and John Purdy of the Patton Museum at Fort Knox were of great help in answering questions on extremely short notice. They also found rare photographs and permitted access to the Museum's vehicle collection. Many test reports on the early Shermans would have been unobtainable without the efforts of Mrs. Forst and Mrs. Patchell in the Technical Library at Aberdeen Proving Ground. Additional information also was obtained from Daniel O'Brien at the Ordnance Museum. Colonel Tasman Graham, Miss Zenich, and Mrs. Braund of the Corps of Engineers were extremely helpful in locating photographs and data regarding equipment developed by the Corps.

Some of the more interesting photographs came from the collection of my old friend the late Colonel G.B. Jarrett. Many of these were taken by the Colonel himself during his Middle East service in 1942. Most of the photographs showing the American Shermans in action were located by Mrs. Destafano of the U.S. Army Audio-Visual Activity or George Craig of the U.S. Marine Corps Museum. Many views of the Sherman in production at the Detroit Tank Arsenal came from Chrysler Corporation through the efforts of Robert Heath. Thomas Tracy and Gloria Wheeler of the National Archives sorted out innumerable boxes of documents for my inspection.

A particularly difficult problem was to obtain information on the British modifications of the Sherman which almost equaled our own in number. As during some of my earlier research, Colonel Peter Hordern made available all of the resources of the Royal Armoured Corps Tank Museum and provided answers to some very difficult questions. Many rare photographs came from the superb collection of Peter Chamberlain. On the Canadian vehicles, both photographs and data were obtained from the Public Archives of Canada through the efforts of Joe Sauve. George Bradford also tracked down sources for many obscure items. The Australian War Memorial provided photographs of M3s and M4s which served in Australia and Burma. Much information on the Israeli Shermans came from Kenneth Brower and Mordechai Dessaur.

A few incidents in the Sherman's battle record were quoted from the writings of those who fought and the histories of the units engaged. I greatly appreciate the permission of the following to quote from the books and documents listed below.

Colonel Henry Gardiner from his unpublished manuscript, "Tank Commander."

Captain Kenneth Koyen from his history "The Fourth Armored Division from the Beach to Bavaria", published 1946.

Brigadier General Paul McDonald Robinett from his book "Armor Command", published 1948.

Colonel Martin Philipsborn from "Paths of Armor" the history of the Fifth Armored Division, published by Albert Love Enterprises, 1950.

Colonel George Kenneth Rubel from "Daredevil Tankers, the story of the 740th Tank Battalion", published 19 September 1945.

Phil Dyer made a detailed study of the vehicles shown in his drawings. Such work not only aided in the preparation of the drawings, it also clarified several points for me as well. Uwe Feist did his usual excellent job on the cover drawing and Don White deserves special thanks for his help with the artwork.

Others who provided help to the research project included William Auerbach, James Berry, Gary Binder, Norman Cary, Howard Christenson, Major Fred Crismon, Colonel James Daulton, Lieutenant General Welborn G. Dolvin, Peter Frandsen, Lieutenant Colonel Elmer Gray, William Hamberg, Donald Hayes, Major General Louis Heath, George Hofmann, Brigadier General Joseph Holly, Ian Hogg, Sam Hunt, Lieutenant Colonel James Loop, George Luckett, Lonsdale MacFarland, Dale McCormick, Gilbert McMurtrie, Stanley Poole, Walter Spielberger, John Storer, William Tauss, Paul van Thielen, Captain Geoffrey Tillotson, Lieutenant Colonel George Witheridge, Clifford Wrigley, and Charles Yust. For all these contributions, I am deeply grateful.

FOREWORD
by
General I.D. White, U.S. Army (Ret)

When I learned that Richard Hunnicutt was writing a history of the development of the U.S. medium tank I was delighted. His magnificent work on the history and development of the M26 Pershing Tank published in 1971 was an outstanding achievement and I was convinced that the long overdue account of the evolution of the Sherman would likewise be a thorough and interesting documentation. The result, as shown in this book, more than justifies my expectations.

Since one of the battalions of my 67th Armored Regiment may have been the first U.S. unit to employ the Sherman in combat in North Africa, I have more than a passing interest in this versatile, ubiquitous creation with which I saw service in two wars.

Mr. Hunnicutt's career is not that of a professional writer although his work would so indicate. He is a highly qualified and successful engineer whose technical expertise and analytic mind has produced two of the most thorough and interesting accounts of armor development in this country. His engineer skills have insured technical accuracy, but there is just enough about the actual employment of the various versions as they evolved to make the book as interesting to the layman as to the serious armor buff.

Probably one of the most interesting features in the evolution of the Sherman is the manner in which basic elements such as hull, suspension system and turret were adapted to many other uses. Various combinations were used for the mounting of different types of tank guns, howitzers, mortars, and for recovery vehicles, engineer vehicles, flame throwers, personnel carriers and even ambulances. This versatility was certainly a welcome asset in the eyes of the logistic and maintenance people. The commonality of major parts and assemblies is not always so successfully attained in the varied weapon systems and vehicles with which armored fighting units are equipped. This greatly simplified the problems usually associated with the issuing of new items to the user. When a new medium tank was received during training or combat operations, it was just an improved version of one with which the troops were already familiar.

To those of us who pitted our out-gunned Sherman against German armor, the book does not entirely indicate the seeming insensitivity to the realities of the battlefield on the part of those responsible for the design and procuring of our fighting vehicles. Some of us, even at the time, were aware of the bureaucratic and often ignorant wrangling and delays that occurred before our medium tanks were fitted with a tank gun that gave us a reasonable degree of equality against our enemy. The author indicates that the British were far more aware of the problem than our own people.

Why did it take our Ordnance Department until 1942 to realize that the low velocity 75mm tank cannon was not going to be adequate in the face of the known German development of much greater armor protection on their tanks? Perhaps it was because of the conflict between the Armored Force and Army Ground Forces regarding the role of tanks. The Armored Force considered the tank to be the best defense against enemy tanks. AGF on the other hand, firmly believed throughout the war, that the role of the tank was to support the infantry and the tank threat should be countered by fast, mobile tank destroyer units and the artillery. It was not until after World War II that the Armored Force doctrine became official policy in the U.S. Army.

In his conclusion, the author states that the need for a powerful, high velocity gun was not realized until it was too late to provide one. This is probably true as far as the policy making echelons were concerned. However, from my own experience in the early days of the Armored Force and later as a battalion, regimental, combat command and division commander in the 2d U.S. Armored Division in WWII, I know that the junior officers—those who actually used the medium tanks—constantly asked for a better gun and ammunition.

I believe that far too many decisions were made in the development of the medium tank without due consideration for the comments and advice of those who had the invaluable experience of the user. Mr. Hunnicutt gives some indication of this in his great book, but it is probably just as well that he did not clutter history with too much controversy. Nevertheless, there is enough material on the subject to fill another book and perhaps he will undertake this later as another interesting project.

INTRODUCTION

Although the end product of the U.S. prewar development program, the Sherman was in many ways an Anglo-American tank. Not only did it incorporate the results of the early British battle experience, it also served as the basic chassis for numerous exclusively British modifications. These ranged from simple stowage changes to the installation of new more powerful armament. Many of these tanks were extensively rebuilt for highly specialized tasks. Close armored support during amphibious landings was achieved by modifying the Sherman so that it could swim in under its own power with the assault troops. A new concept of armored night warfare appeared with the introduction of the searchlight or CDL tanks. These were only a few of the British developments which were applied to the M4 or to its immediate predecessor the M3. Many of these innovations were also adopted by the U.S. Army.

Produced from February 1942 until the latter half of 1945, the Sherman experienced a myriad of changes, but the same basic design was retained. The need for ever increasing production under the pressure of war required that substitutes be found for many vital components. This was particularly true for the power plant with no less than five being standardized and many others were tested experimentally. To meet the changing battle conditions, new armament and better protection were incorporated into the later production tanks. These modifications increased the weight requiring the development of new suspensions and tracks to maintain the vehicle's mobility. Thus the Sherman of 1945 was vastly improved over the tank which entered production in 1942. The ease with which the design absorbed the changes necessary to meet the ever increasing demands from the front was one of its most valuable features.

In addition to the fighting tanks, the Sherman chassis provided the basic motor carriage for many thousands of tank destroyers and other self-propelled artillery. The use of a common chassis greatly simplified maintenance procedures and the supply of spare parts.

The objective of this volume has been to describe the technical evolution which led up to the Sherman and its further development during production. Because of space limitations, only a brief outline could be given of the tanks operational history. Proper treatment of such a subject would require a separate volume many time this size. The few incidents described are intended to show the tank's introduction into action and to illustrate the wide range of combat conditions under which it was required to perform. The detailed coverage of its battle history more properly belongs in the unit histories which tell the stories of the men who so gallantly took it into action, frequently against a much more powerfully armed enemy.

The description of operations may result in some confusion from the designations of the organizations involved. The U.S. armored divisions and tank battalions underwent several changes during the war. On 15 September 1943, the divisions were reduced in size with the two armored regiments being replaced by three tank battalions. The tank battalions were also reorganized dropping the light and medium designations. The new battalions were all alike consisting of one light and three medium tank companies. The 2nd and 3rd Armored Divisions retained the larger regimental structure throughout the war and the 1st Armored Division in Italy was not reorganized until the Summer of 1944. The remaining armored divisions went into battle with the new "light" organization. Although the latter were less cumbersome to handle, they did not have the staying power of the older "heavy" divisions.

In the British Royal Armoured Corps, the regiment was quite different from that in the older U.S. armored division. It was roughly equivalent in size and organization to the U.S. tank battalion. Since each unit is referred to by its official designation in the text, consideration must be given to these differences.

The task of collecting information for this book has extended over a period of many years. Perhaps the most difficult decision in a project such as this is to determine when the research is sufficiently complete for the book to be written. The key word here is sufficiently, for it is obvious that all of the questions which arise cannot be answered and that if the book is to be published, many gaps must remain in the story. Past experience indicates that new information frequently appears soon after publication and it is hoped that will be the case for this book. The author will greatly appreciate any new material or corrections to the present text in order to complete the Sherman story.

R.P. Hunnicutt
Belmont, California
August 1977

PART I

THE SEARCH FOR A MEDIUM TANK

The legacy of World War I. From left to right, the Ford 3-ton, the 6-ton M1917, and the 40-ton Mark VIII.

THE BIRTH OF THE MEDIUM TANK

In the decade following World War I, tank units of the U.S. Army were equipped with the leftovers from that conflict. These were tanks purchased from the Allied nations during the war or manufactured in the United States too late to see action. The latter equipment consisted mainly of two types. The first, and far more numerous, was the 6-ton light tank based on the French Renault FT 17. Nine hundred and fiftytwo of these vehicles were completed in the early postwar period. In addition, fifteen of the small 3-ton Ford tanks were constructed. The second major type was the 40-ton Mark VIII heavy tank designed in cooperation with the British and based on their experience in designing large trench crossing tanks. One hundred Mark VIIIs were assembled by the Ordnance Department at Rock Island Arsenal starting 1 September 1919 and finishing 10 June 1920. These tanks, together with the light 6-ton vehicles, were destined to provide almost the sole tank component of the U.S. Army until the late 1930s.

Since the Army was equipped with these two essentially obsolete types, a portion of the limited budget had to be directed to the task of upgrading these vehicles and improving their efficiency. This work covered such items as new gun mounts, improved communication equipment, and the development of tank compasses and an odograph. Although the importance of these items cannot be denied, this work reduced the already limited funds available for the really essential task of developing a new tank chassis.

Since 1919, interest in the United States and Great Britain had centered on the development of improved light and medium tanks with much greater mobility than the wartime models. In the United States, medium tank development followed two parallel paths. The first was the series of full-track tanks developed by the Ordnance Department while the second was the convertible wheel or track vehicles proposed by J. Walter Christie. Each of these lines of development will be discussed in turn.

The mock-up of the medium tank M1921 and the 6 pounder gun mount are shown above.

MEDIUM TANKS M1921 AND M1922

The Ordnance Department program dated from a work order of June 1919 which approved the design of a new medium tank similar to the British medium D, then under development. Major R. E. Carlson, an Ordnance officer formerly with the Anglo-American Tank Commission, played an important role in defining the characteristics of the new tank. These characteristics were outlined by Brigadier General S. D. Rockenbach in a paper dated 18 August 1919 and called for a tank not exceeding 18 tons in weight with a power to weight ratio of 10 horsepower per ton. A maximum speed of 12 miles/hour was required with a cruising radius of 60 miles. The tank was to be armed with one light cannon and two machine guns and have armor protection against armor piercing (AP) rifle caliber bullets. On 4 November 1919, the Ordnance Committee approved the specification adding the requirement for armor protection against .50 caliber AP rounds at close range. The detailed design work began along with the construction of a full size wooden mock-up. The newly constituted Tank Corps Technical Board examined the mock-up on 2 April 1920 and recommended the construction of a pilot medium A tank with a few minor modifications. After the approval of these recommendations, the Ordnance Department was authorized on 13 April 1920 to construct two pilot medium tanks. The first of these, medium A tank #1, was designated medium tank M1921.

About the time construction was approved for the medium A pilots, information became available regarding the British experiments using a flexible cable type suspension system. To explore the possibilities of such a suspension, it was authorized for use on the second pilot subsequently designated medium tank M1922.

Rear views of the gun mount mock-up showing the telescopic sight and coaxial machine gun.

The medium tank M1921 (above and below) at Aberdeen Proving Ground in May 1922.

The first pilot tank, medium tank M1921, was completed at Rock Island Arsenal in December 1921 and delivered to Aberdeen Proving Ground on 20 February 1922. As completed, the M1921 had a loaded weight of 41,000 pounds with a four man crew. According to the manufacturer, the Murray and Tregurtha engine was rated at 220 horsepower (hp) at 1200 revolutions per minute (rpm) giving a power to weight ratio of 10.7 hp/ton. However, proving ground tests showed this value to be optimistic with only 195 hp being obtained at 1250 rpm. The tank was armed with a 6 pounder (57mm) cannon mounted coaxially with a .30 caliber Browning machine gun in the turret. The cupola on top of the turret carried an additional .30 caliber machine gun. Armor protection ranged from 1 inch on the vertical surfaces around the fighting compartment to 3/8 inches over the engine. The track width of 18 inches resulted in a ground pressure of 10 pounds per square inch (psi) at zero penetration. The maximum speed was 10.1 miles/hour with the engine turning over at 1200 rpm.

Details of the rear deck and gun mount on the M1921 can be seen below.

The views on this page show the medium tank M1922 as it appeared in May 1922 at Aberdeen Proving Ground. Note the wooden track shoes.

Testing continued at Aberdeen and Camp Meade, Maryland until 1926. The major problems centered on the engine which lacked reliability and sufficient power to provide the speeds desired by the using service. At one point in the test program, the engine was replaced by a 338 hp Liberty 12 normally used in the Mark VIII heavy tank. This resulted in a considerable speed increase, but caused numerous failures in the overloaded power train components. In 1926, a special 200 hp Packard 8-cylinder engine was installed as part of the development program for the medium tank T1. During its career, the M1921 served as a test vehicle for numerous experimental components such as the stroboscope vision device, the Winkley odograph, and the Sperry gyroscopic tank compass.

The second pilot, medium tank M1922, was similar to the M1921 except for the installation of the flexible cable type suspension. With this suspension the tracks were higher at the rear than at the front. Wooden track shoes 18 inches wide were carried in steel brackets pivoted at the center where they were attached to the cable.

After completion at Rock Island, the M1922 was also shipped to Aberdeen arriving 1 March 1923. The test program revealed rapid wear of the steel cables requiring their replacement by chains. Despite the wear and maintenance problems, the flexible suspension gave very good riding qualities and one high speed test at Aberdeen reached a speed of 16.2 miles/hour. The Murray and Tregurtha engine, identical with that in the M1921, suffered from similar problems of low power and poor reliability. Like its sister, the M1922 was used to test various components and when interest shifted to the development of the medium tank T1, it was retired to the Ordnance Museum.

Details of the M1922's cable type suspension can be seen in the two photographs above. The outside armor plates have been removed in both views exposing the suspension.

The Murray and Tregurtha engine is visible in the open engine compartment at the right. Note the air louvers on the rear deck.

The left and right sides of the driving compartment are shown below through the open doors in the hull front. The 6 pounder ammunition racks are located on each side of the driver's seat.

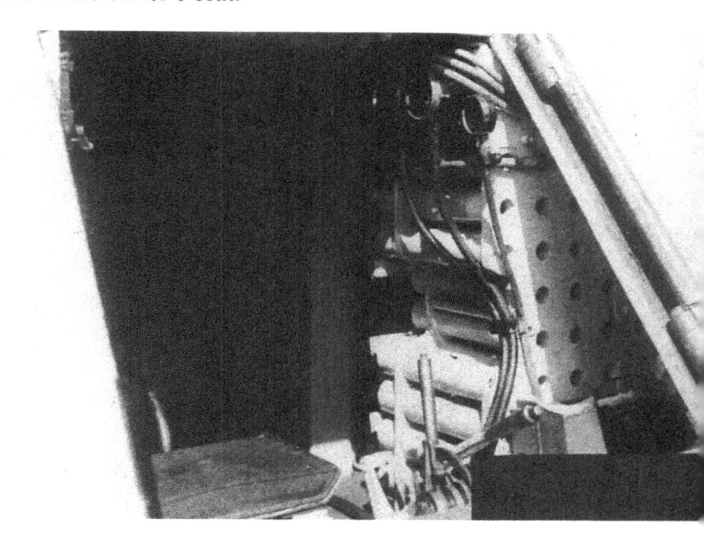

The medium tank T1 at Aberdeen Proving Ground in December 1927.

MEDIUM TANKS T1 AND T1E1

The test program on the M1921 and M1922 revealed their major problems were associated with the Murray and Tregurtha engine. This was a modified marine engine originally intended for large speed boats. When it proved unsuitable for tank use, a survey was made of other commercially available engines. The survey failed to produce a satisfactory candidate and the Packard Motor Company was awarded a contract to develop a special tank engine to meet Ordnance specifications. This project was very successful with the first engine being completed in June 1925. As mentioned previously, the engine was installed for test in the medium tank M1921. Other redesigned components were also being tested in the M1921 and at this stage it was referred to as the Phase 1 medium tank. The intention was to incorporate the design features which proved successful in a later Phase 2 medium tank. The latter vehicle was subsequently designated the medium tank T1.

Further development of the M1921 tank was approved on 11 March 1926. This approval resulted from the successful pontoon bridge tests on 25 June 1925. At that time the M1921, now weighing approximately 23 tons, crossed the medium pontoon bridge under its own power. The test indicated that a tank of this weight could operate with the troops using such bridging equipment. Further studies were authorized to incorporate the changes found necessary by the test program, but maintaining essentially the same weight and overall design. The Ordnance Committee also

The medium tank M1921 during the pontoon bridge tests in June 1925. The turret armament has been removed and the opening for the gun mount is covered by a flat plate.

The forged steel open tracks are clearly visible in these views of the medium tank T1.

permitted the use of soft steel plate on the new experimental tank since it would cost only $5200 compared to approximately $52,000 for armor plate. The new vehicle, medium tank T1, was completed at Rock Island Arsenal in May 1927 and, after shop tests, was shipped to Aberdeen Proving Ground in September of that year.

In outward appearance, the T1 greatly resembled the M1921. Differences were apparent in the rear deck engine louvres and the new forged steel open track shoes. The T1 weighed in at 43,900 pounds giving a power to weight ratio exceeding 9 hp/ton with the new 200 hp Packard engine. Although the new engine was "rugged and dependable" to quote the test report, it still suffered from insufficient power. The highest average speed obtained was 11.28 miles/hour with 14 miles/hour being reached on at least one occasion. Despite the low maximum speed, both Aberdeen Proving Ground and the Tank Board stated that the T1 was an improvement over previous models tested and the Ordnance Committee recommended its standardization on 24 January 1928. The standardization was approved as the medium tank M1 on 2 February 1928, but was withdrawn later that Spring.

The medium tank T1 with crew at Aberdeen in September 1929.

The medium tank T1 armed with the 75mm pack howitzer is shown above. The effect of the 75mm shell on the 6-ton M1917 light tank can be seen below.

The sole example of the T1 continued to serve as a test vehicle and in July 1928, the 6 pounder was replaced in the turret by a 75mm pack howitzer M1920. For this installation, the powder charge was reduced, limiting the muzzle velocity to 650 feet per second (ft/sec) and the recoil to less than 1 foot. Ammunition racks on both sides of the driver carried 36 rounds of 75 mm ammunition. Tests showed the howitzer was extremely destructive when fired against the 6-ton light tank.

In April 1932, the T1 was modified by replacing the Packard engine with the 338 hp Liberty. With the new engine it was redesignated as the medium tank T1E1. The increased power greatly improved the tank's performance giving a maximum speed of approximately 25 miles/hour. However, as with the M1921, the more powerful engine overloaded the power train resulting in early failures.

Racks for the 75mm shells were located on each side of the driver (below left). Note the changes in the rear deck (below right) compared to the M1921 and M1922.

The medium tank T2 is shown above bridging a trench during tests at Aberdeen in early 1931. Below is a model of the early design concept designated as the medium tank M1924.

MEDIUM TANK T2

The order of 11 March 1926 which permitted work to continue on the medium tank T1 also directed the development of a medium tank with a maximum weight of 15 tons. This gave new impetus to a design study known as the model 1924 tank then in progress at Rock Island Arsenal. Fund limitations held up the construction of the 15-ton vehicle until 1929 when the design was completed as the medium tank T2. By this time its appearance had radically changed. The final configuration, carrying a four man crew, was based on the light tank T1E1 manufactured by James Cunningham, Sons and Company who also received the contract for the new medium. With its front mounted engine, the new tank bore a considerable resemblance to the British Vickers medium tanks of the same period.

A loaded weight of 31,200 pounds and a 338 hp Liberty engine gave the T2 a power to weight ratio of approximately 20 hp/ton resulting in improved mobility and a maximum road speed of 25 miles/hour. The latter was limited to 20 miles/hour by a governor to extend the life of the running gear and power train components.

As completed in 1930, the turret of the T2 was armed with a semiautomatic 47mm gun mounted coaxially with a .50 caliber Browning machine gun in the combination mount M4. Initially the gunner stood on the tank floor, but later a seat was attached to the gun cradle allowing him to move with the mount. To

The 37mm gun is installed in the bow mount in these photographs of the T2 taken at Aberdeen during the Winter of 1930-1931.

balance the added weight of the gunner, counterweights were fixed to the gun barrel just in front of the turret face. The original T2 also carried a combination mount T3E1 in the right bow fitted with a 37mm gun and a .30 caliber machine gun. This mount proved limited in flexibility and interfered with the operation of the turret mount. In 1931 the bow combination mount was removed and replaced by a single .30 caliber machine gun. At the same time another .30 caliber machine gun was added on an antiaircraft mount. The combination mount T3E1 was later installed in the light tank T1E3. Armor protection on the medium tank T2 ranged from 7/8 inches down to 1/4 inches.

The T2 underwent a test program starting in December 1930 and lasting until January 1932. With its high speed, good mobility, and excellent firepower, the T2 was reported to be the best tank yet designed by the Ordnance Department. However, with limited funds available during the depression, the single example of the T2 remained as an experimental type and was not proposed for standardization. Like the T1, it was used to test a variety of components and accessories for use in future tanks. One result of the test program was the recommendation to develop a better steering mechanism than the clutch-brake system then in use. The clutch-brake arrangement was unsatisfactory for service in high speed tracked vehicles.

The bow cannon has been replaced by a .30 caliber machine gun in the views below dated October 1931. Also, note the counterweight fitted to the 47mm gun mount to balance the weight of the gunner.

Note the flat track shoes on the T2 (above and left). The bow machine gun mount also is clearly visible. These photographs were taken at Aberdeen in January 1932 and the turret gun mount had been removed during this phase of the test program.

An experimental gyro compass is shown below at the left. A similar compass was installed at the left rear of the driver's seat in the T2 (below right).

The Christie M1919 is shown here with the tracks installed. The photograph below was taken as the tank was loaded for shipment at Hoboken, New Jersey.

CHRISTIE MEDIUM TANKS M1919 AND M1921

During World War I, major tank losses were often incurred by mechanical breakdowns during the approach march before the tanks were ever committed to action. One method of reducing these mechanical failures was to carry the tanks on transporters to the place of employment. In the postwar period, use was made of trucks or trailers capable of carrying the heavy vehicles. Another approach was to design a tank to run on either wheels or tracks. Since most of the mechanical problems were associated with the tracked suspension, the tank could be driven to the jump-off point on its wheels and the tracks installed just before it went into battle. Such a design was proposed by Mr. J. Walter Christie in late 1919. In the Fall of that year, a Christie self-propelled gun mount with a wheel or track suspension was demonstrated to the Tank Corps at Camp Meade. An order for one tank based on this design was placed with Christie's Front Drive Motor Company of Hoboken, New Jersey on 22 November 1919. After some changes, the complete specification for this tank was approved on 8 June 1920.

The new tank designated by Christie as the M1919 was demonstrated at the factory in January 1921 and delivered to Aberdeen Proving Ground on 5 February. As completed, the M1919 weighed 27,000 pounds empty and was powered by a 120 hp Christie engine. The suspension consisted of four large unsprung road wheels, one at each corner of the chassis. The rear pair of wheels were powered and all four were fitted with rubber tires for quiet operation. A 2-wheel bogie with coil springs was located midway between the large road wheels at each side of the tank. The center bogies could be raised or lowered and normally were raised when running without the tracks. In the lowered position, the bogies could carry the entire weight of the tank lifting the four road wheels off the ground. The 15 inch wide steel tracks had a pitch of 9 3/4 inches and were driven by engaging the teeth on the inside of the track shoes with the holes in the rear drive wheels.

The Christie M1919 on its wheels (above). Note the stowage of the tracks. An original sketch of this vehicle is reproduced below.

The M1919 was armed with the 6 pounder (57 mm) in a coaxial mount with a .30 caliber machine gun in a round turret. This combination gun mount was the same as used on medium tanks M1921 and M1922. A cupola on top of the turret carried an additional .30 caliber weapon. Armor protection ranged from a maximum of 1 inch down to 1/4 inches and was well sloped on the front hull. A crew of three was carried with the driver in the front hull and two men in the turret.

Testing at Aberdeen continued until 21 April 1921 when the program was suspended at Mr. Christie's request to allow modification of the vehicle. During the time at Aberdeen, the M1919 was driven 374 miles of which only 37.5 miles were on tracks. The tests showed a maximum speed of approximately 13 miles/hour on wheels and 7 miles/hour on tracks. The fuel capacity of 59 gallons permitted a range of 75 miles on wheels and 35 miles on tracks.

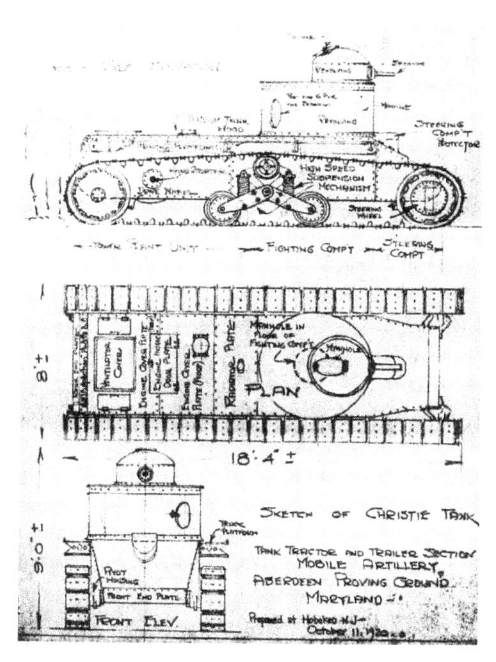

The effect of lowering the bogies is illustrated below. In the right photograph, the front road wheels have been lifted off the ground.

The Christie M1921 without tracks is shown above and below.

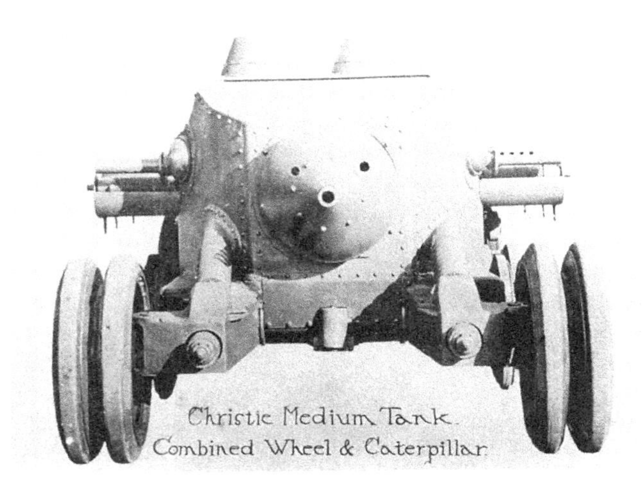

Tests of the M1921 on tracks at Aberdeen, June 1922.

The Ordnance Committee agreed to the modification request and approved a contract covering the cost on 15 June 1921. The modifications were completed and the vehicle returned to Aberdeen on 28 March 1922. Christie designated the rebuilt tank as the M1921 and its appearance was quite different from the M1919. The turret was eliminated, but the same combination gun mount was moved to the front of the hull. Two additional .30 caliber machine guns were fitted, one in each front corner of the hull. The crew, now enlarged to four, consisted of two gunners at the front with the driver and tank commander moved back to the center. The driver was on the left side. Armor protection varied from 3/4 inches to 1/4 inches. The rear road wheels were still unsprung and were driven by the same 120 hp engine as in the M1919. However, the front pair of road wheels were sprung with large coil springs mounted in the sides of the front hull. Two large road wheels were mounted on a pivoting bogie at each side. The same 15 inch wide, 9-3/4 inch pitch tracks were retained as on the M1919.

Testing was resumed at Aberdeen continuing until 24 October 1922. The M1921 was driven 341.5 miles including 161 miles on tracks. An additional 66 miles were driven at Camp Meade in tests which ended in March 1923. The speed was approximately the same as the M1919, but an increase in fuel capacity to 67 gallons extended the range to 100 miles on wheels and 60 miles on tracks. However, maneuverability was poor and the vehicle was mechanically unreliable. The crew compartment was considered too small for efficient operation. Further tests were discontinued and the M1921 was consigned to the Automotive Museum at Aberdeen on 10 July 1924.

The Christie M1928 (above and below) as originally demonstrated.

CONVERTIBLE MEDIUM TANKS T3, T3E1, T3E2, AND T3E3

After the rejection of his M1921 and some later amphibious vehicles, Christie's efforts in tank design turned to the development of a new lightweight high speed chassis. His Front Drive Motor Company was reorganized as the U.S. Wheel Track Layer Corporation located in Rahway, New Jersey. Using the funds he received from selling his patent rights to the U.S. Government, he concentrated on the development of the new vehicle which was to have a profound effect on tank design throughout the world. Designated by Christie as the M1928, it was exhibited on 28 October of that year at Fort Myer, Virginia.

Weighing 8.6 tons and powered by a 338 hp Liberty engine, the M1928 had a power to weight ratio of 39 hp/ton. However, its most important feature was the suspension consisting of four large independently sprung road wheels on each side of the chassis. Each wheel was mounted at the end of a pivoted arm supported by a large adjustable coil spring. This spring allowed a wheel movement of 11 inches beyond the normal compression due to the weight of the vehicle. The wheels were fitted with dual solid rubber tires which helped to damp out vibration and reduce the noise. Able to operate on either wheels or tracks, about 30 minutes were required for a trained crew to remove or install the tracks. When operating on wheels, power was transmitted by a chain drive to the two rear road wheels. With tracks, a large tongue on the inside of alternate track shoes engaged rollers between the two halves of the rear drive sprocket. They also passed between the dual road wheel tires, holding the track in place. The track shoes were steel stampings with both the pitch and track width being 10 inches.

During a test for the Tank Board on 19 November 1928, the M1928 averaged 28 miles/hour on a run from Fort Meade to Gettysburg and return. The outbound trip was made on wheels and the return on tracks. At times it reached a maximum of 70 miles/hour on wheels and 42-1/2 miles/hour on tracks. Such performance received wide publicity and aroused interest in obtaining such vehicles for the Army. At this point numerous difficulties arose from the dispute between Christie and the Ordnance Department over the service requirements for a tank. After protracted negotiations, Christie received a contract for one vehicle now referred to as the M1931. This was finally delivered over four months late on 19 January 1931. Tests at Aberdeen revealed the need for additional modifications and the tank was returned to Christie on 27 March 1931. After further negotiations, Christie was awarded a contract for seven M1931s on 12 June 1931. They were officially designated as the convertible medium tank T3.

Medium tank T3 running on its wheels. Note the stowage of the tracks above the fenders.

The first T3 was delivered to Aberdeen for test on 9 October 1931 and the seventh was accepted in March 1932. After tests, three T3s were assigned to Fort Benning, Georgia to serve with Company F, 67th Infantry (Medium Tanks). The other four were delivered to the Cavalry at Fort Knox, Kentucky where they were redesignated as the combat car T1. This was necessary, since at that time the law required all tanks to be assigned to the Infantry. The medium tank T3 and the combat car T1 differed only in armament. The T3 was armed with a 37mm gun M1916 and a .30 caliber machine gun in the turret combination mount T1. In the combat car T1, the 37mm gun was replaced by a .50 caliber machine gun. Both vehicles had a two man crew consisting of the driver in the front hull and the gunner in the turret. An outstanding feature was the highly sloped armor which ranged in thickness from 5/8 to 1/2 inches.

Like the M1928, the T3 was chain driven when operating on its wheels. A later version using a gear drive to the rear wheels was designated the convertible medium tank T3E1. A single example of this type was tested at Aberdeen Proving Ground.

With a loaded weight of 22,220 pounds, the T3 achieved a maximum speed of 46.8 miles/hour on wheels and 27.3 miles/hour on tracks. In practice the speed was limited to 40 miles/hour on wheels and 25 miles/hour on tracks. Despite its excellent mobility, the fighting efficiency of the T3 was approximately that of a light tank. This was due to its two man crew and limited firepower. The lightweight armor was also insufficient for the infantry support role. After tests during 1931 and 1932, the Infantry and Ordnance Department produced a specification for an improved version of the T3. Further disputes with Christie followed and the contract for five new tanks was not awarded to him, but to the American-La France and Foamite Corporation of Elmira, New York.

Medium tank T3 on tracks. The long pitch Christie single pin tracks are clearly shown in this photograph.

Further details of the medium tank T3 on wheels and tracks can be seen above. Note the mufflers mounted on the rear plate and the drive chain stowed on the fender (below left).

With the side plates removed, the suspension springs are exposed (above left). The driver's controls and the 37mm ammunition racks can be seen above. At left is the combination gun mount T1 used in this vehicle.

Note the increased machine gun armament and the short pitch track in these views of the medium tank T3E2.

The new vehicle, designated the convertible medium tank T3E2, was wider in front permitting a gunner to sit alongside the driver manning a .30 caliber bow machine gun. The turret was enlarged to carry two men and three additional machine guns were fitted, one in each side and one in the rear. The combination mount with the 37mm gun and the .30 caliber machine gun was retained in the front of the turret. The suspension was similar to that on the T3, but a new forged link track was provided with a width of 12 inches and a pitch of 5 inches. The T3's Liberty engine was replaced by a Curtiss D-12 developing 435 hp at 2300 rpm. Maximum speed was about 58 miles/hour on wheels and 35 miles/hour on tracks, but in practice the vehicle was governed to a much lower speed. Major problems during test concerned the weak transmission and final drive. As with the earlier vehicles, a basic flaw was the clutch-brake steering system which repeatedly proved unsuitable for high speed tanks. Some 60 minor modifications were applied as a result of tests at Fort Benning. All five tanks were then redesignated as the convertible medium tank T3E3.

Medium tank T4 with tracks installed. The chains on the fenders were used to secure the tracks when running on wheels.

CONVERTIBLE MEDIUM TANKS T4 AND T4E1

The last medium tank based on Christie's convertible design was built at Rock Island Arsenal in 1935 and 1936. Sixteen vehicles designated as the convertible medium tank T4 were produced during this period. Carrying a four man crew, the T4 weighed 13.5 tons giving a power to weight ratio of 19.8 hp/ton with the 268 hp Continental engine. The crew was divided with the driver and bow machine gunner in the front hull and the tank commander and gunner in the turret. Armament consisted of a single .30 caliber bow machine gun with one .30 caliber and one .50 caliber machine gun in the turret. The latter two weapons were on separate mounts. Armor protection ranged from 5/8 inches down to 1/4 inches.

The suspension was based on Christie's patents with four large rubber tired road wheels on each side. The tracks were 12 inches wide with a 4-3/4 inch pitch and were driven by a sprocket at the rear of the suspension. When operating without tracks, the rear pair of road wheels were chain driven from the final drive. One of the most important improvements over the earlier tanks was the use of controlled differential steering. This replaced the earlier clutch-brake system which had been so unsatisfactory for fast tracked vehicles. At 2400 rpm, the air-cooled radial engine produced maximum speeds of 37.8 miles/hour on wheels and 23.9 miles/hour on tracks.

The appearance of the T4 on wheels and tracks can be compared above and below.

Details of the medium tank T4 are shown above and at the left below. Note the short pitch track compared to the earlier Christie suspensions. The main armament was a .50 caliber machine gun in the right front of the turret.

The short barreled .50 caliber machine gun is shown above in its mount. Below is the driver's compartment viewed through the front hull door.

Medium tank T4E1 on tracks. Note that the barbette extends out to the full fender width.

Three examples of a second version known as the convertible medium tank T4E1 were produced. These vehicles retained the four man crew, but differed from the T4 in that the turret was replaced by a barbette structure on the upper hull. Three additional .30 caliber machine guns were installed at the sides and rear of the barbette giving a total armament of one .50 caliber and five .30 caliber weapons. With the additional space available inside the barbette, larger fuel tanks were fitted in the T4E1. The fuel capacity was 79.5 gallons for the T4E1 compared to 41.5 gallons for the T4.

Service tests at Aberdeen Proving Ground and Fort Benning indicated that the T4 was underpowered for its weight. Standardization was recommended for both the T4 and T4E1 on 6 February 1936. The Office of the Adjutant General rejected the recommendation on the grounds that the offensive power of these tanks was no greater than that of the light tank M2 and they cost twice as much. With the approach of the war in Europe, standardization was again recommended on 30 March 1939. This time it was approved designating the T4 and T4E1 as the convertible medium tank M1, Limited Standard. Eighteen of these tanks were in service at Fort Benning until March 1940 when they were declared obsolete.

Medium tank T5, Phase I with the early wooden turret and superstructure. A proposal drawing prepared by Captain G. H. Rarey for a medium tank based on the Christie chassis is reproduced below.

MEDIUM TANKS T5, T5E1, and T5E2

Item 12876 of the Ordnance Committee Minutes (OCM), dated 21 May 1936, recommended the development of the medium tank T5. The approval of this recommendation initiated the program which eventually led to the most widely produced tank in United States history, the M4 General Sherman. Although the appearance of the Sherman prototype was over five years away, it was a direct descendant of the T5.

After the problems encountered with the convertible wheel or track vehicles, the T5 was a new effort to develop a tank meeting the service requirements specified by the Infantry Board. Essentially the T5 was an enlarged version of the successful light tank M2. Using many of the same components, it was intended to have greater protection and firepower. A weight limit of 15 tons was imposed by the Infantry Board to permit tank units to operate over the bridges found on primary highways in the United States. The first pilot vehicle designed to meet this weight limit, was referred to as the medium tank T5, Phase I.

Two arrangements of armament had been under consideration for some time. The first mounted the main weapon in a turret with full 360 degree traverse as in the medium tank T4. The second replaced the turret with a barbette as on the T4E1 having the appearance of a mobile pillbox. As early as April 1934, Captain G. H. Rarey proposed a combination of the two in a design based on a Christie chassis. A .30 caliber machine gun was placed in each of four rotors mounted in the sponsons at the corners of the fighting compartment. The main armament was carried in a turret on top with full traverse. This arrangement was finally adopted for the T5, although in the original design the two forward sponson machine guns were mounted in auxiliary turrets. Two .30 caliber machine guns were also fixed in the front armor plate for use by the driver. Provision was made for antiaircraft mounts for two additional .30 caliber weapons. The turret was designed to carry the new high velocity 37mm antitank gun then under development by the Ordnance Department. When the tank was delivered, a dummy gun was installed to simulate this weapon. This was later replaced by an interim installation of twin 37mm guns M2A1 in mount T10. These were to have been replaced by the single high velocity gun when it became available. However, this never occurred and the single T5, Phase I still carries the twin 37s and is on display today at the Patton Museum at Fort Knox, Kentucky. Its registration number is W-30369.

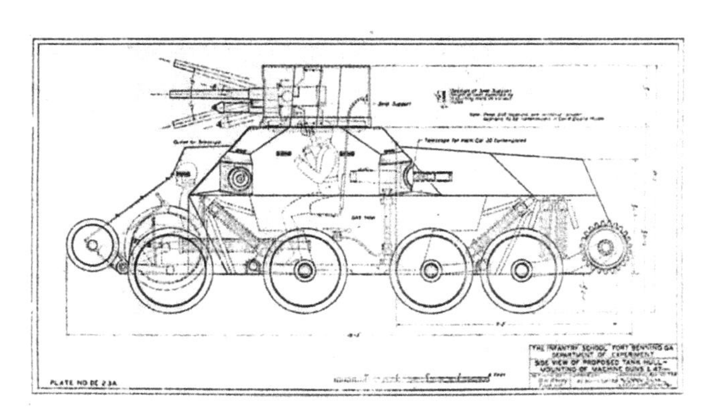

Medium tank T5, Phase I with the steel turret and superstructure. A dummy 37mm gun is installed. Note the cooling fins on the final drive housing.

Other changes during the early development of the T5, Phase I included moving the driver's seat from the floor on the left front of the hull to its final position in the center above the rear of the transmission. During the first stage of tests from 16 November to 29 December 1937, the tank was fitted with a wooden turret and superstructure which differed in configuration from the final design. Early in 1938, the steel superstructure was completed and the steel turret installed, still fitted with the dummy cannon. Soft steel plate was used instead of armor and assembly was by welding. The tank was then shipped to Aberdeen Proving Ground on 16 February 1938.

The driver's controls on the T5, Phase I (below). The fixed machine guns in the front plate are clearly visible.

Medium tank T5, Phase I armed with the twin 37mm guns M2A1. Note the plates on the rear corners of the tank to deflect fire from the sponson machine guns.

With a five man crew and armor protection ranging from 1 inch down to 1/4 inches, the T5, Phase I had a loaded weight slightly over 15 tons. An 11-5/8 inch wide rubber block track gave a ground pressure of 9.6 psi at zero penetration. The tank was powered by a Continental air-cooled radial engine developing 268 hp at 2400 rpm. The engine, located at the rear, transmitted its power through a multiple disc clutch and a long drive shaft to the constant mesh transmission at the front of the vehicle. The transmission, with five speeds forward and one reverse, drove the tracks through a controlled differential and final drive. The latter was fitted with a 12 tooth sprocket. The vertical volute spring suspension, based on the proven design of the light tank M2, carried the weight of the tank on three 2-wheel bogies per track. With a power to weight ratio over 16 hp/ton, the maximum road speed was 31 miles/hour. The fuel capacity of 125 gallons allowed a cruising range of 125 miles.

A number of minor modifications were made during test including the installation of bullet deflector plates at both sides of the rear hull plate. These plates deflected the fire from the rear sponson machine guns into the blind area behind the tank or into any hole or trench the tank crossed.

The test results at Aberdeen and Fort Benning were generally satisfactory and the Chief of Infantry recommended the standardization of the T5 with the 37mm high velocity gun and numerous minor modifications. The Ordnance Committee concurred and standardization of the T5, Phase I as the medium tank M2 was recommended by OCM 14529 on 2 June 1938 and later approved by OCM 14576.

With the acceptance of the T5, Phase I, work continued on the development of a tank with improved performance and the maximum armor protection that could be obtained within a weight limit of approximately 20 tons. The new vehicle was designated as the medium tank T5, Phase III. No medium tank T5, Phase II was ever built as the designation was reserved only for a design study.

Tested at Aberdeen Proving Ground during November and December 1938, the T5, Phase III was similar in appearance to the earlier Phase I machine. The most obvious difference resulted from the shift of the driver's position back to the floor on the left side of the transmission. This moved the driver's vision port to the left and changed the configuration of the front armor giving it an asymmetric appearance. The design for the vertical volute spring suspension also was modified moving the track return roller from the side to the top of each bogie. Brackets were added outboard of the tracks connecting the bogie frame to the sponson on the center and rear bogies of each track.

Medium tank T5, Phase III as originally delivered (above) in November 1938. New mufflers with shields were installed in December (below right). The original muffler arrangement is shown below at the left.

Medium tank T5, Phase III under test. Note the asymmetric appearance of the front hull with the driver shifted to the left of the transmission.

The driver's position and the left front sponson mount can be seen above. Below are two views of the 37mm gun T3 in mount T1.

The machine gun armament remained the same as on the Phase I vehicle, but a high velocity 37mm gun T3 in mount T1 was installed in a new cast armor turret. The armor protection was increased to a maximum of 1-7/16 inches on the turret and 1-1/4 inches on the hull. The hull armor was assembled using carbon steel angles and nickel steel rivets. All of the joints were sealed with a plastic rubber compound. The 9-cylinder Wright air-cooled radial engine was rated at 400 hp, but only developed 346 hp at 2400 rpm during test. With a loaded weight of over 21 tons, the power to weight ratio was about 14 hp/ton. Maximum speed at 2400 rpm was 32.9 miles/hour. However, the cruising range dropped to 103 miles despite an increase in fuel capacity to 132 gallons. The ground pressure went up to 12.2 psi even though the track width was increased to 16 inches. Considerable development work was required on the controlled differential steering during the test program. However the tank was rated as a very satisfactory tactical vehicle, although somewhat larger and about a ton heavier than the military characteristics originally specified.

At this time the Guiberson air-cooled radial diesel engine was an attractive alternative as a tank power plant. Procurement of one of these 400 hp engines was recommended for installation in the T5, Phase III. The designation medium tank T5E1 was assigned for this modification in OCM 14702 dated 20 September 1938.

The medium tank T5E2 is shown above and at the right. Note the folding armor around the howitzer mount.

To evaluate the use of heavier caliber cannon in tanks, OCM 14967 authorized the construction of a pilot mounting the 75mm howitzer M1A1. Since the medium tank T5, Phase III was already available, it was modified to carry the howitzer in the right front of the hull. A subcarriage was manufactured to adapt the top portion of the standard M3A1 field carriage to the tank hull. A new smaller turret was installed armed with a .30 caliber machine gun and carrying a range finder. A modified Model 1917 panoramic sight was provided for direct laying of the howitzer. The two fixed machine guns in the hull front and the three remaining sponson machine guns were retained. With these modifications, the vehicle was redesignated as the medium tank T5E2.

Tests at Aberdeen from 20 April 1939 to 8 February 1940 indicated the effectiveness of the howitzer against both point and area targets. It was concluded that such a mount was practical for tank installation. With the European war now in progress, the experience gained from these tests was to prove of great value in only a few months time.

The pack howitzer mounted in the right sponson of the T5E2 (below). The side door can be seen at the right of the photograph.

Medium tank M2, number 2, at Aberdeen in August 1939. Note that some cooling fins are retained on the final drive housing.

MEDIUM TANKS M2 and M2A1

As standardized, the medium tank M2 differed somewhat from the prototype T5, Phase I. The high velocity 37mm gun M3 was installed in the turret replacing the dual 37mm guns M2A1. The .30 caliber machine gun armament, consisting of two fixed guns in the front hull, four sponson guns, and two anti-aircraft guns, was retained as on the T5. The hull and turret were assembled from face-hardened armor plate using structural steel angles and nickel steel rivets. Thicknesses ranged from 1-1/8 inches on the front of the differential housing to 1/4 inches on the floor. The top plate of the hull was 3/8 inches thick structural nickel steel.

A new power plant was installed in the production vehicles with a 350 hp Wright air-cooled radial replacing the lower power engine of the T5, Phase I. With a loaded weight of about 19 tons, the new engine gave a power to weight ratio of 18.4 hp/ton. The maximum allowable speed was 26 miles/hour which was reached in 5th gear at approximately 2000 rpm of the engine. Despite in increase in track width to 13-1/4 inches, the ground pressure rose to 18.8 psi for the fully loaded tank.

Eighteen M2s were authorized from funds for the Fiscal Year 1939 and production started in the Summer of 1939 at Rock Island Arsenal. The second production tank was delivered to Aberdeen for test in August. An additional 54 M2s were authorized for the Fiscal Year 1940, but rapid changes in the world situation and improvements resulting from the development program stopped further production of the M2.

The bullet deflector plates are still fitted, but they are now rectangular in shape.

Medium tank M2, number 1, with the .30 caliber antiaircraft machine guns in firing position (above) and stowed (at right).

Medium tank M2, number 2, showing the outside stowage (below). Note the panoramic telescope in the turret roof. The driver's controls and the SCR 245 radio on the rear wall of the fighting compartment can be seen in the bottom photographs.

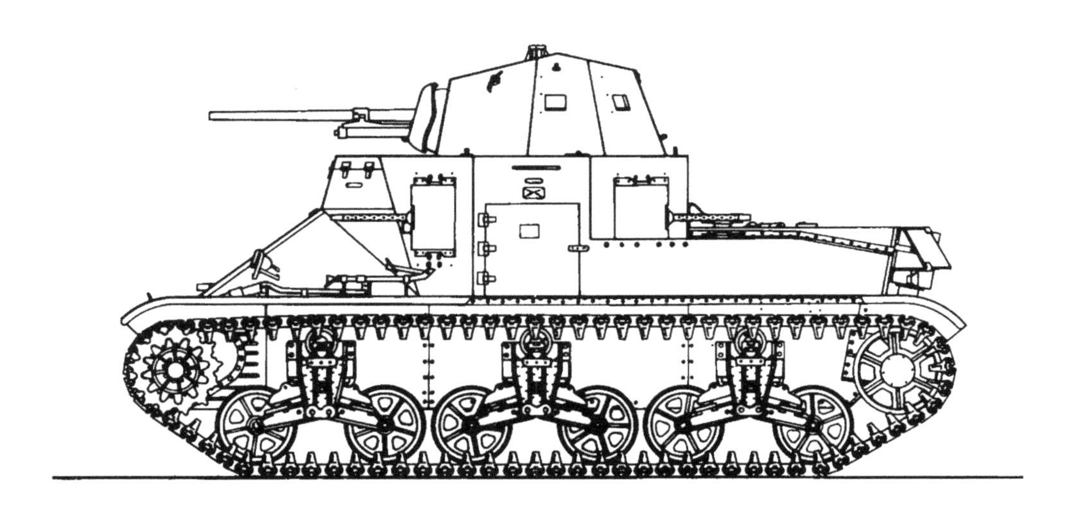

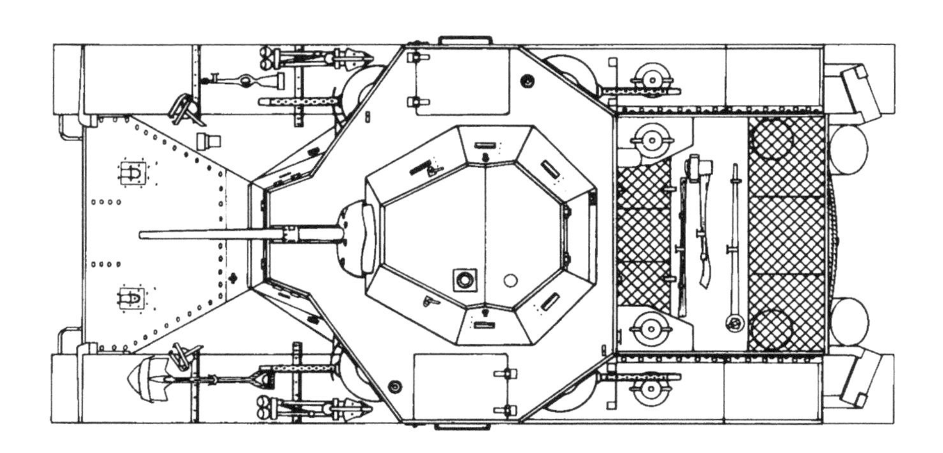

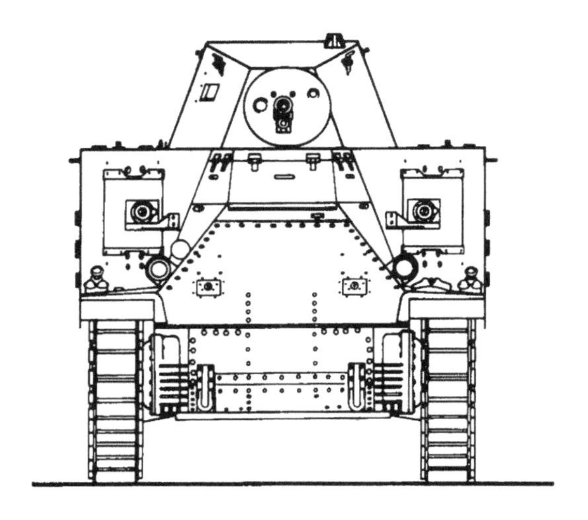

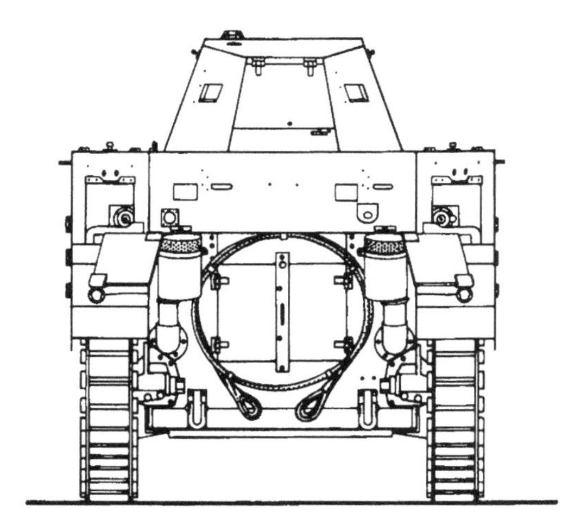

Scale 1:48

Medium Tank M2

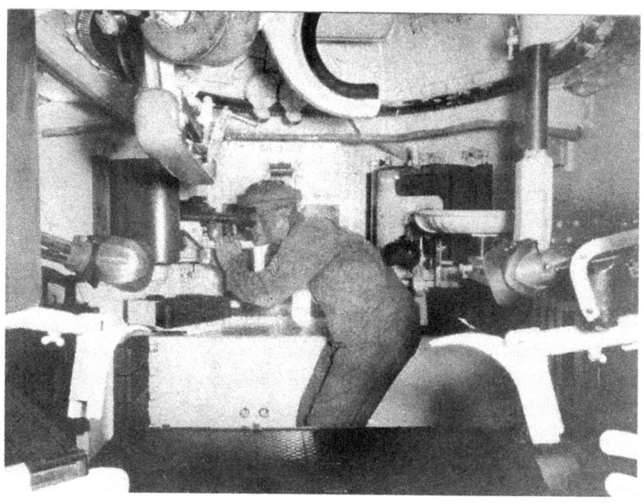

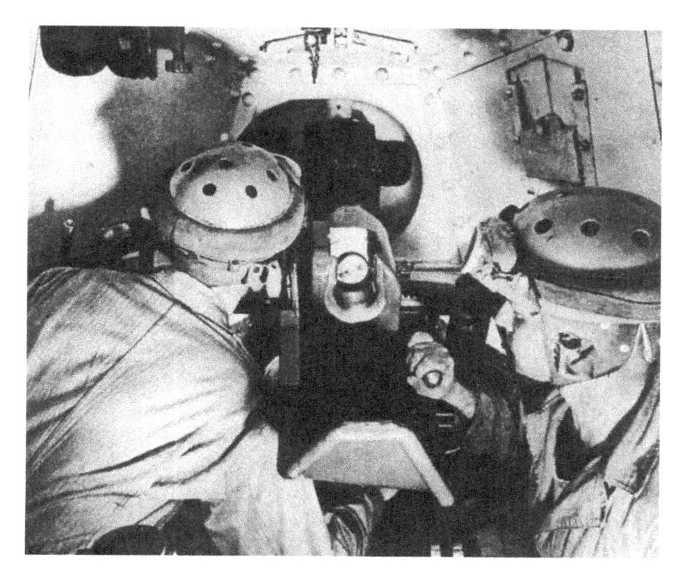

The M2's fighting compartment is shown above. Looking through the left side door (top right), a crew member is seen sighting the right front sponson machine gun. At the left, the crew mans the 37mm turret gun.

Medium tank M2, number 2, fitted with the M2A1 type turret with the early pistol ports during development tests at Aberdeen. It is on display today with this same turret at the Ordnance Museum.

The medium tank M2A1 is shown on this and the opposite page as it appeared at Aberdeen in September 1940. Note the improved pistol port covers compared to the M2.

The 37mm gun mount has better protection than on the M2 and shields have been added to the sponson machine gun mounts.

Lessons learned from the development program and the service test of the M2 indicated the need for increased armor protection and engine power. The most obvious change was a roomier turret with vertical sides replacing the sloped walls of the M2 turret. Pistol ports were installed in the turret sides and the door was moved from the rear to the roof. Armor protection was increased to 1-1/4 inches on all vertical surfaces.

The modified tank, designated the medium tank M2A1, was fitted with the Wright air-cooled radial engine model R975 EC2. This was quite similar to the M2's engine, but the rated power was increased to 400 hp at 2400 rpm. Even with a loaded weight of about 21 tons, the power to weight ratio improved to about 19 hp/ton. However, the maximum allowable speed remained at 26 miles/hour. The track width was increased by 1 inch reducing the ground pressure to 15.3 psi.

The 37mm gun mount M19 was similar to that in the M2, but additional protection was provided for the gun barrel and the recoil system. Each of the sponson machine guns was fitted with a tubular sight and a shield in front of the rotor. An hydraulic steering mechanism was added to reduce the steering effort. Numerous minor modifications were made to the traversing mechanism, suspension, and fuel system.

Steel angles have been attached to the front plate to deflect bullet splash and the panoramic telescope has been eliminated from the turret roof.

The top view (below) shows that the engine compartment was relatively unprotected from above. The hole in the turret hatch was to permit the use of signal flags.

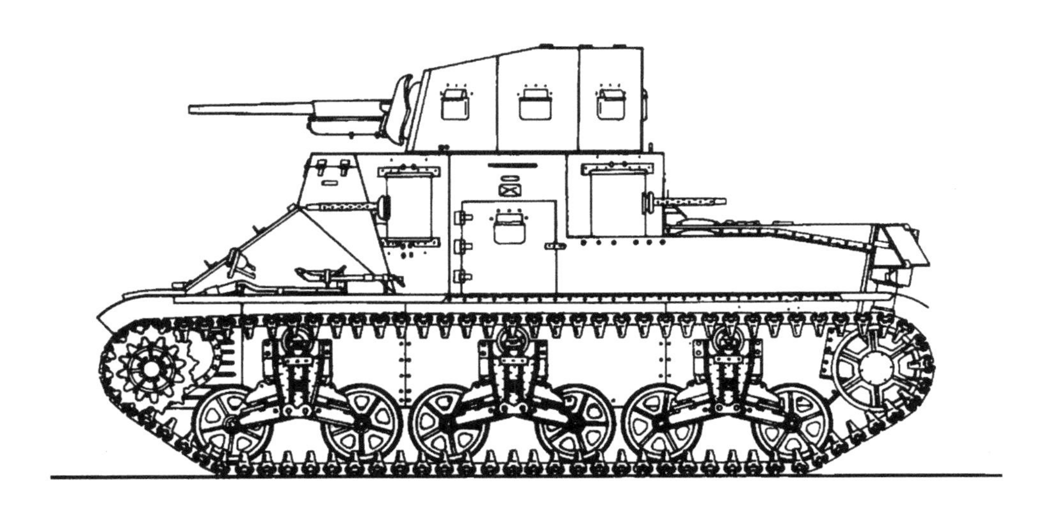

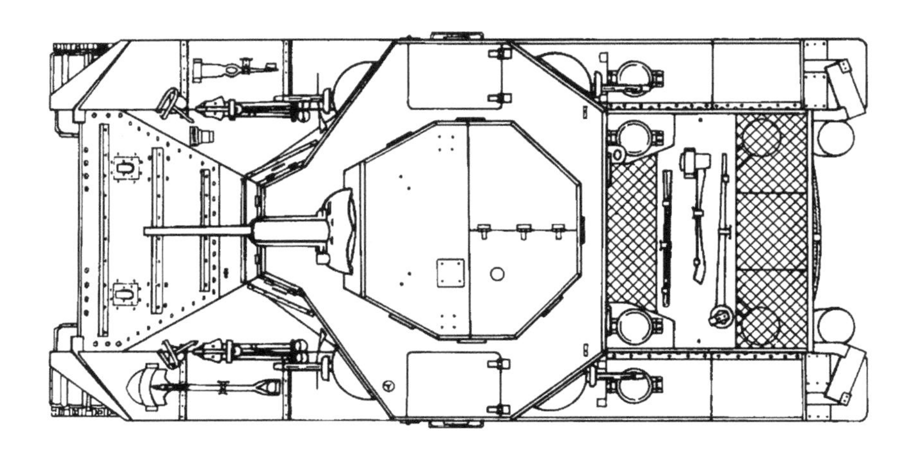

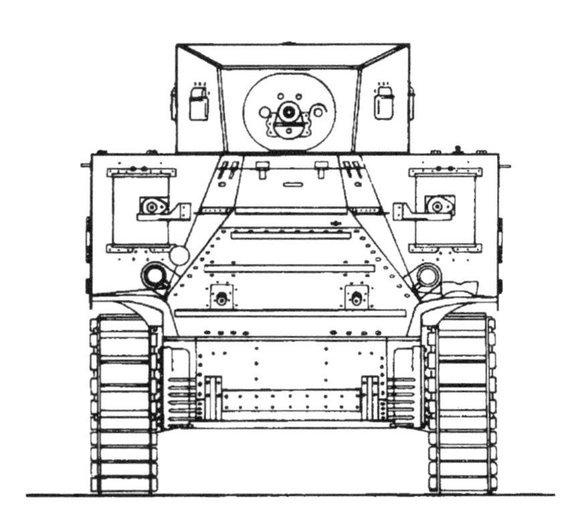

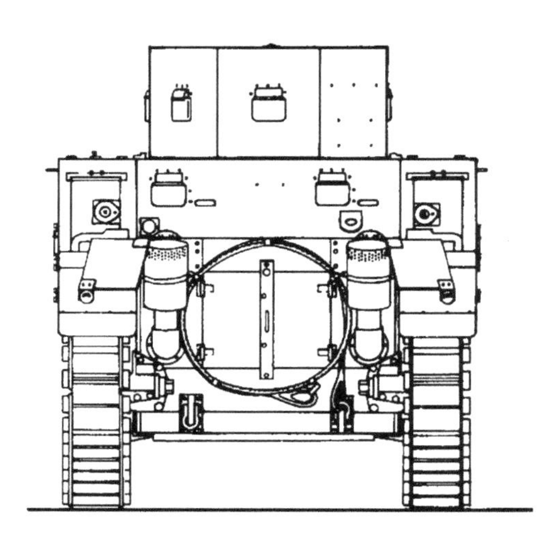

Scale 1:48

Medium Tank M2A1

The front plate has been removed in the view at right exposing the driver's controls. His seat can be seen mounted on top of the transmission.

The radio installation on the rear wall of the fighting compartment and the external antenna base are shown below.

The .30 caliber machine gun sponson mount is at the right. Below are two views of the 37mm gun mount M19. Note that all mounts are equipped with telescopic sights.

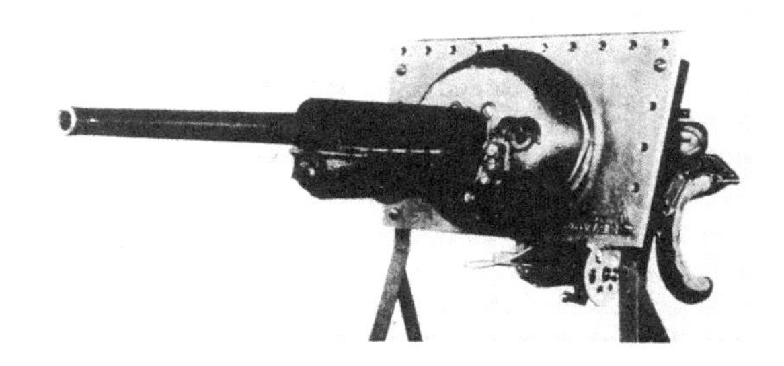

The preproduction mock-up constructed at Chrysler to check out the arsenal drawings.

The M2A1 was intended to replace the M2 for 1940 production, but events in Europe caused drastic changes in the production plans. In May, with the German breakthrough in France, the need for rapid rearmament became clearly apparent. It also provided incentive for the reorganization of the tank troops which had been under study since the success of the German Panzer divisions in Poland the previous Fall. This resulted in the formation of the separate Armored Force under Major General Adna Chaffee on 10 July 1940. Although it consisted initially of only two armored divisions and one separate tank battalion, insufficient tanks were available to arm even this small force. Out of a total strength of approximately 400 tanks, only the 18 M2s could be considered as modern medium tanks. The remainder consisted of light tanks including the Cavalry combat cars and the 18 obsolete M1 convertible tanks at Fort Benning. Production of the light tank M2A4 had started in May and these vehicles were beginning to reach the troops.

Although the "Blitzkrieg" attack had earlier defeated Poland, the sudden fall of France and the British evacuation at Dunkirk awakened the United States to the weakness of its armed forces as nothing had done before. The facilities at Rock Island Arsenal were far too limited to produce the quantity of tanks now required. Previous plans called for production contracts to be issued to locomotive and railway car builders whose experience with heavy equipment would be applicable to tanks. Their excellent production record during the coming years would fully justify this decision. However, it was believed that the vast potential for mass production in the automobile industry must also be applied to the problem of producing tanks. As early as 7 June 1940, William S. Knudsen telephoned K.T. Keller, President of Chrysler Corporation, and arranged a meeting in Detroit. Knudsen, formerly President of General Motors, had been appointed on 29 May 1940 to direct military production. A man who got straight to the point, he asked Keller if Chrysler would build tanks for the Army. When Keller agreed, plans were quickly made to introduce them to their new product. This vehicle, which the Chrysler people had never seen, was the medium tank M2A1, now ready for production. After a quick trip to Rock Island where the Arsenal was building three pilot tanks, a full set of blueprints weighing 186 pounds was shipped to Detroit arriving on Monday 17 June 1940. For the next month, the small group of men who were to form the nucleus of the future tank arsenal worked long hours on the top floor of the Dodge Conant Avenue building. They produced a detailed estimate of the costs required for quantity production of the M2A1 including the land, buildings, and machine tools. During this period, a wooden mock-up was constructed to check the accuracy of the drawings and to enable the engineers to detect assembly problems in the full size tank.

After some changes in requirements and refiguring of the costs, Chrysler received a contract dated 15 August 1940. It was for the production of 1000 medium tanks M2A1 to be delivered by August 1942.

Wooden mock-ups of the auxiliary armor for the M2A1 are shown below.

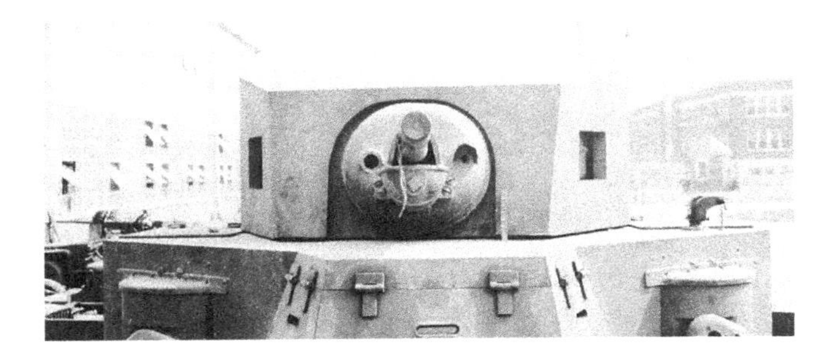

At top left is an M2A1 with full stowage at Fort Knox and at top right, another is about to cross a 2nd Armored Division treadway bridge at Fort Benning.

The new tank arsenal was to be complete by 15 September 1941 and production was to rise from three tanks in the 12th month to 100 in the 15th month and continue at that level until the order was complete.

Meanwhile, staff studies of intelligence reports from the fighting in Europe were concerned with the use by the Germans of the 75mm gun in the Panzer IV. A meeting between Ordnance and General Chaffee, commanding the new Armored Force, concluded that a 75mm gun was a prime requirement for the new medium tank. Thus the M2A1, armed with only a 37mm gun, was rendered obsolete by the rapidly changing tactical requirements. To meet the new situation, a design was prepared based on the M2A1, but carrying a 75mm gun in the right front hull. The new vehicle was designated the medium tank M3. The contract for the M2A1s was cancelled on 28 August 1940 and replaced by a similar contract for 1000 M3s.

Although outmoded for combat use, the M2A1 was still valuable for training purposes. Also, the existing facilities at Rock Island Arsenal would be able to produce limited numbers of the M2A1 long before the new M3s appeared. Thus a contract was let to Rock Island to build 126 M2A1s. Production started in December 1940 and continued until August 1941. By that time, production of the M3 had reached 80 tanks per month and was rapidly increasing. The contract for the M2A1 was then cut to the 94 already produced cancelling the remaining 32.

The M2A1 served, along with the M2, as a training tank in the new Armored Force as well as for experimental purposes. One of the latter programs investigated the use of auxiliary armor to improve the protection against antitank guns. Auxiliary homogeneous armor weighing 9500 pounds was designed for the M2A1 with a maximum thickness of 3 inches in addition to the original face-hardened plate. The program recommended the development of similar auxiliary armor for the medium tank M3.

Another experimental program used an M2, registration number W-30451, as a flame thrower tank. The E2 flame gun was installed in the turret replacing the 37mm gun. The sponson and fixed machine guns were retained. Both the M2 and M2A1 were declared obsolete by OCM 19099 in late 1942.

An M2 and a M2A1 lead the light tanks in this demonstration at Fort Knox in May, 1941.

The mock-up for the medium tank M3 alongside an M2A1. Note the M2A1 type differential and final drive housing.

MEDIUM TANK M3

News from Europe in the late Spring of 1940 emphasized the urgent necessity to rebuild America's Armed Forces. The overwhelming success of the German "Blitzkrieg" required not only that the new forces be reorganized, but that they also be armed with equipment second to none. The move toward an organization for the new mode of warfare started with the formation of the separate Armored Force combining the tank elements previously belonging to the Cavalry and Infantry. A key item in its equipment was intended to be the medium tank M2A1. Although the latest product of the Ordnance development program, dispatches from Europe indicated that its 37mm gun and light armor were already inadequate for a modern medium tank and that it would be obsolete before it reached production. The 75mm short barreled cannon in the German Panzer IV clearly showed that a weapon at least as powerful would be required for the new medium tank.

On 13 June 1940, the characteristics of a tank incorporating the updated requirements were outlined in OCM 15889. The new vehicle was standardized on 11 July 1940 as the medium tank M3. The urgency of the world situation required that it be standardized and ordered into production long before the design was complete.

With the fall of France, the British Army lost the bulk of its armored vehicles during the evacuation at Dunkirk. Thus it was of vital importance to equip these as well as new units at the earliest possible date. A British Tank Mission headed by Mr. Michael Dewar arrived in the United States to arrange for the procurement of armored vehicles. Initially, they hoped to obtain the production of British designs in American factories. Since this would cause a dispersion of effort and an inefficient use of the resources available, they were informed that only designs acceptable to the U.S. Army would be produced. However, some modifications would be permitted on the equipment manufactured under British contracts. On this basis, the British placed orders for the M3 with a modified fighting compartment and a new turret.

British production contracts for 685 tanks were placed with the Baldwin Locomotive Works parallel to a U.S. contract for a similar number. Two other orders for 500 tanks each were issued to the Pullman Standard Manufacturing Company and the Pressed Steel Car Company. An additional order for 100 was given to the Lima Locomotive Company, but because of a late start, production at Lima was later changed to the M4.

During the Summer of 1940, considerable change occurred in the design of the M3. The original concept was to thicken up the armor and install a 75mm gun in the front of the right sponson on the M2A1, similar to the arrangement on the T5E2. The Tank Committee, composed of manufacturers involved in the production program, visited Aberdeen on 26 August 1940. At that time they, along with representatives of the Armored Force, were shown a full size wooden mock-up of the proposed tank hull. The main armament was a short barreled 75mm gun installed in a rotor at the

Mock-up of the final design for the medium tank M3 with the three piece differential and final drive housing.

right front of the hull. This weapon was an adaptation of the unsuccessful 75mm gun T6. The latter was a most improbable weapon, a low velocity antiaircraft gun. As modified for tank use, it was redesignated as the 75mm gun T7.

This early version of the M3 design attempted to retain the full machine gun armament of the M2A1. The loss of the right front sponson machine gun, displaced by the 75mm cannon, was made up by the installation of a small auxiliary turret in the left front of the hull. This auxiliary turret carried two .30 caliber machine guns. A 37mm gun was turret mounted on top of the hull coaxial with another .30 caliber machine gun. On top of the turret, a cupola was fitted with an additional .30 caliber weapon for antiaircraft use. Armor thickness was increased to 2 inches in front and 1-1/2 inches at the sides and on the highly sloped front plate.

The major weakness in the design was the limited traverse of the hull mounted 75mm gun. However, Ordnance pointed out that no turret had yet been designed in this country to carry such a powerful weapon with full 360 degree traverse. On the other hand, many of the design problems in the sponson mount had already been worked out with the pack howitzer in the T5E2. Using this experience, such a mount could be put into production almost immediately. The Armored Force suggested that the M3s be limited to a small number such as 360 and full production be held up pending the design of a 75mm gun turret. However, the urgent need for large quantities of new tanks, particularly by the British in the Middle East would not permit the interruption of the production plans already in progress. Ordnance requested that full production of the M3 begin immediately. At the same time, a new tank would be designed using the same basic chassis, but carrying a turret mounted 75mm gun. Because of its similar chassis, the new vehicle would replace the M3 on the assembly lines with only a small loss of production. This program was adopted and full production was approved without further delay.

Another outcome of this meeting was the revision of the M3's military characteristics which was approved by OCM 16111. All of the sponson machine guns were eliminated and pistol ports were installed to cover these areas. The radio set was moved to the left front sponson where the auxiliary turret had been located. The fuel capacity was increased and the turret compartment floor was lowered to give more head room. Better seats, safety belts, and improved vision devices were provided for the crew. The wooden mock-up was rebuilt incorporating the various changes.

The British turret was designed by Mr. L. E. Carr to fit the standard 54.5 inch diameter turret ring, but it was enlarged to allow more room for the crew and to carry the radio set in a large bustle. The cupola was eliminated and replaced by a circular hatch fitted with a rotating split hatch cover. A periscope was mounted in one half of the cover. The British designation for their version of the M3 was the General Grant I. The standard U.S. model was referred to as the General Lee I. It was obvious which one they considered the winner.

Mock-up of the British turret for the M3 installed on a modified medium tank M2 to check the arrangement.

Medium tank M3, serial number 1. This is the pilot tank built at Rock Island Arsenal.

Once the basic configuration had been established, the tremendous task of detail design began. Close coordination was required between the design team at Aberdeen and the manufacturers to allow the earliest possible start of production. Preliminary drawings were issued to permit the purchase of materials and the necessary machine tools. Representatives of the manufacturers worked with the Aberdeen designers to insure that each part was simplified as far as possible for production.

In the meantime, construction of a pilot tank was started at Rock Island Arsenal. Based on the preliminary drawings a turret was cast and shipped to Aberdeen. After being equipped with the 37mm gun mount and the power traversing system, it was installed on a medium tank M2 for demonstration to the Tank Committee on 20 December 1940. Another pilot turret based on the British design was installed on the M2 during this same period. At this time, the production drawings were about 90% complete.

By the end of 1940, plans called for a total production rate of 14-1/2 tanks per day. Eight of these were from U.S. contractors and 6-1/2 from British orders. It was apparent by now that tank production for the U.S. and Britain could not be handled as separate accounts and a Joint Tank Planning Committee was formed. In April of 1941, this Committee was pushing for 1000 tanks a month and by July, a target of 2000 tanks a month was planned. After meetings between Prime Minister Churchill, President Roosevelt, and Lord Beaverbrook, the production targets were set at 25,000 medium tanks in 1942 and 45,000 in 1943.

The initial design job was finished on 1 February 1941, although a multitude of revisions were to follow. The pilot at Rock Island was rapidly completed and first moved under its own power on 13 March 1941. The following day it was shipped, without a turret, to Aberdeen, arriving on 21 March. The turret was installed and preliminary testing began. The cupola on this first turret differed from those on later vehicles in that it was equipped with only one vision port located on the right side. All later cupolas, as well as the final wooden mock-up, had two vision ports, one on each side. Production pilot tanks were rapidly completed by the various manufacturers and shipped to Aberdeen for test with the first arriving from Detroit Tank Arsenal on 5 May 1941.

The appearance of the Rock Island pilot at Aberdeen in late March 1941. Note that there is only one vision slot in the cupola.

The first Chrysler production pilot, serial number 2 (above), completed in April 1941 at Detroit Arsenal. It served as a test vehicle at Aberdeen during the war and was returned to the Arsenal in 1945 (at right). The early Chrysler production line is shown below with tanks 32 and 41 (registration numbers W-301030 and W-301039) being loaded for shipment.

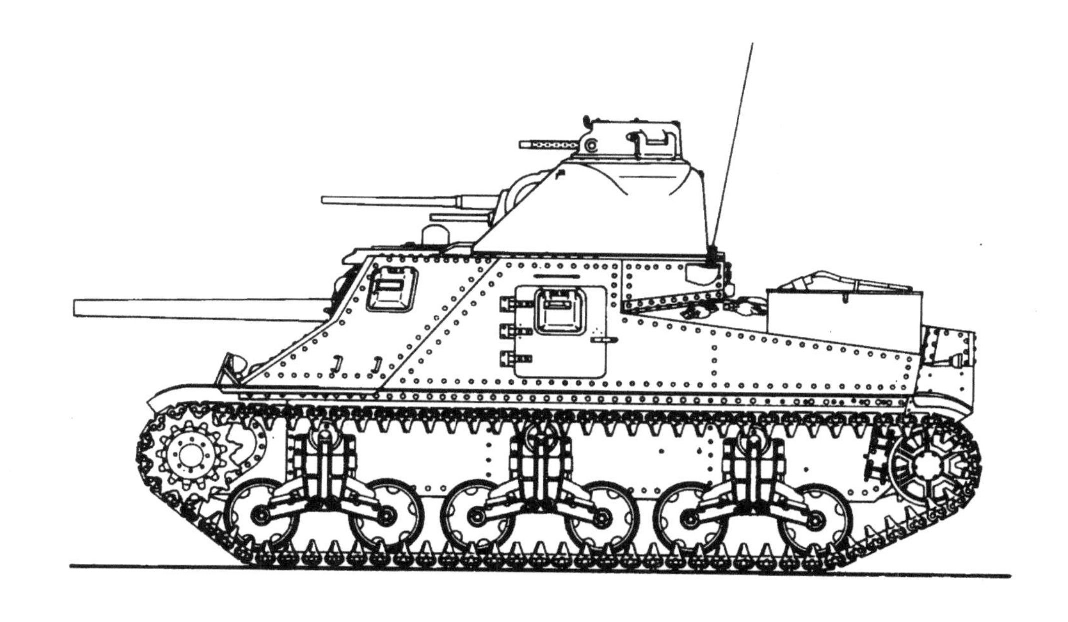

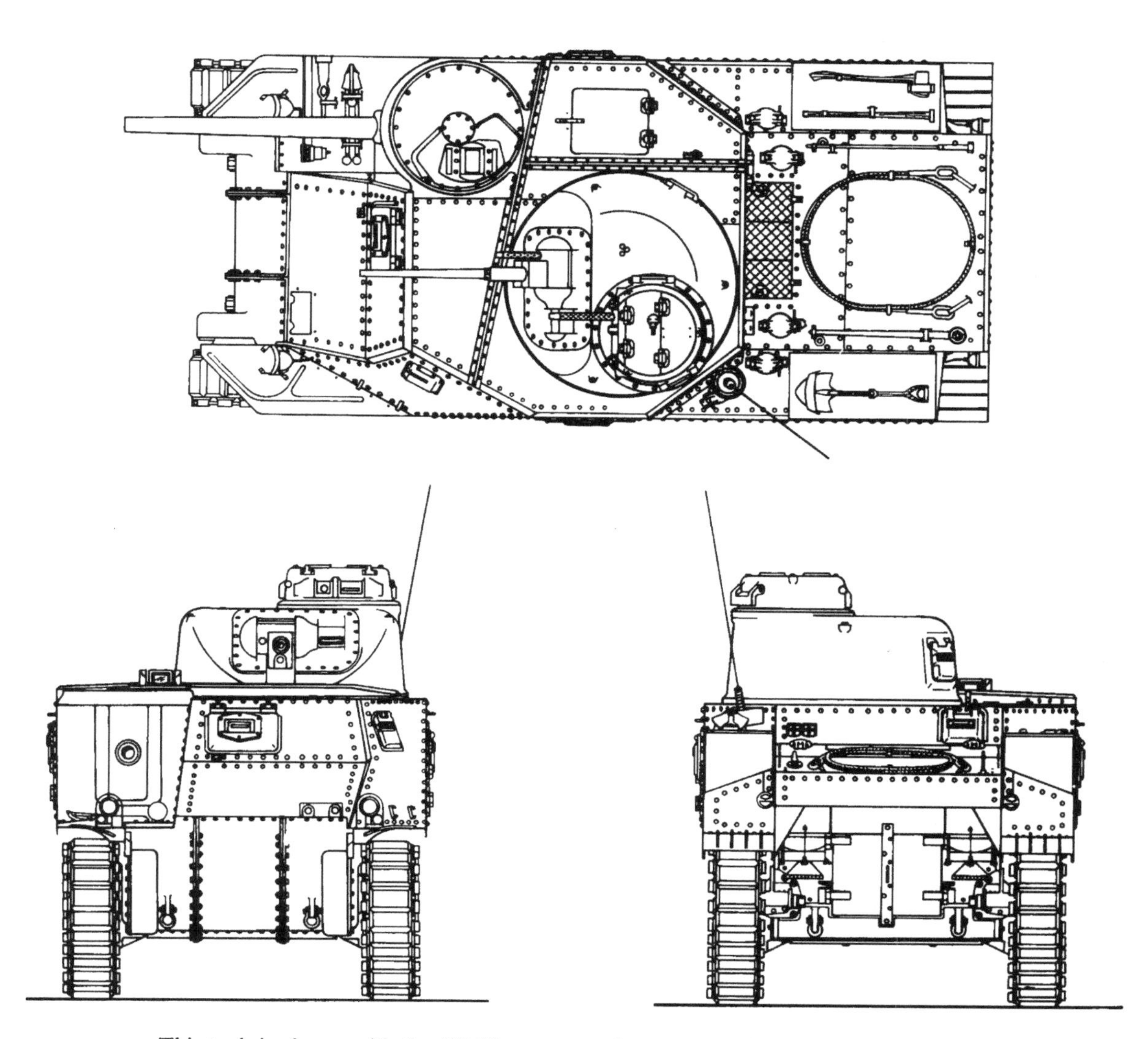

This tank is shown with the M3 75mm gun and a counterweight below the 37mm gun.

Scale 1:48

Medium Tank M3

Production of M3s at Detroit Arsenal (above) in November 1941. The chalk numbers on the front armor indicate these to be the 505th and 510th M3s built by Chrysler. Below a line of completed tanks await shipment.

Production of the medium tank M3 was in full swing by the late Summer of 1941 at four manufacturers. These were the American Locomotive Company, Detroit Tank Arsenal (Chrysler), Pressed Steel Car Company, and Pullman Standard Car Company. The latter two were building the General Grant for British service. Production of the M3 continued until August 1942 reaching a total of 4924 tanks. This total included the standard U.S. M3 as well as the General Lee I and the General Grant I for Britain.

The first Grant tank built for the British by the Pullman Standard Car Company is shown at the right above on 25 July 1941. At the left, the first two Grant tanks are prepared for shipment without guns.

Assembly of the first Grant at Pullman Standard can be seen above. In the bottom photograph, 12 Grants are ready for shipment. At the right is the first Grant completed at the Pressed Steel Car Company on 15 July 1941.

Above is the Grant production line at Pullman Standard. The views below show the assembly of the hull by riveting and the installation of the turret.

A special fixture is used to install the 75mm gun (below left) and the air-cooled radial engine can be seen through the doors at the rear of the hull (below right).

A fully equipped Grant at the Pullman Standard Car Company in November 1941. Note the factory installed sandshields.

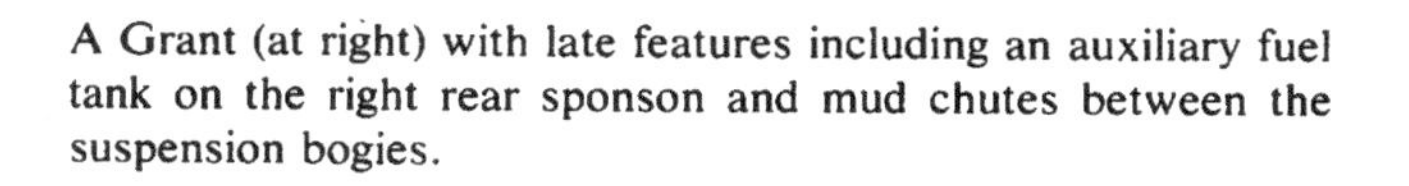

A Grant (at right) with late features including an auxiliary fuel tank on the right rear sponson and mud chutes between the suspension bogies.

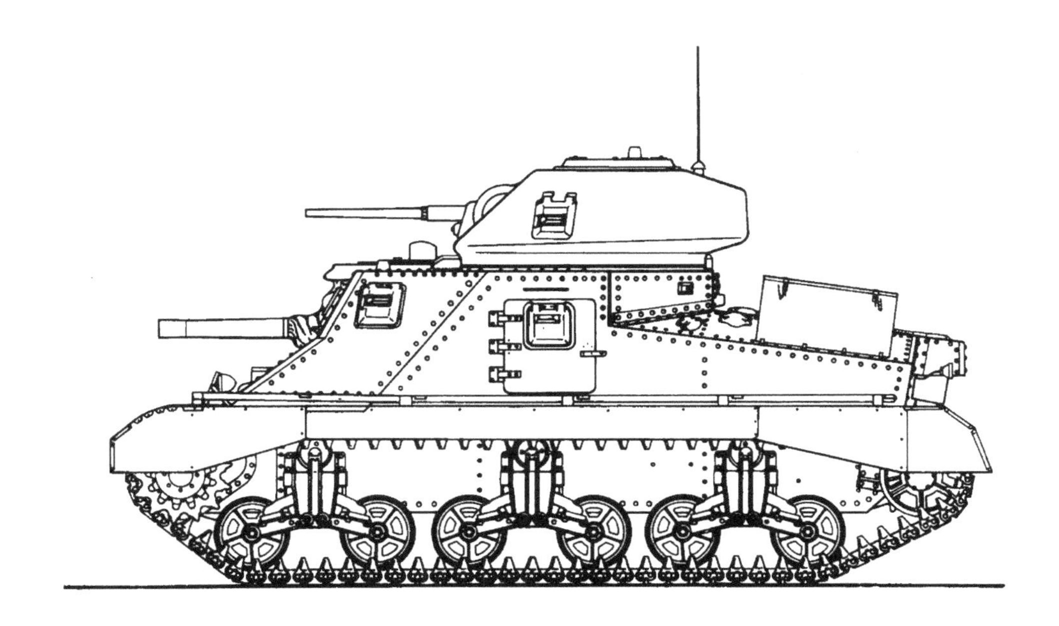

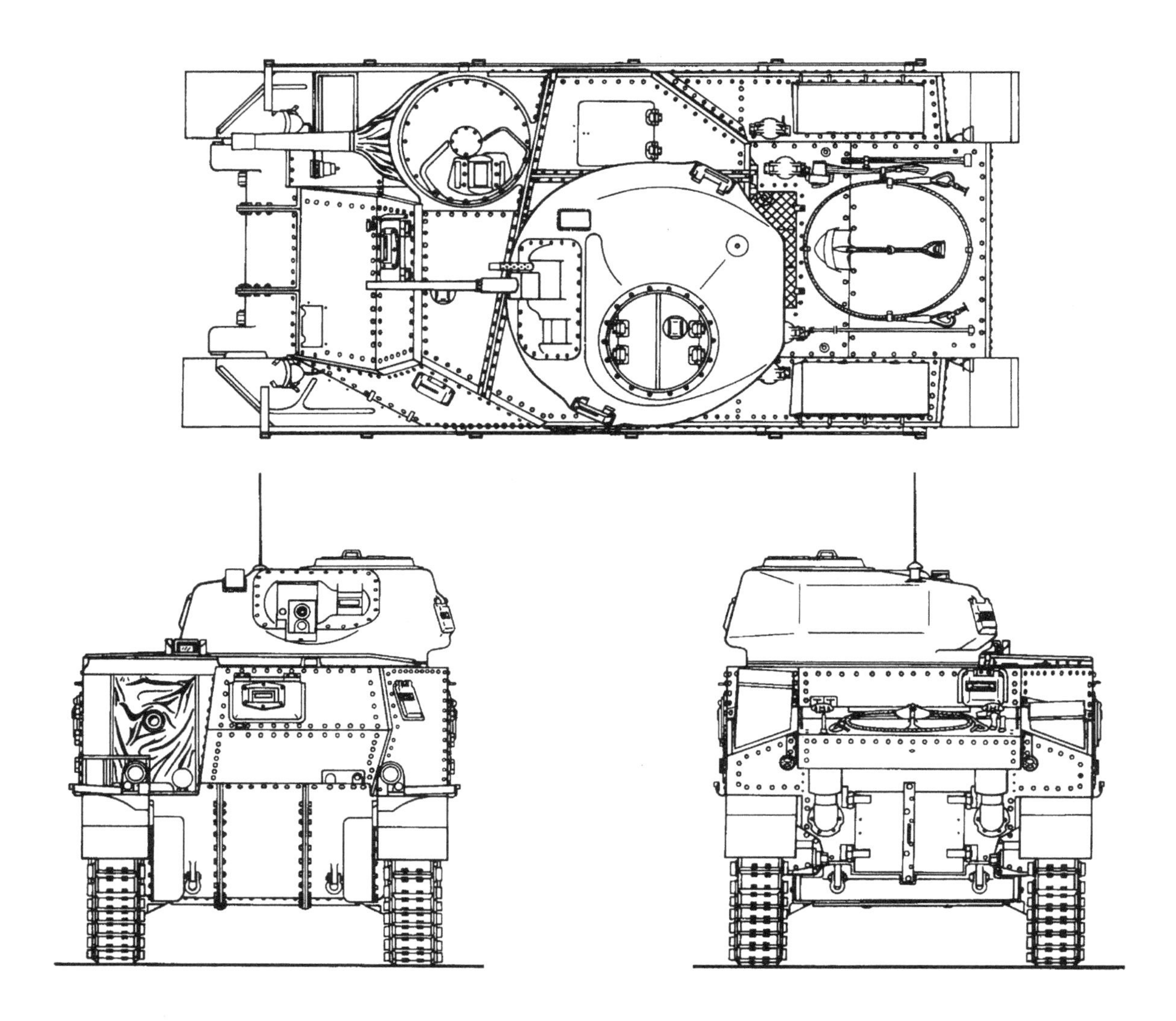

Scale 1:48

Cruiser Tank Grant I

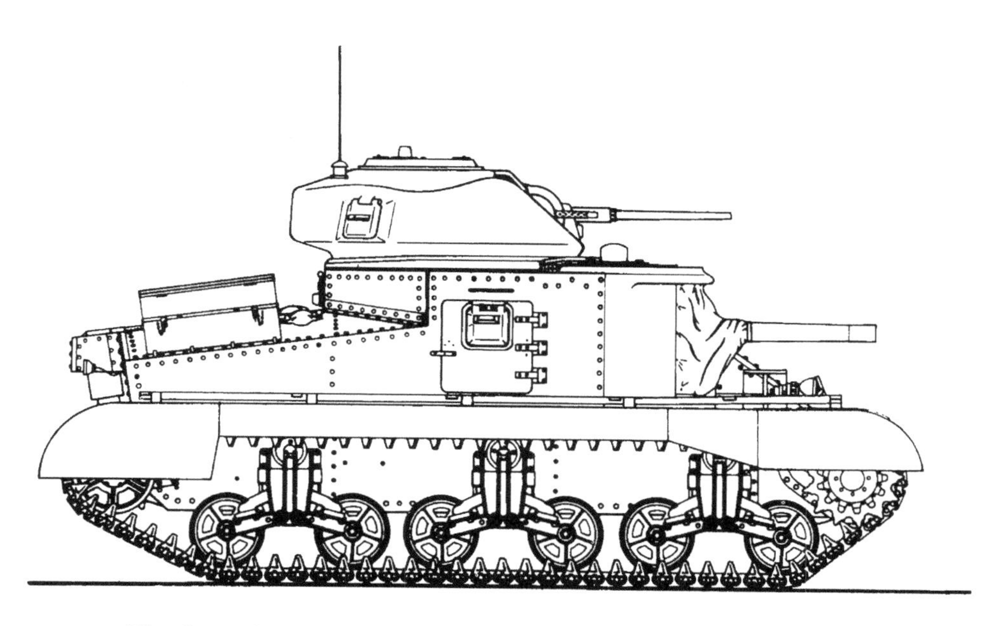

The Grant above is fitted with sandshields of an alternate design.

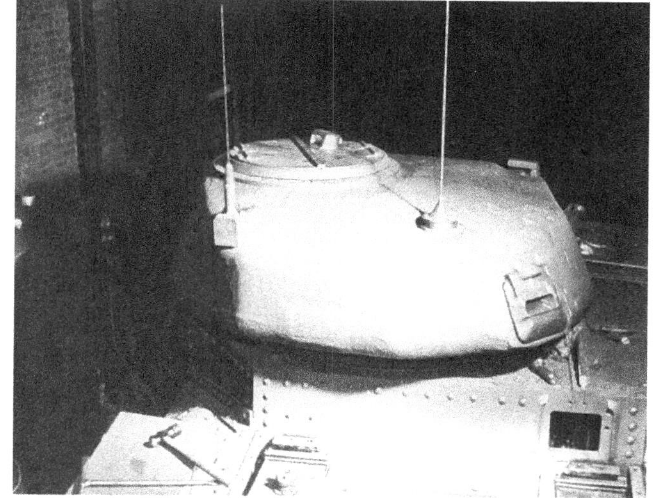

The British Number 19 radio set is installed in the Grant turret bustle with its two antennas (above). With the gun mount removed, the stowage on each side of the turret can be seen (below).

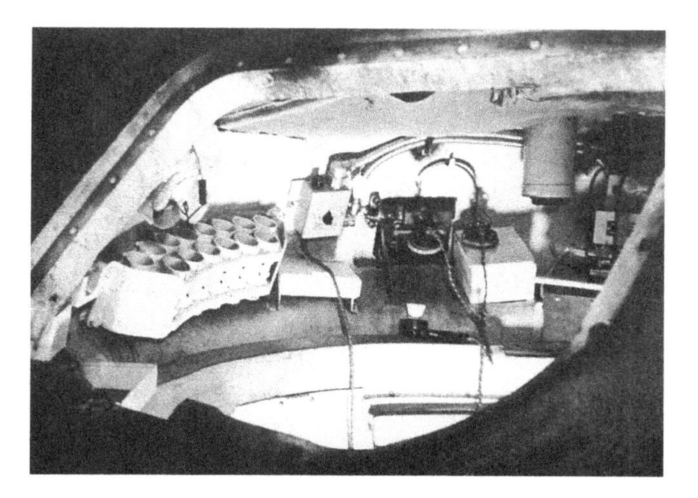

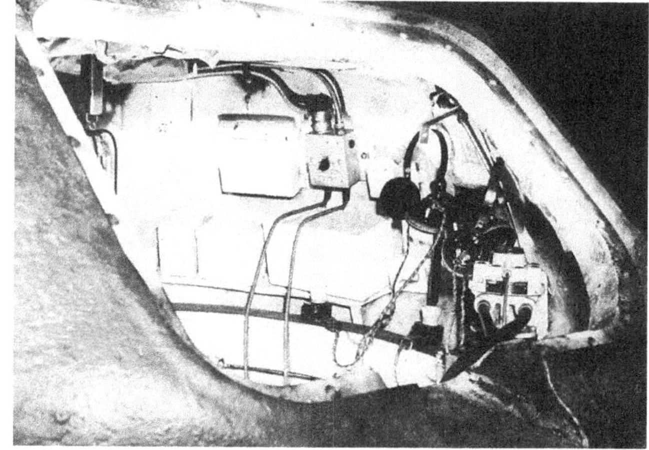

This Grant appears to have full external stowage except for the machine gun tripod on the left front. Note that only one antenna is fitted. The tank is equipped with the British WE 210 double I rubber track shoes.

The views below and at the left show the Grant turret casting installed on the modified medium tank M2. The latter vehicle served as a steel mock-up during the development program.

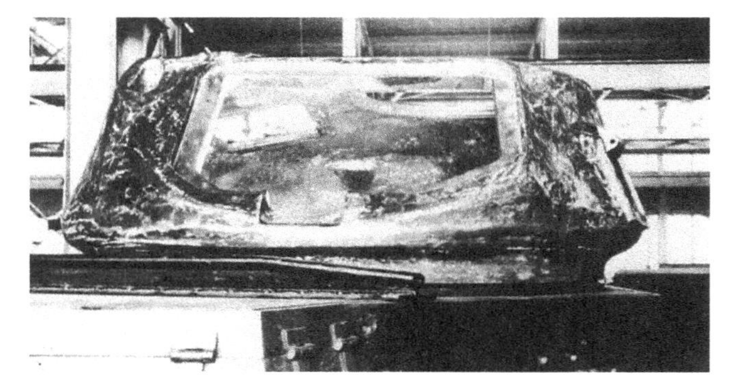

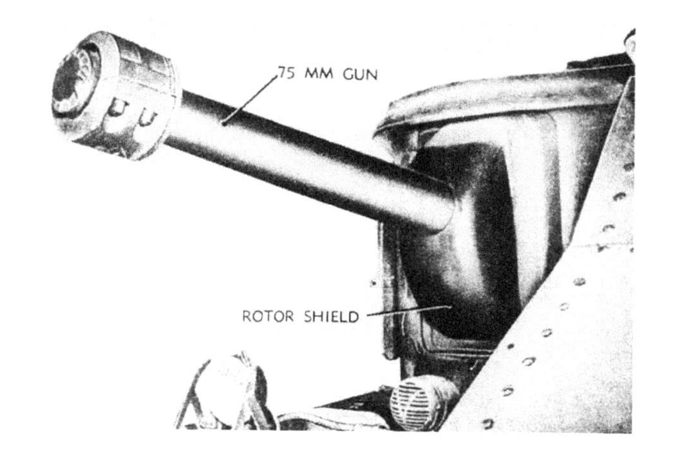

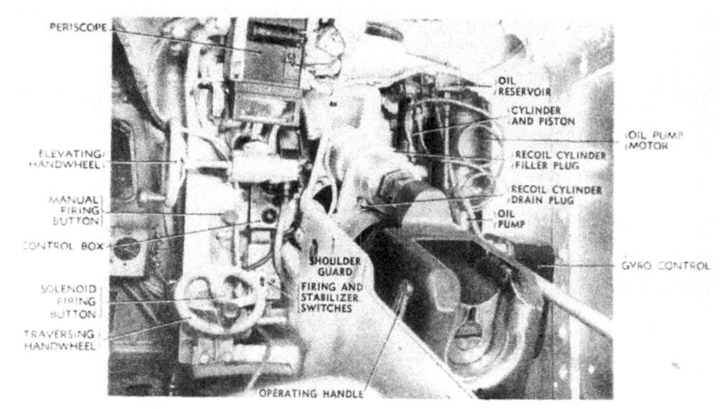

Above the 75mm gun is installed in the medium tank M3. The view at the right is from the gunner's position. Note the counterweight near the muzzle (at left) to balance the short barreled M2 gun.

Main armament of the first pilot M3 was the 75mm gun T7 number 1. This was the modified version of the 75mm gun T6 retaining its bore length of 84 inches. It was chambered to use the standard 75mm ammunition issued for the 75mm gun M1897. The latter was the French 75 adopted by the U.S. during World War I. With a slightly shorter barrel, the muzzle velocity of the T7 was 1850 ft/sec compared to 1950 ft/sec for the field gun. Initially, the 75 was considered as support artillery and not as the primary antitank weapon, so there was little or no concern about muzzle velocity or armor piercing performance. In fact, experiments were carried out shortening the barrel to 71.25 inches, but the muzzle blast was considered excessive so the 84 inch length was retained. Equipped with a semiautomatic vertical sliding breechblock, the T7 was standardized as the 75mm gun M2. The hull mounting was designated as the 75mm gun mount M1.

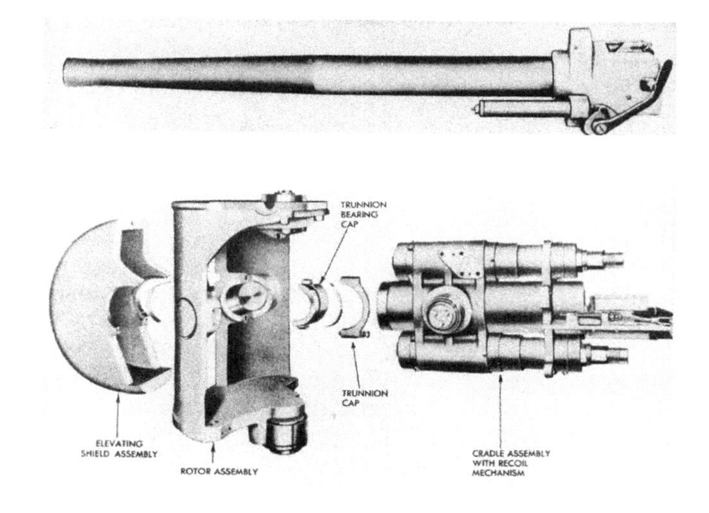

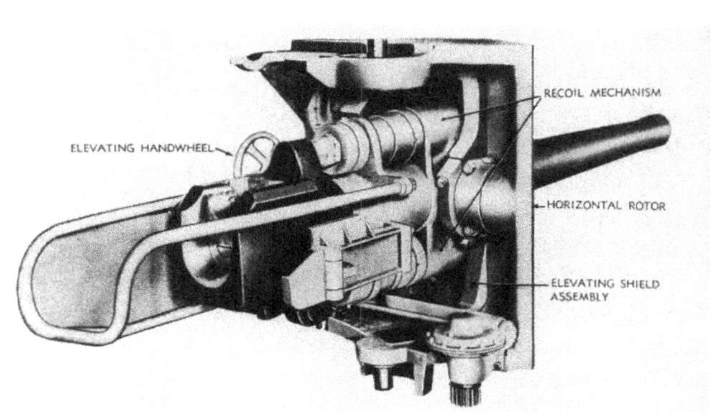

The photographs at the right show (top to bottom) the 75mm gun M2, an exploded view of the gun mount, and two views of the weapon assembled in the mount.

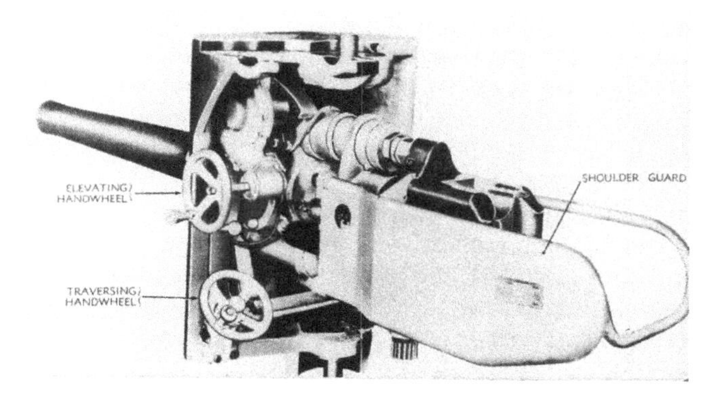

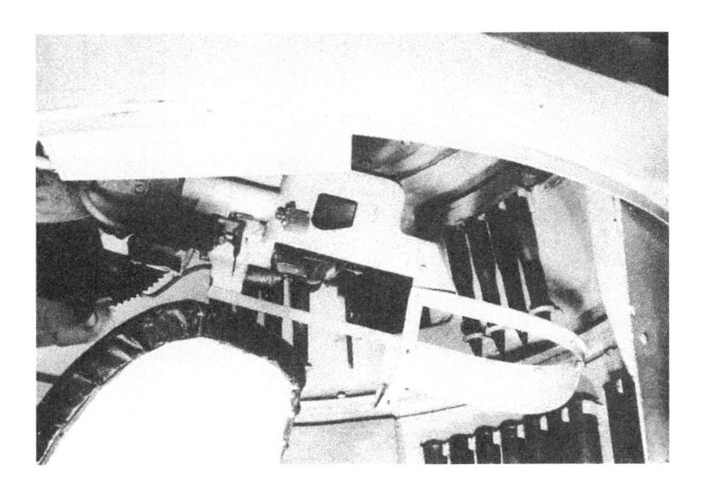

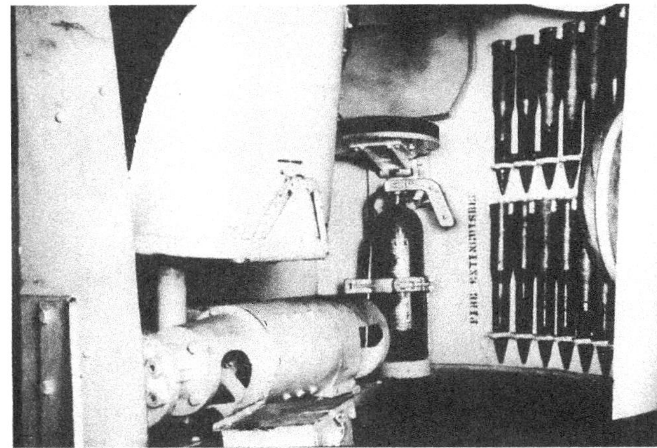

The turret stowage on medium tank M3, number 1026, is shown above. Note the 37mm ready racks in the turret basket.

The turret armament in the M3 consisted of the 37mm gun M6 in a coaxial mount with a .30 caliber machine gun. The same combination mount M24 was used in the British turret. The cupola installed on top of the U.S. turret carried an additional .30 caliber machine gun. Other armament on the production tanks included two .30 caliber machine guns fixed in the front plate for use by the driver.

The 37mm gun M6 was equipped with a semi-automatic breechblock. Early in the production program, shortages forced the substitution of the 37mm gun M5 in some tanks. The barrel of the latter was six inches shorter and the breechblock was manually operated. Both the 75mm and 37mm guns were fitted with elevation gyrostabilizers on the pilot tank. During installation, it was noted that both weapons were out of balance and high friction in the 75mm mount prevented proper operation of the stabilizer. Modifications reduced the friction to an acceptable level and counterweights were added to balance both guns. On the 37mm gun M6, the counterweight was a steel cylinder installed on the mount just below the gun barrel. With the 75mm gun M2, a round counterweight was clamped around the muzzle end of the gun barrel itself. Since future plans were to replace the M2 gun with a longer barreled 75mm cannon, it was not desirable to add the weight to the mount. The longer barrel balanced the new gun so counterweights were not required. The new weapon was the 75mm gun T8 subsequently standardized as the M3. Developed for the medium tank T6, the 75mm gun M3 had a bore length of 110.63 inches and was designed to operate the semiautomatic breechblock in the horizontal direction. Otherwise it was identical to the M2 gun, however, the longer barrel increased the muzzle velocity to 2030 ft/sec with the same ammunition. In the medium tank M3, the longer weapon was installed in the mount M1 with the breechblock moving in the vertical direction, the same as the M2 gun.

The 37mm gun M6 (above) was installed in the 37mm gun mount M24 (below).

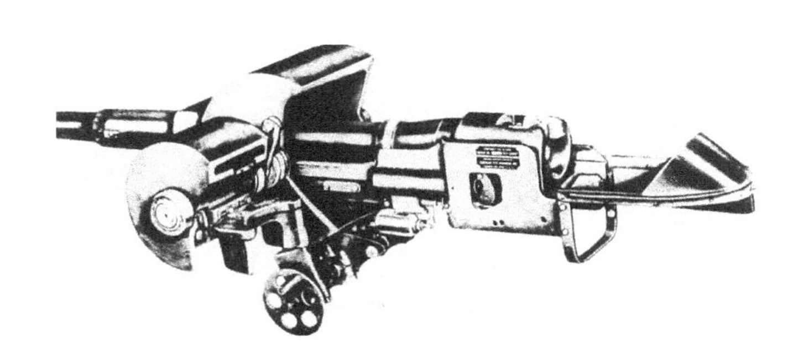

Tests in April 1941 showed that the power traverse and elevation stabilizer greatly improved the effectiveness of the 37mm gun when the tank was in motion. With the tank moving at 10 miles/hour over a zig-zag course, the crew rapidly engaged targets ranging from 200 to 700 yards in all different directions. Over 60% hits were repeatedly obtained using the T1 telescopic sight. As result of these tests and the subsequent solution of the friction problem in the 75mm gun mount, the Ordnance Committee recommended the standardization of stabilizers for both cannon in June 1941. By November, stabilizers had been introduced into production at Detroit Tank Arsenal and a schedule was planned to provide stabilizers for all production M3s starting in January 1942.

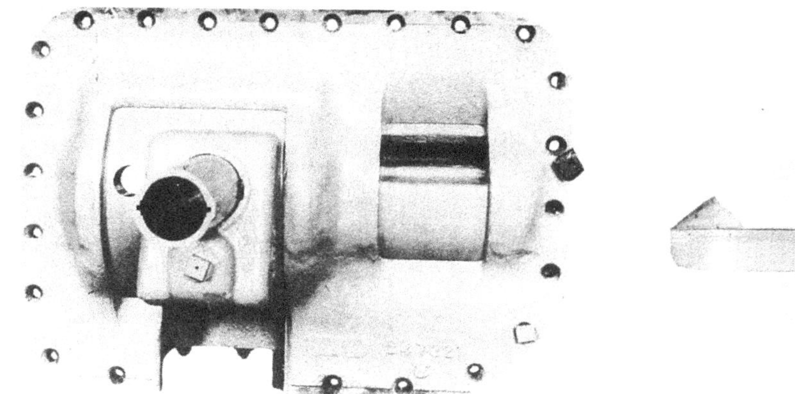

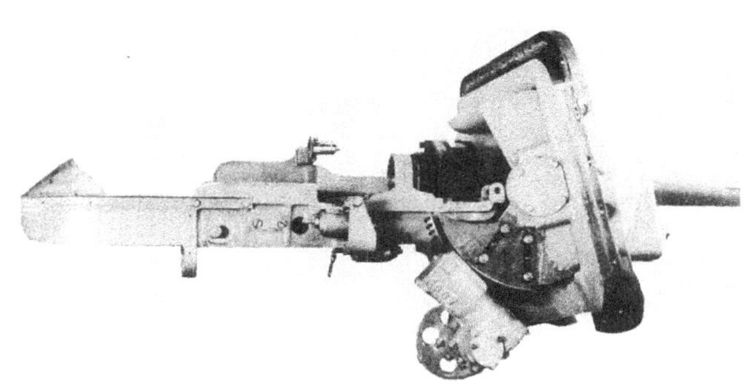

Details of the M24 gun mount without the cannon can be seen above. This is the early mount before the addition of the counterweight.

The counterweight was attached just below the gun barrel (at left) to balance the mount and permit the proper operation of the stabilizer.

The driver's twin fixed machine guns were installed to the left of his seat (below left). The location of the various items of armament and ammunition stowage can be seen below at the right.

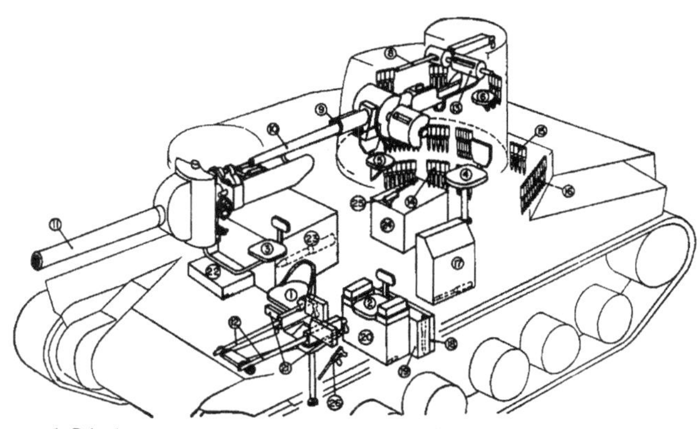

1. Driver's seat.
2. Radio operator's seat.
3. 75-mm gunner's seat.
4. 37-mm gunner's seat.
5. 37-mm gun loader's seat.
6. Tank commander's seat.
8. Cal. .30 machine gun.
9. Cal. .30 machine gun.
10. 37-mm gun.
11. 75-mm gun.
12. 2 cal. .30 machine guns.
13. Protectoscopes.
14. 51 rounds 37-mm ammunition carried in turret.
15. 13 rounds 37-mm ammunition.
16. 11 rounds 37-mm ammunition.
17. 42 rounds 37-mm ammunition.
18. Ten 100-round belts cal. .30 ammunition.
19. 20 rounds 37-mm ammunition.
20. Fourteen 250-round belts containing 225 rounds cal. .30 ammunition.
21. Two 250-round belts containing 225 rounds cal. .30 ammunition.
22. Twenty-five 100-round belts cal. .30 ammunition.
23. 41 rounds 75-mm ammunition; six 100-round belts cal. .30 ammunition.
24. 42 rounds 37-mm ammunition.
25. Submachine gun.
26. Submachine gun. Carried in tank but not shown on drawing are 9 rounds 75-mm ammunition carried in cartons and twenty-four 50-round clips cal. .45 ammunition.

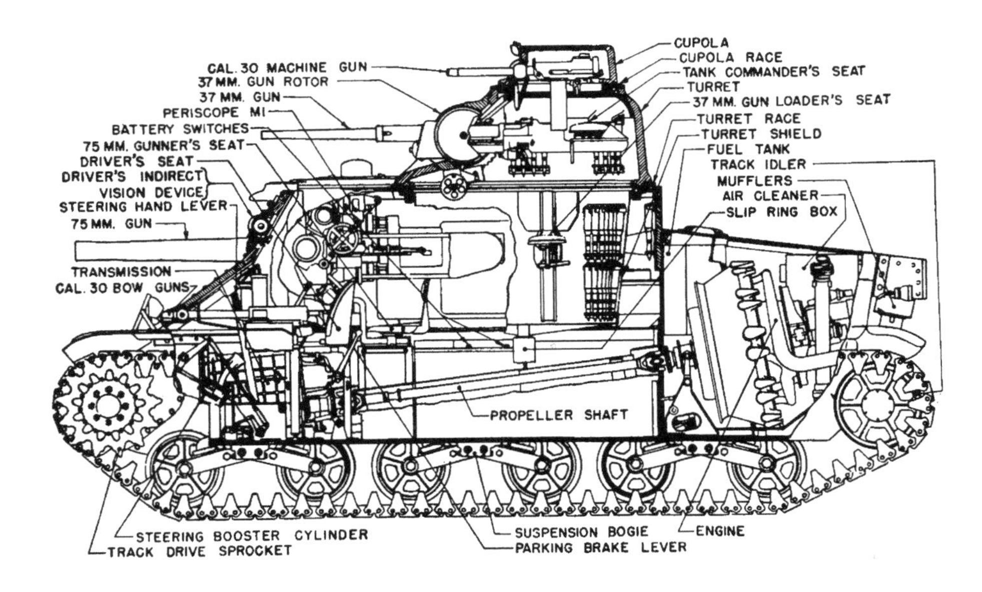

The interior arrangement of the M3 is shown in the sectional drawing above. The stowage in the fighting compartment appears in the three photographs below. Note the early 50 round ammunition drums for the .45 caliber Thompson submachine gun.

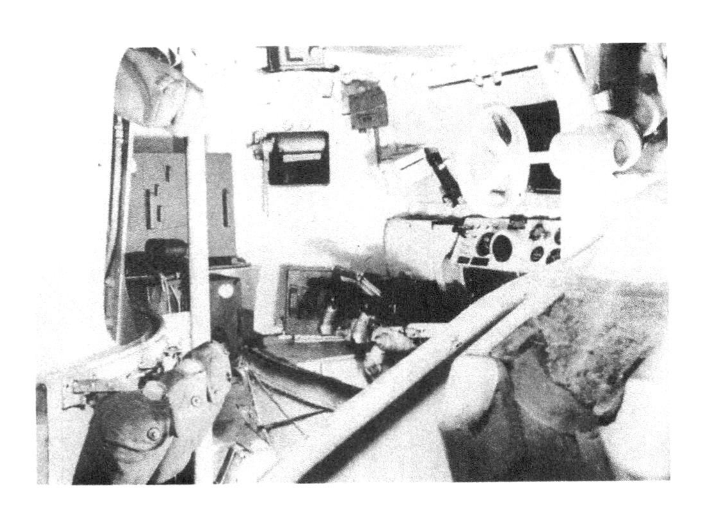

Constructed of rolled homogeneous armor assembled by riveting, the early production M3 had a loaded weight of approximately 31 tons. The turret and cupola were both cast armor. Originally, the crew consisted of seven men, but this was later reduced to six with the driver taking over the duties of the radio operator. The 400 hp Wright R975 EC2 engine was installed in the rear of the hull separated by a bulkhead from the fighting compartment. The propeller shaft extended forward below the turret basket to the 5-speed synchromesh transmission located just below the driver. The power was transmitted through the controlled differential and final drive to the sprockets at the front of each track. The three piece cast housing for the final drive and controlled differential bolted together to form the lower front of the hull.

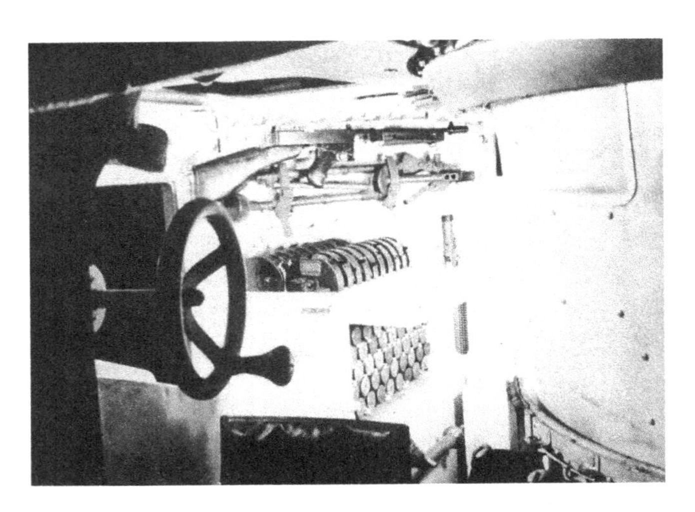

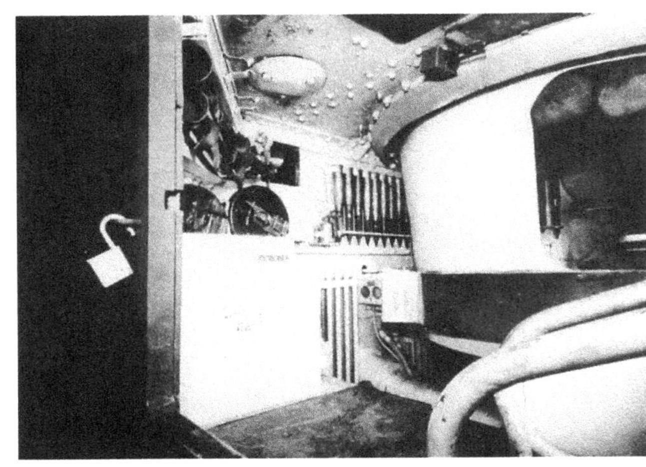

The steel angle stiffeners across the hull bottom are visible on the M3 at right. This early vehicle with side doors does not have a floor escape hatch.

Three M3s were shipped from Aberdeen in August 1941. One went to the Armored Force at Fort Benning and two were sent to Great Britain. By September, 20 tanks had been shipped under the Lend-Lease agreement. All of these vehicles were equipped with a new transmission oil cooler shown to be necessary by the test program. From this time on, increasing numbers of M3s were shipped to meet the urgent British requirements. These tanks all carried the 75mm gun M2, since the new M3 gun was not yet available. Many of the tanks issued to the U.S. Armored Force during this period were without 75mm guns.

The Aberdeen test program, plus information from the troops receiving the new tanks, produced a long list of required changes. One problem concerned the Hycon hydraulic power boost for the steering brake control system. Installed in all of the early production tanks, it proved unreliable and erratic in service. Modifications to the Hycon system were introduced into production beginning 1 November 1941 and modified parts were made available to retrofit the early tanks. However, as early as 26 August, a new, all mechanical, long lever steering system was authorized for use at Detroit Tank Arsenal. In February 1942, the Ordnance Committee recommended the long lever system for all future M3s because of its reliability.

Tests at Aberdeen showed dangerously high concentrations of carbon monoxide inside the tank if the guns were fired with the hatches closed. After evaluation of five different designs, new ventilators were installed at three locations. One was placed on top of the turret alongside the cupola and another on the left front of the hull roof. During the experiments, the third ventilator was installed in the hatch cover on the right side of the hull roof. This increased the weight of the cover and made it awkward to handle so the ventilator was shifted to the hull roof at the rear of the hatch for the production vehicles. With the new ventilators in operation, the carbon monoxide was reduced to a safe level during firing.

The suspension components on the M3, designed for use on earlier much lighter vehicles, had a relatively short life under the high stresses imposed in service. To improve their performance, the bogie assembly was redesigned and heavier volute springs were installed. The most obvious change in the new bogie was the relocation of the track return roller from the top of the bogie frame to a bracket extending to the rear. A steel track skid was attached to the top of the new bogie frame. Released for production, the new design appeared on only the very late tanks of the M3 series. Modification of the track shoes increased the original width of 16 inches to 16-9/16 inches and this remained the standard width for later track shoe designs.

Three ventilators are installed experimentally on the M3 below. Note the ventilator in the hull roof hatch.

A late production M3 without side doors is shown above and below. This tank is armed with the long barreled 75mm gun M3.

Ballistic tests revealed the vulnerability of the side doors to damage from both high explosive and armor piercing projectiles. Aberdeen recommended that both side doors be eliminated and an escape hatch be provided in the floor of the tank. These recommendations were applied to the later production vehicles with the escape hatch being located in the floor at the right rear of the fighting compartment. The door mounted pistol port was also eliminated on the left side, but was retained on the right.

The British had objected very early to the high silhouette of the M3 design. To lower the height of the tank, it was recommended that the cupola be replaced with a flat circular hatch similar to that on the Grant turret using the same type of split hatch cover. This modification was adopted for some production vehicles and was frequently observed on tanks in British service.

The rotors mounting the 75mm and 37mm cannon were easily damaged by small arms fire. Although the small projectiles did not penetrate, they scarred the rotor surface sufficiently to cause interference preventing movement of the gun mount. Auxiliary shields were designed to protect the rotor surface on both the 37mm and 75mm gun mounts.

Auxiliary armor shields are fitted over the 37mm and 75mm gun mounts to protect the rotor surface (at left).

The model above illustrates the final modifications authorized for the medium tank M3. Note the driver's periscope and the late heavy duty suspension bogies.

In June 1942, the Ordnance Committee proposed eliminating both of the driver's fixed machine guns, the two machine gun tripods, and one of the .45 caliber submachine guns. However, approval was granted to drop only one of the fixed guns and one tripod. On the later production vehicles, the empty machine gun port was filled with a steel plug.

Service tests revealed considerable difficulty in maintaining proper alignment between the periscope mounted telescopic sight and the 75mm gun. To correct this, an M15 direct sight telescope was installed coaxial with the cannon on the left side of the mount. It proved far easier to hold accurate alignment with this telescope than with the periscope mounted version. Another late improvement was the installation of a periscope for the driver in the hull roof just above his position.

To insure an adequate engine supply, a contract was let to Continental Motors to produce the Wright R975 EC2. With Wright heavily involved in the aircraft program, Continental became responsible for production of these tank engines as well as their later modifications.

The installation of the M15 direct sight telescope in the M1 mount is shown below. Note that an additional cover was added around the telescope objective in the photograph of the auxiliary armor on the opposite page.

The Chrysler assembly line late in the production life of the M3. The side doors have been eliminated or welded up on these vehicles. A turret is installed on a late M3 (below right) and the last M3 comes off the line (below left) in August 1942.

Medium tank M3A1, serial number 1962, during tests at Aberdeen Proving Ground. Note that counterweights have not been fitted to balance the 75mm and 37mm guns.

MEDIUM TANK M3A1

The successful use of cast armor for the M3 turrets led to the consideration of even larger castings. Ballistic tests of a cast open hearth steel upper hull proved satisfactory, although a slightly greater thickness was required for penetration resistance equal to rolled homogeneous armor plate. However, the casting process permitted the use of a smooth streamlined shape providing approximately the same protection for the equivalent weight. The hazard from rivets fracturing under shot impact and flying around the interior of the tank was also reduced by the cast upper hull. The lower hull was still assembled by riveting. The Ordnance Committee authorized the use of the upper hull casting as an alternative method of medium tank construction in June 1941. On 9 October 1941 this version was designated as the medium tank M3A1 by OCM 17301.

Except for the minor modifications required by the hull casting, the M3A1 was identical to the M3. One difference was the location of the hatch in the right side of the hull roof. On the streamlined M3A1, it was moved to an angled position at the rear where the hull roof sloped down toward the engine compartment. On early M3A1s, the hatch was hinged at the front requiring it to swing up and forward to open. This arrangement proved awkward and was reversed on later tanks with the hinges being moved to the rear. With the cast hull, the pistol port in the rear wall of the fighting compartment was also eliminated.

Additional views of M3A1 number 1962. This tank does not have ventilators and the hull roof hatch is hinged at the forward edge.

The side doors of the early tanks were dropped from the late production vehicles, retaining only the pistol port on the right side. The three ventilators were added to the late model M3A1s in the same locations as on the M3, except for the right side of the hull roof. Since the roof hatch was shifted to the rear on the M3A1, the ventilator was placed just forward of the hatchway.

Production of the medium tank M3A1 began at the American Locomotive Company in February 1942 continuing through August of that year. A total of 300 were produced.

In July 1941, a test program was started at Aberdeen Proving Ground to evaluate the Guiberson T-1400-2 diesel engine in medium tanks of the M3 series. When designating the medium tanks M3, M3A1, and M3A2, the Ordnance Committee specified that they could be powered either by the Wright R975 engine or the Guiberson diesel engine. In the latter case, each tank would carry the additional designation (Diesel).

The Guiberson T-1400-2 had been previously tested in the medium tank M2A1. It was removed from that vehicle and installed in an M3A1 for a test program which ran from 2 July to 8 October 1941. This tank was then shipped out for use as a manufacturing pilot and another M3A1 was fitted with a Guiberson engine to continue the test work. The original tank was returned to Aberdeen on 30 April 1942 and testing resumed until 23 June. The engine was then removed for inspection. Test results showed superior performance with the diesel engines, mainly because of the greater torque available at low engine speed. The range was approximately doubled because of the lower fuel consumption of the diesel. However, the Guiberson was unreliable in service requiring frequent repairs and Aberdeen recommended that further tests of the T-1400-2 be discontinued. Additional engineering studies were proposed to improve the reliability of the engine for future use. In the meantime, however, the Adjutant General directed that the use of the Guiberson be discontinued as soon as other engines were available. It had been intended to use the Guiberson diesel in the M3A1 production at American Locomotive. However, because of this decision, only 28 were completed using this engine.

The M3A1 (above) from the Demonstration Regiment at Fort Knox is representative of the early production tanks with the side doors. On later vehicles, such as this 4th Armored Division tank (below), the side doors have been eliminated by welding up the openings.

The two tanks below from the 4th and 7th Armored Divisions represent the final production version of the M3A1. Note that the hull roof hatch is hinged at the rear and no traces remain of the side doors.

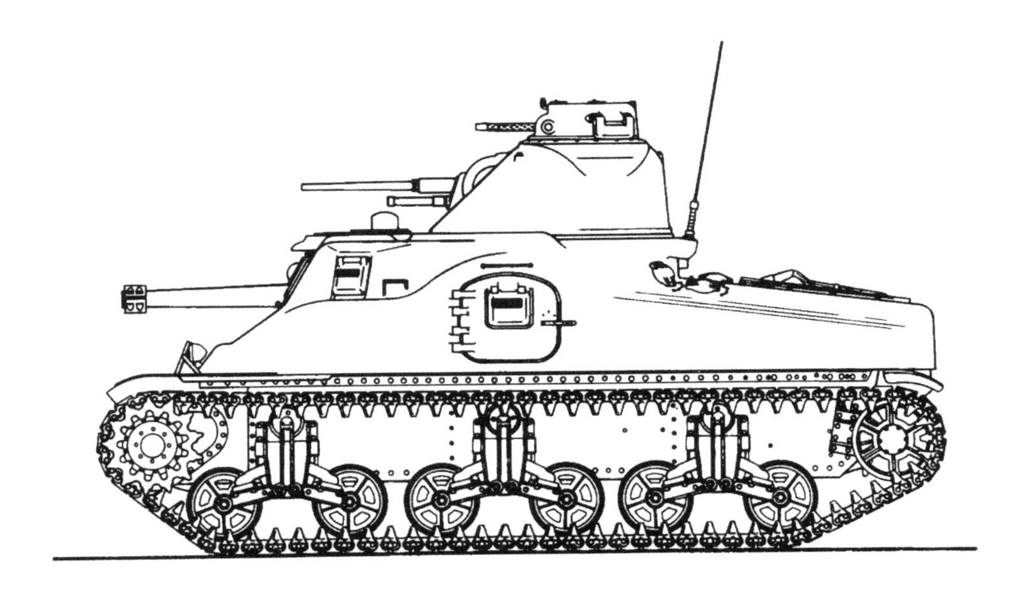

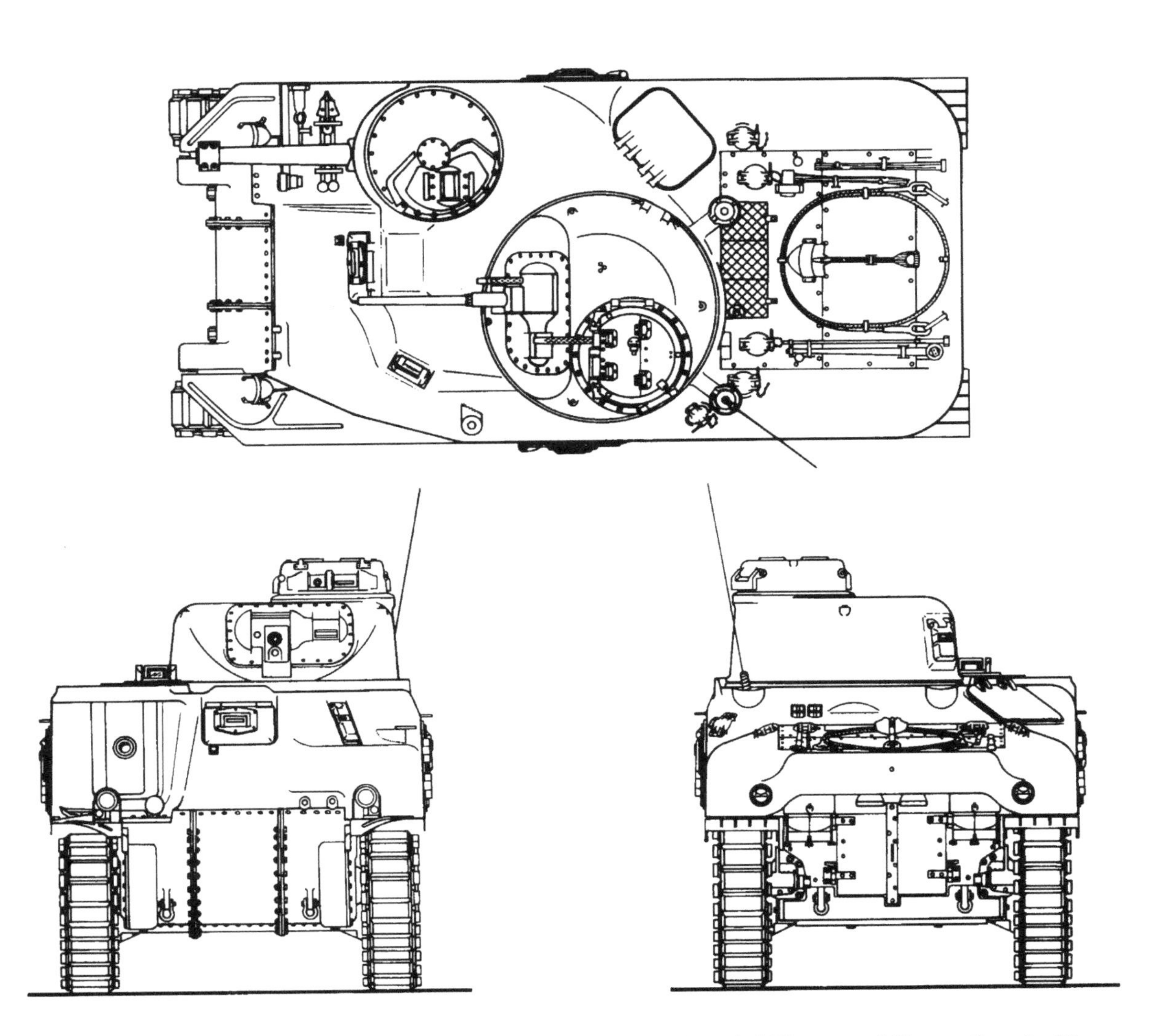

On this tank, counterweights are attached to balance the short barreled 75mm gun M2 as well as the 37.

Scale 1:48

Medium Tank M3A1

The markings indicate that these two late production M3A1s are from the 31st Armored Regiment, 7th Armored Division (above) and the 37th Armored Regiment, 4th Armored Division (below). Note that the lower tank is fitted with ventilators, but the upper one is not.

A welded hull M3A2 built by Baldwin Locomotive Works is shown here at Aberdeen Proving Ground. These photographs were dated 1 January 1942.

MEDIUM TANK M3A2

Successful ballistic tests of a welded turret resulted in a contract to Rock Island Arsenal for the construction of a welded hull for the medium tank M3. Two hulls were built, one of which was assembled into a medium tank M3 using a cast turret. Ordnance Committee action in August 1941 had designated the tank with a welded hull and a cast turret as the medium tank M3A2. In all other respects, it was identical to the standard M3.

Tests at Aberdeen showed that the welded hull offered improved strength and ballistic resistance for a somewhat lower weight than the riveted hull. It also, of course, eliminated the danger from flying rivets and the entrance of bullet splash through the riveted joints. The interior surfaces were smooth without the steel angles and rivet heads present in the standard M3. The simple construction also reduced costs and time required for fabrication.

Production of the M3A2 began at the Baldwin Locomotive Works in January 1942, but was discontinued in March after a total run of only 12 M3A2s. Baldwin then shifted to production of the diesel powered M3A3, also with a welded hull.

Additional views of M3A2 number 1040 at Aberdeen. Except for its welded hull, this tank was identical to the early production M3 with side doors and without ventilators.

Medium tank M3, serial number 28, (above and below) after conversion to diesel power. Extra lights have been rigged on the front and rear of the tank at Aberdeen for use in the test program.

MEDIUM TANKS M3A3 AND M3A5

It was apparent by the Summer of 1941 that a limiting factor in tank production would be the availability of suitable engines. The air-cooled radial of the type used in the medium tank M3 was also required for use in training aircraft and future production for tanks might be greatly restricted. To develop an additional source of tank engines, a contract was issued in August 1941 for the experimental installation of a pair of General Motors diesel engines in the medium tank M3. The new power plant, known as the Model 6046, was assembled from a pair of standard General Motors 6-71 diesel truck engines which were already in quantity production. A fortunate feature of this engine was its symmetrical engine block. Although both engines rotated in the same direction, it was possible to assemble the accessories on opposite sides of the two blocks so that they were located on the outside of the combined power plant. Although anchored together structurally, each engine could be operated independently and drive the tank if the other failed. Power was transmitted from each engine through its respective clutch to a helical gear that meshed with a common collector gear. This gear was mounted on a propeller shaft connected to the standard M3 transmission.

Larger in size than the radial engine it replaced, the twin diesel required some modification of the engine compartment. To protect the radiators installed at the rear, the side and rear armor plates of the engine air outlet were extended down to the level of the tracks and the rear plate was sloped about 10 degrees from the vertical. A single lower rear plate replaced the engine compartment doors of the M3 and a deflector was installed to reduce the amount of dust stirred up by the

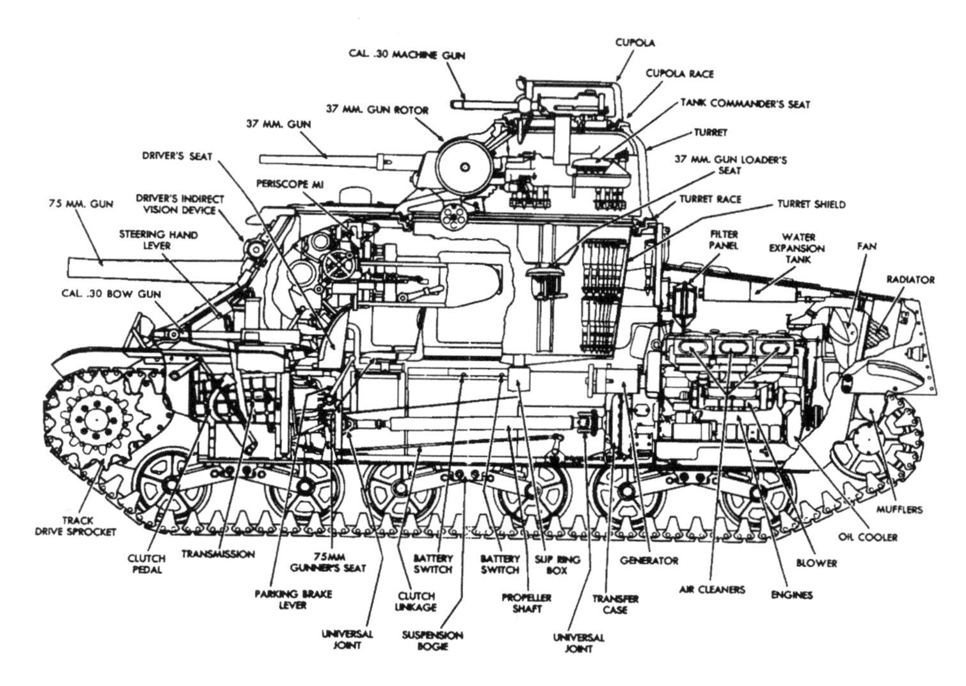

The installation of the GM diesel engine can be seen in the sectional view above. Compare with the similar section of the M3 on page 62.

blast of cooling air and exhaust gases. Two armored doors with intake louvers were located on the deck over the engine compartment. The length of the two engines required the shifting of the lower part of the engine compartment bulkhead about 12 inches into the fighting compartment. However, the fuel economy of the diesel engines permitted a reduction in the fuel tank capacity to 148 gallons even though the range was increased to approximately 160 miles.

The twin diesel was installed in medium tank M3, serial number 28, originally built at Detroit Tank Arsenal. Shipped to Aberdeen for test, it was so satisfactory that the Ordnance Committee authorized the use of the twin diesel as an alternate power plant in October 1941. The new engine increased the weight of the tank by approximately a ton, but its torque characteristics provided superior performance at low engine speeds compared to the standard installation.

Ordnance Committee action standardized the tank powered by the General Motors 6046 as the medium tank M3A3, but later restricted this designation to vehicles with welded hulls. The need for increased production also required the use of the new engine in riveted hulls and this version was designated as the medium tank M3A5. Production of the twin diesel powered tanks started at Baldwin Locomotive Works in January 1942 and continued until December. A total of 322 M3A3s and 591 M3A5s were produced.

Medium Tanks M3A3 (below left) and M3A5 (below right). The only difference between these vehicles is the method of hull construction.

The M3A3 (top left) and the M3A5 (left and top right) are late production tanks with ventilators and welded up side doors.

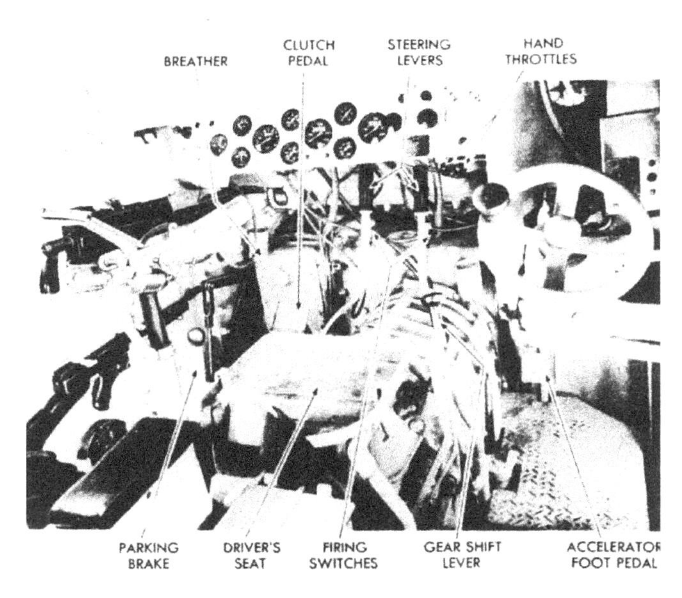

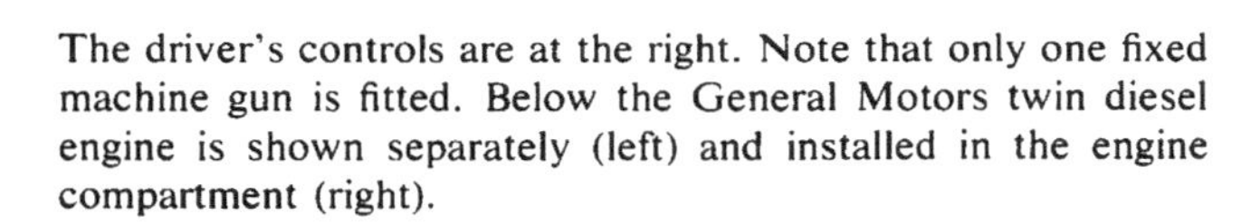

The driver's controls are at the right. Note that only one fixed machine gun is fitted. Below the General Motors twin diesel engine is shown separately (left) and installed in the engine compartment (right).

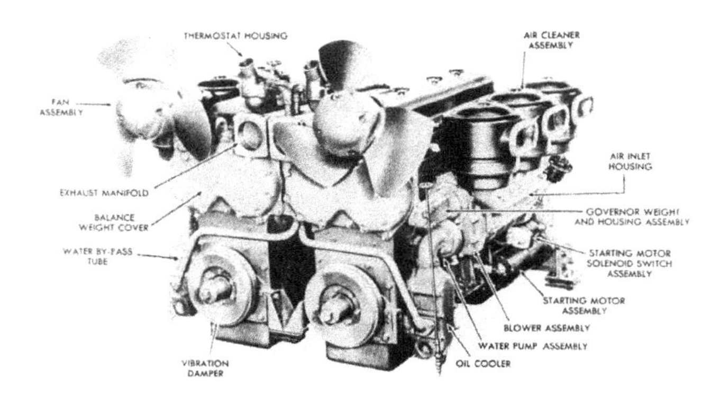

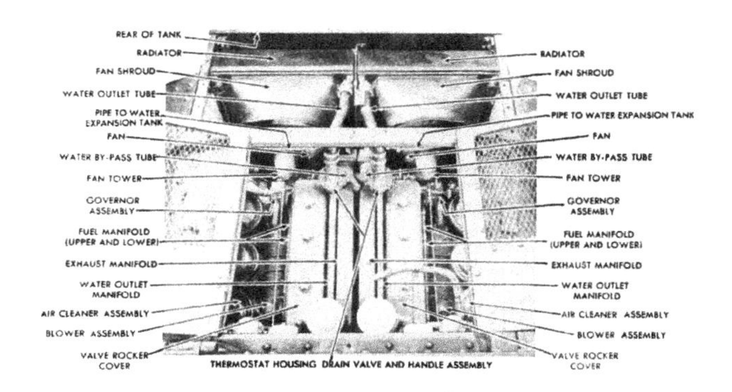

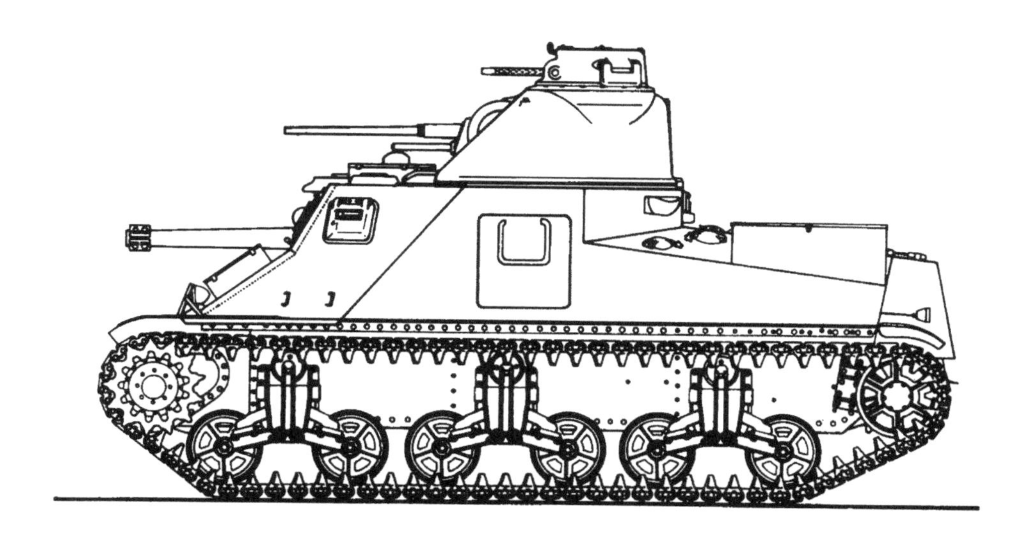

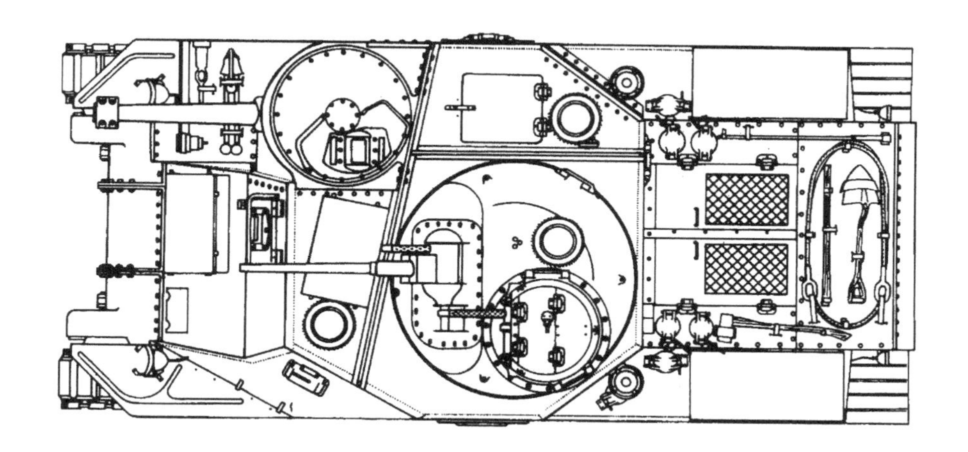

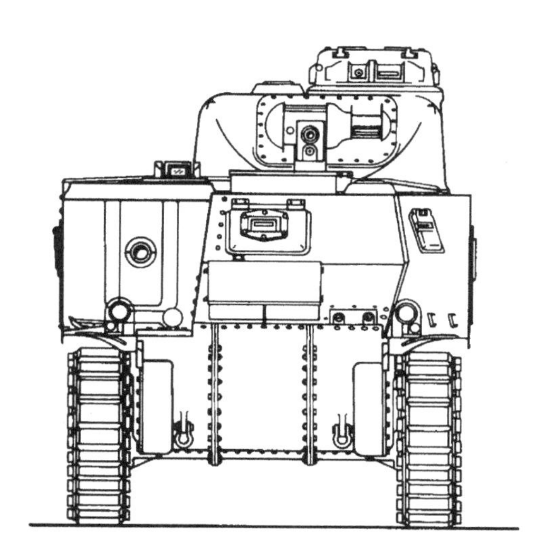

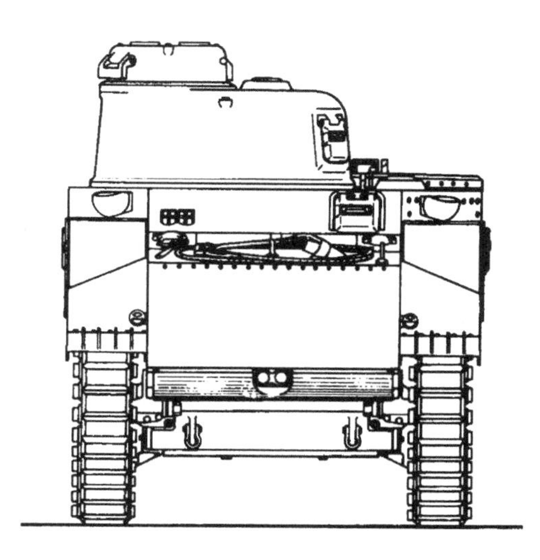

Scale 1:48

Medium Tank M3A3

Medium tank M3A5, serial number 1465, during its acceptance tests at Aberdeen in December 1942. This tank includes late production features such as ventilators, welded up side doors, and counterweights to balance both the 37mm and 75mm guns.

The pilot M3A4 at Aberdeen in February 1942. Note the extended hull and the increased spacing between the suspension bogies.

MEDIUM TANK M3A4

During a visit to Chrysler Engineering in June 1941, Mr. William Knudsen outlined the critical situation in the production of tank engines. These engines were needed to power the increasing numbers of tanks being demanded not only by the Armored Force, but also to meet worldwide Lend-Lease commitments. He requested Chrysler to develop a tank engine which could be rapidly put into production using tooling already in existence. Chrysler's solution to the problem was to combine five automobile engines, each with six cylinders, in a star configuration. Geared together to operate as a single unit, the 30-cylinder power plant developed 425 hp at 2850 rpm. Dubbed the A57 multibank engine, it was much bulkier than any previously used in the M3. The first experimental engine was installed in a pilot tank on 15 November 1941 and in December, the Ordnance Committee standardized the vehicle as the medium tank M3A4.

The large power plant required modifications to the standard M3 hull. The engine compartment was lengthened by 11 inches and the hull upper rear plates were moved back 15 inches. A 4-1/4 inch blister in the floor provided clearance for the fan. Another bulge on top of the rear deck covered the single radiator assembly which cooled the entire power plant. It was

Because of its late start, the production M3A4 incorporated all of the late design features. Note the heavy duty suspension bogies.

also necessary to remove the two vertical fuel tanks in the M3's engine compartment. Their loss was compensated by enlarging each of the two sponson tanks to 80 gallons.

The longer hull of the M3A4 required some modification of the suspension system. The center and rear bogie assemblies were moved to the rear increasing the distance between bogies by about 6 inches over the standard M3 suspension. This placed the center of gravity of the tank over the center bogie. Each of the longer tracks required 83 shoes compared to 79 for the M3.

In February 1942, the pilot M3A4 was shipped to Aberdeen for testing. After over 42 hours of operation on all types of roads, the original experimental engine was removed and replaced by a new production model. Reports indicated generally satisfactory performance with ample power. Testing continued with the second and third engines until October 1942 resulting in numerous modifications which were applied to production.

Production of the medium tank M3A4 began at Detroit Tank Arsenal in June 1942 continuing into August with a total of 109 tanks completed. At this time, the Tank Arsenal shifted to the production of the M4 series and the same multibank power plant appeared in the medium tank M4A4. Because of the late period of their construction, the production M3A4s incorporated many of the improvements developed for the M3 tank series. These included the elimination of the side doors, installation of the three roof ventilators, and the late model bogie assembly with the track return roller at the rear. The latter was continued in the new M4 production.

The M3A4 was armed with the long barreled 75mm gun M3 which did not require a counterweight to balance the weapon.

In addition to the wide bogie spacing, the M3A4 could be easily identified by the radiator cover on the rear deck.

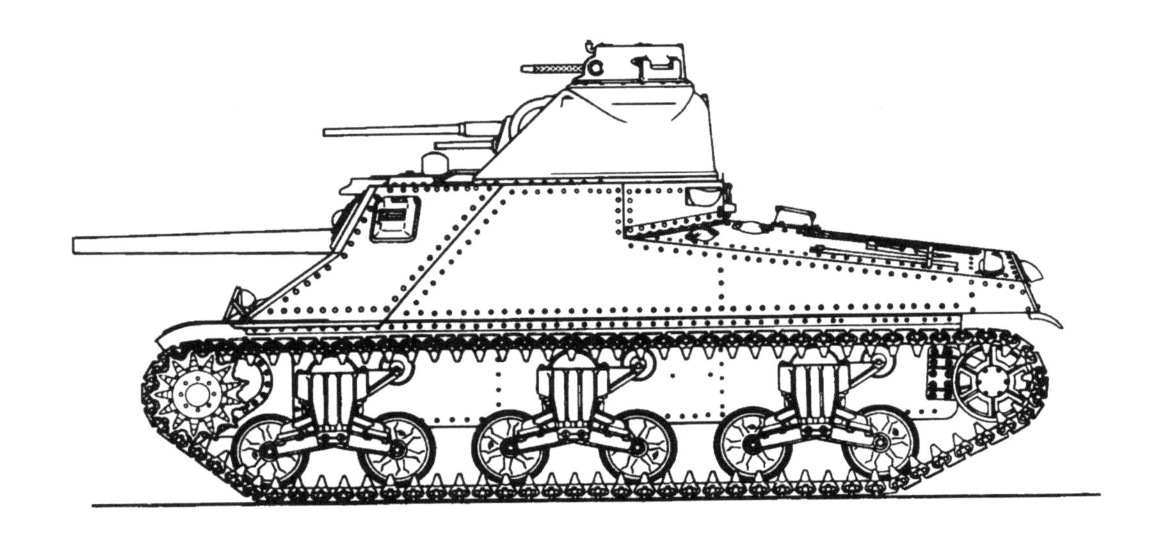

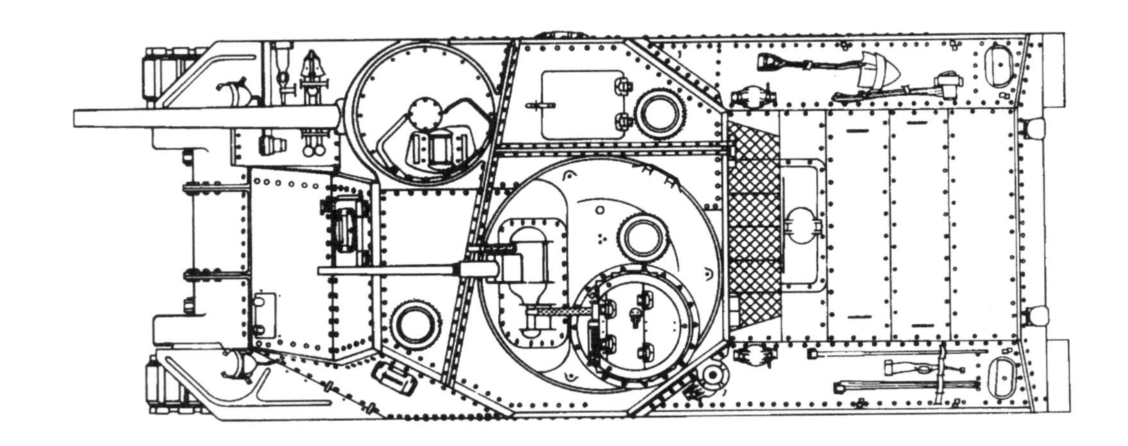

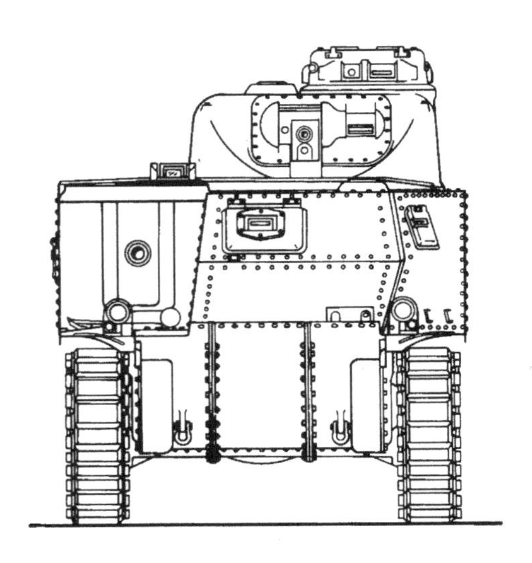

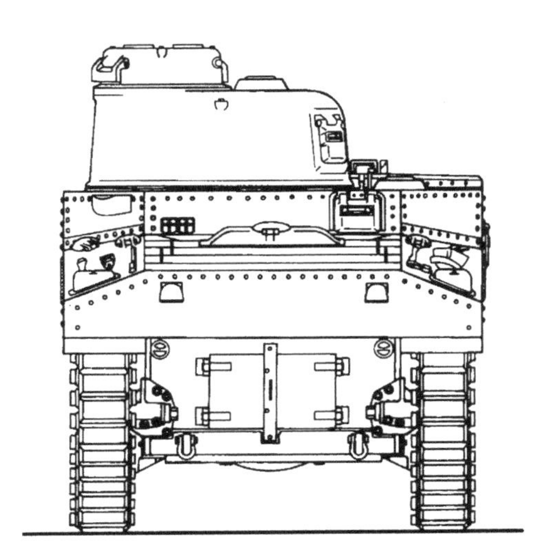

Scale 1:48

Medium Tank M3A4

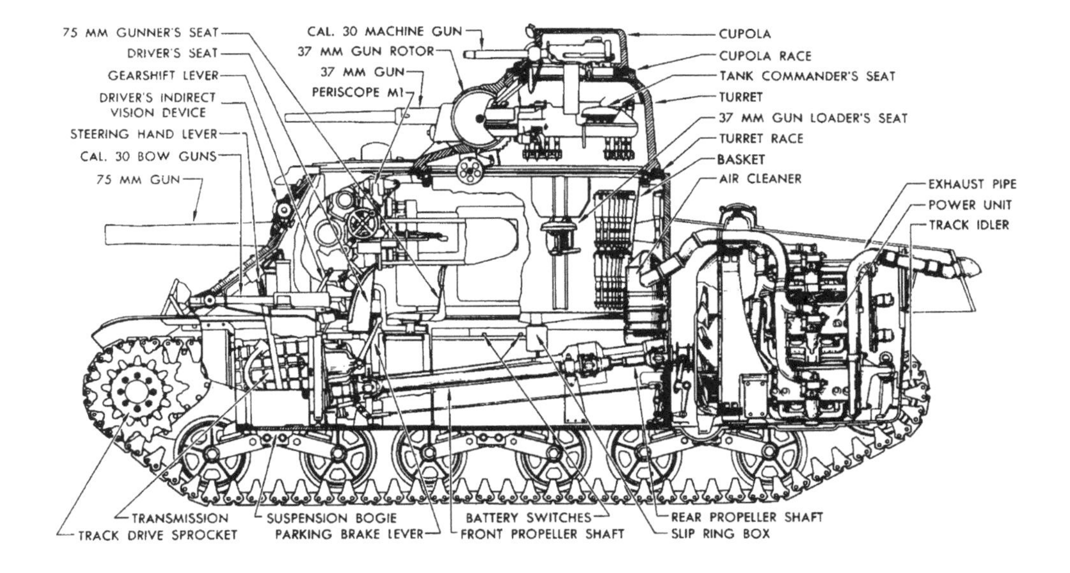

This sectional view of the M3A4 is incorrect as far as the suspension is concerned. Note that it retains the bogie spacing of the M3. A wartime draftsman probably traced a standard M3 suspension to save time. The hull length is correct resulting in the overhang seen above. Compare with the proper drawing on the opposite page. The M3A4 driver's controls are below at the right and a sketch of the long lever control linkage appears below at the left.

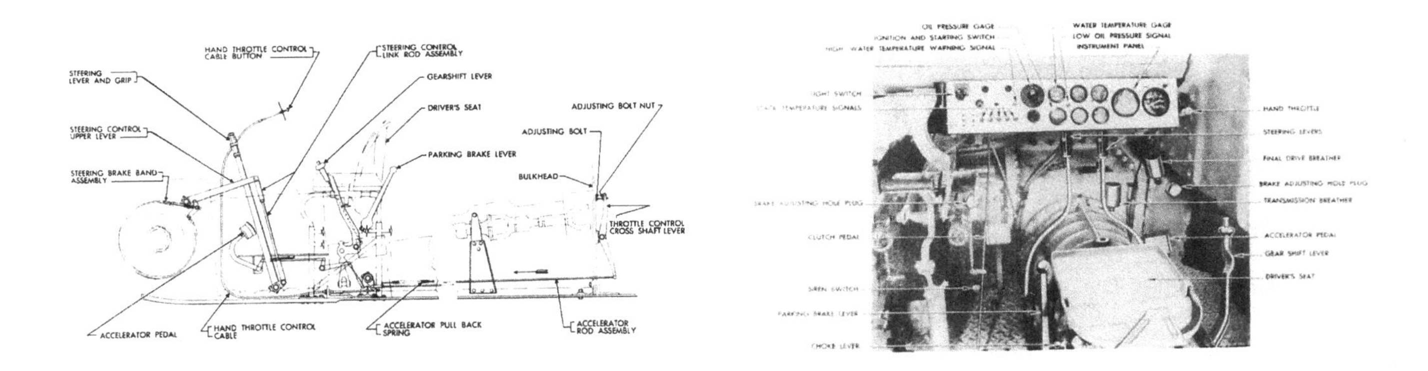

Two stages in the removal of the multibank power plant are illustrated below. Because of the size and complex configuration of the engine, removal was necessary for even simple maintenance operations.

Medium tank M3, serial number 935, fitted with the early horizontal volute spring suspension. Note that the shock absorbers have not been installed on the front and rear bogies.

EXPERIMENTAL VARIANTS OF THE MEDIUM TANK M3 SERIES

Tanks of the M3 series were used in a variety of experiments to improve the vehicles and to develop components for the new M4s. The problem of adequate engine supply continued to plague the production program. In addition, the new M4 series would be somewhat heavier than the M3s and would require more power for satisfactory performance. Efforts were underway to increase the power of the air-cooled radial R975, but the quantities available were limited. The improvised engines such as the twin General Motors diesel and the Chrysler multibank were heavy and bulky. To design a new engine specifically for tanks was a time consuming process and in the Fall and Winter of 1941, time was a very scarce commodity. However, the Ford Motor Company had under development a liquid-cooled V-12 aircraft engine which might be modified for tank use. Shortened to a V-8, the experimental engine developed about 500 hp at 2600 rpm. To evaluate the engine for future use in the M4 series, it was installed in a medium tank M3. Ordnance Committee action designated the test vehicle as the medium tank M3E1 on 19 February 1942. Tests at Aberdeen were successful and the engine was subsequently used to power the medium tank M4A3 and a number of other vehicles.

Medium tank M3, serial number 935, was used as a test vehicle in the suspension development program. Although rugged and reliable, the standard vertical volute spring suspension gave a very rough ride at high speed. In an effort to improve its performance, the bogies were redesigned with the volute springs rotated 90 degrees to an horizontal position. This arrangement permitted the use of shock absorbers to smooth out some of the bumps. An early version of this suspension was installed on M3 number 935 for test. Other suspension tests on the M3 included the use of a trailing idler to increase the ground contact length and reduce the ground pressure.

Above is the experimental installation of the early horizontal volute spring suspension with the trailing idler. The front bogie has been fitted with a shock absorber. Below are drawings of the early horizontal volute spring suspension with and without the trailing idler. On these drawings, the shock absorber appears only on the front bogie.

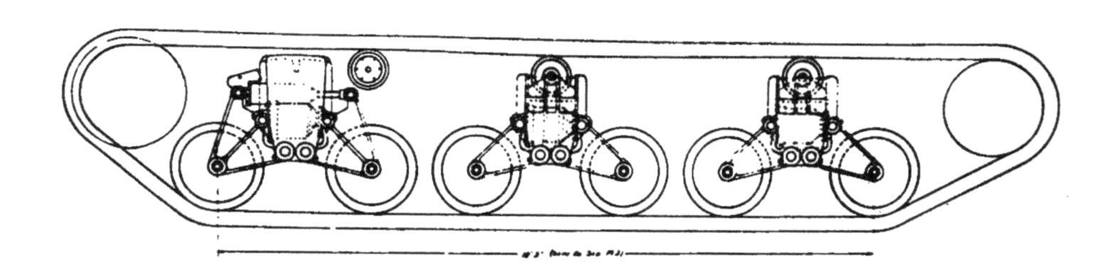

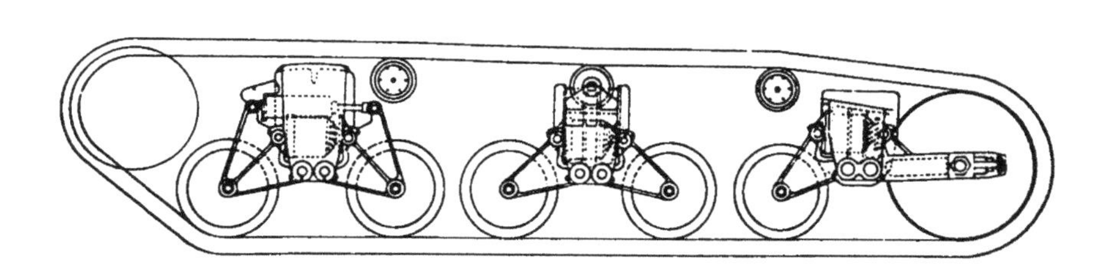

Medium tank M3A1E1 (above and left) during the test program in May 1942.

Another effort to alleviate the engine shortage produced the Lycoming T1300 tank engine. This power plant combined three 6-cylinder air-cooled Lycoming aircraft engines into a single unit. With 18 cylinders and a displacement of 1300 cubic inches, it developed 560 hp. Installed in M3A1, serial number 1986, the vehicle was designated medium tank M3A1E1 in February 1942. Unofficial tests reported a maximum speed of about 40 miles/hour, the fastest attained with any power plant. Both General Motors Proving Ground and Aberdeen reported few mechanical difficulties, although the experimental clutch was hard to operate. However, maintenance was extremely difficult with the crowded engine compartment. For example, the power plant had to be removed from the tank for a spark plug change. By the time the tests were complete, a sufficient number of other engines were available to meet the demands of production and further work was discontinued.

The engine compartment doors in the rear hull are shown open and closed at the left. Below is the Lycoming T1300 engine removed from the tank.

Medium tank M3A5E1, serial number 398, at Aberdeen in March 1942. The bicycle wheel is part of the performance test equipment.

Among Aberdeen's recommendations, after test of the M3s, was the suggestion that automatic transmissions be considered for use in the medium tank. One vehicle so equipped, designated the medium tank M3A5E1, was completed in early January 1942. The General Motors twin diesel power plant was fitted with two Hydramatic transmissions. Test runs at Aberdeen showed improved performance over both the M3 and M3A5. The new transmission provided the tank with greater acceleration, driver comfort, and firing platform stability than previous vehicles tested. Further experiments were recommended and the designation medium tank M3A5E2 was assigned for a similar tank driving through a single heavy duty Hydramatic transmission.

This Grant I is fitted with WE210 double I tracks and sandshields for service in the desert.

INTRODUCTION IN THE DESERT

After the retreat to Gazala in early February 1942, a lull settled over the desert front. The British Eighth Army held positions stretching from Gazala on the Mediterranean to Bir Hacheim about 35 miles to the south southeast. Both sides took advantage of the quiet period to resupply their troops. A major item received during this time by the British forces was new M3 General Grant tank with its 75mm gun. By the end of March, a total of 666 Grants had been completed under the British contracts and sizable numbers had been shipped to the Middle East.

Training programs were immediately started to familiarize both the maintenance and combat troops with the new tank. The advent of the 75mm gun required a new approach in gunnery training. The 2 pounder and 37mm guns of the earlier tanks were direct fire weapons using only a simple telescopic sight. They fired solid armor piercing shot since their small caliber prevented the development of an adequate high explosive round. The larger 75 however, had an excellent high explosive shell in addition to its armor piercing projectile. For the first time, the tankers had an effective weapon to engage the enemy antitank guns. However, the required gunnery techniques were more closely related to those of field artillery then the methods previously used by tanks. The necessary instruction required considerable improvisation as the early Grants were not fitted with proper fire control equipment. For example, the 75mm gun had no range scale or clinometer. This problem was solved by the simple expedient of filing notches in the elevation handwheel corresponding to different range settings. The azimuth was indicated the same way on the traversing wheel. Both vane and bore sights were improvised and hoods were fabricated to shield the periscopes from the glare of the sun. Most importantly, the troops learned the workings of the new tank and how to effectively use it in action.

The training program also revealed serious problems with the high explosive (HE) ammunition. Although a highly effective HE round had started production in the United States, much of the stock available in Egypt was of World War I vintage. Some of this ammunition had deteriorated with age until it was dangerous to use. A number of fatalities resulted from premature explosions during the training program.

Also, the fuzes were designed not for the flat trajectories frequently used with tank guns, but for the high angle indirect fire of field artillery. In order to function properly, they required an impact on an almost perpendicular surface. If fired at a low angle, the projectile might strike on the side of the ogive and the fuze would not fire. The shell would then go bounding over the desert, frequently without ever exploding. What was needed was a creep element in the fuze which would fire, even if it only grazed the target. These early U.S. fuzes did not have such an element, but the original French World War I fuzes did. A British mission located a stock of the French fuzes in Syria and shipped 90,000 of them to Egypt. Since the U.S. ammunition was based on the French design, the fuzes were readily fitted to the American shells. This provided high explosive ammunition which could be used in ricochet fire against enemy personnel and antitank guns. When fired at the ground in front of the enemy position, the shell would ricochet into the air before exploding with a deadly fragmentation effect.

Another problem, not so easily solved, concerned the armor piercing ammunition. The armor of the Panzer III and IV being used by the Germans was either face-hardened or reinforced with face-hardened plate. Effective penetration of such plate required the use of a capped armor piercing projectile. Such a round had been developed for the 75mm tank gun, but it was not yet available in the Middle East. This was the APC M61, an armor piercing capped projectile with a ballistic cap (APCBC) to reduce wind resistance and extend its effective range.

During the development period of the APC M61, it had been necessary to introduce an interim round to meet the requirement for large quantities of armor piercing ammunition. This was the AP M72 monobloc shot. Rushed into production, this solid steel shot was variable in quality and tended to break up against face-hardened armor. Tests carried out near Cairo in March 1942 against several German tank hulls revealed that the M72 shot was relatively ineffective against the frontal armor at ranges over 500 yards.

A successful effort to provide effective armor piercing rounds resulted from the brilliant idea of Major Northy, an Australian serving with the British Royal Army Ordnance Corps. Early in 1942, about 50,000 tons of assorted German ammunition captured during the relief of Tobruk were moved to the Ninth British Army Depot along the Suez canal. Among this vast supply were many of the explosive loaded APCBC rounds for the Panzer IV's 7.5cm Kampfwagenkanone (KwK) L/24. Major Northy noted that if the rotating band was modified, the German projectile could be fitted into a U.S. cartridge case and fired from the M3's 75. Checking with Major G.B. Jarrett, an Ordnance ammunition expert with the U.S. Mission in the Middle East, he found that Jarrett not only agreed as to the feasibility of the project, but gave it his enthusiastic support.

With pennants attached to their radio antennas and lots of unofficial stowage, the Grants below are in service with the British Eighth Army in the desert.

The modified explosive loaded German APCBC projectile (left) fitted into a U.S. cartridge case is compared above with the inert U.S. APC M61 (right).

The German projectile differed from its U.S. counterpart in having a much wider and thicker rotating band, but the basic dimensions of the round were essentially the same. A number of the German projectiles were removed from their cartridge cases and the rotating bands turned down to the U.S. dimensions in a lathe. The rounds were then successfully assembled into U.S. cases and they chambered properly in the M3's 75mm gun. These were explosive loaded armor piercing projectiles fitted with a base detonating fuze. This fuze was armed by the projectile rotation when the round was fired. Fortunately, the lathe rotation was insufficient to arm the fuze during the machining operation.

Some of the converted ammunition was test fired against a Panzer III hull in comparison with a few of the new U.S. APC M61s which had been flown out to Cairo. Like the German round, the M61 was fitted with an armor piercing cap, but it was inert loaded since the development of a suitable base detonating fuze was not yet complete. The tests showed the penetration performance of the two rounds was identical, but the damage resulting from the German projectile was much greater. Both penetrated the front of the Panzer III at a 1000 yards, but the German round exploded inside the tank. In combat such an explosion would almost always set off the stowed ammunition.

With the approval of Middle East Headquarters, the new round was designated as the 75mm AP-Composite and conversion began at full speed. A total of about 17,000 rounds were converted of which 15,000 were the explosive loaded APCBC. The remaining 2000 were high explosive and smoke which were also modified as any reliable round was most welcome for the M3's gun. U.S. AP M72 and HE Mk I ammunition was used to provide the primed cartridge cases and propellant charges. Much of the old ammunition was found to contain variable weights of propellant so all the charges were dumped together, mixed, and reweighed to insure a uniform muzzle velocity.

The conversion work took two to three weeks and the composite rounds were sent forward before the action opened on the Gazala line in late May. No information seems to be available on what use was made of the new ammunition. About 6000 rounds were captured by the Germans in the dumps at Capuzzo during the retreat to Alamein. They were then moved to the German base dump at Tobruk where they were recaptured the following November.

A Grant (at left) test firing the new U.S. APC M61 ammunition near Cairo in the Spring of 1942.

A Grant with typical desert stowage. The guns on this tank are balanced for use with the stabilizer. Also, note the .30 caliber machine gun fitted to the commander's hatch ring.

The heavy use during training revealed other problems with the tanks themselves. The engines on the first Grants were burning out before completing 25 hours of operation. It was known that the M3 was somewhat underpowered and in this case, the situation was aggravated by using the wrong grade of lubricating oil. This was easily corrected, but engine life was also drastically reduced by ingesting the sand and dust from the desert. This required the installation of suitable filters in the engine air intakes. At one time, a lack of engines threatened to immobilize the force, but an air lift of new engines over the south Atlantic ferry route saved the situation. The training of the crews and the adaptation of the Grant to desert conditions continued at full speed so as to be ready when the war again became active.

By late May 1942, 167 Grant tanks were divided between the British 1st and 7th Armoured Divisions. The latter was destined to be the first to take it into battle. The limited number of Grants available posed a problem. For morale purposes it was desirable that every unit get some of the new tanks, but it was far more efficient from a maintenance and supply standpoint that an organization be equipped with a single type. The result was a compromise with some regiments having two squadrons of Grants and one squadron using the light M3 General Stuart. This was the plan followed in the 4th Armoured Brigade. The 3rd Royal Tank Regiment along with the 5th RTR and the 8th Hussars made up the tank elements of the 4th Armoured Brigade in the 7th Armoured Division, the famous "Desert Rats". Equipment tables dated 15 March 1942 allotted 20 Stuarts and 24 Grants to each regiment. However, because of shortages the 3rd RTR, commanded by Lieutenant Colonel G.P.B. Roberts, had only 16 Stuarts and 19 Grants available on the morning of 27 May 1942.

Commanded by Brigadier G.W. Richards, the 4th Armoured Brigade leaguered about 15 miles east of Bir Hacheim on the night of 26 May. Unknown to them, General Erwin Rommel had launched his operation "Venezia" that afternoon. Powerful Axis forces consisting of the Italian Ariete Division, the German 15th and 21st Panzer Divisions, and the German 90th Light Division swept southeast around Bir Hacheim. The Italians moved to attack the Free French defending Bir Hacheim, but the German force moved northeast to cut behind the British positions.

The heavy dust cloud thrown up by the tracks obscures the Grant and Crusader above in the desert.

Early on the morning of the 27th, reports reached the 4th Armoured Brigade of strong enemy forces south of Bir Hacheim. Originally ordered to move south at first light to their prepared battle positions, the movement was delayed in the confusion over the enemy's intentions. The brigade was finally ordered to rendezvous at 8:15 AM and the 3rd RTR, which was to lead, moved out at 7:30 AM. With the light squadron of Stuarts about 2000 yards in front, the 19 Grants moved in line with B Squadron commanded by Major George Witheridge on the right and C Squadron under Major Cyril Joly on the left. Colonel "Pip" Roberts was in the center, also in a Grant.

They hardly had been moving ten minutes when the light squadron reported large dust clouds and numerous vehicles about three miles to their front. As the Grants closed up on the Stuarts, large numbers of Panzer IIIs and IVs were identified. Moving in lines of about 20 tanks, six to eight lines were visible before disappearing into the dust clouds. Led by the 8th Panzer Regiment, these were the tanks of the 15th Panzer Division.

Ordering A Squadron's Stuarts to protect the flank, Colonel Roberts moved the Grants into a battle line along a small ridge. When the range closed to about a 1000 yards, the regiment's 19 tanks opened fire with a devastating effect. As Rommel's own notes show, the Grant's 75mm gun was a drastic shock to the Germans. For the first time, British tanks could engage the enemy beyond the effective range of the 5cm gun of the Panzer III or the short barreled 7.5cm weapon in the Panzer IV. None of the new Panzer IVs with the long barreled KwK 40 were available for this action.

Despite their heavy losses, the weight of the German attack was not to be denied and shortly past noon the surviving Grants, their ammunition exhausted, were forced to withdraw. The C Squadron Leader's tank had been knocked out and he was slightly wounded. Major Witheridge, leading B Squadron, was on his fourth tank after three Grants had been shot out from under him. Out of the original 19 Grants, seven, including Colonel Roberts, arrived at the rendezvous point to replenish their fuel and ammunition. Three other tanks had been sent on to the rear since their guns had been damaged rendering them useless for combat. Fighting continued in the afternoon and by the end of the day, the 3rd RTR had been reduced to five Grants and eight Stuarts.

The Grants below are moving across flat desert terrain. The view at the left is through the driver's hatch.

A Grant passing a burning German light tank. Note the camouflage pattern on the British tank.

The 8th Hussars, commanded by Lieutenant Colonel G. Kilkelly, had fared even worse during the morning. The powerful enemy force appeared about 7:30 AM before they could clear their leaguer area. C Squadron under Major J.W. Hackett was the first to engage the enemy with A and B Squadrons forming up on either side of them. A Squadron bore the brunt of the initial assault losing all but two of its tanks followed shortly by the complete loss of B Squadron and the regimental headquarters tanks. The regiment claimed the destruction of 30 enemy tanks, but they had been almost wiped out with only two Grants surviving the day.

The 5th RTR was much more fortunate than its sister regiments ending the day with only light casualties. Thus the M3 was introduced to battle. Although they had suffered severe losses, a heavy toll had been exacted from the enemy serving notice of things to come. In the future, the Panzer IIIs and IVs would have to contend with much more heavily armed and armored adversaries than in the past. The high explosive capability of the 75mm gun would also go a long way toward reducing the threat from the antitank gun.

It was during this same period that the first U.S. tankers received their baptism of fire in the M3. Three crews under Major Henry Cabot Lodge were attached to the Eighth Army for combat experience to aid in training the new tank units in the United States. At the opening of the battle, they were in a reserve area near Tobruk. On 11 June, they brought their tanks forward joining the 1st RTR, now part of the 4th Armoured Brigade. During the next few days, they participated in the heavy fighting between Knightsbridge and Acroma to hold open the escape route for the two divisions still on the original Gazala line. In the fighting, they claimed the destruction of nine enemy tanks. After the battle, the three crews returned to Fort Knox and were assigned to U.S. armored units.

A U.S. Army tank crew serving with the British Eighth Army poses with their Grant in the desert.

Above is a British General Lee which operated alongside the Grant in the desert. Below are two views of a Grant command tank modified to resemble the Sherman.

The M3 medium tank continued to play a major role in the desert fighting after Gazala. In addition to the General Grants, the British were also receiving many of the General Lees under Lend-Lease arrangements. On the eve of the battle of Alamein, 170 M3s were ready for action with the various armored formations. By this time, the Sherman was arriving in quantity and the M3 had fulfilled its role as an interim tank. However, it continued to serve the British throughout the remainder of the African campaign and many were then shipped to other theaters of war.

Many of the British M3s had been converted to command tanks by the installation of additional communication equipment and the replacement of some armament with dummy weapons. With its relatively roomy interior, the M3 was well suited to this role. When the Sherman came into service, many commanders were reluctant to give up the convenience of the M3, although its distinctive appearance made it an obvious target among a group of the newer tanks. Some of these command tanks were modified by the addition of sheet metal and a larger dummy gun to give a silhouette similar to the Sherman. This way they could still operate with the new tanks without being easily detected.

Both of these photographs show late British modifications to the M3. The Lee (above) and the Grant (below) have the later stowage box arrangement and auxiliary fuel tank. Both are fitted with mud chutes between the suspension bogies.

M3s of the U.S. 2nd Armored Divison training at Fort Benning in February 1942. Note the Air Corps type insignia on these tanks. The arrival of the M3 finally gave the troops a real medium tank with which to train. Prior to that time, light tanks were used frequently marked with a large M (below right).

THE M3 IN THE U.S. ARMORED FORCE

The lack of medium tanks greatly hampered training during the first year of the new U.S. Armored Force. At that time, it was common practice to designate light tanks as mediums by the simple expedient of marking them with a large M. Photographs taken during maneuvers frequently show these tanks with their 37mm gun turrets labeled "75mm gun". By the fall of 1941, production of the medium tank M3 was in full swing and for the first time, it was possible to equip the tank battalions with a real medium tank.

The M3 filled the role of training tank for all of the early armored divisions and was widely used in the maneuvers of 1941 and 1942. When their training was complete, the armored divisions exchanged their M3s for new M4s before going into combat. The only exception to this was the 1st Armored Division. When this division embarked for Northern Ireland in May 1942, the medium battalions of both armored regiments were still equipped with the M3. These tanks then saw further heavy use in training exercises during the Summer and Fall. When the Center Task Force was formed for the November landings near Oran in North Africa, only one medium tank battalion was included. Dock facilities were required for landing the medium tanks since the M3s were a little too tall for the bow door opening on the early Maracaibo type tank landing ship. The unit selected was the 2nd Battalion of the 13th Armored Regiment commanded by Lieutenant Colonel Hyman Bruss and it went to Africa with the M3s it had trained on in the United States.

The U.S. 1st Armored Division training with their M3s in Northern Ireland during the Summer of 1942. The censor has deleted the identifying marks on many of the tanks. Note that all of the U.S. tank guns are balanced for use with the stabilizer and many vehicles are armed with the 75mm gun M3.

Landing early on the morning of 8 November 1942, two light tank battalions supported the infantry and quickly overcame the opposition from obsolete French tanks without any help from their heavier sisters. After the end of the hostilities on 10 November, the various elements of the 1st Armored Division were concentrated in the Oran area as Combat Command B under Brigadier General Lunsford Oliver. Colonel Paul Robinett, who had led one of the invasion task forces became Deputy Commander of CCB.

Events in Tunisia soon provided a new mission for the armored troops. Reacting quickly to the Anglo-American invasion, German air units flew into Tunis as early as 9 November and a buildup of ground troops rapidly followed. Late on 15 November, Blade Force commanded by Colonel R.A. Hull began moving from Algiers toward the east. Consisting mainly of elements from the British 6th Armoured Division, this provisional armored group was the advanced striking force for the corps under Lieutenant General Kenneth Anderson. The objective of General Anderson's command was to move rapidly east and seize Tunis and Bizerta.

The most readily available armored reinforcement for General Anderson was CCB still located near Oran. Both the medium and light battalions soon started the move east. The former, Bruss's 2nd Battalion of the 13th Armored Regiment, drove their tanks to Algiers and were moved by sea to Bone. They then resumed the road march for two days reaching the forward area on 24 November. About this time, Colonel Robinett and Brigadier General Oliver were promoted to Brigadier General and Major General respectively.

On their arrival, the tanks had driven about 700 miles and their tracks were badly worn. Bivouacking first near Souk el Arba and then near Souk el Khemis, the battalion received its first mission. Confusion and misinformation were the order of the day and the tanks deployed to attack a hill that the Germans had already abandoned.

Lieutenant Charles Davis (far right) and crew with their M3 at Souk el Khemis, Tunisia on 23 November 1942, five days before the attack at Djedeida.

M3, registration number W-309056, from the 2nd Battalion, 13th Armored Regiment at Souk el Khemis, Tunisia on 17 December 1942. This tank was in action from 29 November until 12 December. Note the badly worn condition of the tracks and bogie wheel tires.

After some other false starts, the first serious encounter with the enemy occurred on the 28th. With the 5th Battalion of the British Northhamptonshire Regiment, the battalion was ordered to seize Djedeida and the nearby airfield. The combined attack jumped off at 1:00 PM with the infantry riding on the tanks. For this operation, the tank battalion was reduced to Company D, one platoon of Company F, and the battalion headquarters tanks. Company E was detached at this time and the remainder of Company F had not yet arrived from Algiers. The enemy held their fire until the attacking force was fully committed and had moved into a flat exposed area. Well camouflaged heavy antitank guns then opened fire from the left front destroying the tanks of the leading platoon under Lieutenant Charles Davis. The remaining tanks engaged the guns which could be located only by the muzzle blast when they fired. The tanks and infantry withdrew to a defilade position along the original start line. Major Henry Gardiner, the battalion executive officer, went forward and observed four tanks burning with black columns of smoke rising from each. Numerous wounded were scattered in the exposed area. Despite Major Gardiner's efforts to reach them in the medical half-track, most of them could not be evacuated until after nightfall.

These losses were only the first in a series of painful lessons inflicted over the next few days and it soon became apparent that the Allies had lost the race for Tunis. Fighting continued to flare all along the front with the 2nd Battalion's medium tanks suffering further heavy losses. A few days later on 2 December, Major Gardiner had his own tank destroyed while leading part of the battalion. This tank, an M3 named Henry I, was the first of three that were shot out from under him during the Tunisian campaign.

In the fierce fighting southwest of Tebourba on 6 December, the 2nd Battalion took additional losses including a full platoon of the new Shermans which had been attached from the 2nd Armored Division. At the end of the day, the Battalion was reduced to 22 badly worn M3s. General Oliver relieved Colonel Bruss and Captain James Simmerman assumed temporary command until Major Gardiner returned from the hospital.

A few M4s were received as replacement tanks, but the M3 played a major role until the end of the Tunisian fighting. The remainder of the 1st Armored

Division arrived from England and Lieutenant Colonel B.G. Crosby's 3rd Battalion of the 13th Armored Regiment was also still equipped with the M3. The two medium tank battalions of the 1st Armored Regiment had been able to exchange their M3s for Shermans before leaving England for North Africa.

Although the M4 was certainly a far superior tank, the quality of equipment was not the only consideration. Troop experience and leadership were far more important factors. General Robinett fully realized this fact in early February when asked by General Anderson to choose between the two medium tank battalions under his command. At that time Anderson expected that it would be necessary to detach one of the battalions and he asked Robinett which one he preferred to retain. The choice was between Lieutenant Colonel Alger's 2nd Battalion of the 1st Armored Regiment which had a full complement of the new Shermans, but had not yet seen action, or the 2nd Battalion of the 13th Armored Regiment. Although the latter was understrength and still mostly equipped with its well worn M3s, it had become an experienced battlewise unit under the leadership of Henry Gardiner, now a Lieutenant Colonel. Although careful to show his respect for Alger's battalion, Robinett chose Gardiner's outfit knowing full well that their battle experience far outweighed the deficiency in equipment. His selection was to be justified more rapidly than he expected.

One of the 13th Armored Regiment M3s which was knocked out and burned. Note the 88mm hole alongside the driver's hatch.

These two photographs show 1st Armored Division M3s in action near Sened early in 1943. The camouflage pattern was obtained by applying streaks of light colored mud over the normal olive drab paint.

M3s of the 1st Armored Division move across open country near Kasserine on 20 February 1943.

On 14 February 1943, the Fifth Panzer Army launched an offensive in central Tunisia striking through Faid Pass toward Sidi bou Zid. This opened the series of battles that were popularly known as the battle of Kasserine Pass, although action did not occur in that area for several days. A counterattack by Lieutenant Colonel Louis Hightower's 3rd Battalion, 1st Armored Regiment was unable to stop the enemy, but delayed his progress during a stubbornly fought withdrawal. Fortyfour Shermans were lost during the day including those that were immobilized for maintenance in Sidi bou Zid. Only seven of Hightower's tanks reached the rallying point at dusk. When the strength of the German attack became apparent, Colonel Alger's battalion was detached from CCB and ordered south to retake Sidi bou Zid and relieve the U.S. troops cut off in that area. The battalion attacked on the morning of 15 February, but was decimated by fire from skillfully deployed enemy tanks and antitank guns. Only four Shermans survived the day and Colonel Alger was captured.

Falling back toward Sbeitla, Combat Commands A and C organized a defensive line east of the town. Their armor consisted of the survivors from Hightower's battalion and the M3s of Crosby's 3rd Battalion, 13th Armored Regiment. CCB was now released from its assignment at Maktar and General Robinett rushed it south joining the division on the morning of the 16th. For the next week, the M3s and a few M4s were engaged in a fighting withdrawal to the west through Kasserine exacting a heavy toll from the advancing Germans.

On the 17th, Gardiner's battalion ambushed the enemy destroying five of his tanks with the opening burst of fire and completely breaking up the attacking formation. They had learned a lot since the first action at Djedeida. On the 21st, the same battalion again played a decisive role when CCB stopped a German thrust toward Djebel el Hamra. On 22 February, Rommel gave up the attack and began to retreat toward the east. With the enemy on the defensive, the Allied forces could begin the advance that was to end the African campaign early in May. Replacing battle losses, larger numbers of Shermans came into action, but many M3s fought throughout the campaign. At the end, 51 M3s were still on strength in the 1st Armored Division. These were turned over to the French for driver training when the division moved west from Tunisia.

Above, another 1st Armored Division M3 operating near Kasserine on 20 February 1943. Below, the final phase of the Tunisian fighting. The M3s move into Bizerte on 8 May 1943.

An M3 of the 193rd Tank Battalion returns from action (above) on Butaritari Island in the Makin atoll on 24 November 1943. Below the 193rd fires on the hulks of some wrecked ships occupied by the enemy at Butaritari.

U.S. Forces made no further use of the medium tank M3 as a fighting tank in the Mediterranean or European theaters of operation. However, in the Pacific they saw action during the seizure of the Gilbert islands in late 1943. From 20 to 23 November, the 193rd Tank Battalion used their M3s to support the 27th Infantry Division in the fighting on Butaritari island of the Makin atoll. The only Japanese armor on the island consisted of a few light tanks which were dug in to serve as pillboxes. Without armored opposition, the M3s were limited to an infantry support role much like that envisaged in the prewar studies at Fort Benning. Thus ended the fighting career of the M3 in U.S. service. OCM 20076, dated 1 April 1943 had redesignated the M3 series as Limited Standard and in April 1944 it was declared obsolete.

An Australian General Lee without the turret cupola. Note that this tank is a late production model without side doors and armed with the long barreled 75mm gun M3.

THE LEE-GRANT IN THE FAR EAST

Although declared obsolete in April 1944, the M3 soldiered on until the end of the war against Japan. Large numbers of both Lees and Grants served with the British Fourteenth Army in the Burma campaign until the fall of Rangoon. Referred to collectively as the Lee-Grant, these tanks were often equipped with the U.S. turret minus the cupola. The latter was replaced by the same type of split cover circular hatch used on the Grant turret.

Large numbers of M3s were shipped to Australia after the end of the African campaign. Their service with the Australian forces continued until the end of the war. As in Burma, the absence of strong Japanese armored forces restricted their role to that of infantry support. So the M3 finished its career performing the task for which its basic design, that of the M2, had been intended. The prewar planners who wrote the original specifications would have been happy to know that it carried out this job remarkably well.

Another Lee without the turret cupola at Mandalay Hill in Burma.

These Grants are in Australia. Above is the 1st Australian Armoured Division being reviewed by General Sir Thomas Blamey at Puckapunyal in June 1942. Below, auxiliary armor has been added by the Australians to protect the differential and final drive housing.

A Soviet M3 captured by the Germans. It is marked with the original U.S. registration number W-304850, the Russian 147, and the cross of its captors.

THE M3 IN RUSSIA

Little information is available regarding the employment of the 1386 M3 medium tanks assigned to the Soviet Union under the Lend-Lease program. Most available photographs are from German sources showing captured or destroyed vehicles. The M3s were used in action by the Soviet tank troops and on at least one occasion, they were employed in an amphibious operation. The latter occurred at Ozereyka Bay on the Black Sea in early 1943. At this time Stalingrad was completely surrounded and the German Seventeenth Army was retreating toward a beachhead on the Taman peninsula. In an attempt to cut off and destroy these forces, the Soviets launched their amphibious attack in the early morning hours of 4 February 1943. The landing failed because of heavy German resistance and a failure of the Soviets to reinforce the successful initial assault. Thirtyone American built tanks were counted as destroyed by the Germans after the battle. These consisted of M3 medium tanks and some General Stuart light tanks.

At the left below, are a number of M3s knocked out on the battlefield in Russia. The tank at the right, manned by its Soviet crew, moves through the ruins of a Russian town.

The Canadian Ram I pilot tank (above and below) at Aberdeen Proving Ground in August 1941.

CANADIAN MEDIUM TANKS RAM I AND RAM II

Although the U.S. production authorities permitted modification of the M3 by installation of the Grant turret, this was considered an interim solution which did not completely meet British requirements. Instead of waiting for the redesigned vehicle which would eventually emerge as the M4, the British Tank Mission in collaboration with the Canadian General Staff designed a modified M3 for production in Canada. The new tank was to use the standard M3 power train and running gear, but the hull and turret would be a Canadian design.

Production facilities were established at the Montreal Locomotive Works with some support from the parent company, the American Locomotive Works in the United States. The new design featured a low silhouette cast turret mounting a British 6 pounder as main armament coaxial with a .30 caliber Browning machine gun. An additional .30 caliber gun was stowed on the outside of the turret and could be mounted on the hatch ring for use against aircraft. The upper hull was a single large casting with the driver located in the right front and a small auxiliary turret on the left. The latter was similar to the cupola on top of the M3 turret and also carried a single .30 caliber machine gun. A door was provided in the sponson on each side of the hull and a small water tight hatch with a quick release catch was located just below the bow gunner's feet. This was for use with special equipment such as the snake, a long pipelike explosive charge used to detonate minefields.

It was originally expected that Britain would provide production drawings for the 6 pounder turret mount. When these did not materialize, it was necessary to equip the first 50 vehicles with the 2 pounder using the mount already in production for the Valentine tank. The Canadian War Department numbers for these tanks were CT-39781 through CT-39830. A new 6 pounder mount was designed and tested in time to enter production in January 1942. The tanks armed with the 2 pounder were designated as the Ram I and those with the 6 pounder as the Ram II.

Compare the pilot tank (above) with the fully stowed production Ram I (at right).

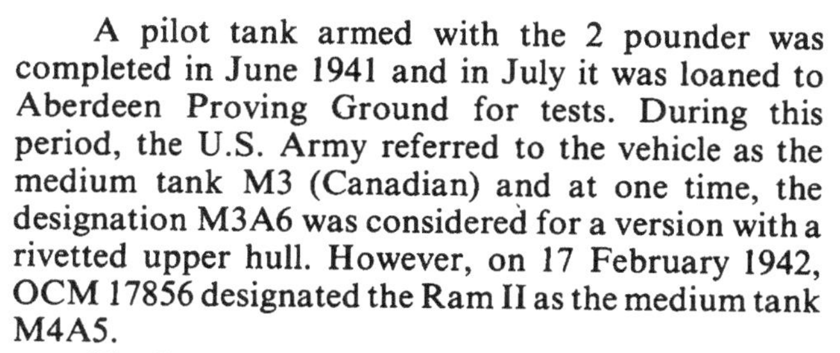

A pilot tank armed with the 2 pounder was completed in June 1941 and in July it was loaned to Aberdeen Proving Ground for tests. During this period, the U.S. Army referred to the vehicle as the medium tank M3 (Canadian) and at one time, the designation M3A6 was considered for a version with a rivetted upper hull. However, on 17 February 1942, OCM 17856 designated the Ram II as the medium tank M4A5.

The Ram could be fitted with any of the standard U.S. tracks for the M3 or M4 series of medium tanks. It also used the Canadian dry pin steel track. This track had a 4.6 inch pitch compared to the 6 inch pitch of the U.S. tracks and it required the installation of a special sprocket with 17 teeth. The Canadian track was 15-1/2 inches wide and required 206 shoes per tank or 103 shoes per track.

Below are the Ram I production lines at the Montreal Locomotive Works.

A total of 1899 Ram II tanks were produced at Montreal Locomotive Works ending in the Summer of 1943. The Canadian War Department numbers assigned to these vehicles were CT-39831 through CT-40937 for the first 1107 tanks and CT-159402 through CT-160193 for the remaining 792. A number of changes were instituted during production. On the later vehicles, the rear opening in the turret casting was eliminated and the tanks were equipped with the late model suspension bogies having the track return rollers offset to the rear. On the Ram II, the side door pistol ports were replaced by blowers and a mushroom ventilator was substituted for the gunner's periscope. The side doors in the hull were eliminated at tank number CT-40131. The auxiliary turret on the left bow was replaced by a ball mount machine gun at vehicle number CT-159502. At the same time, a floor escape hatch was installed just behind the bow gunner. Late production Ram IIs were powered by the Continental R975 C1 replacing the earlier R975 EC2. The new engine had a lower compression ratio permitting operation on 80 octane gasoline. At tank CT-159599 a new mantlet was introduced for the 6 pounder gun.

By 1943, sufficient quantities of the M4 Sherman were available to meet all requirements and further production of the Ram was discontinued Although it was never used in combat, the Ram provided a valuable training tank for the Canadian armored troops. However, as a fighting vehicle, it suffered from the same disadvantage as other tanks armed with the 6 pounder. That was the lack of an adequate high explosive projectile, particularly for use against enemy antitank guns. In this respect, the original M3, with its sponson mounted 75, was superior.

Early Ram IIs are shown above and below. Still equipped with side doors, these tanks are fitted with the WE210 double I tracks.

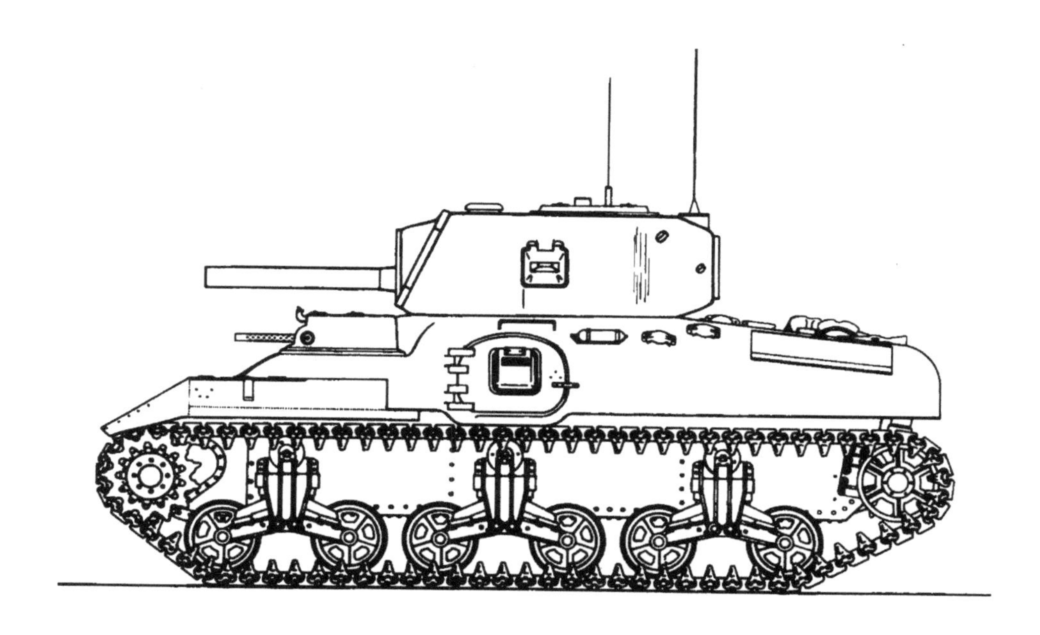

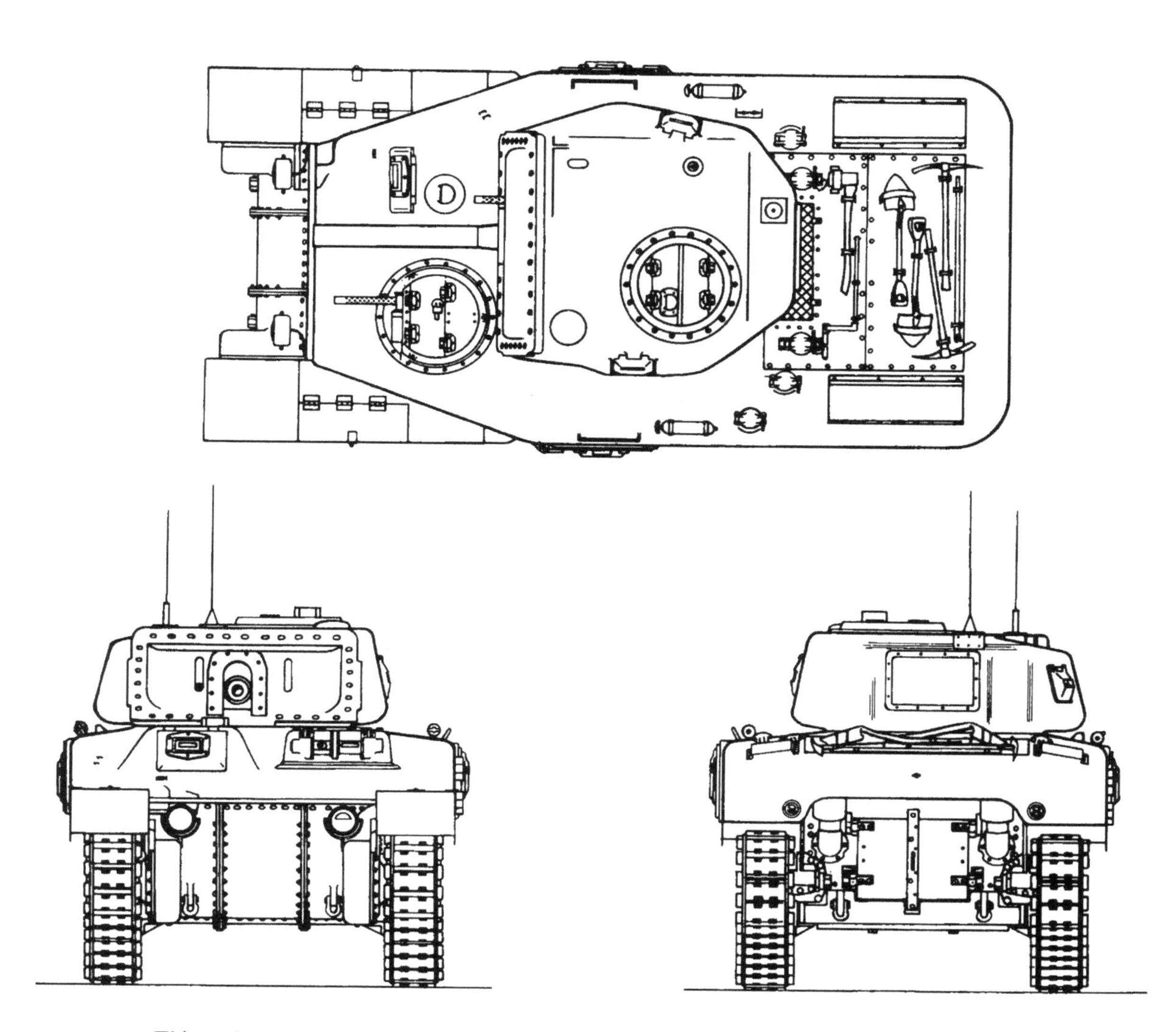

This early production Ram II retains the side doors and the auxiliary machine gun turret.

Scale 1:48

Cruiser Tank Ram II

The late production Ram II. The side doors and pistol port have been eliminated and a ball type bow machine gun mount replaces the auxiliary turret.

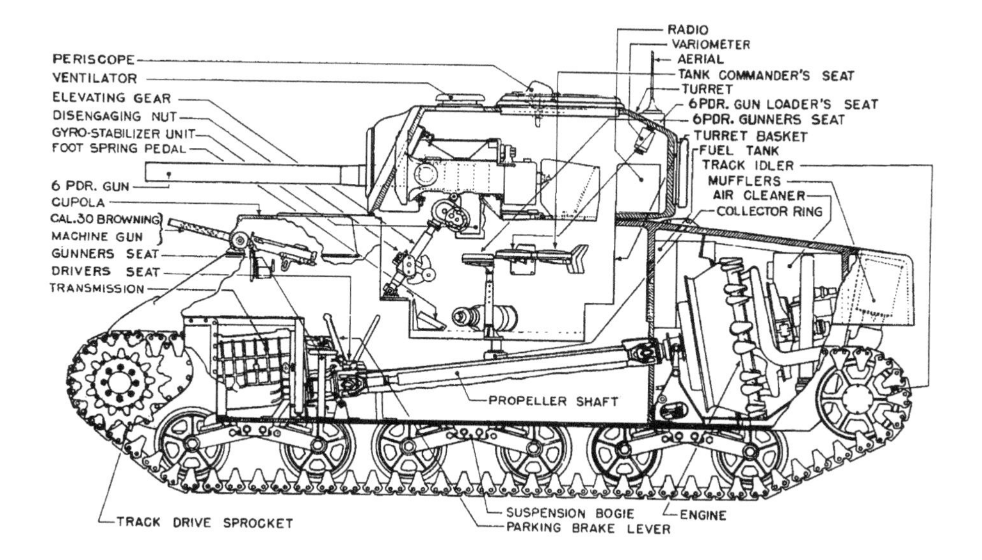

The interior arrangement of the Ram II can be seen in the sectional view above. The mount for the 6 pounder and its coaxial .30 caliber machine gun is shown below (left). Unlike the U.S. built tanks, the driver in the Ram was seated to the right of the transmission as can be seen below (right).

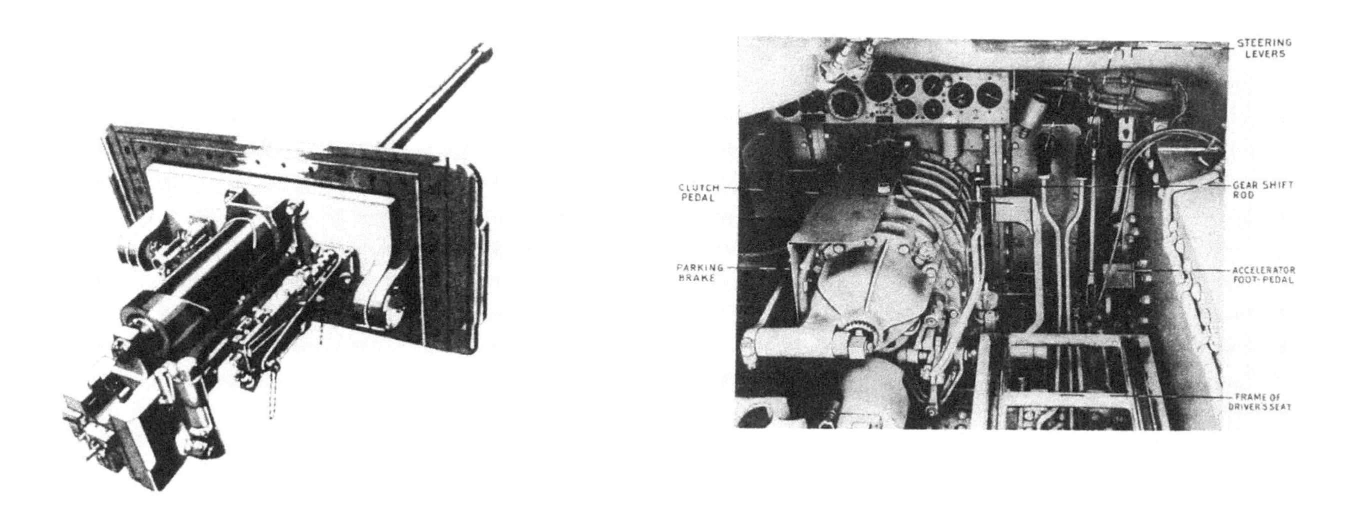

Starting with the 1258th tank, the ball type machine gun mount (below) replaced the auxiliary turret in Ram production.

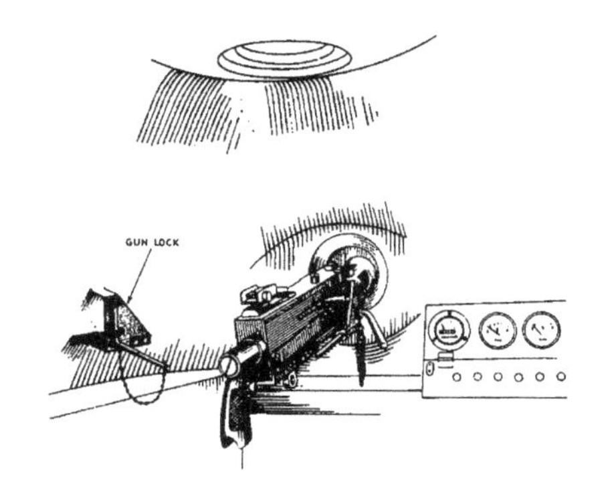

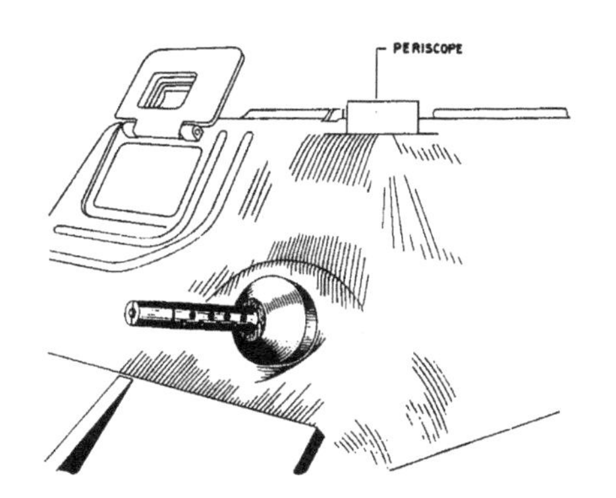

The production Command/Observation Post tank above is based on the late model Ram without the side doors or auxiliary turret. Note the extra radio antennas and reels of communication wire.

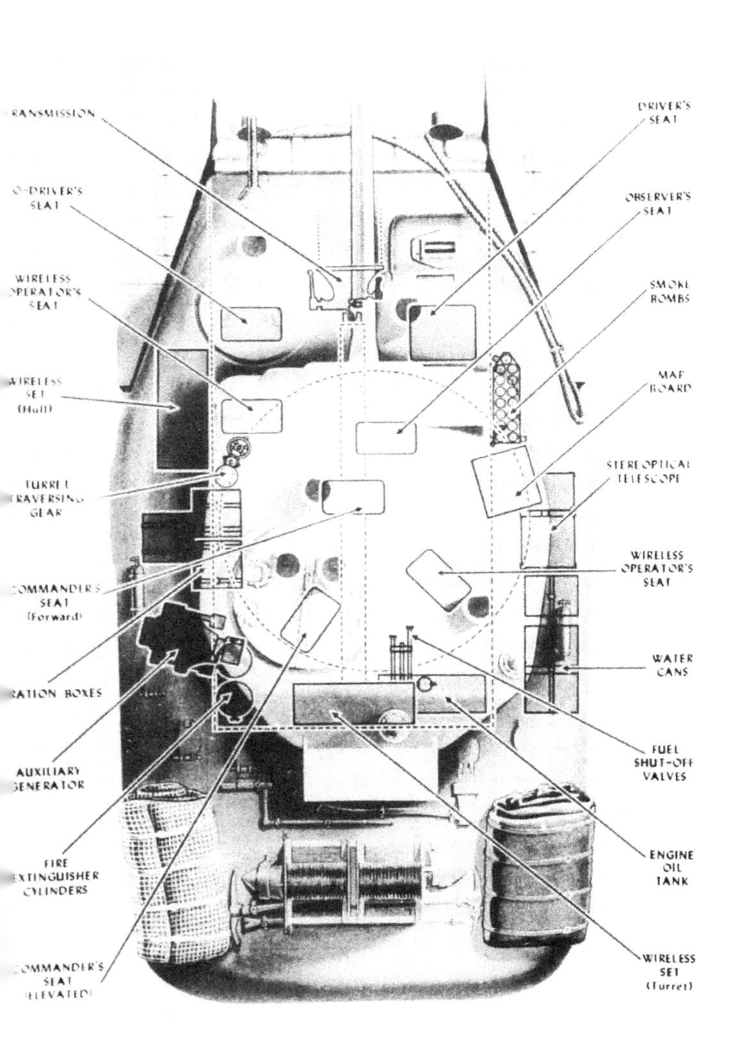

The Ram also provided the basic chassis for numerous other vehicles. One of these was the Command or Observation Post tank. Eightyfour of these were produced at Montreal during 1943 and additional vehicles were converted from Ram IIs in the United Kingdom. During conversion, the 6 pounder and its coaxial machine gun were eliminated and replaced with a dummy gun. The turret basket and hydraulic traversing gear were removed and the manual rotation was limited to 90 degrees. This provided sufficient room for a six man crew with the necessary seats and a map table. Two radio sets were installed, one in the turret bustle and one in the left sponson. Additional line communication equipment was fitted and a forward observation post was located at the front of the turret with a sliding door view port just below the dummy 6 pounder gun. Artillery fire control equipment was carried and the rotating turret hatch was calibrated so that the hatch periscope could be used as a direction finder. Armament was limited to the .30 caliber bow machine gun and the .30 caliber antiaircraft gun fitted to the turret hatch.

Unlike the Ram II on which it was based, the Command/Observation Post tank was widely used by the Canadian armored divisions during operations in northwest Europe.

The general arrangement of equipment appears in the phantom view of the Command/Observation Post tank at the left.

PART II

THE APPEARANCE OF THE SHERMAN

The medium tank T6 mock-up at Aberdeen Proving Ground in August 1941.

MEDIUM TANK T6

In recommending the immediate production of the medium tank M3, the Ordnance Committee directed that work start as soon as possible on the design of an improved tank. Such a tank would correct the major flaws of the M3, but would be close enough in design to use many of the same major components. The new vehicle could then replace the M3 on the assembly line with a minimum loss of production. The Armored Force submitted detailed characteristics for the new medium tank on 31 August 1940. However, the design team assembled at Aberdeen was fully engaged during the Fall and Winter of 1940 completing the production drawings for the M3. When this job was finished on 1 February 1941, a directive was received from the Chief of Ordnance to proceed immediately with the detailed design of the M3's replacement.

The major objection to the M3 was, of course, the location of the 75mm gun in the limited traverse hull mount and the first task was to design a suitable turret for this weapon. The Armored Force requirements also suggested a reduction in height and the provision of antiaircraft protection. A conference at Aberdeen on 18 April 1941 confirmed the major features of the new design. The basic chassis of the M3 was retained including the lower hull, engine, power train, and suspension. Although designed around the Wright R975 EC2, the engine compartment was wide enough to accommodate the larger more powerful Wright G100 or G200 engines when they became available. The upper hull was to be either cast or welded and would use as many components as possible from the M3 in order to expedite production.

With the 37mm gun eliminated, the 75mm weapon was mounted with a coaxial machine gun in a 360 degree traverse, power operated turret. The turret ring diameter was enlarged to 69 inches and the armor thickness was increased to a maximum of 3 inches in the front. The turret was designed with a removable front plate permitting the installation of different armament combinations. Five basic arrangements were considered. These were (1) one 75mm gun M2 coaxial with one .30 caliber machine gun, (2) two 37mm guns M6 with one .30 caliber machine gun, (3) one 105mm howitzer with one .30 caliber machine gun, (4) three .50 caliber machine guns mounted for high angle antiaircraft fire, and (5) one British 6 pounder high velocity gun coaxial with one .30 caliber machine

Additional views of the T6 mock-up at Aberdeen.

gun. Such a design was expected to simplify production since the wide variety of weapons would permit the same basic tank to be armed for many different tactical missions. The commander's cupola from the M3 was retained on top of the turret with its high angle .30 caliber antiaircraft machine gun. Two fixed .30 caliber machine guns were located in the front armor plate for use by the driver similar to those on the M3. These guns could be locked in any position from +8 to –6 degrees elevation.

The crew in the new tank was reduced to five men and their arrangement was to become standard on U.S. tanks for many years. The gunner was located at the right front of the turret alongside the 75mm gun with the tank commander just behind him under the cupola. The loader was on the left of the cannon where he could load the main weapon and service the .30 caliber coaxial machine gun. The two remaining crew members rode in the front of the hull with the driver's seat on the left alongside the transmission. The assistant driver or bow gunner rode in a similar seat on the right side of the transmission. He manned the .30 caliber flexible machine gun mounted in the right front armor plate.

Ordnance Committee action in May 1941 recommended the construction of a full size wooden mock-up as well as a pilot tank. This was approved by OCM 17316 in June with the new vehicle designated as the medium tank T6. After finishing the wooden mock-up, Aberdeen was directed to assemble a complete pilot tank using a cast upper hull. Rock Island Arsenal was assigned the task of building another pilot with a welded upper hull, but without a turret. The latter design required some modification to reduce the number of plates and the length of welded joint.

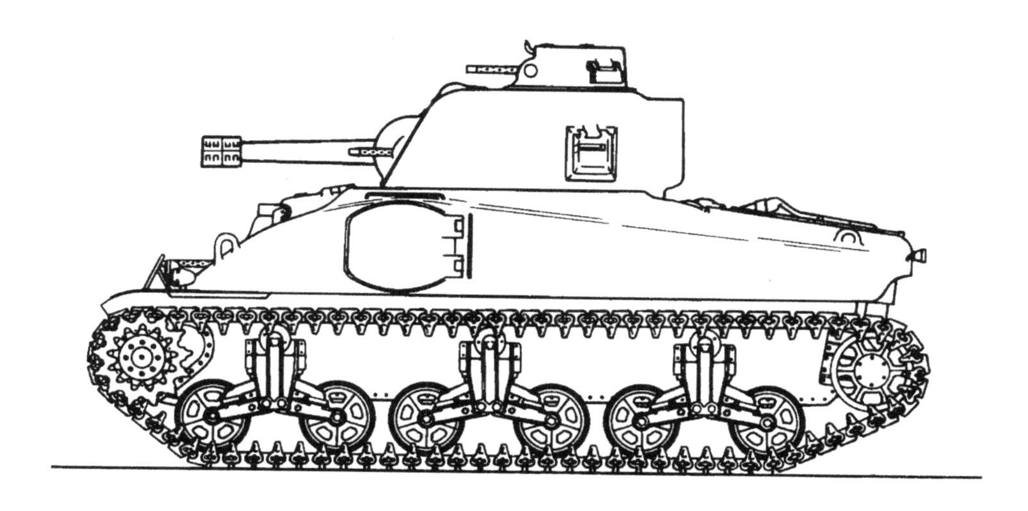

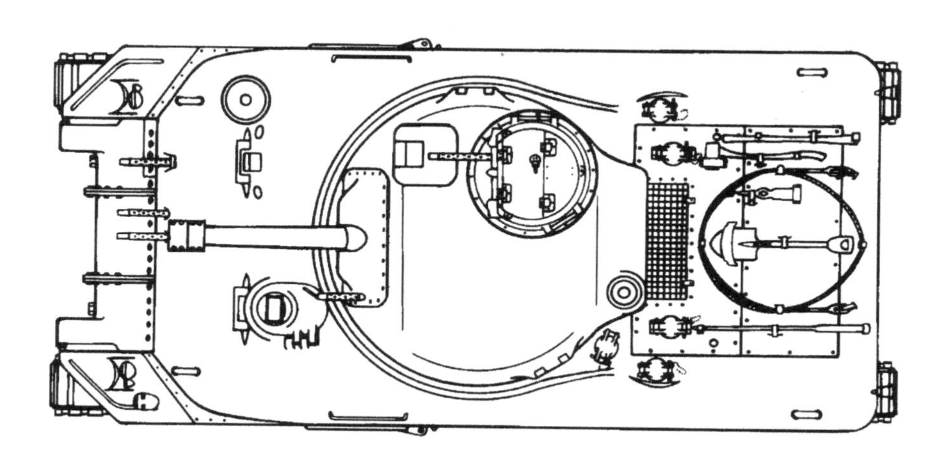

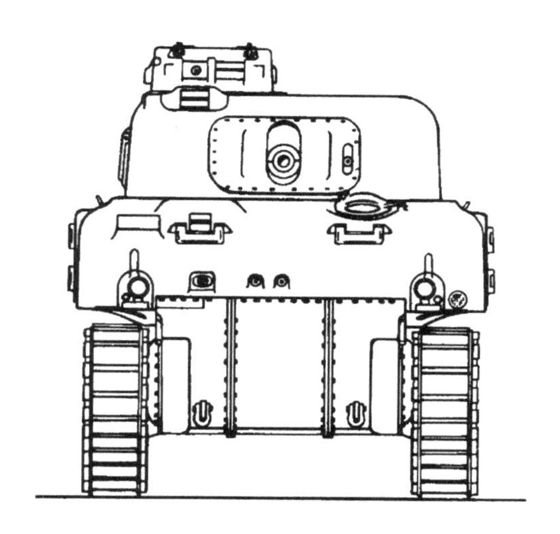

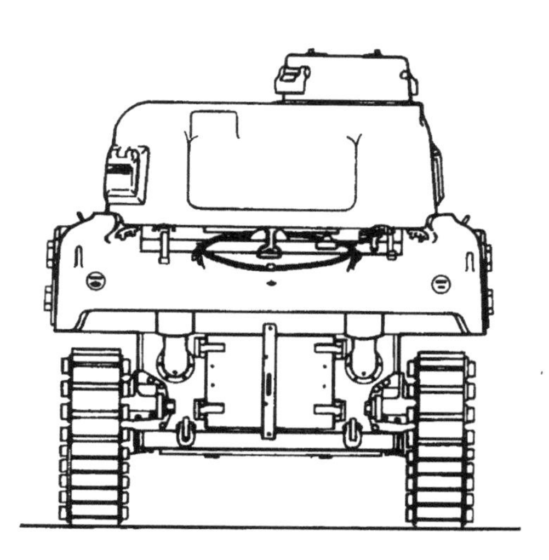

This drawing shows the T6 as originally designed with the turret cupola.

Scale 1:48

Medium Tank T6

At the top left, the new T6 is displayed alongside the medium tanks M3, M3A1 and the light tank M3. The tall officer with his back to the camera (arrow) is Major Robert J. Icks. At the top right, the T6 is at full speed during the demonstration.

The Aberdeen pilot was complete on 2 September 1941 and inspected by representatives of the Armored Force and the Ordnance Department. As completed, the T6 was fitted with side doors in the sponsons on each side of the hull. Unlike the M3, the side doors were solid without any protectoscopes or other vision devices. A hatch was located over the driver's seat and a floor escape hatch was installed just behind the assistant driver's position. The flexible bow machine gun was linked to a sight rotor in the upper hull in front of the assistant driver. Direct vision slots were provided for both the driver and the assistant driver and the former also had a periscope mounted in the hatch cover above his head. An adjustable seat permitted the driver to ride with his head out of the open hatch or to drop down inside and use the periscope or vision slot when the hatch was closed.

A pistol port with a protectoscope was located in each side of the turret. The mount carrying the 75mm gun M2 was linked to a special sight rotor in the top front of the turret for use by the gunner. This linkage moved only the top mirror of the periscope type telescopic sight maintaining the alignment between the sight path and the 75mm gun. If damaged, this mirror could be quickly replaced from a magazine containing a supply of mirrors included as part of the sight. The 75mm gun M2 was installed with the breechblock moving in the horizontal direction for easy right hand loading. In the combination gun mount T48, the elevation ranged from +25 to −12 degrees. With the full 360 degree power traverse, the advantage over the old M3 was obvious. Since the mount was designed for the new longer barreled 75mm gun T8 (M3), it was badly out of balance with the short M2 gun. Double counterweights were installed near the gun muzzle to balance the weapon and permit proper operation of the elevation stabilizer. This gyrostabilizer was essentially the same unit used with the 37mm gun M6 in the medium tank M3. Minor differences included an improved oil reservoir and the addition of a small bleeder valve to facilitate rapid charging of the hydraulic system.

Below: The T6 on 20 September 1941. Note the two antennas installed for the SCR 508 in the turret bustle and the SCR 506 in the right sponson.

The T6 photographed on 16 September 1941. The views below show the cannon at maximum and minimum elevation.

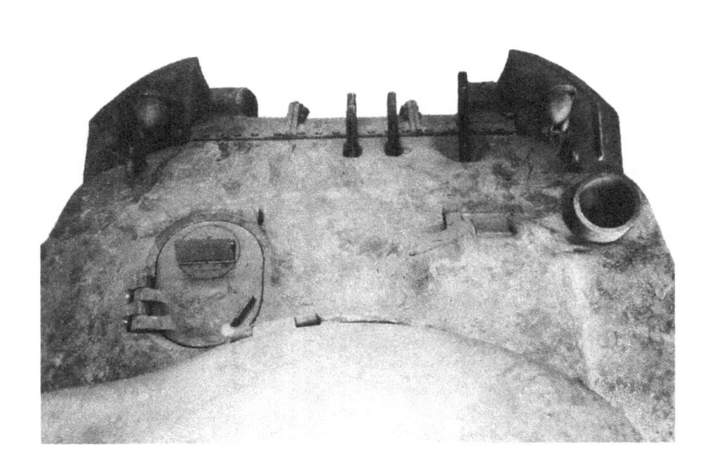

Note the absence of a roof hatch or periscope for the bow gunner (top left). Except for the direct vision slot, his only view was through the sighting device coupled to the bow machine gun. The view of the rear deck (top right) reveals the lack of overhead protection for the engine air intake as on the M3. The external stowage in this area also is similar to that on the M3. The view below with the top plate removed shows the installation of the R975 EC2 engine.

The T6 was equipped with two radios. An SCR 508 for voice communication was located in the turret bustle and an SCR 506 was carried in the right front sponson for operation by the assistant driver. The latter radio for both voice and code had a longer range and was standardized for use only in command tanks. Although these two radios were considered standard for U.S. tanks, an installation was developed for the SCR 245 as a substitute for the SCR 506 because of expected shortages of the latter. The turret brackets were also designed to mount the British Number 19 radio set.

Discussions between the Armored Force and Ordnance after the inspection on 2 September led to a number of modifications to the T6. The most obvious of these changes were the elimination of the commander's cupola and the sponson side doors. The cupola was about one foot high, but the overall height of the tank was not reduced by that amount since some height was added by the flat circular hatch and antiaircraft machine gun mount that replaced it. Although the cupola was part of the wooden mock-up, the writer has no evidence that it was ever installed on the pilot tank. During the inspection on 2 September, the tank had an open hole in the turret roof. Elimination of the side doors strengthened and improved the armor protection of the hull. With these and other minor changes, the Ordnance Committee recommended on 5 September 1941 that the vehicle be standardized as the medium tank M4. The recommendations were approved in October with the requirements that, if possible, a .50 caliber antiaircraft machine gun be installed and a ball mount be provided for the flexible bow machine gun.

Construction of production pilots started in November and additional manufacturers were brought into the program. OCM 17578 of 11 December 1941 assigned the designation medium tank M4 to vehicles with a welded hull and those with a cast upper hull became the medium tank M4A1. Under the latter designation, the T6 served as a test vehicle at Aberdeen to develop components and assemblies for use in production tanks. In the U.S. Army, all models of the medium tank M4 series were referred to as the General Sherman. The British designated the M4 as the Sherman I and the M4A1 as the Sherman II.

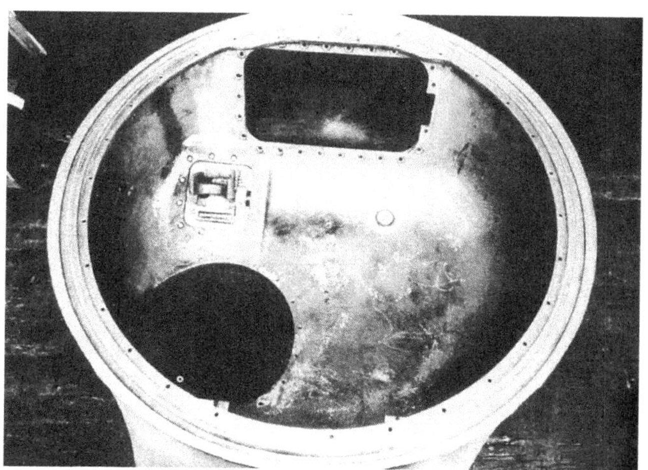

The T6 turret and fittings including the 75mm gun mount and turret bustle radio can be seen in the four upper photographs. Note that the new flat circular hatch has not yet been installed to replace the cupola. The lower three photographs show the driving compartment.

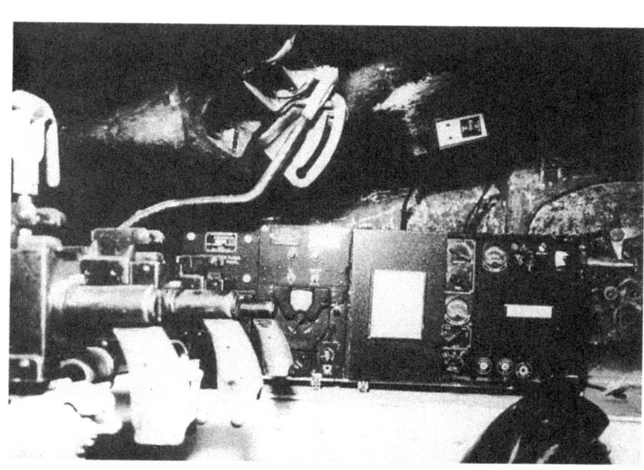

The first M4A1 (above and below) manufactured at the Lima Locomotive Works photographed on 11 March 1942.

MEDIUM TANKS M4 AND M4A1

Production of the medium tank M4A1 started in February 1942 on the assembly line established by the British contract at Lima Locomotive Works. A month later they were also being produced at the Pressed Steel Car Company. These early production tanks incorporated the modifications specified for the T6. The side doors were eliminated, although the first tank built at Lima used a T6 upper hull casting with the holes for the side doors welded up. This tank was taken over by Ordnance for test purposes, but it retained its British WD number, T-25189, throughout its service in the U.S. Army. The second tank, T-25190, used a new hull casting with the side doors completely eliminated. Both vehicles were equipped with the short barreled 75mm gun M2 fitted with double counterweights since the new M3 cannon was not yet available. T-25190 was shipped to England bearing the name MICHAEL on its sides probably in honor of Michael Dewar, head of the British Tank Mission.

MICHAEL, the second production M4A1 which originally carried the number T-25190 after completion at the Lima Locomotive Works (above) and on display in London (below). The counterweights were added to the gun muzzle before shipment.

A later photograph of MICHAEL showing its new number. Note that the 75mm gun M2 has been replaced by the longer M3 weapon.

Early 1942 production at Lima Locomotive. The tanks are still armed with two fixed bow machine guns and have the original suspension bogies.

Above: Early production M4A1s parading in Louisville, Kentucky on Army Day, 6 April 1942.

Further modifications were introduced in the production tanks. A rotor shield was added to the front of the T48 mount and it was standardized as the combination gun mount M34. This shield, about 2 inches thick, was to prevent small arms fire from scarring the rotor surface and locking it against the main gun shield which served as the front plate of the turret. It also reduced the possibility of bullet splash entering the turret and acted as a counterweight to help balance the 75mm gun. At the same time, another splash guard was added to the bottom section of the front plate to block bullet splash from entering around the gun rotor. A small shield about 1 inch thick was later attached to the barrel of the coaxial .30 caliber machine gun to exclude bullet splash from the machine gun port.

Service experience with the medium tank M3 revealed the need for better ventilation to exhaust the powder gasses from the fighting compartment when firing with the tank closed up. On the M3, the necessary increase of air intake area was obtained by the installation of three armored ventilators. A similar solution was applied to the M4A1 with one ventilator located on the turret roof and two on the top of the hull. One of the hull ventilators was fitted on top of the right front sponson in lieu of the radio antenna socket for the SCR 506. The second was also located on top of the right sponson, but was just to the rear of the turret. In these early tanks, the front hull ventilator and the 75mm ammunition rack in the right front sponson were sacrificed when the SCR 506 was installed. Since the SCR 506 was only used in command or headquarters tanks not usually involved in heavy firing, the problem was not serious.

Below: An early M4A1 under test by the Armored Force at Fort Knox during the Spring of 1942. These tanks all have the original sighting device for the 75mm gun.

The pilot M4A1 from the Pacific Car and Foundry Company (above and below) at Aberdeen on 9 June 1942. The early sighting device for the 75 has been replaced by a periscopic sight in the turret roof.

With the side doors gone, the production tanks were provided with a roof hatch for the assistant driver. It was a mirror image of the driver's hatch also fitted with a periscope, but opening in the opposite direction. The bow machine gun was now installed in a ball mount shielded to prevent damage from small arms fire and to block the entrance of bullet splash. The bow gun could be traversed 20 degrees left or 25 degrees right and had an elevation range of +20 to –10 degrees. Without the sight rotor and connecting linkage, the bow machine gun could be aimed only by using tracer ammunition.

Protection for the engine air intake was improved by the addition of a flat cast armor plate approximately 3 inches above the rear deck. Baffles were welded to the deck to prevent small arms fire from entering the engine compartment.

When the M4 was standardized, it was requested that a .50 caliber antiaircraft machine gun be installed replacing the .30 caliber weapon removed with the turret cupola. A fitting to carry the .50 caliber gun mount was attached to the rotating ring surrounding the split circular hatch that replaced the cupola. The mount could be operated in two positions. The forward position had a range of elevation from +56 to –25 degrees for use against aircraft and ground targets. When operated from the rear position, the elevation ranged from +80 to +36 degrees for engaging dive bombers. Originally, a bracket was installed inside the turret for stowing the gun and mount, but this was later shifted to the outside of the turret.

The question of the antiaircraft machine gun was a difficult one to settle. The British never liked this feature and frequently left them off their tanks. They preferred to leave the defense against aerial attack to special antiaircraft vehicles. The U.S. Army also had difficulty in making up its mind. In September 1942, the Ordnance Committee directed that a .30 caliber machine gun be provided in place of the .50 caliber weapon. However, the following February, combat reports indicated that the .50 caliber gun was essential and its use was standardized once again in April 1943.

Other changes from the T6 included the installation of a periscope for the tank commander in one half of the split circular turret hatch cover. A similar periscope was installed in the turret roof for the loader. Both periscopes, as well as those for the drivers, could be rotated 360 degrees and tilted to change the line of vision. The periscopes could be locked in azimuth and elevation by two knurled set screws. The pistol port on the right side of the T6 turret was left out of the production tanks and the protectoscope was eliminated from the left hand pistol port leaving it with a solid cover. Unlike the T6, the lower hull on the production M4A1s was assembled by welding.

OCM 17906, dated 6 March 1942, revised the armament for the M4 series of medium tanks. This order eliminated the two fixed machine guns in the front plate fired by the driver. In July 1942, one of the two .30 caliber machine gun tripods was also dropped from the tank's approved armament. Tests had also shown that the special sight rotor located in the top front of the turret was vulnerable to damage and in some cases, bullet splash could penetrate into the turret. The rotor was then replaced in production by the periscope M4 which included a telescopic sight. The periscope was installed well back in the turret roof with only the replaceable top exposed. Like the earlier sight rotor, the periscope was linked to the gun mount so that the sight path remained aligned with the 75mm gun.

Another modification was the introduction of a metal vane sight. This enabled the tank commander to roughly lay the gun on target. The front element was a metal blade welded to the front of the turret roof just to the right of the gunner's periscopic sight. The rear sight was a shorter blade attached to the turret hatch door in front of the tank commander's periscope. Looking through his periscope, the tank commander could align the two sight vanes with the target. These metal sights appeared on the Sherman during the Fall of 1942. Later, they were superseded in production by an improved design installed as a single unit on the front of the turret roof to the left of the gunner's periscope. This later design combined a short front element with a taller double blade rear sight in a single assembly and could be used with the hatch open or closed.

The tank above illustrates the early production standard after the elimination of the fixed bow machine guns and the introduction of the gunner's periscopic sight. Compare the steel covered engine air intake with that on the T6 or M3.

A production pilot M4A1 was completed in May 1942 at the Pacific Car and Foundry Company and shipped to Aberdeen for test. The hull casting retained the two holes for the fixed .30 caliber machine guns, but the weapons were not mounted having been eliminated by the order of the previous March. Production of the M4A1 continued at all three manufacturers until September 1943 when it stopped at Lima Locomotive Works. Pacific Car and Foundry built their last M4A1 in November and the Pressed Steel Car Company completed their run in December. During this period, U.S. factories produced a total of 6281 M4A1s with the 75mm gun.

Although the fixed bow machine guns are gone from the front view below, this tank retains the early sighting device in the upper front of the turret.

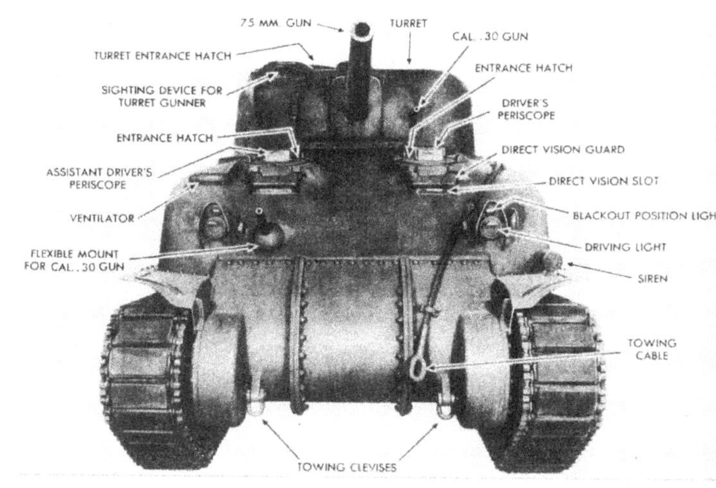

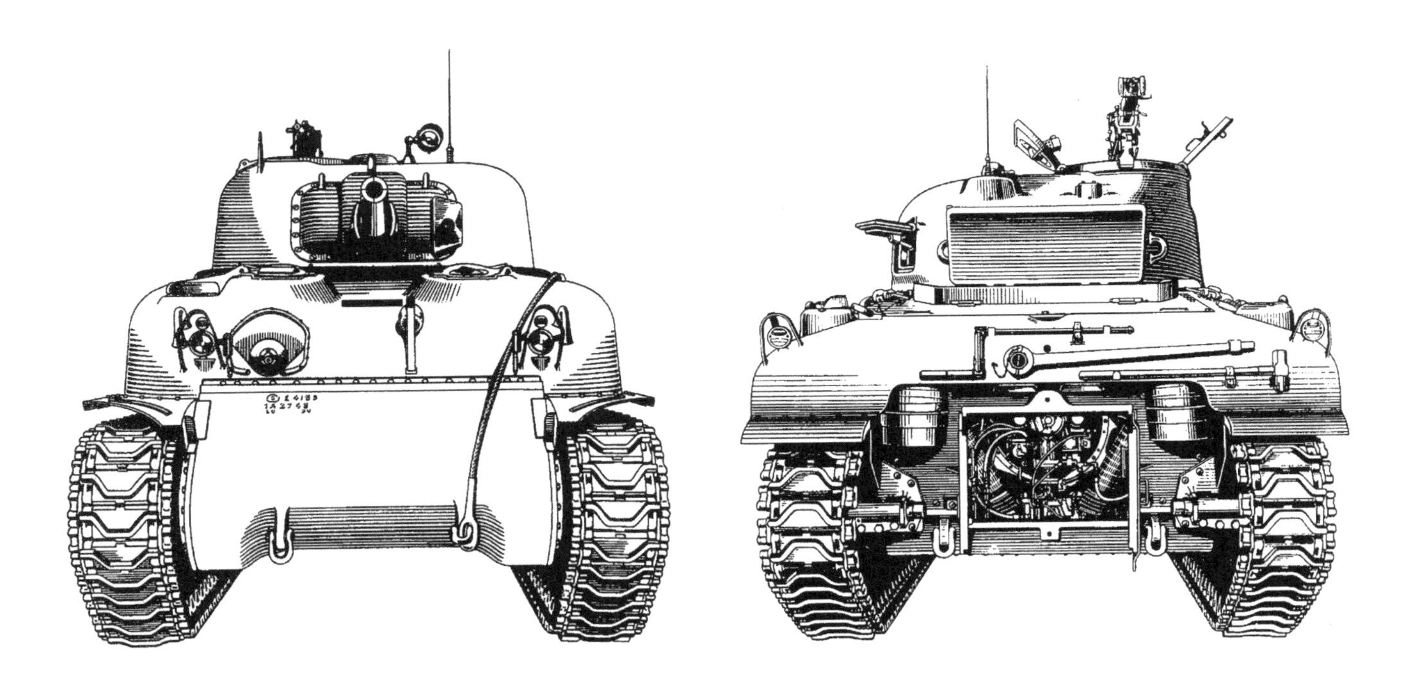

A production M4A1 after the elimination of the drivers' direct vision slots and the installation of the second set of periscopes in the front hull. Note the one piece differential and final drive housing.

The first production Grizzly I built at Montreal Locomotive. A British type stowage box is installed on the turret bustle and the opening for the smoke bomb thrower can be seen in the turret roof just forward and to the left of the loader's periscope.

In September 1942, specifications were issued in Canada for the production of the Sherman modified to meet Canadian requirements. It was intended to replace the Ram II on the assembly lines at the Montreal Locomotive Works. The change over was delayed until August 1943 to minimize any disruption of the production effort. The model of the Sherman selected was the M4A1 designated by the Canadians as the Grizzly I. It was essentially identical to the U.S. version except for British stowage and the installation of a Number 19 radio set and a 2 inch bomb thrower (smoke mortar) in the turret. The latter item was subsequently adopted as standard on U.S. tanks. Some of the Grizzlies were fitted with the short pitch Canadian dry pin track requiring special 17 tooth sprockets. By December 1943, 188 Grizzlies had been built. Production stopped with the end of the year since adequate supplies of tanks were available from U.S. sources. Some of the Grizzlies were shipped to the United Kingdom and the remainder were assigned to training units in Canada.

In July 1942, production of the welded hull M4 started at the Pressed Steel Car Company. The M4 differed from the M4A1 only in details resulting from the welded upper hull construction. The angular welded hull provided a little more room allowing the stowage of 97 rounds of 75mm ammunition compared to 90 rounds for the M4A1. Three ventilators were installed in the hull roof with one on the top front of each sponson and one at the right rear as on the M4A1. In addition, a separate antenna socket was provided on the right side of the front plate for the installation of the SCR 506 radio. The turret was identical to that on the M4A1.

An early production M4 (at right) with the drivers' direct vision slots and the three piece differential and final drive housing. However, the heavy duty suspension bogies have been introduced on this model.

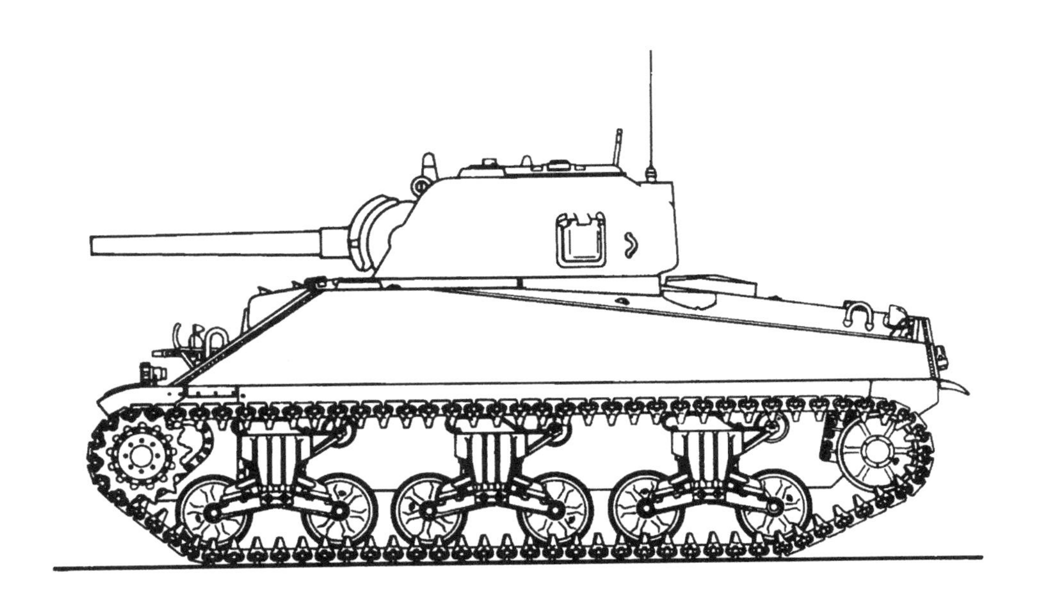

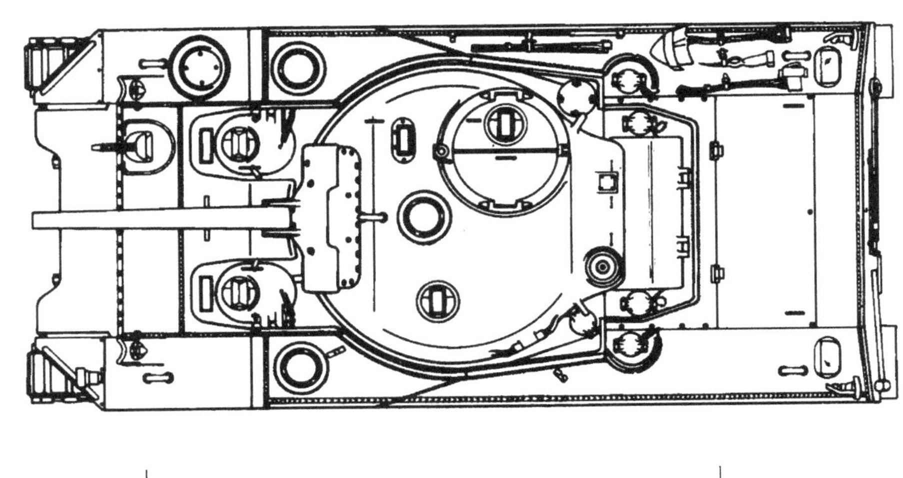

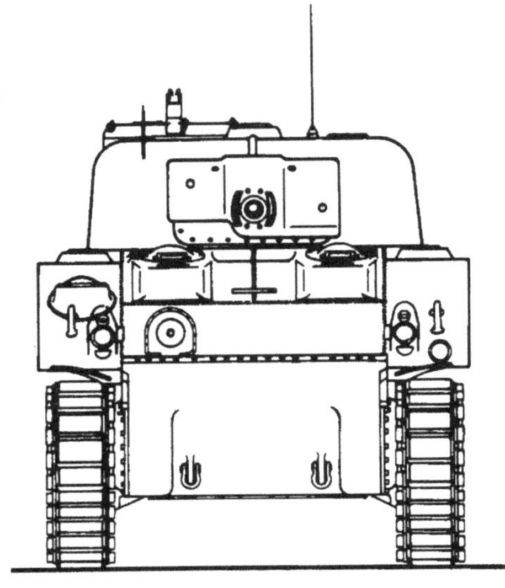

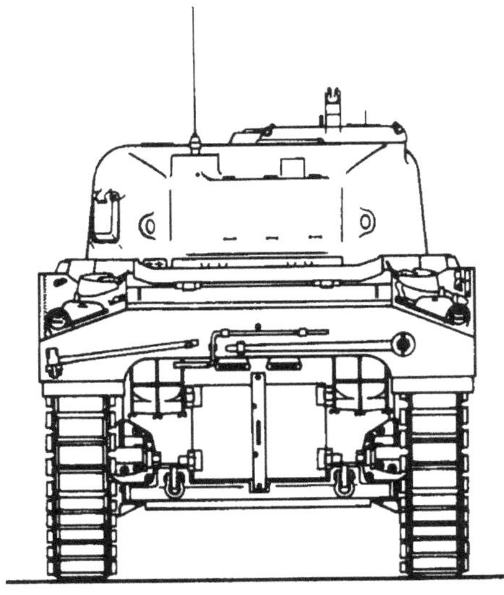

Scale 1:48

Medium Tank M4

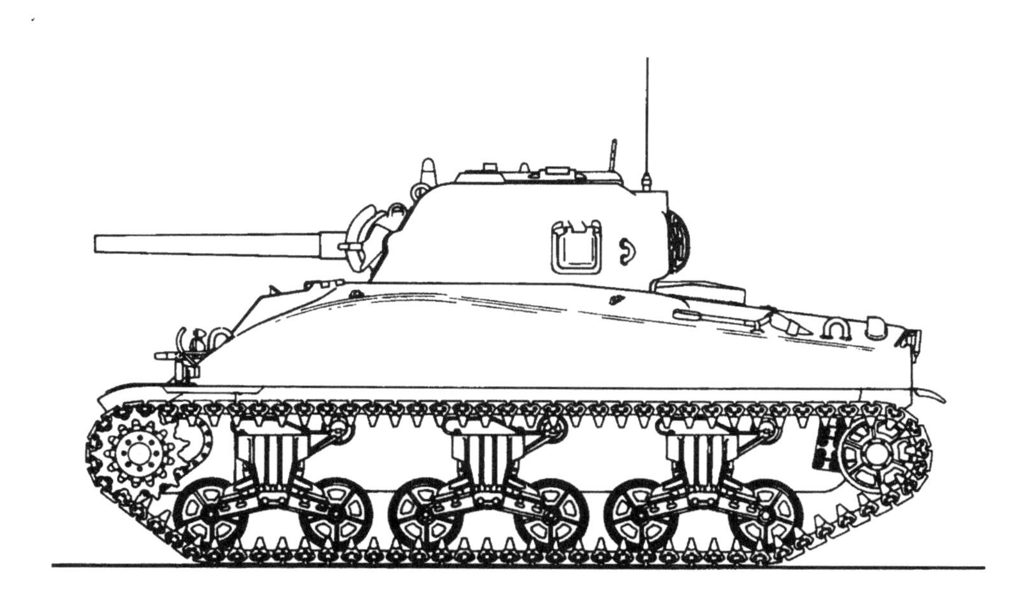

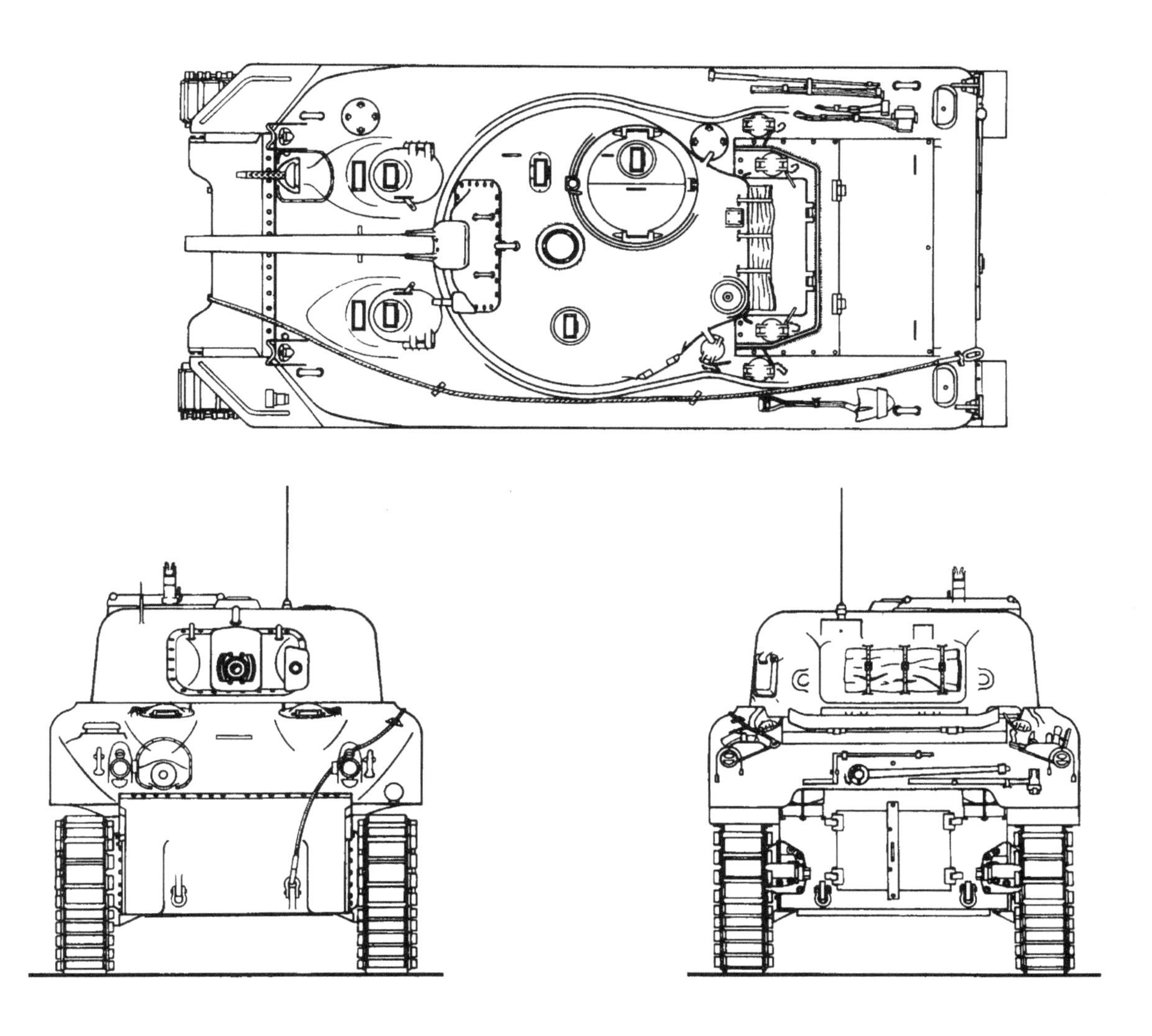

Scale 1:48

Medium Tank M4A1

After the first production tanks, the R975 EC2 engine was superseded by the R975 C1 now manufactured by Continental. With its compression ratio lowered from 6.3:1 to 5.7:1, the new engine developed the same power, but its fuel octane requirement was reduced from 91 to 80. Using this power plant, the M4 and M4A1 reached a maximum speed of 24 miles/hour on roads. A fuel capacity of 175 gallons gave a cruising range of over 100 miles.

Like the earlier medium tank M3, all tanks of the M4 series were equipped with a 50 ampere, 30 volt auxiliary generator. It provided battery charging when the main engine was not running and supplemented the engine generator under high load conditions. Driven by a 2-cycle single cylinder air-cooled gasoline engine, the auxiliary generator was installed in the sponson at the left rear of the fighting compartment.

Front (left) and rear (right) views of the Continental R975 C1 engine are shown above.

The auxiliary generator installation for the early tanks can be seen below at the left. The arrangement on the later production vehicles is shown at the right.

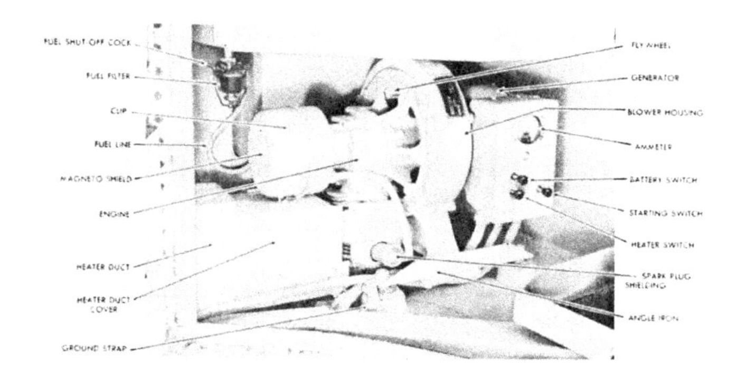

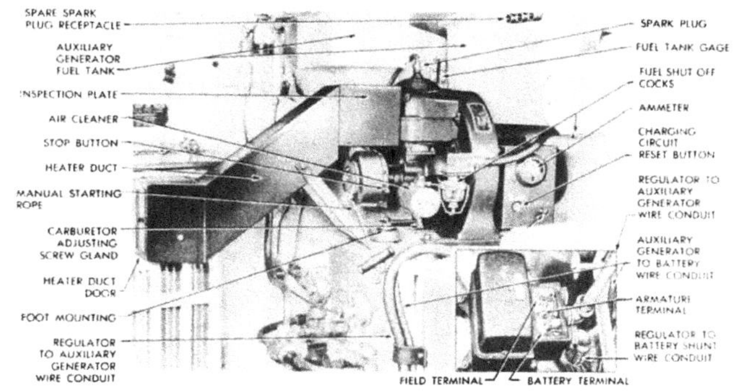

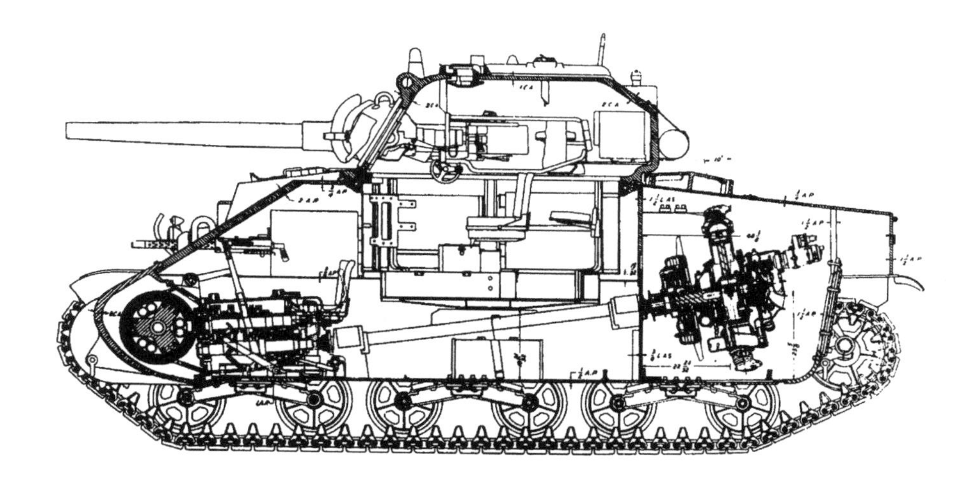

Above is a sectional view of the medium tank M4. Except for the welded hull, the M4A1 was identical. The photographs below compare the early vertical volute spring suspension (upper) with the later heavy duty version (lower). The use of larger volute springs in the latter did not leave sufficient clearance for the track return roller on top of the bogie frame so it was offset to the rear.

By the Summer of 1942, the heavy duty suspension bogies with the rear mounted track return rollers were replacing the earlier type in production. The volute springs were 8 inches in diameter compared to 7 inches on the previous models. The new suspension was designed to reduce the number of spring failures, particularly with the heavier tanks such as the M3A4 and the M4 series. It was released for production on 15 January 1942 for the M3A4 and on 29 January for the M4s, but problems during the test program delayed its appearance and resulted in a number of changes. The trunnion center was raised on the later designs greatly improving the spring stability. The different versions could be identified most easily by the shape of the track skid on top of the bogie assembly. The early skids were heavy strips of steel bowed in the center and bolted to the top of the bogie at each end. The front end of the later skids made a 180 degree loop before being attached to the bogie frame.

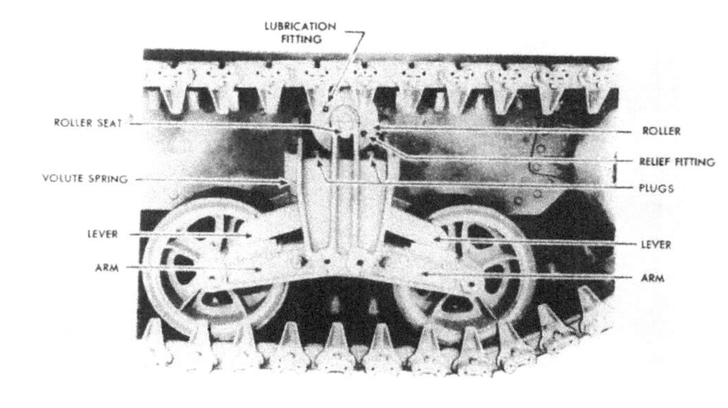

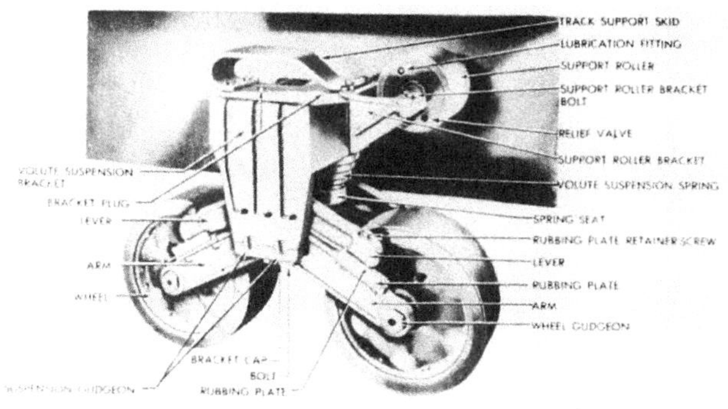

Four stages in the development of the vertical volute spring bogie are illustrated in the drawings below.

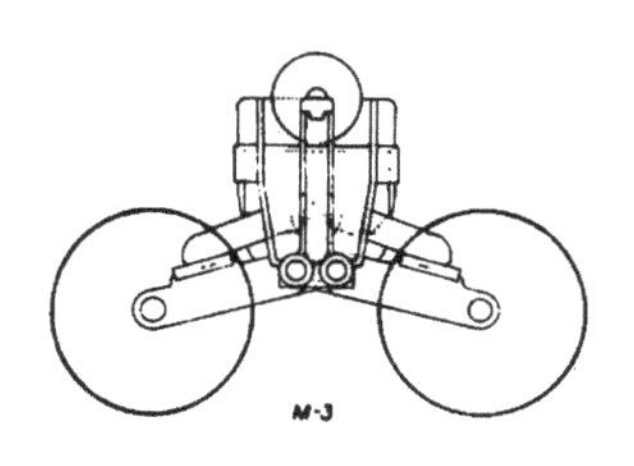

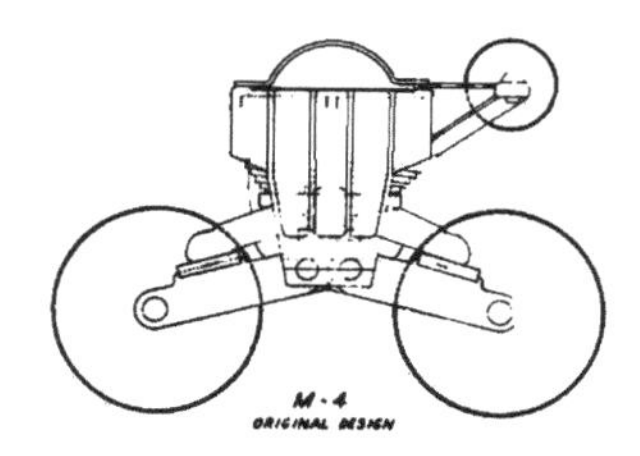

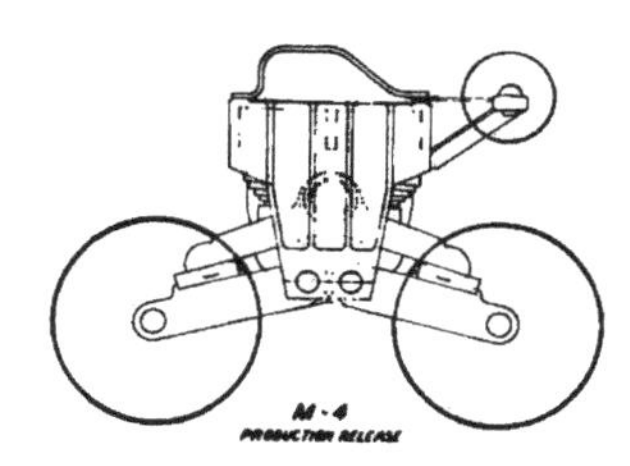

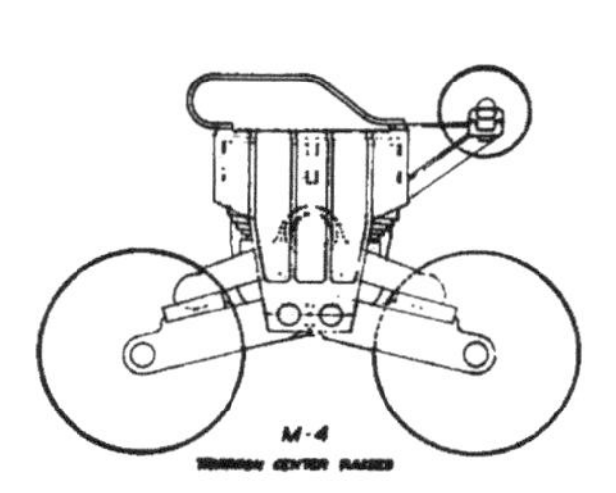

The covers for the auxiliary periscopes which replaced the vision slots can be seen just in front of the drivers' doors. Unlike the periscopes in the doors, they were not capable of rotation.

On the early production tanks, direct vision slots were provided for emergency use by the driver and assistant driver. Production tolerances resulted in gaps between the hull and the direct vision door hinge which permitted the entrance of bullet splash. This was cured by welding 3/8 inch steel plates to the inside of the hull around the door handle. However, with a 2 inch increase in length on the later periscope holders, interference between the drivers' heads and the periscopes prevented easy use of the direct vision slot. The problem was solved by eliminating the direct vision slots completely and providing a second set of auxiliary periscopes. This greatly improved the field of view over the vision slots and smoothed out the front armor increasing the protection it provided.

These two photographs show the driver's controls in the early (left) and late (below) production tanks.

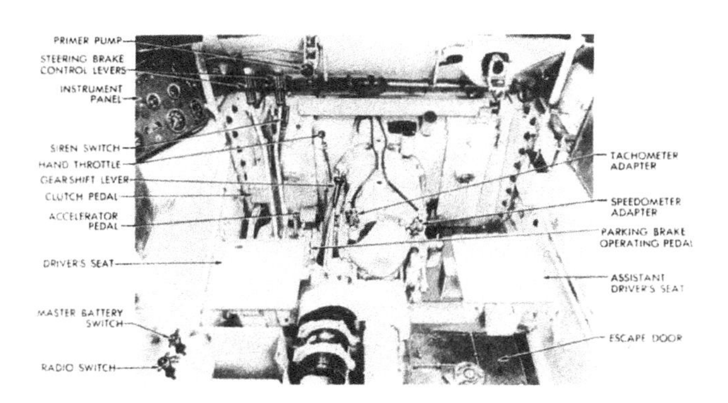

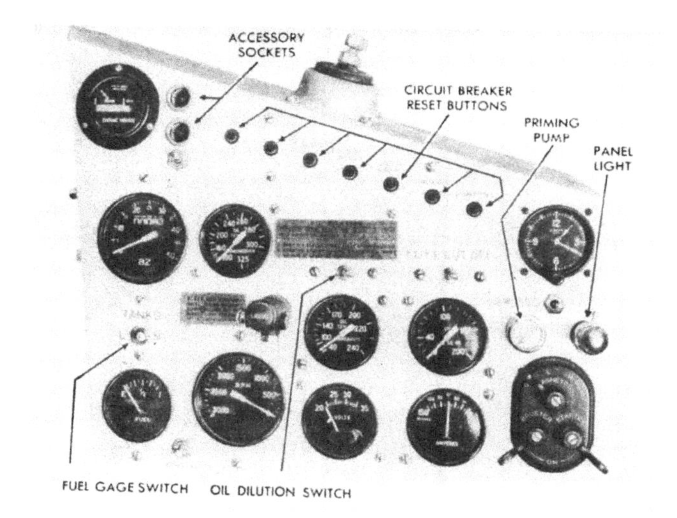

Note the difference between the early instrument panel above and that on the late production tanks at the right.

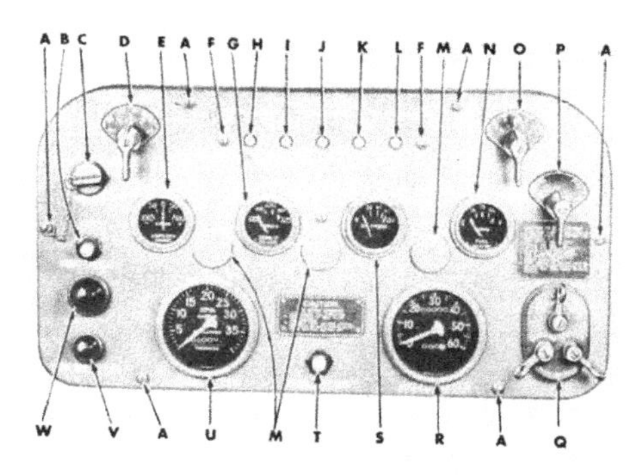

A—PANEL ATTACHING SCREWS
B—FIRE DETECTOR TEST SWITCH
C—OUTLET SOCKET
D—PANEL LIGHT SWITCH
E—AMMETER
F—CIRCUIT BREAKER PANEL ATTACHING SCREWS
G—ENGINE OIL TEMPERATURE GAGE
H—CIRCUIT BREAKER RESET BUTTON (FUEL CUT-OFF)
I—CIRCUIT BREAKER RESET BUTTON (LIGHTS)
J—CIRCUIT BREAKER RESET BUTTON (ACCESSORIES)
K—CIRCUIT BREAKER RESET BUTTON (SIREN)
L—CIRCUIT BREAKER RESET BUTTON (INSTRUMENTS)
M—PANEL LIGHT COVER
N—FUEL GAGE
O—MAIN LIGHT SWITCH
P—FUEL GAGE SELECTOR SWITCH
Q—CRANKING MOTOR AND MAGNETO SWITCH
R—SPEEDOMETER
S—OIL PRESSURE GAGE
T—FUEL CUT-OFF SWITCH
U—TACHOMETER
V—LOW OIL PRESSURE WARNING LIGHT
W—FIRE SIGNAL LIGHT (NOT ON LATER MODELS)

Testing of various power traverse units showed the superiority of the hydraulic mechanism manufactured by the Oilgear Company. This unit had greater control sensitivity and since it used a variable stroke piston pump, tight spots in the turret race or ring gear had little effect on the smoothness of operation. The Oilgear unit was recommended as the standard for all production tanks, but the large numbers required made it necessary to authorize the use of the Westinghouse electric and the Logansport hydraulic equipment as substitutes. Both of these, and particularly the Logansport unit, were affected by tight spots or other variations in friction. All of the power traverse mechanisms were designed to fit the same turret bracket and the two hydraulic units used the same reduction gears. A gear reduction unit was included as part of the Westinghouse equipment. A different gyrostabilizer pump was required for tanks equipped with the electric unit since its motor drive rotated at about 3600 rpm compared to about 2000 rpm for the two hydraulic mechanisms.

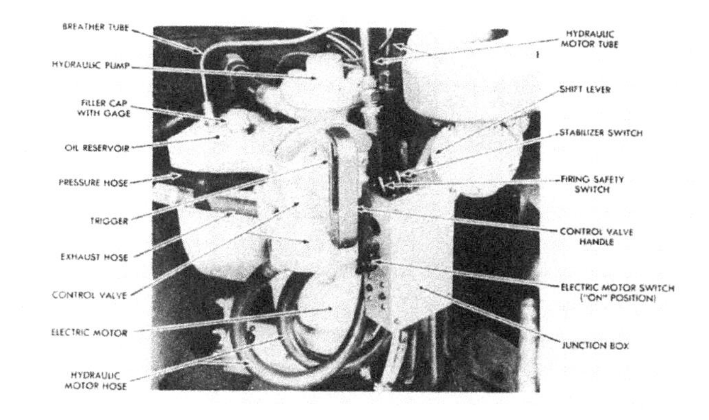

The controls for the Logansport (above), Westinghouse (below left), and Oilgear (below right) turret traversing systems are illustrated here.

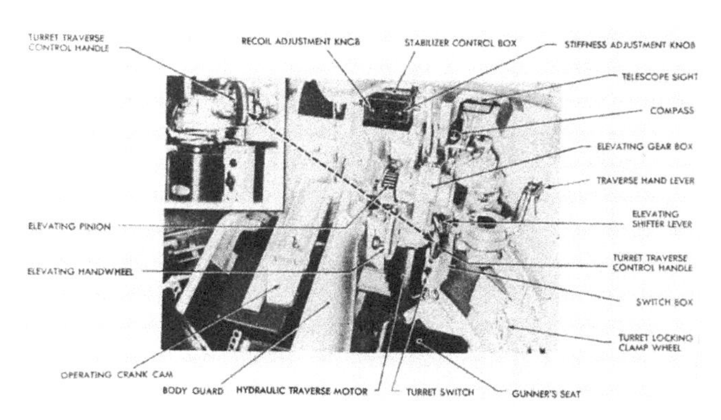

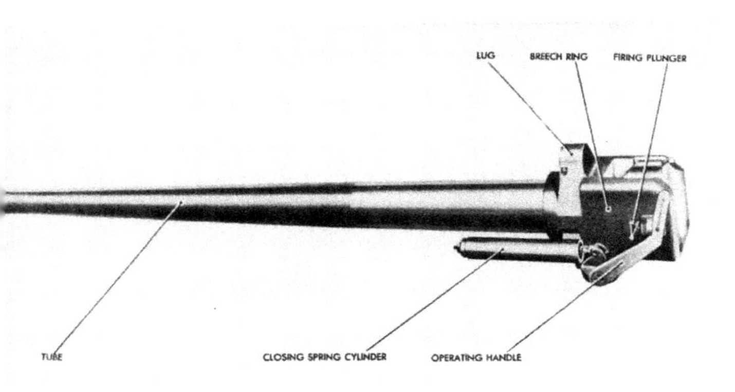

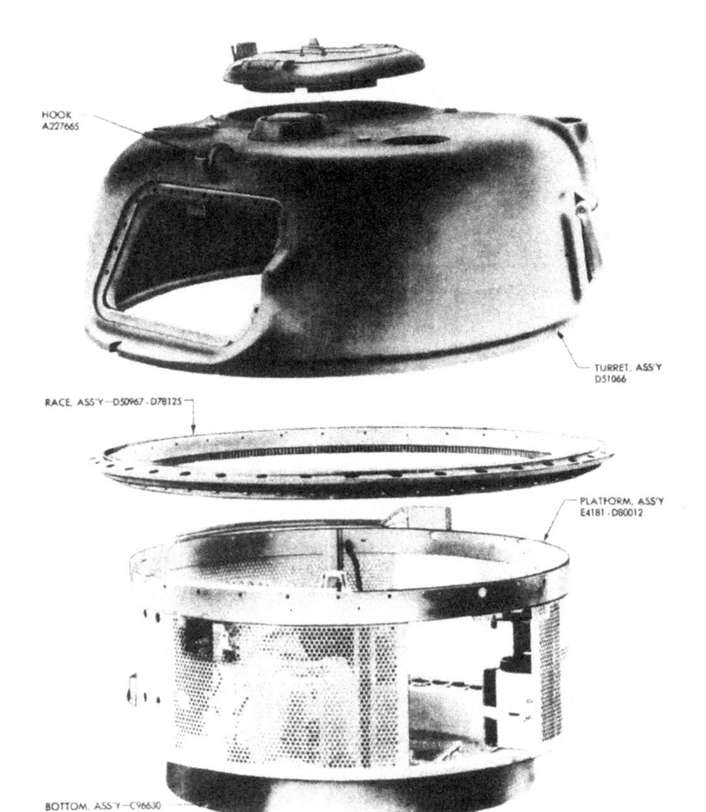

The 75mm gun M3 is shown above. Below, the same weapon is installed in the combination gun mount M34.

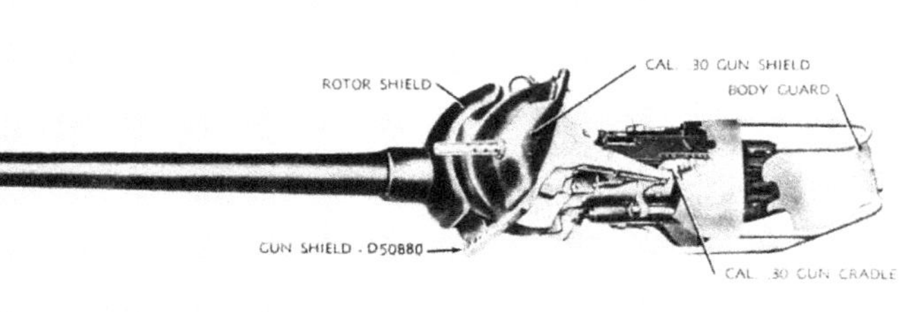

These photographs illustrate details of the turret assembly and the 75mm gun mount M34.

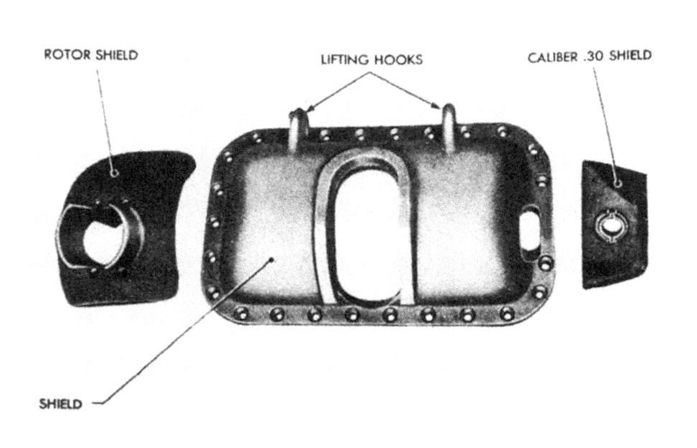

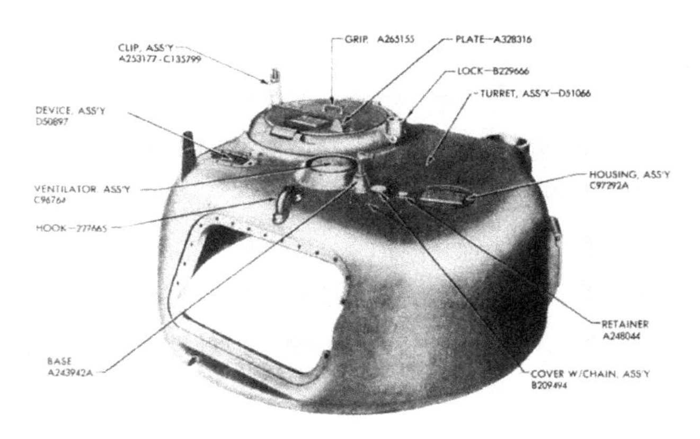

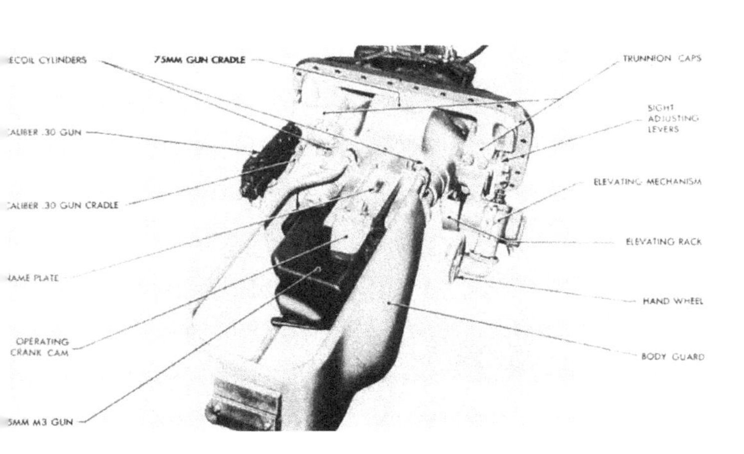

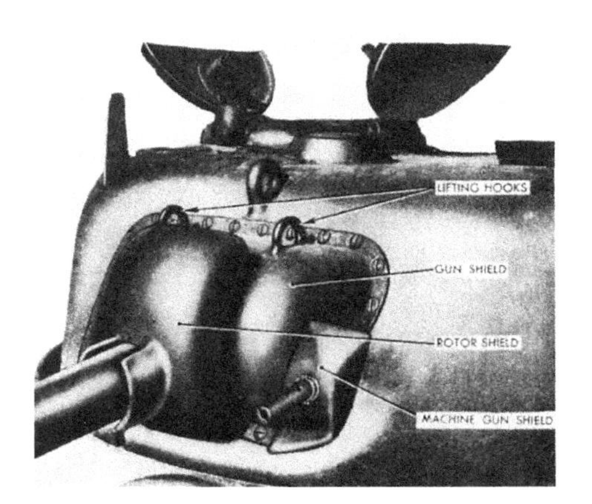

Difficulty in maintaining the alignment between the 75mm gun and the periscope type gunsight led to a request by the Armored Force for a direct sight telescope. The combination gun mount M34 was modified to include a telescopic sight just to the right of the cannon in front of the gunner. Standardized as the telescope M55, it was later superseded by the telescope M70F. The gunner's M4 periscope, incorporating the telescope M38A1, was retained as a backup fire control system. To protect the direct sight telescope, the rotor shield was redesigned and extended. It now covered both the telescope on the right and the .30 caliber coaxial machine gun on the left, eliminating the need for a separate shield on the machine gun barrel. The heavier rotor shield also required two additional mounting bolts which extended through slots machined in the front plate or main gun shield. A counterweight was necessary at the gun breech to balance the heavier mount which was standardized in October 1942 as the combination gun mount M34A1. The range of elevation for the M34A1 mount was +25 to -10 degrees. Some of the M34 mounts were modified to use the direct sight and an extension was welded to the right side of the rotor shield to protect the telescope opening.

Above: The M34 mount is modified to use a direct sight telescope. The arrow indicates the extension welded to the rotor shield. Below is the standard combination gun mount M34A1.

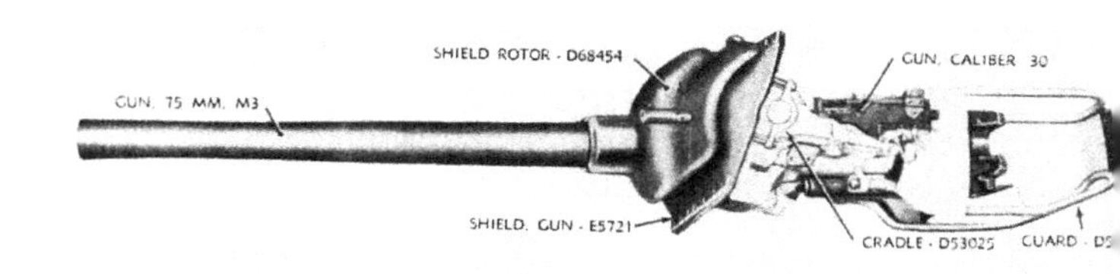

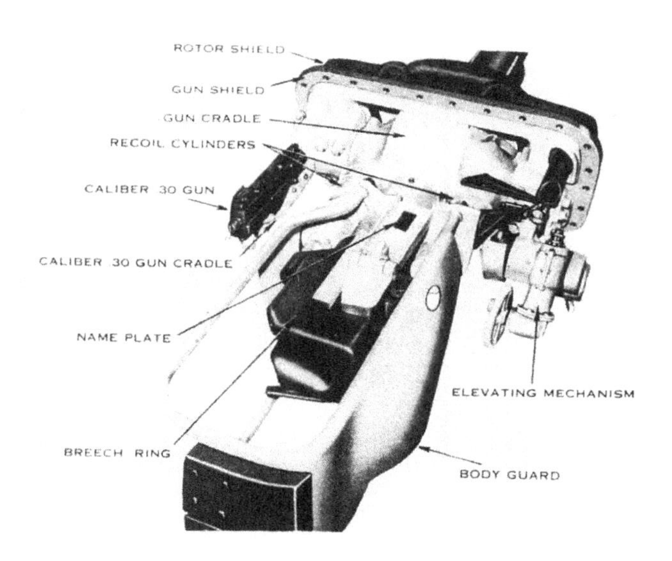

Details of the M34A1 mount are shown in the bottom three photographs.

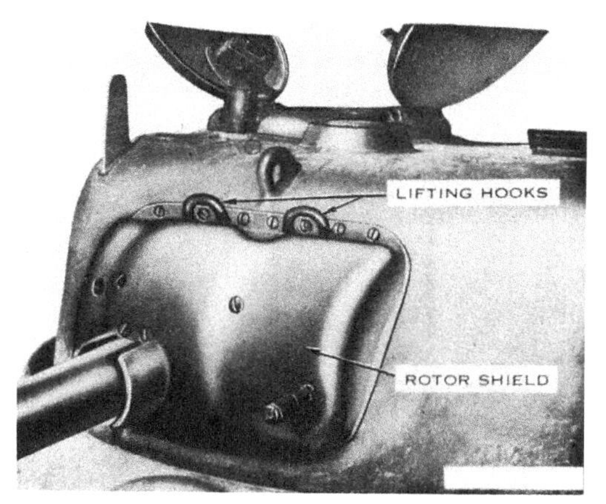

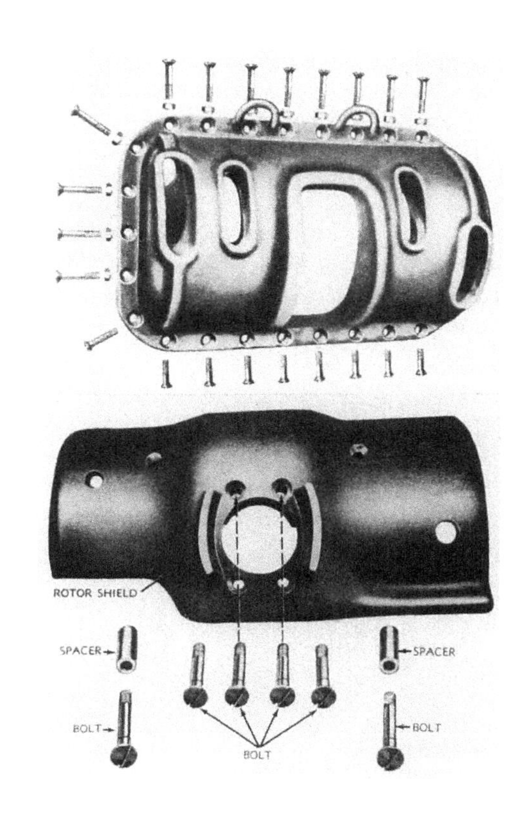

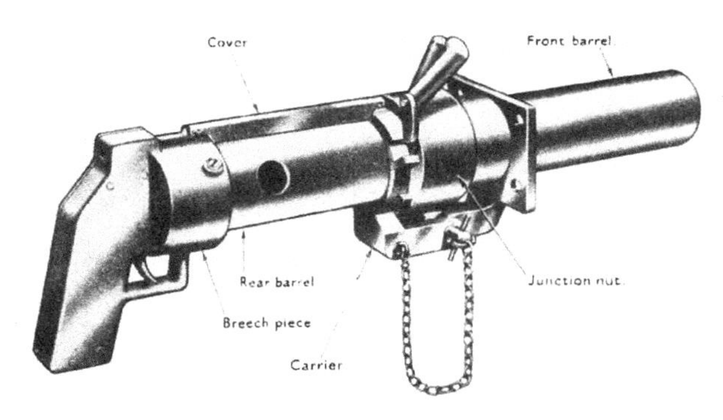

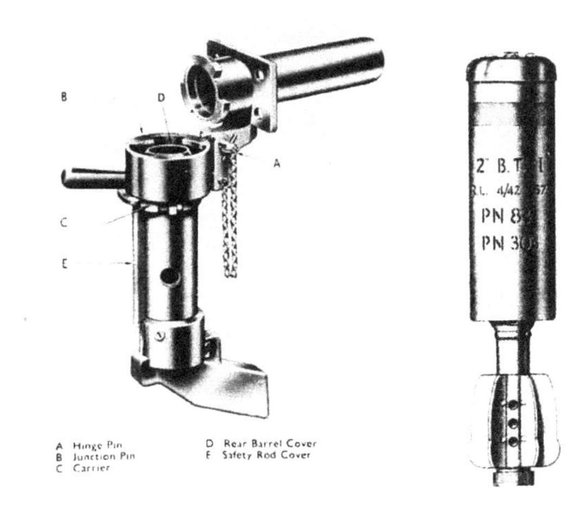

Above is the 2 inch smoke mortar M3 (British bomb thrower Mk I). At the right, the mortar is shown open for loading and at the far right is a round of 2 inch smoke ammunition.

Responding to a request by the Armored Force, the Ordnance Committee recommended in June 1943 that all tanks of the M4 series be equipped with the British 2 inch bomb thrower Mk I and a minimum of 12 rounds of smoke ammunition. This applied to both new production tanks and to tanks already built and destined for overseas shipment. Primarily intended to produce smoke screens, it was designated in U.S. service as the 2 inch mortar M3. The mortar was installed in the left front of the turret roof at a fixed elevation of +35 degrees. The range could be set at approximately 35, 75, or 150 yards by use of a regulator controlling the escape of the propellant gases.

A new single piece cast differential housing was designed to replace the three piece bolted assembly on the early production tanks. The differential gear train fitted into the rear of the armored housing after being assembled with the transmission on a one piece cast steel carrier. The single cast housing made it much easier to install and service both the differential and the final drive. The one piece housing was also more rigid, helping to maintain the alignment of the gear trains. The first of the new housings were 2 inch thick round castings essentially following the contour of the three piece model. However, later versions were cast with a thicker sharp nosed contour to improve the ballistic protection. The final version was referred to at Detroit Arsenal as the "Mary Ann" because of its similarity in profile to a young employee at the Arsenal.

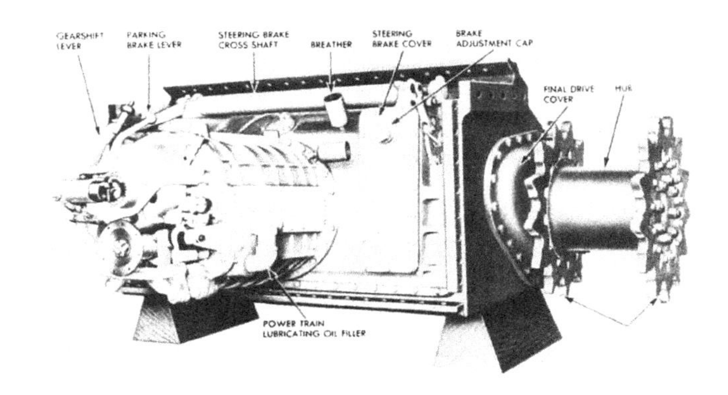

The early (above) and late (below) transmissions are compared in these photographs. Note the parking brake lever on the early transmission. On late model tanks the parking brake was operated by a floor pedal.

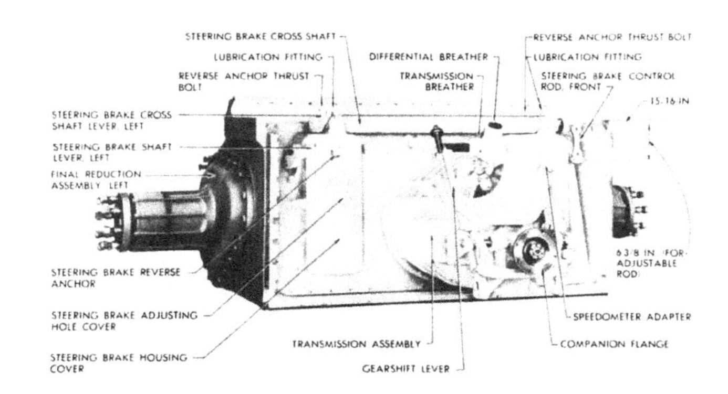

Below, the round single piece differential and final drive housing (left) is compared with the later sharp nosed version (right). These vehicles also are fitted with applique armor over the sponson ammunition racks and in front of the drivers' hoods on the welded hull tank.

Details of the late model M4 with the combination rolled and cast upper hull are shown here. Like most of the later production tanks, it is fitted with sandshields.

Other manufacturers were soon brought into the M4 program. Production started at Baldwin Locomotive Works in January 1943 and one month later at the American Locomotive Company. In May the Pullman Standard Car Company, and in August the Detroit Tank Arsenal, started building the M4 making a total of five manufacturers of the welded hull tank. Production was phased out in August at Pressed Steel Car and one month later at Pullman. American Locomotive continued production until December with Baldwin and the Detroit Tank Arsenal finishing in January 1944. A total of 6748 M4s were produced with 75mm gun.

The construction of the late production M4s built at Detroit Tank Arsenal differed from the earlier welded hull vehicles. The upper front hull consisted of a single armor steel casting extending back past the drivers' doors. This casting was welded to the remainder of the hull which was fabricated as usual from rolled homogeneous plate. Two ventilators were fitted in the casting at the front of each sponson as in the earlier welded assembly and the same separate antenna socket was provided on the right front for the SCR 506.

Several other features are useful in identifying the approximate period of production for these tanks. For example, the early suspensions were equipped with spoked idlers while on the later vehicles they were solid discs. The early tanks had two fuel shut off valves on the rear deck. Both of these were eliminated later in production. Fixed headlights replaced the removable ones on the early vehicles. Periscope guards, sandshields, and a traveling lock for the 75mm gun were features of the later tanks. Even the siren location provides a clue. On the first production vehicles, it was located on the left front fender. Later, it was mounted under a bracket just left of center on the front plate above the differential housing. When the traveling lock for the 75mm gun was introduced, the siren was moved over next to the left headlight and was protected with a guard similar to that for the light. This was the arrangement on the first M4 produced at Detroit Arsenal in August 1943. The same installation also was used on many remanufactured tanks.

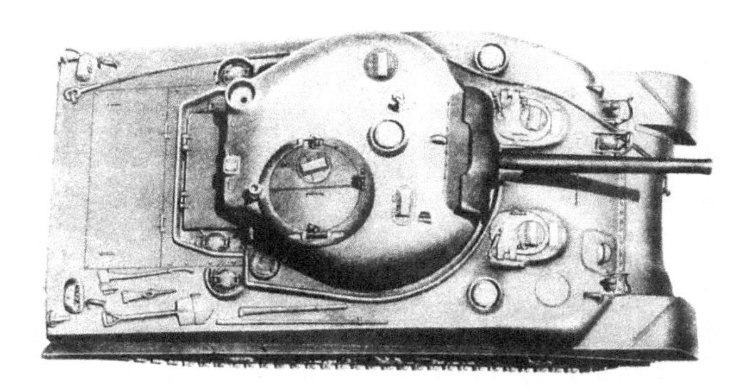

Below, the first M4 produced at Detroit Arsenal is prepared for shipment.

Battle experience showed that a considerable number of losses resulted from ammunition fires inside the tank. These usually occurred after penetration of the armor with the projectile or other fragments setting off the 75mm ammunition in the stowage racks. As an interim solution, sections of 1 inch armor plate were welded to the outside of the hull opposite the sponson ammunition racks. This applique armor increased the protection for the single rack on the left side of the tank as well as the two on the right. All three sponson racks, the 30 round box behind the assistant driver, and the 8 round ready box on the turret basket floor were protected from fragments by enclosing them with 1/4 inch armor plate. The 75mm rounds clipped to the wall of the turret basket were eliminated. The additional armor was introduced not only as a field modification, but also went into production pending the introduction of water protected ammunition or "wet stowage" planned for the improved versions of the Sherman. The latter did not appear until 1944.

Ballistic tests showed wide variations in the armor protection on the front of the Sherman. In an effort to equalize this protection, applique armor also was welded over vulnerable areas on the tank front. To provide adequate clearance for operating the 75mm gun controls, part of the inside turret wall had been machined away thinning the right front armor. Later production turrets were redesigned to thicken this area, but for those already in existence an armor patch was welded over the right front on the outside. A similar solution was applied to the weak areas on the hull front. The vertical surfaces on the front of the drivers' hoods were reinforced by the addition of two 1-1/2 inch thick plates welded at an angle of approximately 35 degrees from the vertical over these areas. This modification was also applied both in the field and on the production line, but only to the tanks with the welded front hull. Because of their better slope in this area, the cast hull fronts already provided fairly uniform protection. The additional armor also was applied to many of the tanks remanufactured after service in training units.

Examples of the applique armor applied to the hull and turret can be seen here. Additional armor was frequently welded on in the field, but it usually did not have the neat appearance of the production jobs.

The pilot medium tank M4A2 under test at Aberdeen in April 1942. Note the fixed bow machine guns.

MEDIUM TANK M4A2

In late 1941, work was started on drawings for a modified version of the M4 powered by the General Motors 6046 diesel engine. Equipped with the same engine and power train as the earlier M3A3 and M3A5, the new tank had a welded hull. OCM 17578 designated the vehicle as the medium tank M4A2 in December 1941. Under the British system it became the Sherman III. A pilot was completed in April 1942 and shipped to Aberdeen for test. Production of the M4A2 started that same month at both the Fisher Tank Arsenal and the Pullman Standard Car Company. It was the first welded hull model of the Sherman to enter production and some of the early tanks were still fitted with the two fixed .30 caliber machine guns that had been abolished by the armament change of March 1942. They were also equipped with the early suspension system having the track return roller mounted at the top of each bogie.

The Aberdeen tests indicated that the M4A2 was superior in power to the medium tanks fitted with the R975 engine and that the twin diesels were at least as reliable. Twelve early production M4A2s were sent to the Desert Warfare Board where they were evaluated by the 5th Armored Division. Their report showed that

The pilot M4A2 still retained the early vertical volute spring suspension with the track return roller mounted on top of the bogie frame.

the tank had a good horsepower to weight ratio and could maintain a speed of 30 miles/hour on dirt roads. The high torque characteristics of the diesel engine at low speed gave it good cross-country performance and its low fuel consumption allowed a cruising range of about 150 miles. However, everything depended on the tank being in first class mechanical condition and the Board particularly criticized the air cleaners, cooling system, and the clutches. They concluded that because of these problems, the M4A2 as originally delivered was not a satisfactory combat vehicle. In addition, the Board noted that the original suspension was inadequate for a tank of this weight. However, this suspension had already been replaced in production by the later heavy duty model. The Board recommended further tests after modification of the tank.

Note the long length of weld joint in the front armor plate. The .50 caliber machine gun is in the rear position for engaging targets at high angles of elevation.

Early production M4A2s operated by A Company of the Demonstration Regiment at Fort Knox.

The M4A2 at the right also is equipped with the early suspension bogies, but it is fitted with the single piece differential and final drive housing. At bottom right, the later suspension has been introduced. The two bottom views show the rear hull armor and the grill type doors in the rear deck over the engine compartment. Both features serve to identify the M4A2.

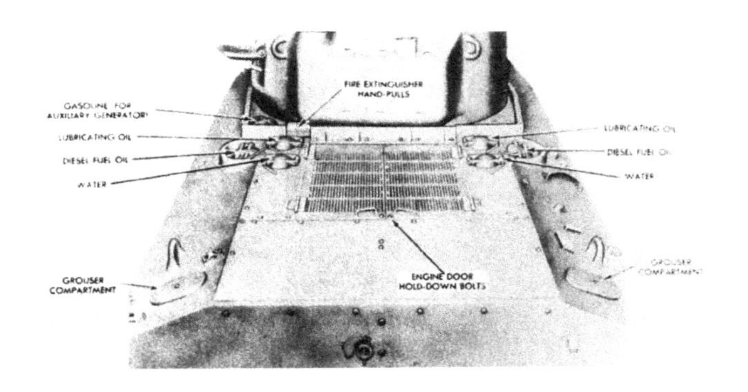

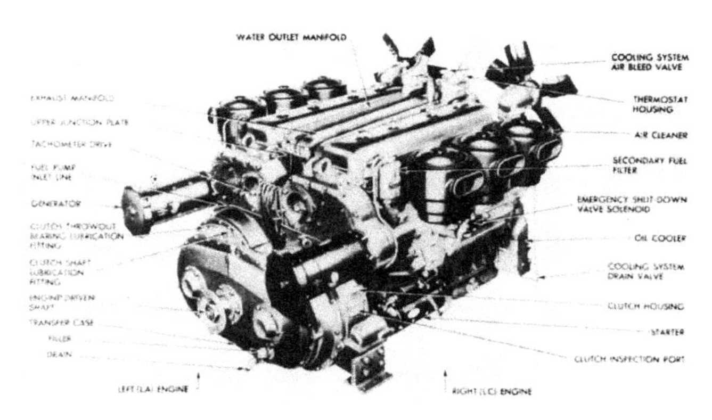

Details of the M4A2 rear deck can be seen above. At the right are two views of the early production GM 6046 diesel engine. This is the version with the dry sump and separate oil tank.

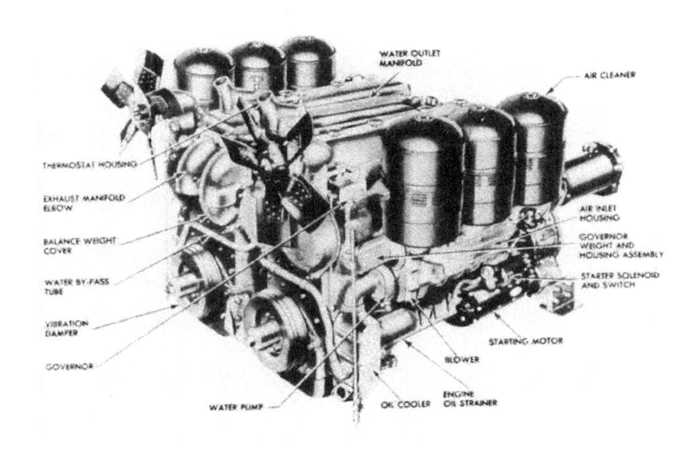

Details of the bow machine gun mount can be seen below. Note the direct vision slot on this early M4A2.

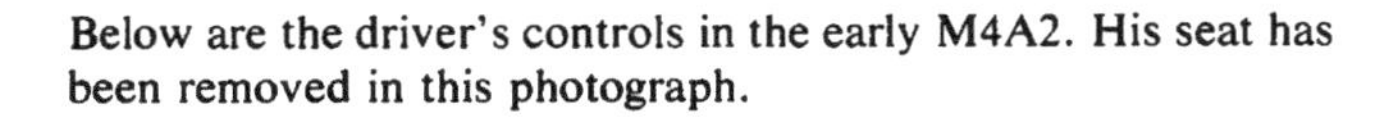

Below are the driver's controls in the early M4A2. His seat has been removed in this photograph.

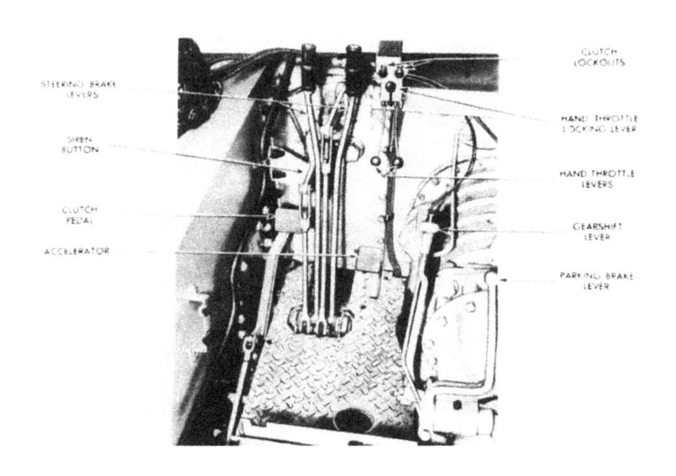

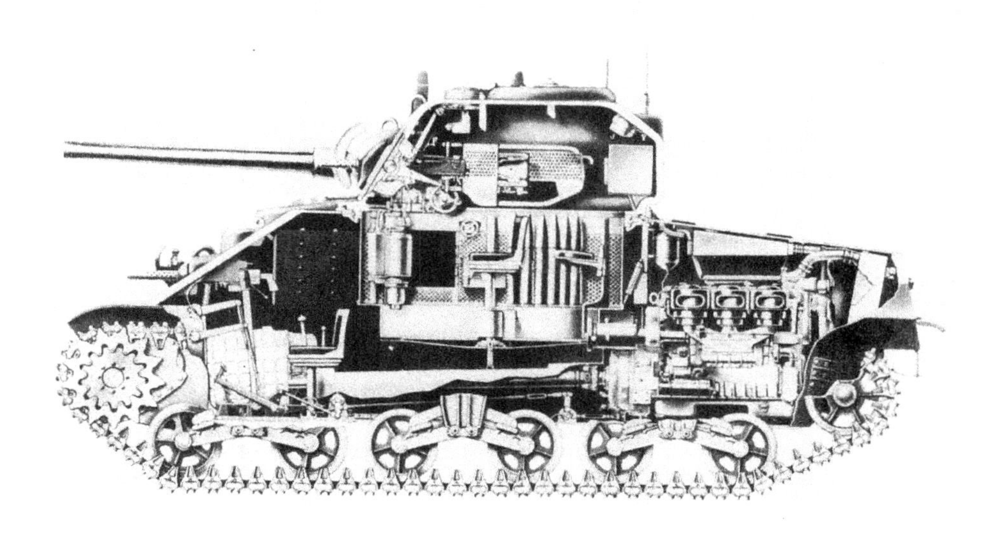

Compare this sectional view of the M4A2 with that of the M4 on page 135 and note the much greater clearance of the low mounted propeller shaft under the turret basket.

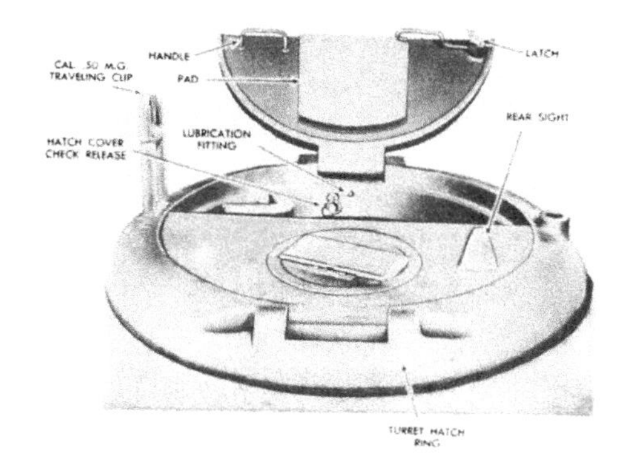

Details of the commander's hatch and the turret interior are shown in the two photographs at the left. Note the empty ammunition ready racks around the edge of the turret basket.

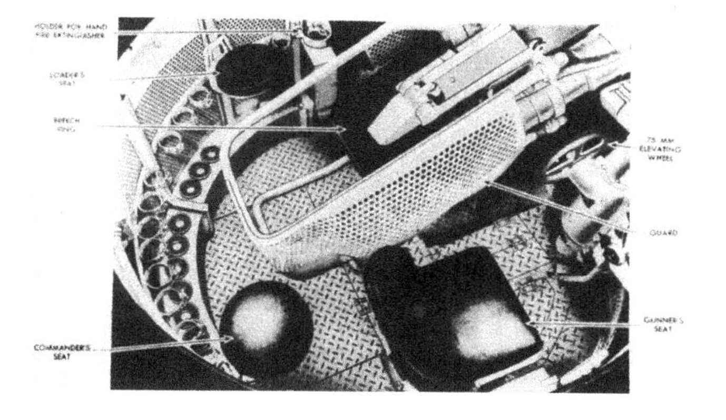

The general arrangement of components and the ammunition stowage in the M4A2 can be seen in the sketch at the right.

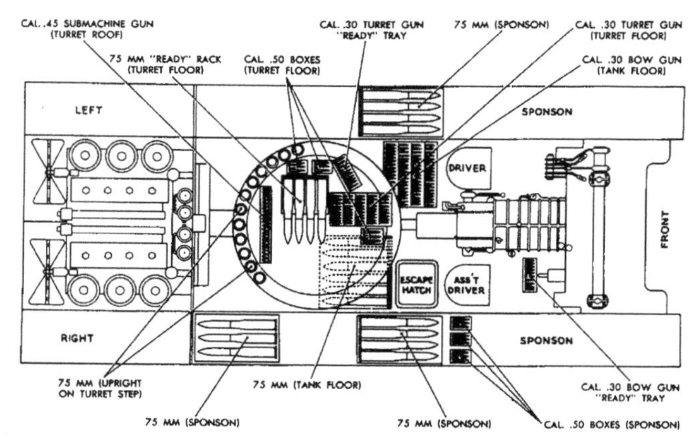

Six M4A2s incorporating numerous improvements were submitted to the Desert Warfare Board in February 1943. Five of these tanks had the same basic engine as the earlier vehicles, but included many improvements in the installation, controls, and accessories. Larger air cleaners and a better cooling system were provided as well as more rugged clutches. Changes in stowage and the engine compartment bulkhead made engine removal easier helping to ease maintenance problems. The sixth tank had all of these changes in addition to a modified engine. The new power plant had an improved lubrication system which eliminated the oil tank and incorporated a wet sump in both engines. The same arrangement of four fuel tanks was retained with one in each rear sponson and a smaller reserve tank on each side at the bottom of the engine compartment. However the shape of the tanks was changed from those on the earlier vehicles.

Further tests by both Ordnance and the Armored Force indicated that the performance of the twin diesel compared favorably to the best engines under test. At that time these included the R975, the Ford GAA, and the Chrysler A57 multibank. The main weakness of the GM diesel was its sensitivity to dirt, frequently resulting in a short endurance life and poor reliability.

As the first welded hull tank in production, many of the fabrication techniques were pioneered on the M4A2. The upper hull was a welded assembly of castings and rolled plates. As originally produced, the hull front alone consisted of seven major sections welded together. These were the two cast drivers' hood assemblies, the casting incorporating the bow machine gun mount, two rolled plate sections, and the two sponson front plates. The cast antenna socket for the sponson radio was welded into one of the latter. Assembled from so many pieces, the front of the tank necessarily contained a considerable length of weld joint. Despite the best of quality control procedures, such joints were always more vulnerable to ballistic attack than a single rolled plate. The rather complicated design, particularly around the drivers' hatches, also presented surfaces of varying obliquity resulting in unequal protection from the front armor. The same condition applied in different degrees to all of the early welded hull tanks and the problem was not really solved until the introduction of the new single piece front hull plate in early 1944.

The heavy demand during peak tank production overloaded the foundries resulting in a shortage of armor castings. To keep the assembly lines moving, Fisher Tank Arsenal developed welded parts to replace many of these castings. Included were the drivers' hoods, drivers' doors, bow machine gun mounts, sponson antenna sockets, turret ring guards, and sponson bulkheads. The welded drivers' hoods were introduced during the Fall of 1943 after the elimination of the direct vision slots and their flat surfaces and sharp corners permit easy identification of the M4A2s manufactured during this period.

The M4A2 below was photographed in July 1943. It features many of the welded components such as drivers' hoods, bow machine gun port, antenna socket, and turret ring guards.

The pistol port has been omitted on this M4A2, serial number 15161. Although difficult to read in the photographs, the registration number is 3056341. The later type of vane sight is mounted in front of the commander's hatch and the 2 inch smoke mortar is installed in the left side of the turret roof.

The various general modifications such as the later gun mount and the applique armor described for the M4 and M4A1 were also applied to the M4A2 as well as other tanks of the series. Another change which occurred in all of the tanks might be described as "The Great Pistol Port Controversy". The early production turrets of the M4 series were fitted with a pistol port in the left side wall. At this time there was considerable discussion as to the value of this port and whether its installation justified the increased vulnerability of the turret in this area. In February 1943, the arguments against the pistol port prevailed and orders were issued eliminating them from the tanks in production. This continued for several months until field reports indicated that pistol ports were necessary after all. Instructions were received in July to reintroduce pistol ports and they reappeared on production tanks by early 1944.

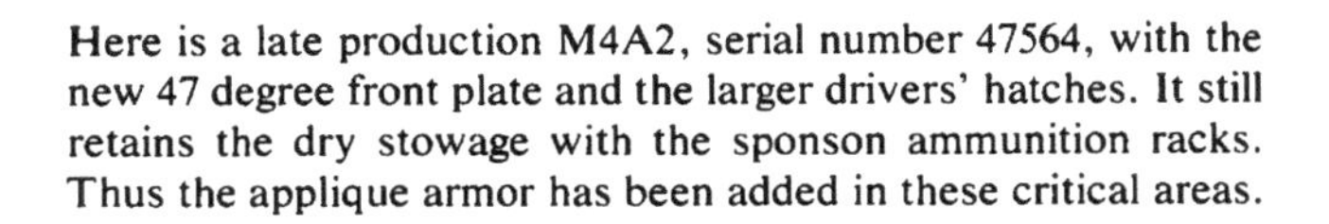

Here is a late production M4A2, serial number 47564, with the new 47 degree front plate and the larger drivers' hatches. It still retains the dry stowage with the sponson ammunition racks. Thus the applique armor has been added in these critical areas.

Another modification introduced late in the career of the M4A2 was the new front hull sloped at 47 degrees from the vertical compared to the 56 degrees of the early models. The protruding drivers' hoods were eliminated and larger hatches were provided in the hull roof. The front plate, increased in thickness to 2-1/2 inches, was unbroken except for the .30 caliber bow machine gun mount. With the elimination of the many weld joints, the one piece front plate greatly improved the ballistic protection.

Battle experience had also shown the necessity for an additional turret hatch. In the original turret, the loader had to duck past the 75mm gun and follow the gunner and tank commander out of the single hatch. Frequently, there was not enough time for him to get out of a burning tank. To correct this, a small oval hatch was designed in December 1943 for installation directly over the loader's position. Intended for all M4 series tanks, this hatch was applied to M4A2 production at tank number 3793. Kits were also available to retrofit tanks already produced.

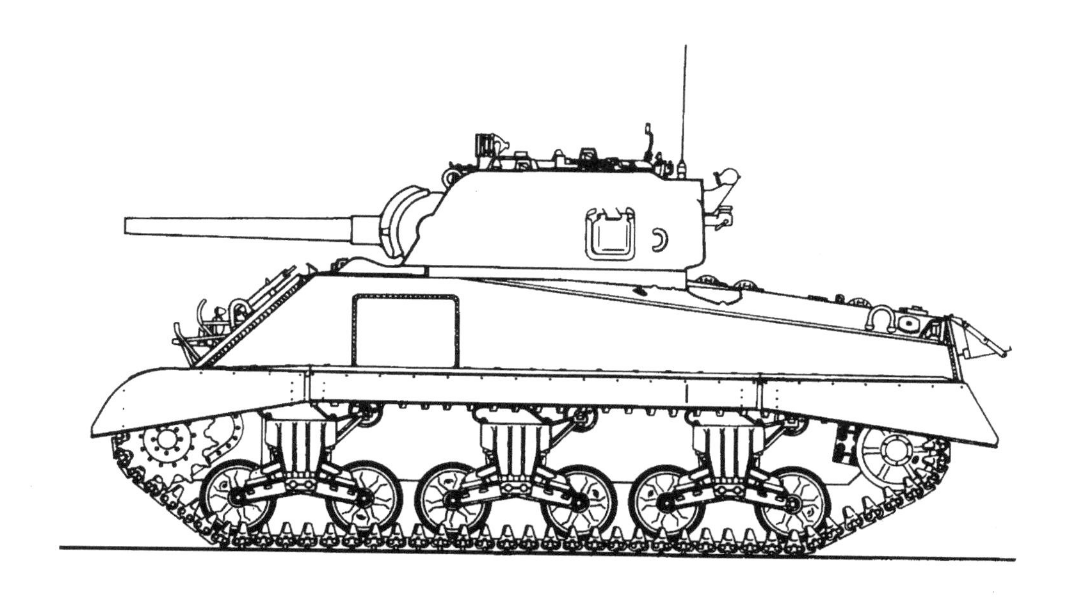

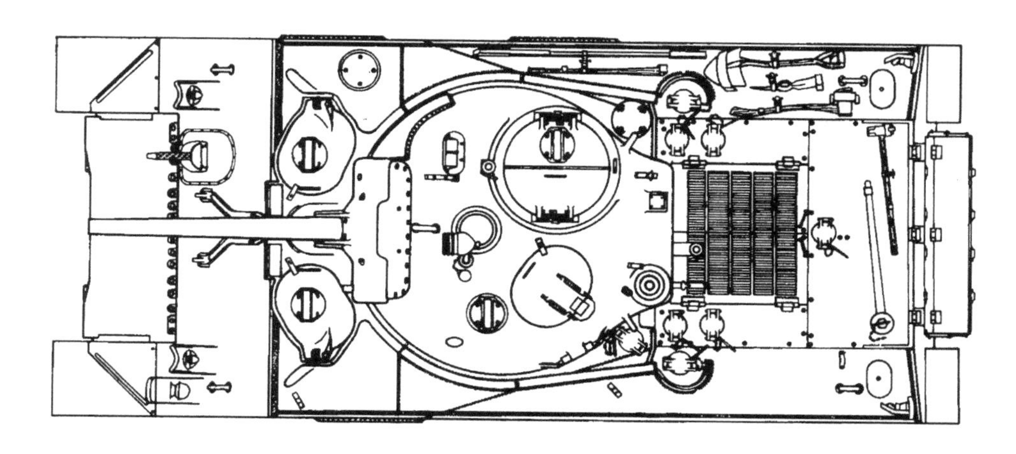

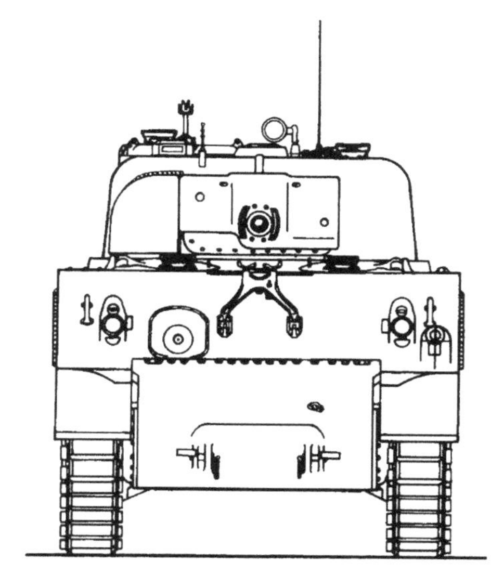

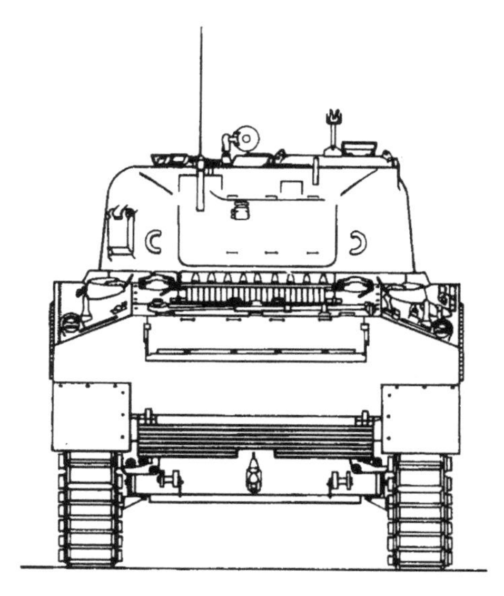

Scale 1:48

Medium Tank M4A2

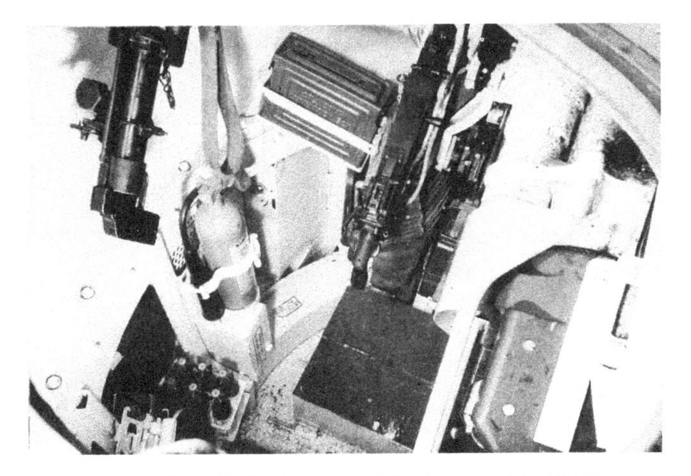

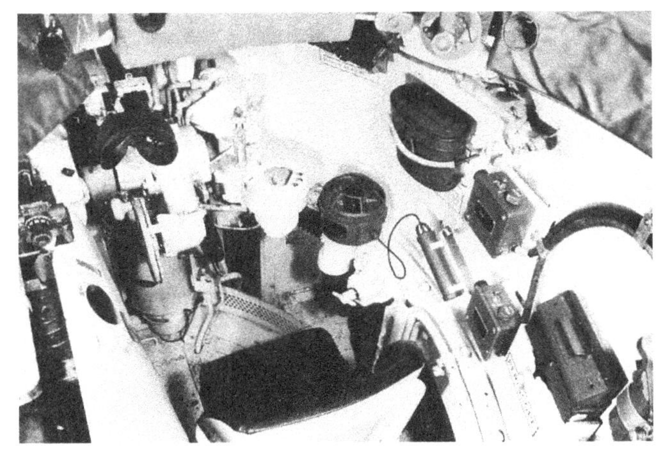

Above is the interior of the late model M4A2 turret. The coaxial machine gun and smoke mortar can be seen at the loader's station on the left. The gunner's position appears at the right.

Like the twin diesel powered tanks of the M3 series, the M4A2 could be identified by the single piece rear armor plate extending down past the sponson level. Below this, an exhaust deflector was mounted to minimize the dust kicked up by the blast of cooling air and exhaust gasses. The grill type engine compartment doors on the rear deck provided another point of identification. Their total width was approximately the same as the rear of the turret bustle, much less than the doors of this type on the M4A3 which had a similar rear armor plate configuration.

As a result of the War Department policy that U.S. troops would be supplied with gasoline powered tanks, an order was issued in March 1942 that diesel powered tanks would not be shipped overseas with U.S. forces. They were employed by training units in the United States and were supplied under Lend-Lease to both the Soviet Union and Great Britain. Some of the tanks intended for the latter were taken over by the 1st Armored Division and used during the crisis in Tunisia. Another exception was the combat use of some M4A2s by the U.S. Marine Corps as late as Okinawa.

In addition to the Fisher Tank Arsenal and the Pullman Standard Car Company, three other manufacturers were brought into the program. Production started in September 1942 at American Locomotive Company, in October at Baldwin Locomotive Works, and in December at the Federal Machine and Welder Company. With the cutback in tank requirements, work was discontinued at Baldwin in November and at American Locomotive in April 1943. Production continued at Pullman until September 1943 and at Federal Machine and Welder until December. Fisher Tank Arsenal completed their run of 75mm gun M4A2s in May 1944. This brought the total production of the M4A2 with the 75mm gun to 8053 from all five manufacturers.

The stations for the driver (left) and bow gunner (right) are shown in the photographs below. The collapsible bad weather hood for the driver is stowed over the transmission above the spare periscope heads. The tails of some smoke mortar bombs can be seen at the lower right.

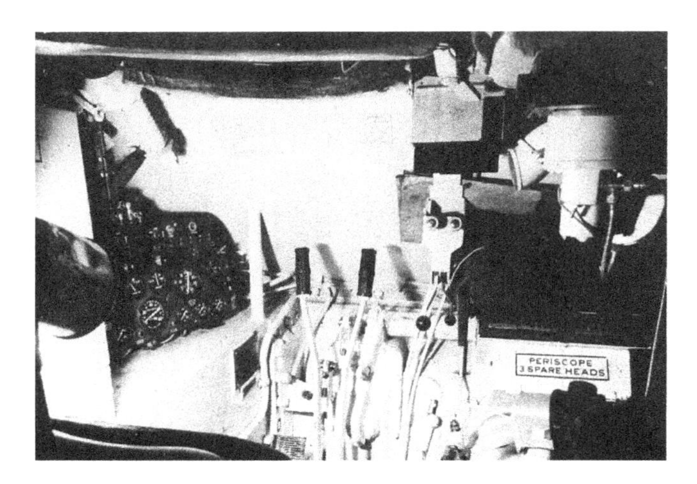

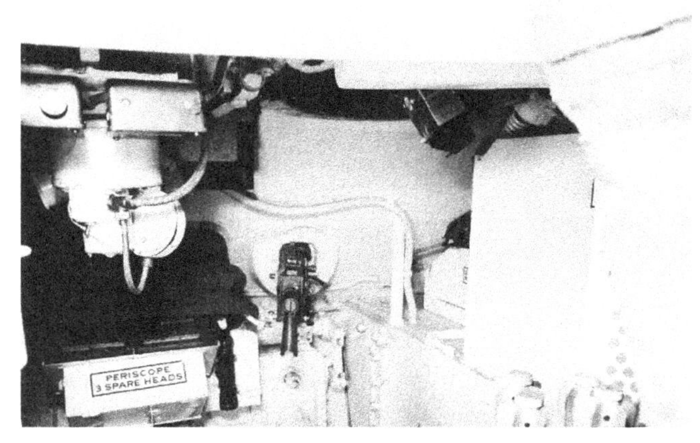

The first M4A3 (above and below) is shown here under test at the General Motors Proving Ground in May 1942. Note the single piece differential and final drive housing.

MEDIUM TANK M4A3

The need to supply power plants for the ever increasing tank production pushed the search for substitute engines which could be rapidly produced in existing facilities. In late 1941, the 8-cylinder modification of the experimental Ford aircraft engine was ready for test. Fueled by gasoline, the liquid-cooled V-8 developed 500 gross horsepower. Destined to become the preferred U.S. tank engine, the first example ran 85 hours on the test stand without any problems. As was mentioned earlier, the second engine was installed in the medium tank M3E1 for test. These tests indicated that the new engine, designated the Ford GAA, was the most promising tank power plant yet evaluated because of its high output, compactness, and excellent power to weight ratio. Ordnance Committee action in January 1942 authorized the Ford engine for use in the Sherman and designated the new version as the medium tank M4A3. This was the basic model of the Sherman that was to serve the U.S. Army for over a decade after the end of World War II. The British designation was the Sherman IV.

The first tank was completed at Ford Motor Company in late May 1942 followed shortly by the second and third. They all were shipped to the General Motors Proving Ground where five different engines with slight variations were tested in the three vehicles. Minor changes were proposed and the Proving Ground recommended acceptance of the M4A3.

An early production M4A3 (above) with vision slots and single periscopes for the driver and bow gunner.

With the tank in full production at Ford, ample numbers were available for further testing by the Proving Grounds and Service Boards. Their reports were generally favorable indicating the engine installation was more accessible than any other tank power plant and hence much easier to service.

The early M4A3s were still equipped with the direct vision slots, but even the pilot tanks were fitted with the later model heavy duty suspension bogies. The single piece cast differential and final drive housing also was used on all M4A3s. Like the other welded hull tanks, the front plate was an assembly of castings and rolled plates, but they were fewer in number than on the earlier M4A2, thus reducing the length of weld joint. The turret was identical to the other tanks of the M4 series, fitted at first with the M34 combination mount and later with the M34A1.

The armor plate on the rear of the hull reached below the sponson line similar to the M4A2, but the grill type engine doors were much wider extending across the flat part of the rear deck to the sponsons on each side. The compact V-8 engine fitted easily into the engine compartment driving the tank through the same power train as the earlier models. The location of the propeller shaft connecting the Ford V-8 to the transmission was much lower than with the radial engine, allowing greater clearance under the turret basket. Four fuel tanks were arranged similar to those in the M4 and M4A1. A 60 gallon horizontal tank was located in each rear sponson and a 27-1/2 gallon vertical tank was fitted in both front corners of the engine compartment. Each tank had a separate drain plug and shut off valve. The latter were located on the bulkhead at the rear of the fighting compartment. The 175 gallons of gasoline gave the M4A3 a range of about 130 miles. Its maximum sustained speed on roads was 26 miles/hour.

Note the wide grill doors on the rear deck of the tanks below. This is a major identification point of the M4A3. The early production vehicle at the left has single periscopes for the driver and bow gunner in addition to the vision slots. On the tank at the right, the auxiliary periscopes have replaced the vision slots.

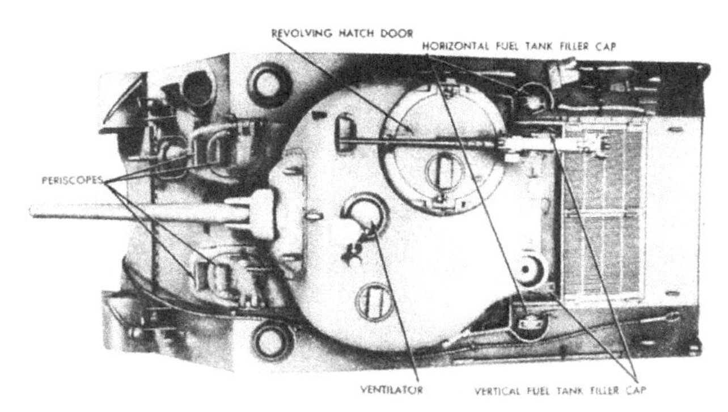

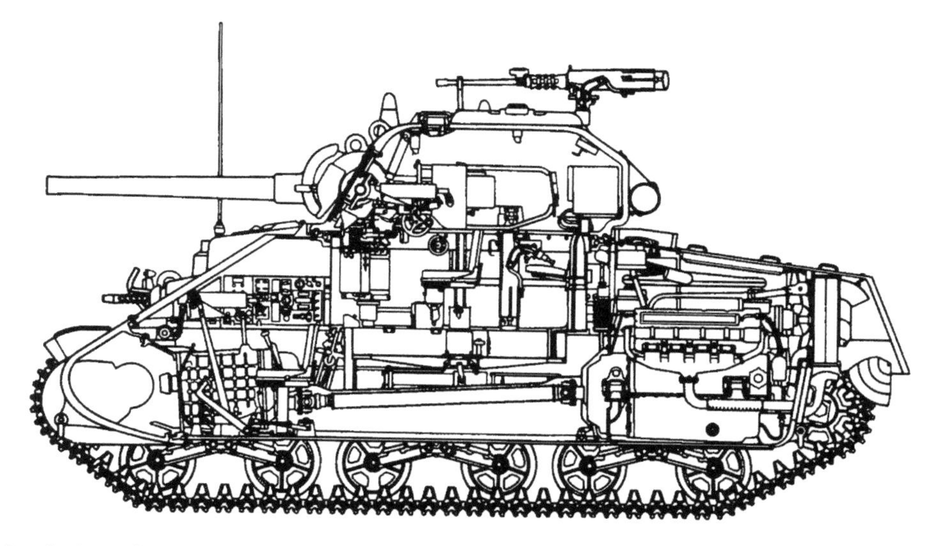

Above is a sectional view of the M4A3. Like the M4A2, the lower propeller shaft provides considerable clearance beneath the turret basket.

The ammunition stowage in the early M4A3 is shown in the phantom view at the right. The three sponson racks which were protected by the applique armor on the later production dry stowage tanks are clearly visible.

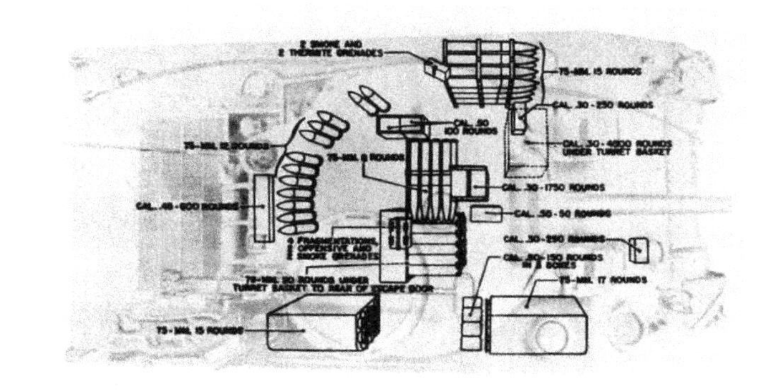

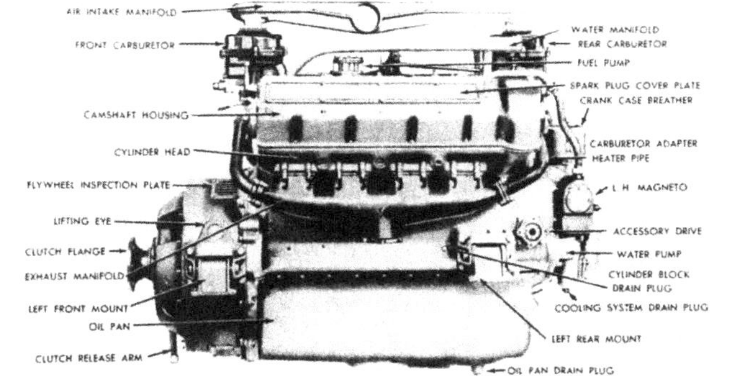

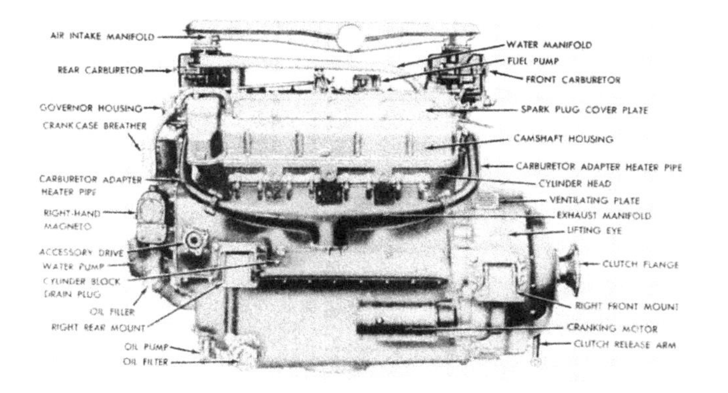

The left side (top) and right side (bottom) of the early production Ford GAA engine appear at the left. The later engines had an oil level bayonet gage on the left side. Below is the fuel system for the M4A3 dry stowage tanks.

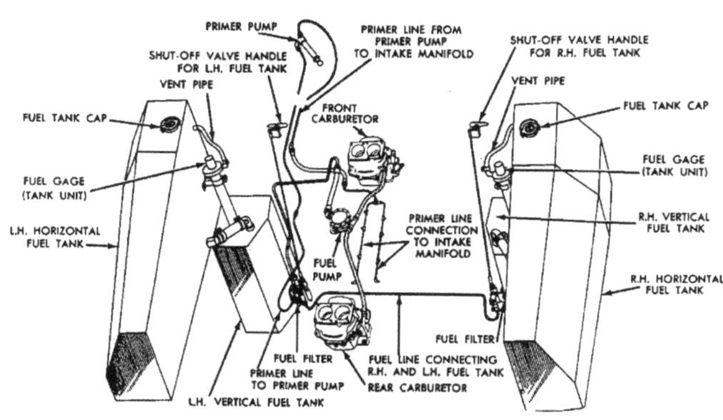

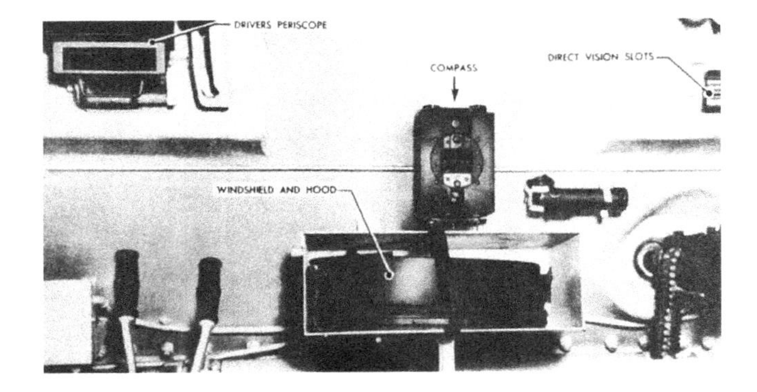

The driver's bad weather hood was stowed over the transmission (top left) between the driver and bow gunner. In use, it was erected over the driver's open hatch (bottom left).

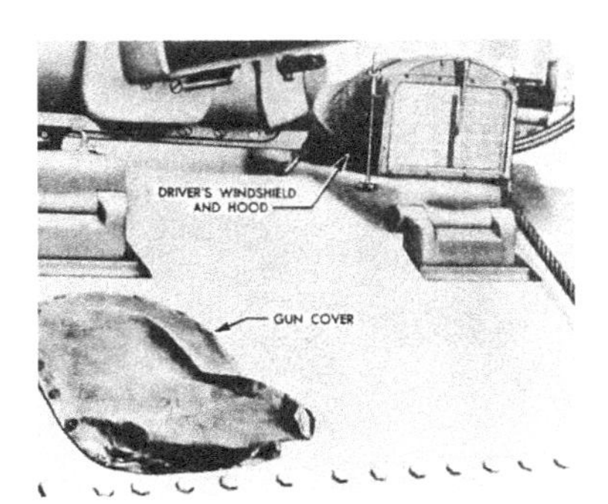

In the Sherman the driver normally rode with his head fully exposed above the open hatch and Ordnance recognized very early the need to provide some sort of hood to protect him from the weather. Such a hood had to give protection from dust, rain, and high velocity air and at the same time permit good visibility. It had to be equipped with a windshield wiper and defroster and be small enough to be taken inside the tank through the hatch opening. The first design was constructed using a double thickness safety glass windshield with the front half sides of plastic and the rear half sides, top, and back of light gage steel. This version served the purpose, but the Armored Force added the requirement that it be collapsible for ease of stowage when not in use. The hood was redesigned retaining the safety glass windshield, but using a folding canvas top, sides, and rear. The new hood did not seal out rain and dust as effectively as the earlier version, but it was lighter and its design permitted the driver to climb through the hatch with it in place. When not in use, the folded hood was stowed inside the front hull between the driver and the assistant driver.

Below is a late production dry stowage M4A3 with the M34A1 gun mount and sandshields. However, this tank has not been fitted with applique armor.

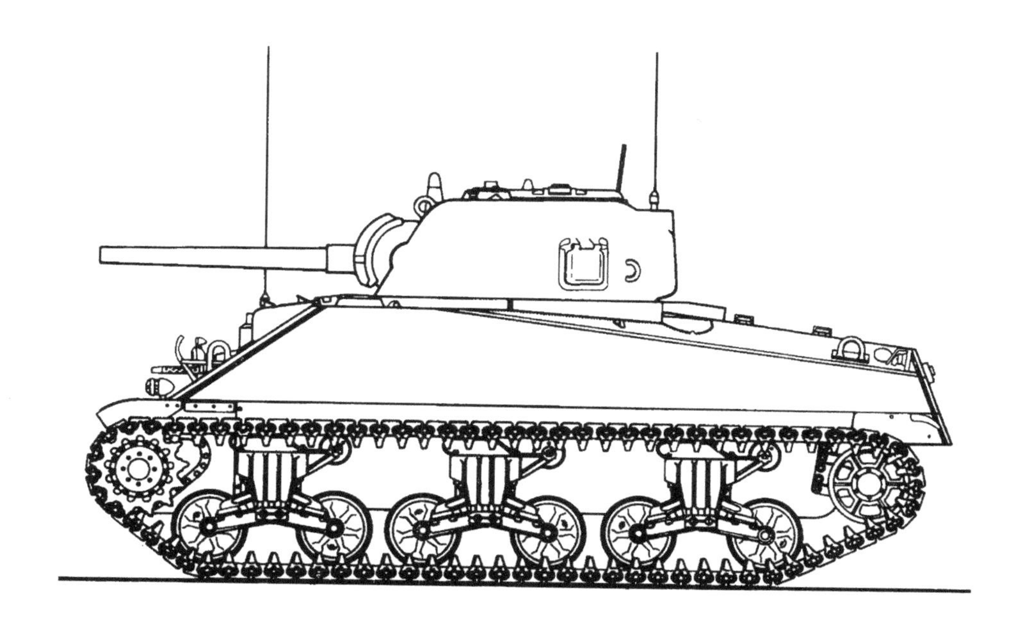

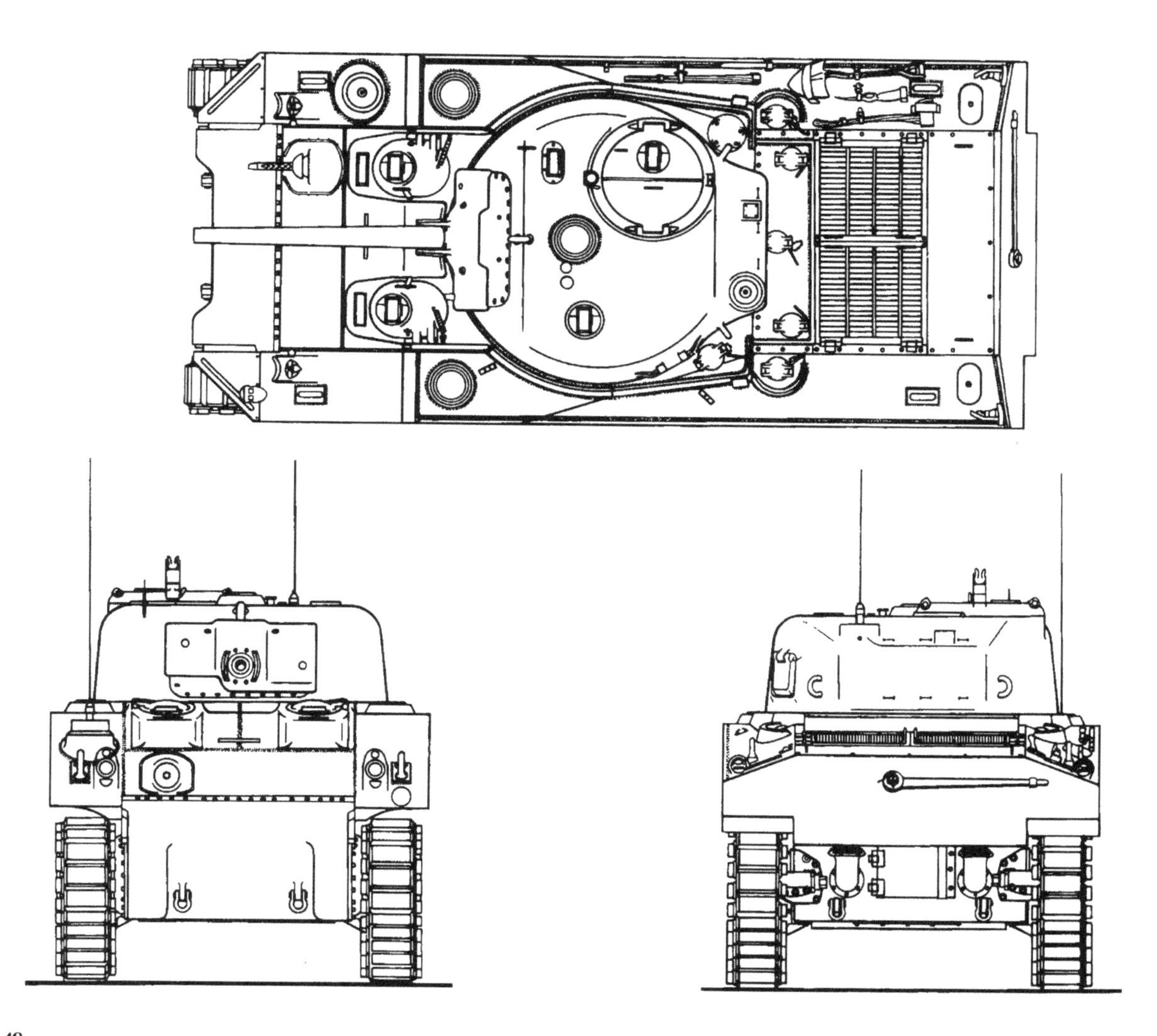

Scale 1:48

Medium Tank M4A3

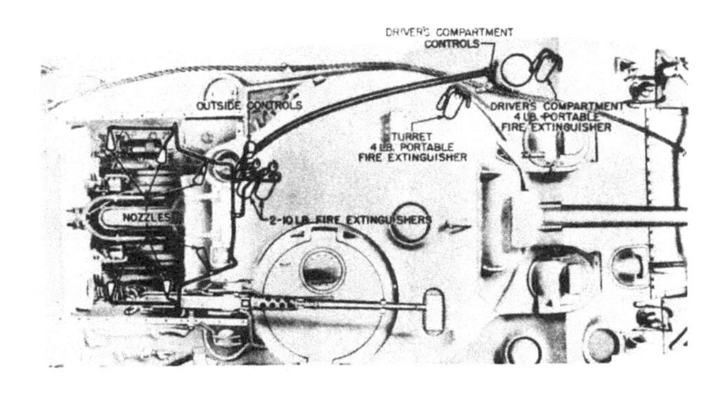

The phantom view above shows the fire extinguisher system on the early M4A3s. Below is the floor escape hatch located just behind the bow gunner or assistant driver.

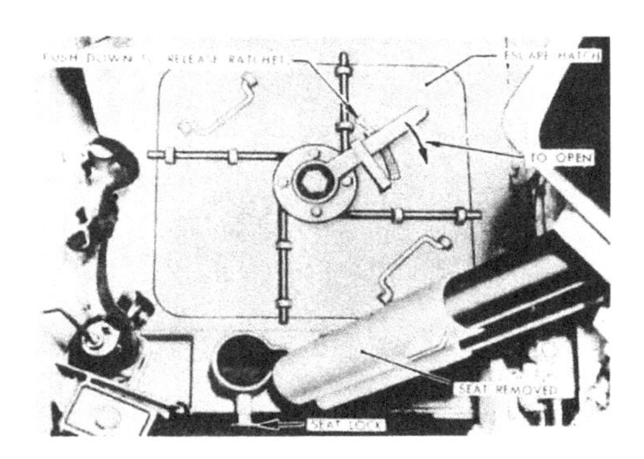

Like all tanks of the M4 series, the M4A3 was equipped with a fire extinguisher system consisting of two 10 pound fixed, and two 4 pound portable, carbon dioxide bottles. The two fixed units were clamped to the bulkhead at the left rear of the fighting compartment and were connected to six nozzles surrounding the engine. These bottles could be activated by two sets of controls, one located outside the tank on the rear deck and the other inside near the driver's seat. One of the portable extinguishers was strapped in a vertical position in the left sponson near the driver and the other was located on the turret basket beside the loader's seat.

The original production run of the 75mm gun M4A3 at Ford was completed in September 1943 with a total of 1690 produced. At that time, Ford left the tank program and future M4A3 production was assigned to other manufacturers. Reports from the field units equipped with the M4A3 and the various test agencies now indicated that the Ford engine was the preferred power plant for U.S. tanks. If sufficient production capacity had been available, all of the future Shermans would have been M4A3s. Battle experience and the test programs had also produced a long list of modifications requested for all models of the Sherman. Their incorporation resulted in almost a new tank. The major part of the M4A3 production consisted of several variations of this new vehicle which began to appear in early 1944. These tanks will be discussed later after the history of the development which led up to them.

The driver's controls in the dry stowage M4A3 can be seen below and at the right is the instrument panel for these tanks.

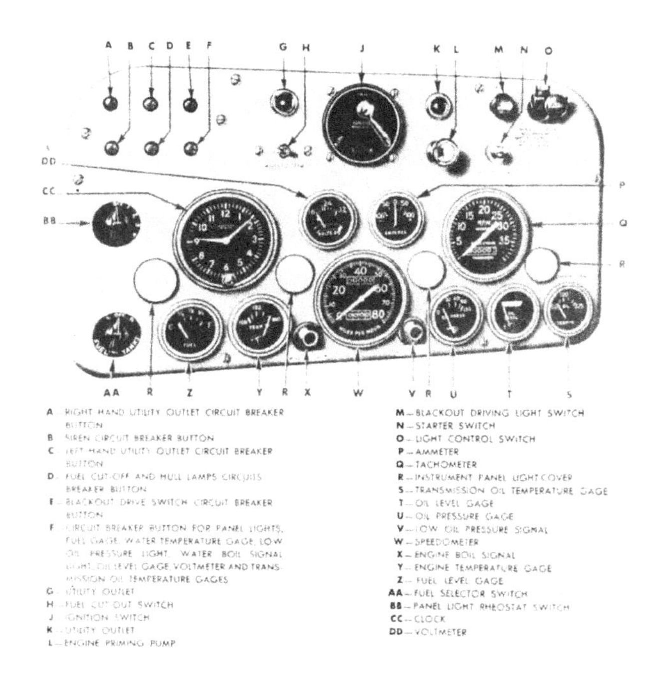

The third pilot medium tank M4A4 (above and below) at Aberdeen Proving Ground on 28 May 1942.

MEDIUM TANK M4A4

To meet the projected production schedules, the Ordnance Committee in February 1942 approved the Chrysler A57 multibank engine for use in the Sherman. With this engine and a welded hull, it was designated as the medium tank M4A4. The power plant developed 425 gross horsepower at 2850 rpm and was identical to that in the medium tank M3A4 which started production in June 1942. The M4A4s followed closely with the first two tanks off the line in July. Chrysler stopped production of both the M3 and M3A4 at Detroit Tank Arsenal in August and for the following year their tank construction program was devoted exclusively to the multibank powered M4A4. A total of 7499 M4A4s were built during the production run ending in September 1943.

Design of the M4A4 was greatly assisted by the development work on the M3A4 which immediately preceded it. The M3A4 had been under test at Aberdeen for about three months when a pilot M4A4 arrived in May 1942. With the same engine and power train, the lessons learned from the earlier tests could be applied directly to the new tank. Although heavier than some earlier Shermans, the M4A4's longer tracks reduced the ground pressure and the multibank engine drove it at a maximum speed of 25 miles/hour. The major problems resulted from the complexity of the power plant. Assembled from five Chrysler engines it

Additional views of the third pilot M4A4 at Aberdeen. This vehicle is representative of the early production tanks.

had a total of 30 cylinders and in the original version, five belt driven water pumps. Because of its size, the engine compartment was extremely crowded and many components were inaccessible unless the engine was removed from the vehicle. Under these conditions, minor adjustments and maintenance were time consuming and difficult to perform. Changes recommended by the test program reduced many of these problems by simplifying the design. For example, the five belt driven water pumps were replaced by a single gear driven model which served the entire power plant. Improvements in components such as valves and piston rings increased the reliability and an intensive training program for maintenance personnel acquainted them with the problems and service procedures peculiar to the multibank engine. These measures greatly improved the serviceability of the M4A4 and were, no doubt, a major factor in its successful performance with the troops.

The long hull, wide spaced bogies, and rear deck bulge characteristic of the M4A4 can all be seen below. Note that a .30 caliber antiaircraft machine gun has been mounted on the tank here.

The first production M4A4, serial number 4805 (above), completed in July 1942. The early version of the Chrysler A57 multibank engine with five water pumps (two left photographs) is compared below with the later single water pump model (two right photographs). The two upper views show the distributor end of the engines and the left sides appear at the bottom.

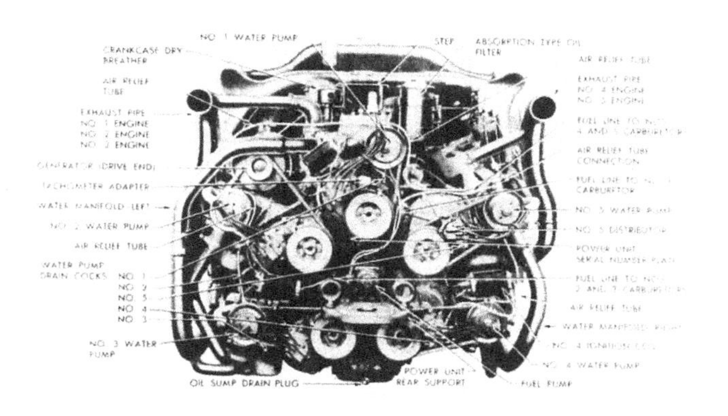

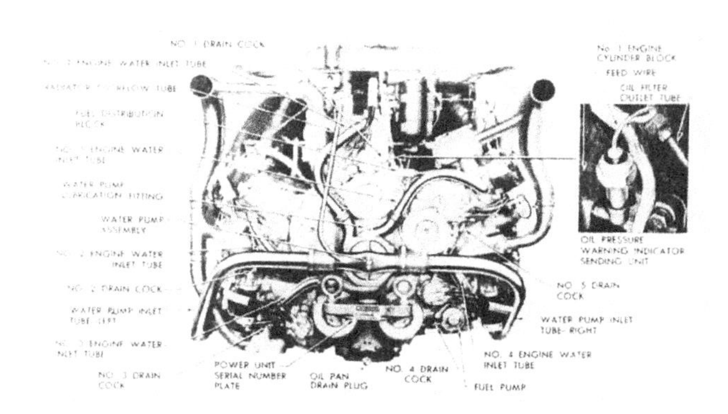

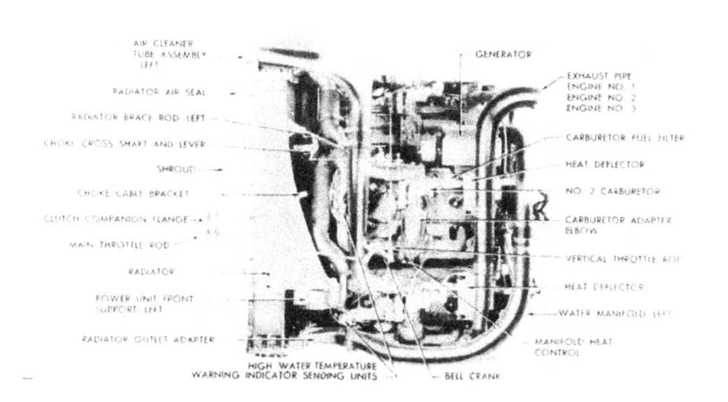

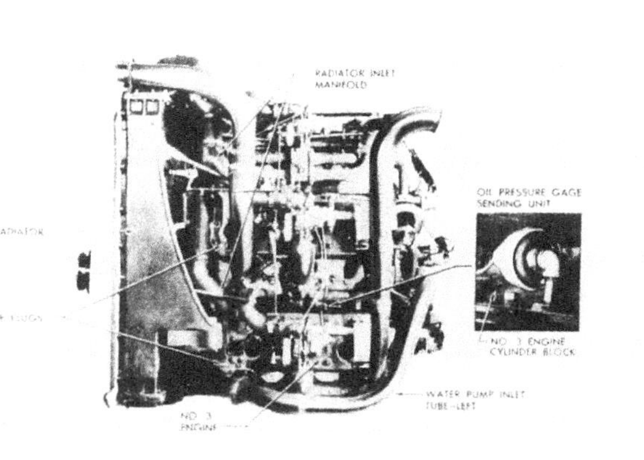

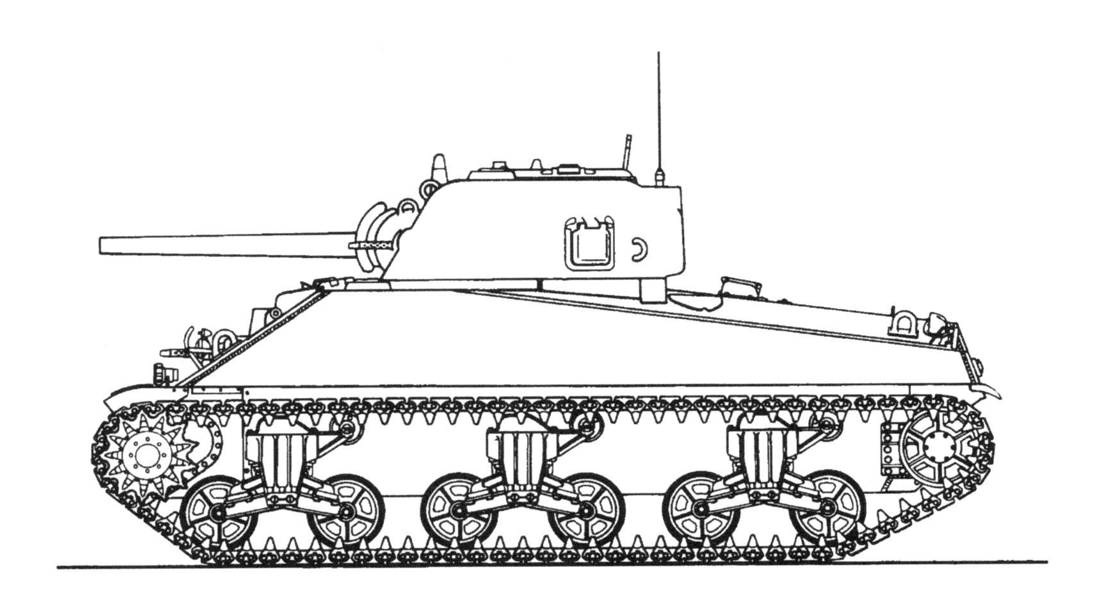

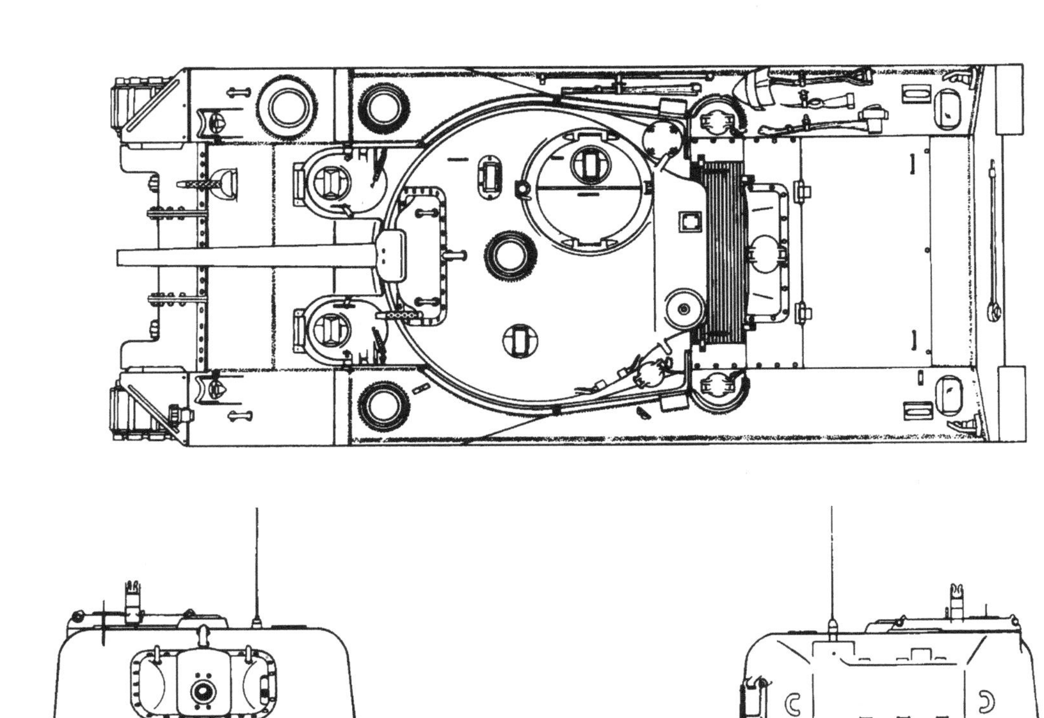

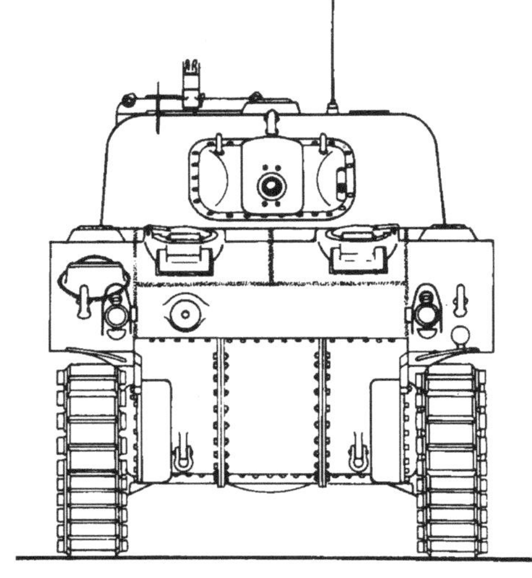

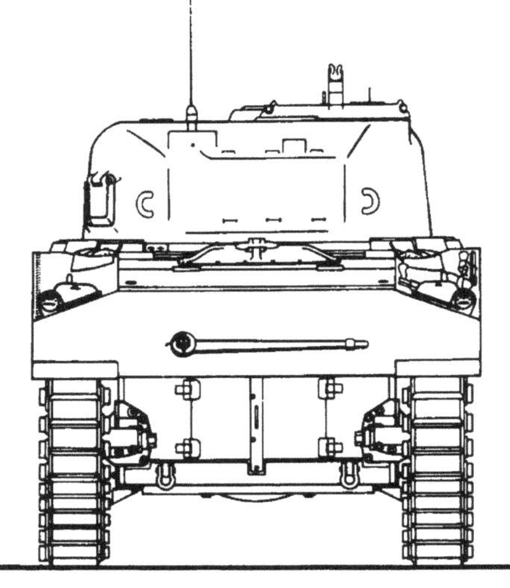

Scale 1:48

Medium Tank M4A4

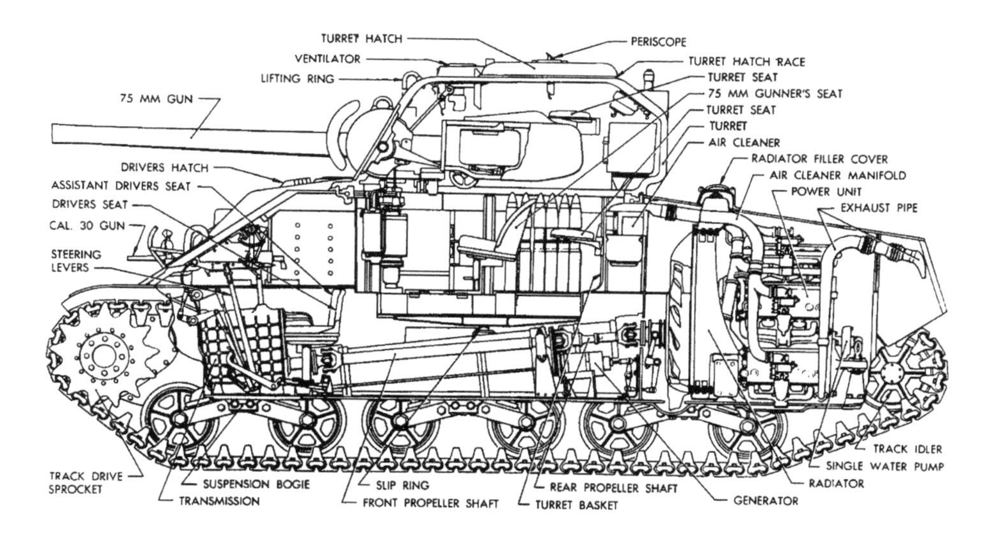

The size of the A57 engine is apparent in the M4A4 sectional view above. Note the incorrect spacing of the suspension bogies in this drawing. The top of the early production M4A4 can be seen below at the left and the arrangement of armament and ammunition stowage appears at the right.

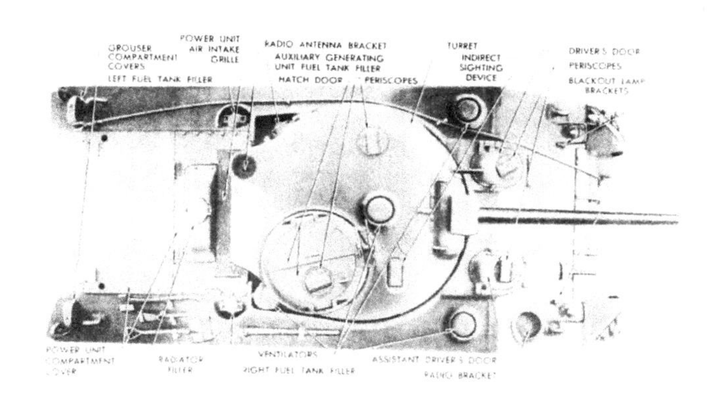

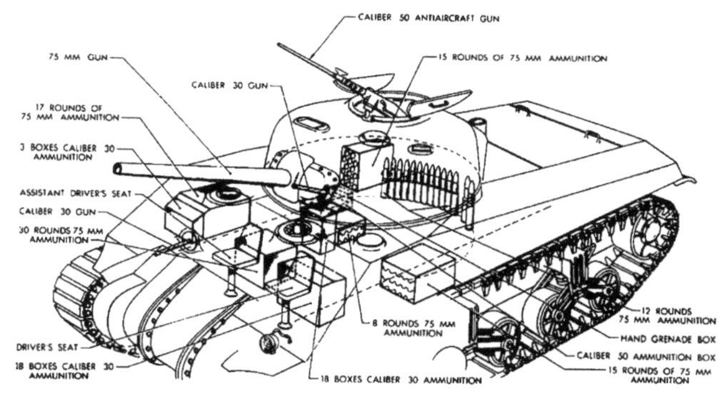

The M4A4 driving compartment is shown below and the instrument panel can be seen at the right.

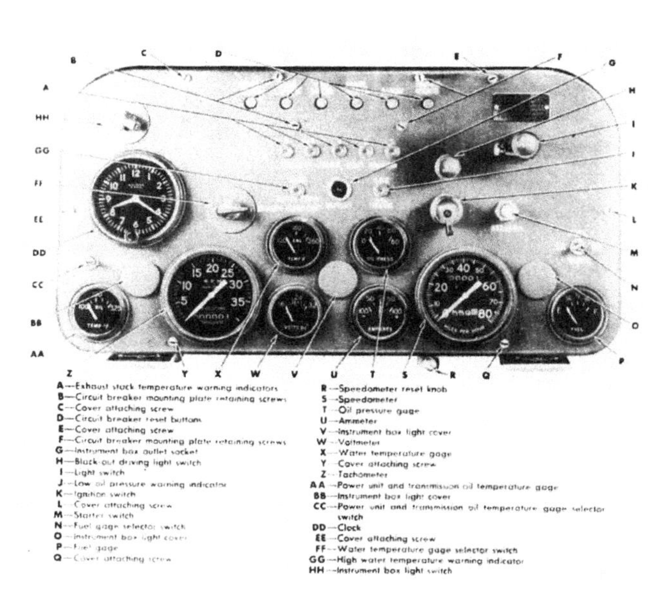

Above: Installation of the early production M4A4 sprockets and suspension bogies on the Chrysler assembly line.

With the tank in production at Detroit, improved versions of the M4A4 were made available for test by Aberdeen, the Armored Force, and the Desert Warfare Board. The latter had already tested five M3A4s and five early M4A4s and concluded that they were unsatisfactory for use in combat. The tests indicated that despite its power, the A57 was the least satisfactory of the engines in production and recommended that it be dropped when a sufficient number of other power plants became available.

The design modifications required to accommodate the Chrysler A57 made the M4A4 easy to identify. The engine compartment was enlarged to fit the bulky power plant by extending the hull 11 inches in length and eliminating the vertical fuel tanks. The loss of the latter was compensated as on the M3A4 by installing larger sponson tanks, each holding 80 gallons. A blister also was necessary in the floor to provide clearance for the engine cooling fan. Another

Details of the 75mm turret casting can be seen above. Below, applique armor is added to the turret and in front of the drivers' hoods on the M4A4.

bulge, rectangular in shape, was located transversely on the rear deck. This covered the upper part of the radiator assembly and the filler cap. To distribute the weight properly, the center and rear bogies were relocated on the longer hull increasing the distance between bogie centers from 57 to 63-5/8 inches. Longer tracks were now required each with 83 shoes increasing the ground contact length from 147 to about 160 inches. The longer tracks and larger spaces between bogies are readily apparent in photographs of the M4A4.

The front armor followed the practice established on the other welded hull tanks and was assembled from castings and rolled plate. However, the design was simplified in comparison to the early M4A2s with the number of major sections being reduced from seven to five.

Early M4A4s were fitted with vision slots for the drivers. As with other models of the Sherman, the slots were replaced on later production vehicles by a second set of periscopes. The M4A4s also received the many modifications such as applique armor common to all tanks of the M4 series. The same 75mm gun turret was installed as on the other Shermans with the M34 gun mount on the first tanks later being replaced by the M34A1.

Above, a late production M4A4 is moved onto a railway car for shipment.

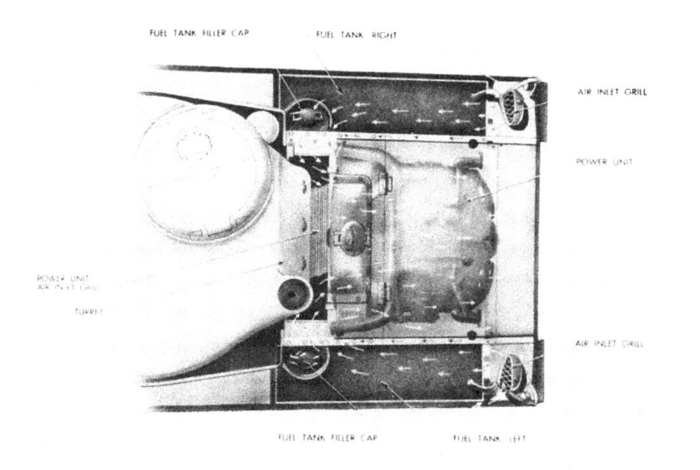

The air flow pattern which cooled the fuel tanks and power unit is shown at the left. Below is the engine compartment (left) with the power plant removed and a plan view of the fighting compartment (right) without the turret.

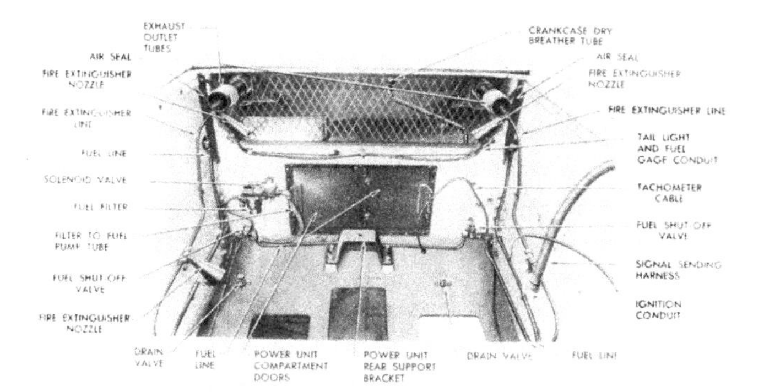

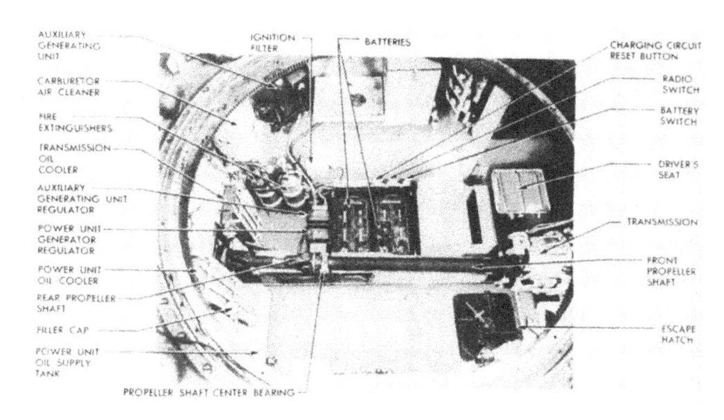

Rejected by the U.S. Army for overseas service, the M4A4 was used by units training in the United States. However, the great majority of the multibank powered tanks were allocated to the British under the Lend-Lease arrangement. Thanks to the modifications resulting from the test program and good maintenance training, the M4A4 established an excellent record in British service. Under their system, it was designated as the Sherman V. Fitted out to meet British stowage requirements, it served both as a standard 75mm gun tank and as the basis for numerous special modifications. Ordnance Committee action in May 1945 reclassified the M4A4 as Limited Standard.

A late production M4A4 stands outside the Arsenal (above) awaiting shipment. Note that even the late production M4A4s retain the three piece differential and final drive housing. Below a shipment of British Sherman Vs in India enroute to the Chinese.

The third medium tank M4E1 under test at the General Motors Proving Ground in June 1943.

MEDIUM TANKS M4E1 AND M4A6

As part of the new engine development program, Caterpillar Tractor Company successfully modified the Wright G200 air-cooled radial to operate as a diesel with fuel injection. The assembly of 28 of these engines for test purposes was authorized in 1942. Designated as the Caterpillar D200A, the modified engine was an early example of a multifuel tank power plant. It was capable of operating on a variety of petroleum products ranging from crude oil to 100 octane gasoline.

The new engine used the supercharger section, crankshaft, bearings, connecting rods, and cylinders of the Wright Cyclone from which it was adapted. The pistons, cylinder heads, crankcase, fuel injection and lubrication systems were designed by Caterpillar. A transfer case was added as an integral part of the power plant. It served the dual purpose of increasing the propeller shaft speed to 1.5 times that of the crankshaft and lowering the propeller shaft thus providing ample clearance under the turret basket. The D200A developed 450 horsepower at 2000 rpm with a maximum torque of 1470 foot pounds at 1200 rpm. These rotational speeds refer to the crankshaft not to the propeller shaft.

Since it was proposed to install 20 of the new engines in tanks of the M4 series, the Ordnance Committee in November 1942 designated the experimental vehicles as the medium tank M4E1. Because of the large size of the D200A, the long hulled M4A4 was selected as the basis for the modification. Built by Chrysler at Detroit Tank Arsenal, the tanks were shipped to Caterpillar for installation of the power plant. The vehicles were essentially standard M4A4s

A top view of the third M4E1 showing the bulge in the rear deck necessary to cover the large power plant.

with minor modifications to accommodate the new engine. Like the original Chrysler A57, the air-cooled diesel was a bit too large for the engine compartment and blisters were required in both the floor and the rear deck. The latter provided an easy point of identification for the M4E1 since it was a round cornered square compared to the narrow rectangular bulge on the M4A4's rear deck. It also consisted of a solid single piece cover without the separate filler cap cover as on the M4A4. The original M4A4 fuel tanks were used consisting of an 80 gallon tank in each rear sponson.

The first M4E1 was completed in December 1942 and began testing at the Caterpillar Proving Ground. The second tank was shipped to Fort Knox in January 1943 followed in May by number four. The third experimental vehicle, with registration number W-3057896, was under test at the General Motors Proving Ground. Some of the M4E1s were fitted with the three piece differential and final drive housing while others used the single piece version. During the tests at Fort Knox, a higher rate of gear train failures was noted for the later model. The failures were attributed to lower specification requirements for the gears used with the single piece housing. This was corrected in later specifications by changes requiring higher strengths in these components.

The tests at Fort Knox revealed numerous difficulties with the original clutch and a modified Lipe clutch was installed. The D200A also frequently failed because of scoring between the pistons and cylinder walls. This was particularly true of the master rod piston and cylinder. Further work on modified piston rings and cylinder wall surface treatments was required to solve the scoring problem. The two vehicles under test at Fort Knox, registration numbers W-3056693 and W-3057623, were also used to evaluate the performance of the vehicle using gasoline for fuel. The tanks ran on either 72 or 80 octane gasoline mixed with engine lubricating oil in a ratio of ten to one. Both vehicles performed satisfactorily on this fuel.

The engine compartment on the M4E1 opened to expose the Caterpillar D200A engine.

The first production medium tank M4A6, registration number 3099687, being shipped from Detroit Arsenal.

The preliminary engine dynamometer tests and the early vehicle performance were so promising that OCM 19630 on 28 January 1943 authorized procurement of 1000 D200A engines. A separate Ordnance Committee action redesignated the D200A as the Ordnance Engine RD1820 and arrangements were made to install 775 of these engines in M4A4 tank hulls for extended service tests. The Ordnance Committee designated this production version of the new vehicle as the medium tank M4A6. These later model production vehicles and engines were not interchangeable with the earlier experimental versions and the latter were disposed of in March 1944. Two of the M4E1s were retained at Fort Knox for further tests using gasoline fuel and one remained at Aberdeen Proving Ground for historical purposes. The remaining M4E1s were salvaged or used for target practice.

Chrysler started production of the M4A6 at Detroit Arsenal with the first tank being shipped on 28 October 1943. However, the run was discontinued in February 1944 after the completion of only 75 vehicles. Changing military requirements and the decision to concentrate on the gasoline powered M4A3 combined with the usual problems on a new tank to kill the M4A6.

As noted earlier, the M4A6 differed from the experimental M4E1. It used a late production version of the M4A4 hull with a cast front section similar to that on the late model M4 produced at Detroit Arsenal. It also included the larger drivers' hatches and was fitted with a traveling lock for the 75mm gun. The single piece sharp nosed differential and final drive housing was used on all of the production tanks. Applique armor was welded over the sponson ammunition racks on each side of the hull, but the turrets were the later reinforced model not requiring the exterior patch. Pistol ports were eliminated from the first production tanks, but were reinstated on later vehicles. Photographs show the 12th production tank to be fitted with a pistol port, but it is absent from the 1st, 5th, 7th, and 13th vehicles. The need to use the stock of available turrets obviously resulted in some overlap between tanks with and without pistol ports. Drawings of the M4A6 dated 17 April 1944 show the pistol port as standard. The late model turret with the pistol port on M4A6 number 12 also included the small oval hatch for the loader. All of the production M4A6s were fitted with the M34A1 gun mount.

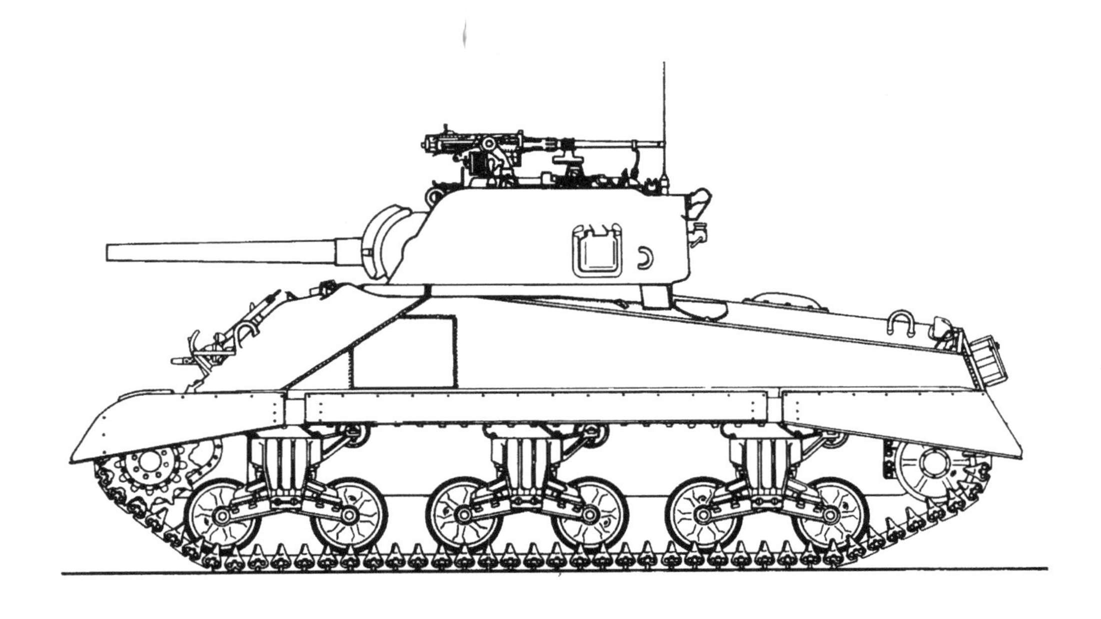

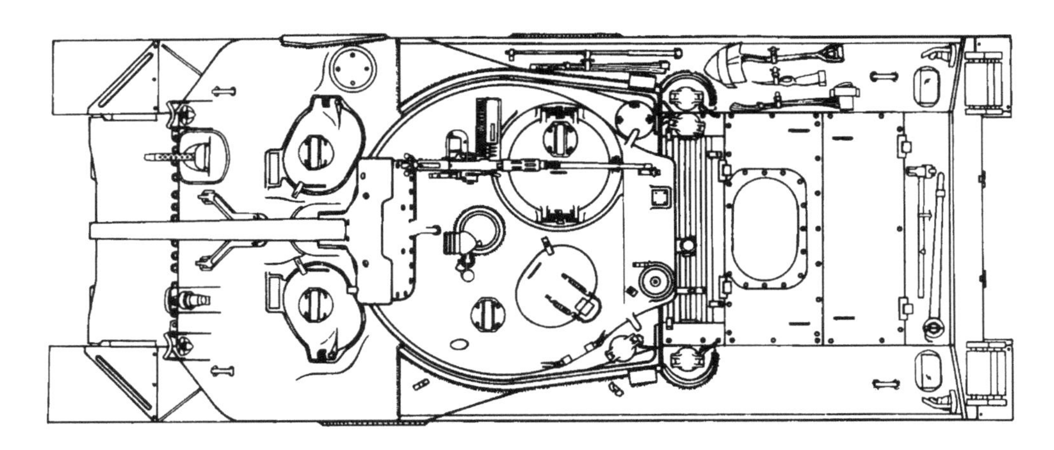

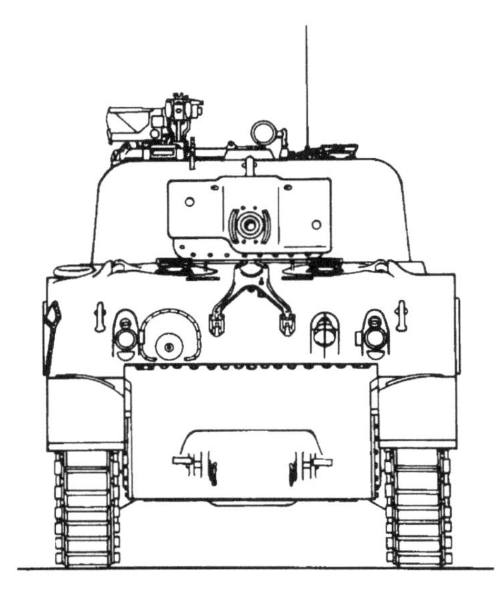

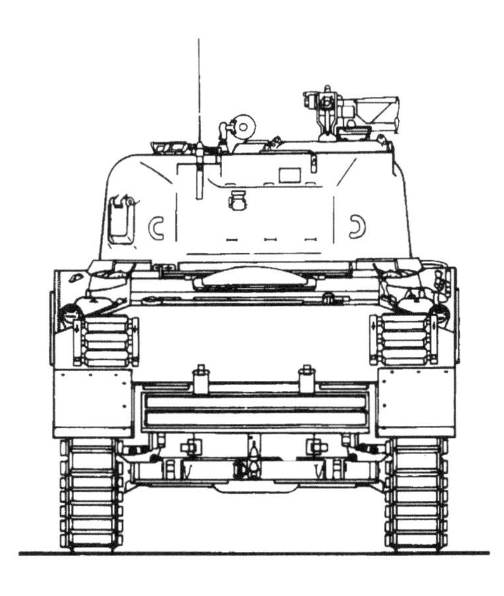

Scale 1:48

Medium Tank M4A6

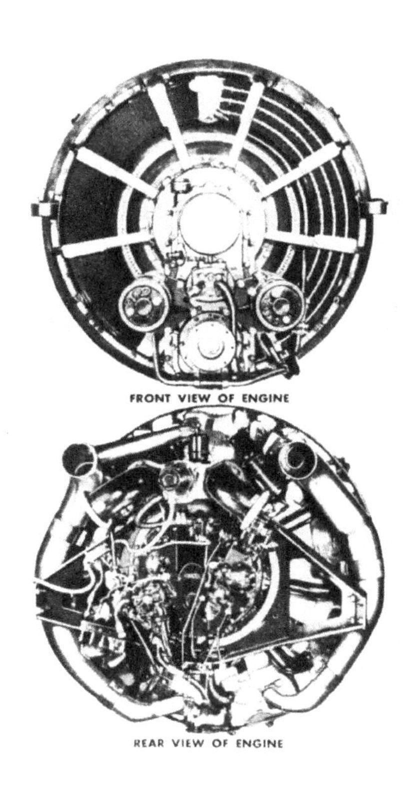

FRONT VIEW OF ENGINE

REAR VIEW OF ENGINE

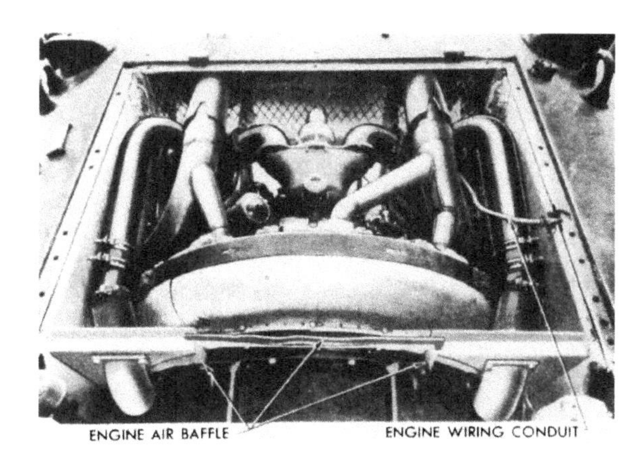

The Ordnance Engine RD 1820 appears at the left and above it is installed in the M4A6. The crowded condition of the engine compartment is obvious.

The driver's controls and the instrument panel in the M4A6 are shown below.

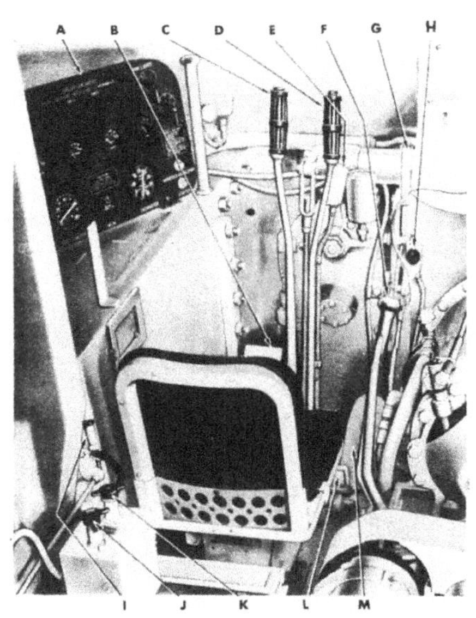

A—INSTRUMENT PANEL
B—CLUTCH PEDAL
C—STEERING BRAKE CONTROL LEVER—LEFT
D—STEERING BRAKE CONTROL LEVER—RIGHT
E—SIREN SWITCH
F—TRANSMISSION GEARSHIFT LEVER
G—GOVERNOR CONTROL HAND LEVER
H—HAND THROTTLE CONTROL
I—FUEL TANK SELECTOR LEVER
J—RADIO MASTER SWITCH (12-VOLT)
K—BATTERY MASTER SWITCH (24-VOLT)
L—PARKING BRAKE OPERATING PEDAL
M—ACCELERATOR PEDAL

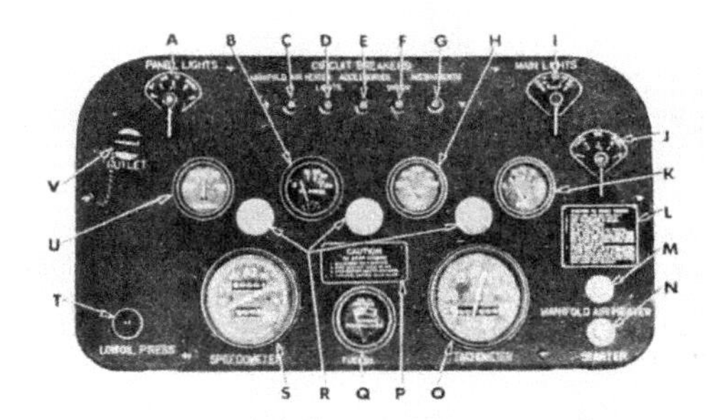

A—PANEL LIGHT SWITCH
B—ENGINE OIL PRESSURE GAGE
C—CIRCUIT BREAKER RESET BUTTON (MANIFOLD AIR HEATER)
D—CIRCUIT BREAKER RESET BUTTON (LIGHTS)
E—CIRCUIT BREAKER RESET BUTTON (ACCESSORIES)
F—CIRCUIT BREAKER RESET BUTTON (SIREN)
G—CIRCUIT BREAKER RESET BUTTON (INSTRUMENTS)
H—ENGINE OIL TEMPERATURE GAGE
I—MAIN LIGHT SWITCH
J—FUEL AND OIL LEVEL GAGE SELECTOR SWITCH
K—FUEL AND OIL LEVEL GAGE
L—INSTRUCTION PLATE (TO START ENGINE)
M—MANIFOLD AIR HEATER SWITCH
N—STARTING BUTTON
O—TACHOMETER
P—INSTRUCTION PLATE (TO STOP ENGINE)
Q—FUEL OIL PRESSURE GAGE
R—INSTRUMENT PANEL LIGHTS
S—SPEEDOMETER
T—LOW OIL PRESSURE WARNING LIGHT
U—AMMETER
V—ELECTRICAL OUTLET

These views of the production M4A6 illustrate its major points of identification. These are the large round cornered bulge on the rear deck, the long hull with wide spaced bogies, and the combination rolled and cast upper hull.

Ten production M4A6s were tested by the Armored Force at Fort Knox starting in March 1944. These tests concluded that the M4A6 was superior in performance to any of the standard M4 series medium tanks. The fuel economy and cruising range were considerably better than any of the other standard versions of the Sherman.

With the end of production, the M4A6s were assigned to training units in the United States and the 777th Tank Battalion at Fort Knox was equipped with the vehicle for battalion service tests. In line with U.S. policy, none of the diesel powered tanks were shipped overseas for U.S. troops and on 3 May 1945, OCM 27512 reclassified the M4A6 as Limited Standard.

The 12th M4A6 is shown above during tests at Fort Knox. The tank below is from C Company of the 777th Tank Battalion.

The second Sherman received by Britain. Like MICHAEL on page 125, it is armed with the 75mm gun M2.

ACTION AT EL ALAMEIN

After the defeat near Gazala, the British Eighth Army fell back toward the Egyptian frontier. Following rapidly, Rommel's forces drove toward Tobruk. The defenses around the port had been neglected since the siege of the previous year and the defenders were badly disorganized by the chaotic conditions during the retreat. Striking early in the morning of 20 June 1942, the assault troops overwhelmed the outer defenses and by that evening the 21st Panzer Division reported that the town itself had fallen. Fighting continued during the night until General Klopper, commanding the garrison, surrendered on the morning of the 21st. A few small detachments managed to break out and rejoin the British forces to the east and some others continued to fight until the morning of the 22nd. However, Rommel's troops were now in full control and had captured over 32,000 men and about 2000 serviceable vehicles.

Prime Minister Churchill was with President Roosevelt in Washington when the news was received of the disaster at Tobruk. In answer to Roosevelt's offer of help, Churchill requested as many of the new Sherman tanks as could be made available. With the arrival of General Marshall at the White House, the details were worked out in a series of meetings during the night. Marshall's first plan was to send a complete U.S. armored division to Egypt equipped with the Sherman. Major General George S. Patton, Jr. was recalled from the Desert Training Center and ordered to prepare the 2nd Armored Division for movement overseas. Since the Sherman was just coming into production, it was necessary to transfer tanks from several units to obtain a full complement of vehicles for the division. Further study of the shipping problem showed that it would be October or November before the complete division could arrive in Egypt. That might well be too late to stop Rommel. General Marshall then offered to withdraw 300 Shermans from the troops in training and ship them direct to Egypt. He also offered to send 100 of the new M7 self-propelled 105mm howitzers. A special convoy carrying the tanks sailed on 15 July, but the following day one vessel was torpedoed and sunk. Another fast ship with 52 additional tanks was dispatched to replace the losses and by 11 September a total of 318 Shermans had arrived in the Middle East. Most of these were M4A1s, but some M4A2s were also included.

Although the emergency shipment brought the first Shermans in quantity, a sample tank had arrived in Egypt in August. This was one of the first M4A1s produced at Lima Locomotive and was armed with the short barreled 75mm gun M2 fitted with double counterweights. At that time it was quite a secret weapon and was used to familiarize the ordnance and armored troops with the new tank.

The first Sherman to arrive in Cairo, August 1942.

After the arrival of the September shipment, work began immediately to modify the tanks for desert conditions and to train the troops with their new weapon. The workshops installed sandshields along with stowage items proven necessary by desert experience. However, time was running out and the work was still in progress when the great battle at El Alamein opened on the night of 23 October 1942. Reports of that evening show that 252 Shermans were fit for action in the forward units of the Eighth Army. Some of these tanks, such as the 36 Shermans belonging to the 9th Armoured Brigade, had only reached their units on the 23rd leaving little time to check them out before going into action. The remaining Shermans available for the opening phase of the battle were divided between the 1st and 10th Armoured Divisions. The 2nd Armoured Brigade of the 1st Armoured Division was equipped with 92 of the new tanks. In the 10th Armoured Division, the 8th and 24th Armoured Brigades had 31 and 93 Shermans respectively. Other tanks available in the forward formations at the start of the battle included 170 Grants, 294 Crusaders, 119 Stuarts, and 194 Valentines.

Sherman IIs and IIIs from the first shipment newly arrived at Tel el Kebir (top left) and test firing (top right) near Suez. Below are the first three Shermans sent from Tel el Kebir to the front.

Below, the stabilized gun on one of the new Shermans is tested near Suez in November 1942.

British crews with their new Shermans (above and below) on the Alamein front.

The 9th Armoured Brigade operated as part of the New Zealand Division supporting the infantry during the initial assault. Their first losses were caused by mines and the antitank guns dug in behind the German infantry positions. A similar situation faced the two armored divisions when they tried to deploy out of the lanes cleared through the enemy minefields. By this time, the first light of dawn was beginning to break and the tanks found themselves easy targets silhouetted against the eastern horizon. The antitank guns were still concealed in the darkness to the west and could only be located by the muzzle flash. These guns were engaged by both the supporting artillery and the tanks firing high explosive. However, the return fire was relatively ineffective until it became light enough to locate the enemy positions.

The Sherman's first encounter with enemy tanks occurred shortly after sunrise. A detachment from the 15th Panzer Division approached the front of the 2nd Armoured Brigade as it moved up through the 51st Highland Division. The enemy tanks were late model Panzer IIIs and IVs armed with the long barreled 5cm and 7.5cm cannon. The latter weapon was the Kampfwagenkanone (KwK) 40 with a muzzle velocity of 2590 ft/sec compared to the 2030 ft/sec of the Sherman's 75. However, the enemy was engaged at a range of 2000 yards and after a short time withdrew to the north leaving several tanks burning on both sides. Thus began the battle career of the Sherman which, in one form or another, was to last for more than 30 years.

German armor at Alamein: The Panzer III (top left) and the Panzer IV (top right). Battle damage suffered by the Shermans during the fighting can be seen below.

After Alamein, the numbers of Shermans in British armored units rapidly increased until it became the most widely used type in service. Older tanks such as the Grant and Lee were transferred to less demanding theaters of war, converted to other uses, or consigned to the scrap heap. By the end of December 1944, 15,153 75mm gun Shermans had been supplied to Britain. These tanks consisted of 2073 Sherman I (M4), 885 Sherman II(M4A1), 5033 Sherman III (M4A2), 7 Sherman IV (M4A3), and 7155 Sherman V (M4A4). Many of these were converted for special tasks or rearmed with the British 17 pounder high velocity gun.

Christmas 1942 on the coast road after Alamein (above right). Below, the Shermans continue the advance toward Tripoli.

A U.S. M4A1 towing a half-track near Sidi bou Zid, Tunisia on 14 February 1943.

U.S. SHERMANS IN NORTH AFRICA

The combat career of the M4 in the hands of U.S. troops began in Tunisia. As mentioned previously, the first medium tank unit of the 1st Armored Division to see action was the 2nd Battalion of the 13th Armored Regiment. Equipped with the medium tank M3, it first clashed with the enemy in late November 1942. The Shermans of the 2nd and 3rd Battalions of the 1st Armored Regiment were first committed to battle in the ill fated attempt to stop the German attack through Faid Pass and to retake Sidi Bou Zid. The destruction of both units in the fighting of 14-15 February has been related earlier. However, it appears that the first U.S. manned Shermans to see action belonged to the platoon from the 2nd Armored Division which was attached to the 2nd Battalion, 13th Armored Regiment. All five of these tanks were knocked out in the fighting southwest of Tebourba on 6 December. Thus the initial action of the U.S. Shermans resulted in disastrous losses mainly from attacks against skillfully deployed enemy tanks and antitank guns. Fortunately, the lessons learned so painfully were rapidly absorbed and applied to future actions.

Company G and part of Company H from the 2nd Armored Division's 67th Armored Regiment arrived in the Beja area of Tunisia on the night of 11-12 December with 26 M4A1s. They provided support for the British 1st Guards Brigade in the fierce fighting around Longstop Hill.

The 2nd Battalion, 13th Armored Regiment, under the redoubtable Henry Gardiner, received 20 M4A1s transferred from the 2nd Armored Division in mid December. With the addition of a few repaired M3s, the battalion was almost back to full strength after the losses of early December. D Company was issued a full complement of the M4A1s with the excess going to E. Company F continued to operate with the M3. The battalion's hard won battle experience is readily apparent in Gardiner's description of their operations in the Ousseltia Valley.

"When asked how long it would take me to get rolling, I said the tanks would be moving in 45 minutes after I left the CP (CCB), and they were. Driving back to the battalion, a flight of friendly fighters swept up the valley and toward the upper

A newly arrived M4A1 (above and below) at the Ordnance Depot in Oran on 5 April 1943. Note that this tank is fitted with the heavy duty suspension bogies and the vision slots have been eliminated.

end a heavy concentration of light ack-ack was thrown up, so there was no doubt about the enemy being in the valley and in considerable numbers. We moved out in a line of companies in column. There was a crosswind and the battalion made a brave sight as we rolled forward, with three tank companies churning up the dust. . .The country was perfectly flat all the way to Ousseltia. There, per our plan of attack, HQ Company and E Company dropped out and D and F Companies continued on without halting. Jim (Capt. Simmerman) stayed with the battalion half-track with that group under his control and I went with the two assault companies in my tank. . .

If we learned nothing else at Tebourba it was the hazard of rushing into an unknown situation. I was determined that we would not get ourselves in a position of being surprised to the point that it would be too late to defend ourselves. We reformed. . .and I put D Company on the left so that with their M4s they could engage any targets that appeared on that flank since that was the side the enemy were supposed to be on. . .It was just getting dusk when suddenly several guns opened up on us from our left front. The D Company boys replied immediately, their turrets all swinging around to the left which gave me the impression of a group of battleships steaming into action. The tank next to mine in which the D Company commander was riding was hit and disabled, but no one was hurt. I gave orders to our group to veer to the right and we moved over a hill firing at the direction of the enemy guns as we moved."

Lieutenant Colonel Henry Gardiner (top left) with Henry III. At the top right is Major Simmerman's tank camouflaged with light colored mud. Below: One of the M4A1s near Kasserine Pass.

The M4s Colonel Gardiner refers to were, of course, M4A1s. He had acquired one himself naming it Henry II replacing his M3 lost on 2 December. Henry II served until 17 February when it was destroyed covering the retreat of Combat Command B from Sbeitla. The 2nd Battalion's performance in the latter action is best described by General Robinett in his book ARMOR COMMAND.

> "About 1730 the final withdrawal was ordered. The artillery moved out without delay, but the tanks found disengagement a difficult task. Colonel Gardiner, though closely engaged by a superior force, gradually broke off the action and moved his battalion toward the rear. Major James S. Simmerman led one company across the deep wadi and down the main road toward Kasserine, while Gardiner, in keeping with his high standard of personal leadership, supervised the withdrawal of the remainder of his battalion on the central route. In breaking off the engagement, the battalion lost nine medium tanks. Gardiner's tank was among those destroyed by enemy action and he was reported missing. Characteristically, he stayed to the very end and was the last to withdraw...
>
> Morning brought news that Colonel Gardiner had not been captured. When his tank was knocked out he succeeded in removing one of the wounded crewmen. After giving the man first aid and placing him beside a trail where he would be found...Gardiner managed to escape and make his way back to friendly troops on foot, a distance of more than 30 miles. Cpl. Orvis Carlock, Gardiner's tank driver, was killed. Gardiner was awarded the Distinguished Service Cross for the action at Sbeitla and Carlock the Silver Star, posthumously.
>
> In the last analysis, the 2nd Battalion, 13th Armored Regiment, was largely responsible for stopping the enemy at Sbeitla at a cost of relatively small losses-two officers, 14 men, ten tanks, and two half-tracks. It had stopped the 21st Panzer Division and covered the withdrawal of other forces from the Sbeitla area."

Henry II was soon replaced by another M4A1 named, in turn, Henry III. The latter had about the same life span as its predecessor lasting until 6 May 1943 when it was destroyed by an antitank gun north of Mateur during the final drive toward Bizerte.

After the end of fighting in Africa, the M4 and M4A1 became the standard tanks in the 1st Armored Division and were used throughout the Italian campaign. They were supplemented by the arrival of late model M4A3s after the fall of Rome in the Summer of 1944.

A famous photograph above illustrates the empty terrain near Kasserine as Captain G. W. Meade of the 13th Armored Regiment scans the area from his turret on 24 February 1943.

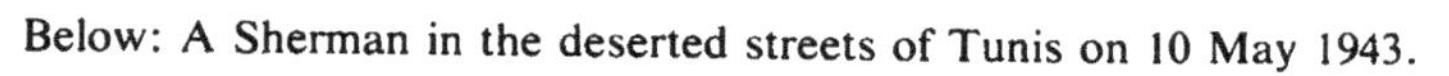

Below: A Sherman in the deserted streets of Tunis on 10 May 1943.

The M4A1s (at left) are backing on to an LST using a treadway ramp during a training exercise at Oran on 6 April 1943. Note the extra 5 gallon gasoline cans stowed on the rear deck.

Below, M4A2s are supplied under the Lend-Lease program to rearm the French in North Africa.

A Sherman moves along the road four miles north of Mistretta, Sicily on 14 August 1943.

WORLDWIDE SERVICE

With the production of the Sherman at full speed, it rapidly became the most widely used tank in the Allied forces. It was supplied not only to U.S. and British units, but also to those of the Soviet Union, the Free French, and several other countries. In addition to the tanks allotted to the British, the Lend-Lease program supplied the Soviet Union with 1991 M4A2s and 2 M4A4s by 31 December 1944. In the same period, the Free French received 382 M4A2s and 274 M4A4s. Brazil received 53 M4s at the same time. All of these tanks were armed with the 75mm gun.

The full details of the Sherman's battle record would be similar in size and scope to the complete history of World War II after 1942. It appeared on almost every major battlefield of the war, but little is known of its role in the Soviet Union where it was overshadowed by the vastly greater numbers of the home grown T34.

Designed as a weapon of exploitation, the Sherman proved remarkably successful at that task. With a weight of about 30 tons and a width of 105 inches, it could cross most of the bridges usually encountered in Europe. The relatively simple maintenance and high reliability provided a tank which could operate over long distances without major repair. These features combined in the Sherman resulted in a weapon ideally suited to deep penetration tactics and the disruption of the enemy rear areas. In the hands of such leaders as Patton, it was a decisive weapon.

In tank versus tank battles, the Sherman easily matched the late model Panzer IV. Although the German tank's 7.5cm KwK 40 was much more powerful than the U.S. 75mm gun M3, the latter could easily

An M4A1 comes ashore in Sicily.

An M4A1 of the 13th Armored Regiment near Capua, Italy on 29 November 1943.

destroy the Panzer IV at all normal combat ranges. The KwK 40 could, of course, also penetrate the Sherman, but the fast power traverse frequently allowed the U.S. built tank to get in the first shot. With proper training, the use of the elevation gyrostabilizer also gave an advantage to the M4s.

Although the Sherman could effectively deal with the Panzer IVs, the appearance of the Panther and the Tiger I on the battlefield drastically changed the situation. The 75mm armor piercing round could not penetrate the glacis plate of either of the new enemy tanks even at pointblank range, but the 7.5cm KwK 42 and the 8.8cm KwK 36 of the Panther and Tiger I could destroy the Sherman from any angle at maximum combat range. New tactics were required to meet these powerful enemy tanks. Superior numbers and the Sherman's good mobility frequently allowed them to outflank the heavier enemy vehicles and attack them from the sides and rear. The Sherman's 75 could penetrate the thinner armor in these areas particularly in the case of the Panther. When the terrain prevented such flanking maneuvers, the Sherman was in serious trouble and usually relied on the heavier gunned tank destroyers, the artillery, or close air support to knock out the dangerous enemy tanks.

Shermans of the 1st Armored Division unload at Anzio (below) on 27 April 1944. Note the track sections added to the hull front for extra protection.

Above, an inflatable dummy tank is used to confuse the enemy at Anzio, 20 May 1944.

Below, Shermans of the 760th Tank Battalion move forward past disabled tanks on the road to San Maria Infante, Italy on 14 May 1944. Note that the first disabled tank still has the early suspension bogies. The M34 mounts on these tanks are fitted with the .30 caliber machine gun shield.

The accuracy of the Sherman's 75 sometimes allowed it to immobilize the turret on the larger enemy vehicles by a hit at the junction of the hull and turret, thus pinning the turret ring. The early Panthers were also vulnerable to a shot from the front striking the curved gunshield below the cannon. Even if it did not penetrate, a hit in this area frequently deflected the projectile down through the hull roof into the drivers' compartment or under the turret.

In any case, the Sherman's greatest deficiency as far as the European Theater was concerned was its inadequate firepower. Ordnance had recognized this problem early in 1942 and numerous experimental programs were in progress to improve the armament. In the meantime, the troops had to soldier on with what was available.

Above, 1st Armored Division Shermans cross the Arno River on 1 September 1944. These tanks are fitted with applique armor on both hull and turret. Below, the 755th Tank Battalion is lined up ready to fire as artillery in the Pietramala area of Italy on 1 October 1944. Note the unofficial stowage on the front armor plate.

The Sherman during its introduction to the Pacific war at Tarawa. Above is Red Beach 3. The M4A2s suffered numerous losses (below) from the well sited Japanese 47mm antitank guns.

The situation in the Pacific was quite different from that in Europe. The rarely encountered Japanese tanks were as inferior in firepower and protection to the Sherman as the latter was to the heavy German equipment. The Japanese had few tanks in action and these were often dug in and used as pillboxes. The major role for Allied armor was in infantry support, both during the island assaults and the campaign in Burma. The tank losses in these battles resulted from concealed guns, mines, and infantry antitank weapons. Thus heavier armor became a prime requirement, particularly on the sides of the Sherman which were easily penetrated by the Japanese 47mm antitank gun. Numerous field expedients were employed such as welding extra plate over the sponsons, but the problem remained until the end of the war.

Armor support for the early Pacific operations was provided by the light tanks of the M3 series. With the availability of suitable landing craft, they were replaced by mediums during the later campaigns. Shermans were first in action with the U.S. Marine Corps at Tarawa in November 1943 playing a vital part

Above, an M4A1 lands from an LST at Cape Gloucester, New Britain in late December 1943.

Late production M4A1s of the 767th Tank Battalion on Ebeye island, Kwajalein atoll (at left), 4 February 1944.

in that battle. After the island was secured, Major General Holland Smith, commanding the Marine assault force, recommended that Shermans replace the light tanks in all future amphibious assaults. This was primarily due to the greater effectiveness of the 75mm gun against the Japanese fortifications compared to the 37mm gun of the light tanks.

After 1943, the Sherman participated in almost every battle of the island hopping campaign across the Pacific. By the time war returned to the Philippines in the Fall of 1944, Sherman equipped separate tank battalions were operating on a regular basis in support of the infantry divisions. None of the armored divisions were deployed in the Pacific although their use was planned for the invasion of Japan.

At left is a Sherman operating with the Americal Division in the Bougainville jungle during February 1944.

Shermans are in action above in the Laruma section of the Bougainville perimeter.

Loading ammunition in a camouflaged Sherman on Bougainville (at right), 13 March 1944. Note the late production features such as the gun traveling lock and the sharp nosed differential housing.

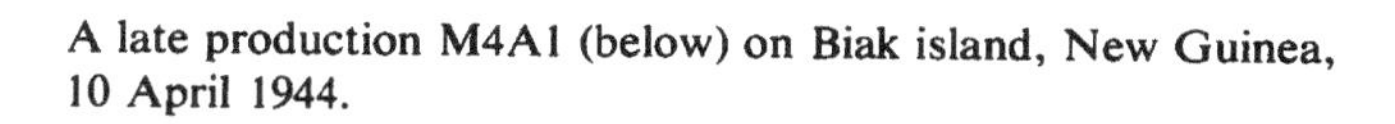

A late production M4A1 (below) on Biak island, New Guinea, 10 April 1944.

U.S. Marine Corps M4A2s on Saipan during June and July 1944. Note the extra wooden protection (above right) against the Japanese magnetic mines. The crew below had destroyed an enemy tank the previous day near Garapan. The welded drivers' hoods, antenna socket, and bow gun mount can be clearly seen in this photograph.

U.S. Marine Corps Shermans with deep fording equipment (top left) come ashore on Tinian, July 1944. Above at the right, U.S. Army late production M4s move through the ruins of Agana on Guam, 2 August 1944.

U.S. forces encountered the largest concentration of Japanese armor on Luzon in the Philippines. Here the Japanese 2nd Tank Division was assigned as part of the Shobu Group under General Tomoyuki Yamashita. Equipped with about 220 tanks, the division was used in the static defense role. By early February 1945, it had lost 180 of its tanks, most of these dug in defending the approaches to San Jose. After this, it was reorganized as an infantry unit and Japanese armor no longer played an important role on Luzon.

Another late production M4 with the combination rolled and cast upper hull moves along a hill overlooking Baguio, Luzon on 27 April 1945.

Above are American manned M4A4s operating with Chinese troops in Burma, 25 February 1945. The British T number is still dimly visible on the side of the nearest tank.

Tanks of the Chinese-American 1st Provisional Tank Group cross the Nam Yao River (at left) during the attack on Lashio, Burma, 6 March 1945. Above, the same unit works to extract on M4A4 from a bomb crater in the Namtu River near Haenwi, Burma.

PART III

MODIFICATION AND DEVELOPMENT

An early artist's concept of an improved tank. Note the sloped side armor on the sponsons and the central position of the driver with no bow gunner.

PROPOSALS FOR AN IMPROVED TANK

Even before the first production model came off the assembly line, work was started to modify and improve the M4. On 8 December 1941, the Office of the Chief of Ordnance wrote to Aberdeen Proving Ground regarding the design of a modified Sherman. Aberdeen was instructed to prepare a design study of an M4 with increased armor protection and mobility. On 13 March 1942, Aberdeen submitted layout drawings and a list of characteristics for the new design.

The proposed tank differed in a number of features from the first production vehicles. The front hull armor remained the same except for the final drive housing. The latter was a single piece casting similar to that which soon appeared on the production tanks. The vertical portion of the housing was thickened to 3 inches and it had a sharper contour to improve the ballistic protection. The sides of the hull were modified to give protection equivalent to 2-1/2 inches of vertical armor. On the sponsons this was achieved by increasing the actual thickness to 1-3/4 inches and sloping the plates at 30 degrees from the vertical. This arrangement increased the upper hull width to 123 inches. The rear plate of the hull was vertical and increased in thickness to 2 inches.

At the time the design was submitted, a shortage was expected in foundry capacity for the production of large castings. To avoid this problem, the turret was designed as a welded assembly of rolled plates giving a sharp angular silhouette to the new tank. The armament was unchanged with the standard 75mm gun M3 being retained still using the M34 combination mount.

To improve the mobility with the increased weight of armor, a more powerful engine was required. Aberdeen proposed the use of the Wright G200 air-cooled radial which was expected to develop 640 net horsepower in this installation. The standard M4 transmission was still used, but the engine was fitted with a transfer case which lowered the propeller shaft increasing the clearance below the turret basket. With a ratio of 1:1.55, the transfer case increased the propeller shaft speed and lowered the input torque to the transmission permitting the use of the standard unit with the more powerful engine. A bulge in the rear deck was required to cover the large power plant.

The additional armor and heavier engine made changes necessary to keep the ground pressure within acceptable limits. Aberdeen's solution utilized a modified version of the suspension from the heavy tank M6. This system had horizontal volute springs in three bogies per track. Each bogie was fitted with two double wheels 18 inches in diameter except for the leading wheels on the front bogies and the trailing wheels on the aft bogies which were 22 inches in diameter. The heavy tank track was 25-3/4 inches wide using steel

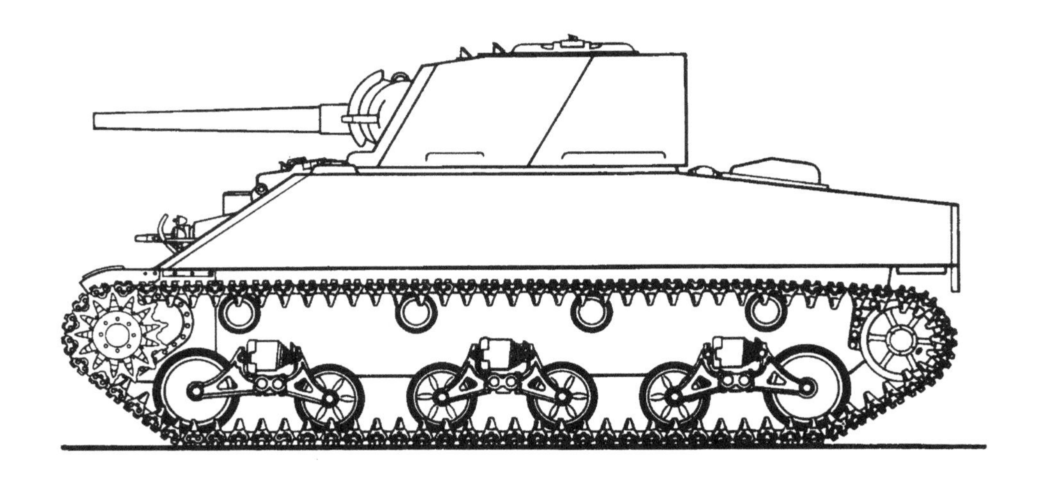

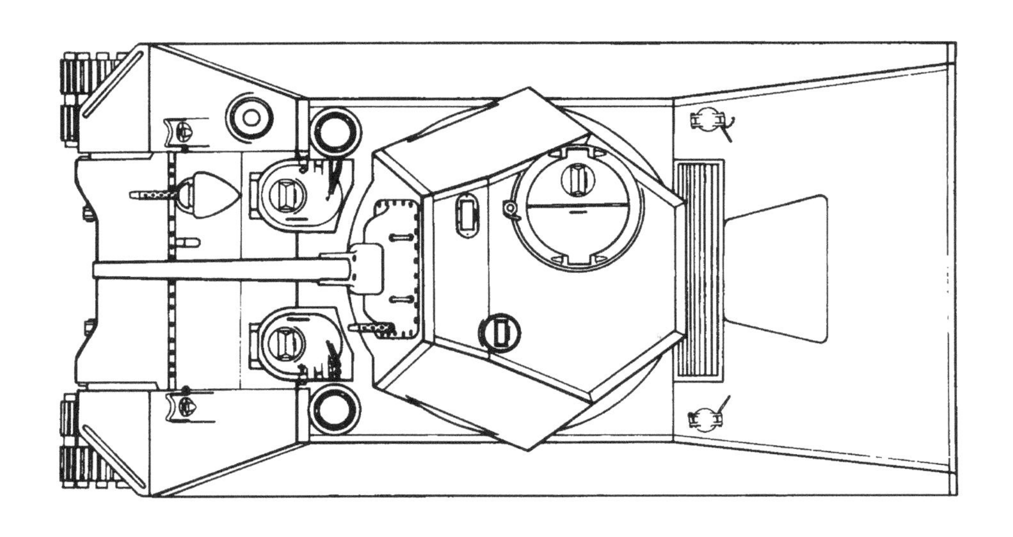

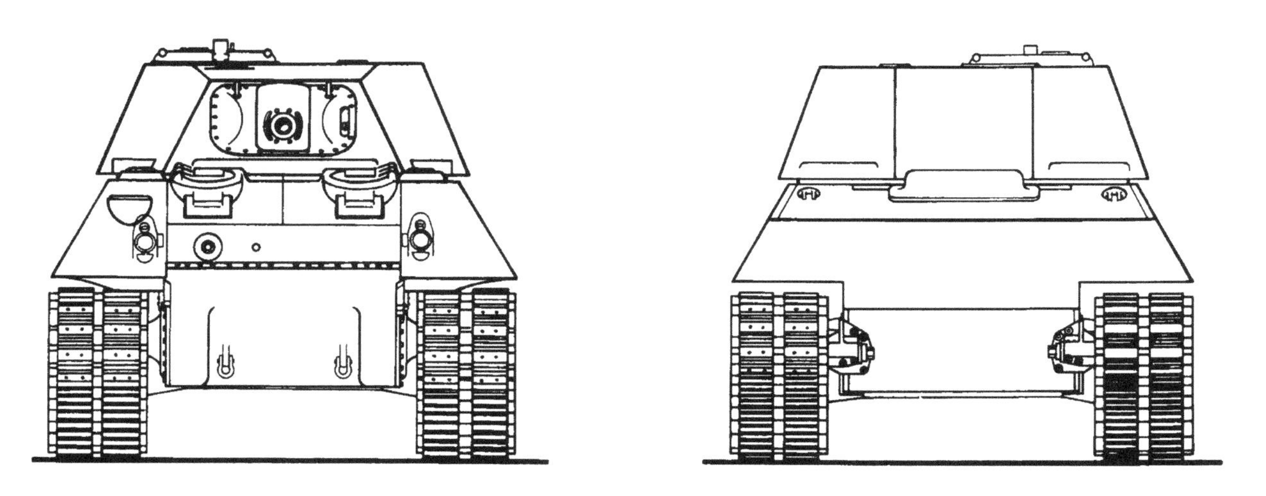

The proposal drawings for an improved Sherman submitted by Aberdeen Proving Ground.

Scale 1:48

Medium Tank M4, Improved

shoes with integral grousers and rubber bushings. Four track return rollers were equally spaced along the top at each side.

The Proving Ground estimated that the modified Sherman would have a combat weight of 83,600 pounds. This provided a horsepower to weight ratio of 15.3 hp/ton and an estimated maximum speed of 35 miles/hour. The wide tracks reduced the ground pressure to 10.0 psi despite the increased weight.

Although the modified tank was not placed in production, the proposal indicated areas where further development was required. Additional studies at Detroit Arsenal produced other modified versions of the Sherman. Drawings dated August 1942 show three types of main armament fitted in either a cast or welded turret. Interchangeable front plates permitted the installation of the 75mm gun, a 3 inch gun, or 105mm howitzer. The combination mounts for these weapons included a direct sight telescope and were similar to the M34A1 which later appeared in production for the 75mm gun.

The weight of the vehicles proposed at Detroit was held to approximately 30-1/2 tons, but protection was improved by better arrangement of the armor. The bulges over the drivers' positions were eliminated from the front plate giving a smooth unbroken slope. The side armor on the sponsons was angled at 30 degrees from the vertical increasing the hull width to 120 inches. Since the weight was not increased, the standard Sherman suspension and tracks were retained.

Three power plants were shown in the proposal drawings. These were the Continental R975 C1, the GM 6046 diesel, and the Ford GAZ. The latter two engines drove the tank through the normal synchromesh transmission, but the R975 was fitted with a transfer case and a torque converter.

Although the new designs included many desirable features, they also contained some serious defects. The increased main armament ammunition supply was still carried in the sponsons. Although convenient for the crew, battle experience was soon to prove that this location was highly vulnerable. The fuel tanks were also relocated from the engine compartment to the bottom of the hull below the turret basket. In this area, any kind of fuel fire certainly would have had disastrous results for the crew.

Even though the studies contained numerous defects, they indicated the intense effort expended to develop an improved fighting vehicle. Many features of these development projects were carried through to success despite the wartime pressures of time and often conflicting requirements. The late production Shermans which began to appear in early 1944 reflected the results of this work.

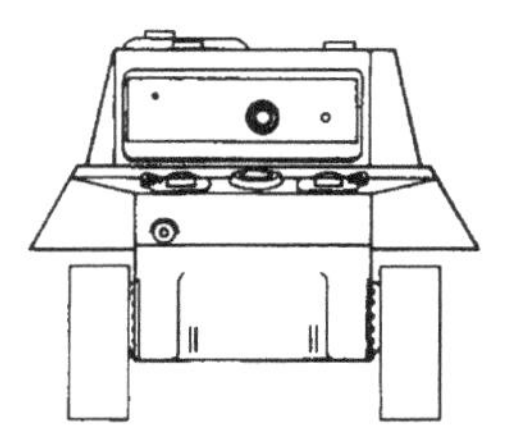

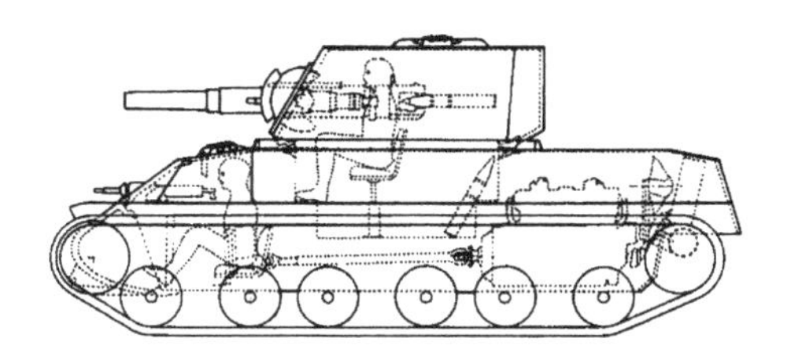

Scale 1:96

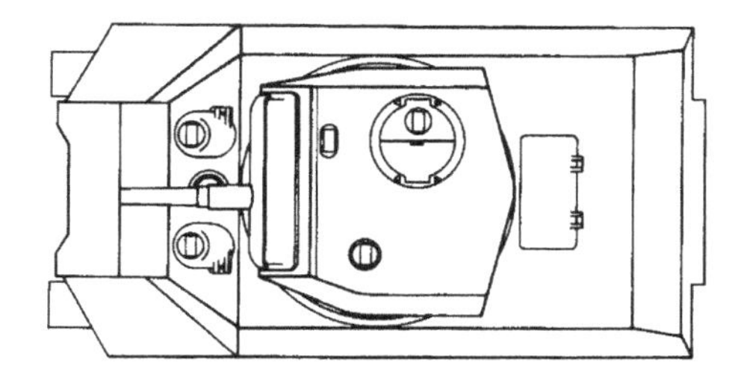

One of the Detroit Arsenal proposals for an improved Sherman. This version is armed with the 105mm howitzer in a welded turret and is powered by the Ford GAZ engine.

The original 76mm gun T1 with the full bore length of 57 calibers installed in the M4A1.

BETTER ARMAMENT AND PROTECTION

OCM Item 17202 of 11 September 1941 outlined the military characteristics of the M4 tank. It included the provision for interchangeable turret face plates which could be used to mount a variety of armament. The proposals for the improved Shermans showed the 105mm howitzer and the 3 inch gun as alternates to the 75mm gun M3. The 3 inch gun M7 had better armor piercing performance and was already standardized as the main armament of the heavy tank M6. However, it was considered too heavy for installation in the medium tank turret. A weapon was needed which would have the armor penetration of the 3 inch gun, but could replace the 75 in the standard M34 mount. To achieve this objective, a development program began for a new gun designated as the 76mm gun T1.

Although referred to as a 76mm gun, the experimental cannon actually had a 76.2mm or 3 inch bore. To shorten the development cycle, the projectiles for the standard 3 inch gun M7 were adopted for the new weapon. The powder charge in a smaller diameter cartridge case was adjusted to obtain the same 2600 ft/sec muzzle velocity as the 3 inch gun. The barrel was lighter in weight than the 3 inch tube and, as originally designed, had a bore length of 57 calibers. Fitted with the same breech ring assembly as the 75mm gun M3, the new weapon could be installed in the standard combination gun mount M34.

The long barrel of the original 76mm gun T1 is obvious in this view with the turret traversed to the left.

Two 76mm guns T1 were manufactured and shipped to Aberdeen Proving Ground for tests starting on 1 August 1942. One gun was fired on a fixed test mount and the other was installed in the turret of an M4A1 (registration number W-3060572). In the M34 tank mount the long barreled cannon was badly unbalanced. This was partially corrected by cutting 15 inches from the muzzle end of the tube and adding weight to the breech ring. After completion of the firing tests, Aberdeen concluded that the 76mm gun T1 was satisfactory for use in the M4 medium tank series with the modifications specified.

Additional photographs of the M4A1 with the original 76mm gun T1. Note that the weapon is fitted into the standard M34 mount.

The 76mm gun M1 at maximum elevation in the medium tank M4A1. Compare the length of the standardized weapon with the T1 on the previous page.

Based on the early test results, the Ordnance Committee on 17 August 1942 recommended that the M4 armed with the 76mm gun be classified as Substitute Standard. The T1 gun also was standardized as the 76mm gun M1 and this was added in parentheses to the tank's designation when it was armed with this weapon. For example, an M4A1 armed with a 76 became the medium tank M4A1 (76M1). At this time it was planned to modify production orders to provide for the manufacture of 1000 76mm gun tanks.

The testing program continued at Aberdeen with a production 76mm gun M1 now installed in medium tank M4A1, serial number 549. This tank, registration number W-3015305, carried the weapon in the newer combination gun mount M34A1 equipped with a direct sight telescope. Elevation for the 76 in this mount ranged from +25 to −12-1/2 degrees. A number of minor changes were also introduced. These included the use of a new turret front plate and spacer which moved the gun forward 2 inches. This provided more room behind the gun preventing interference between the recoil guard and the radio. The gun was balanced by adding weights to the recoil guard. This was necessary to permit proper operation of the gyrostabilizer. Stowage space was provided for 83 rounds of 76mm ammunition.

Like the earlier part of the program, these tests indicated that the 76 could be satisfactorily installed in the M4. They also showed that much greater accuracy was possible using the M51(T60) 3-power direct sight telescope over the earlier periscopic sight. However, the turret itself was badly out of balance when fitted with the long barreled cannon. On a 30 per cent slope, it was extremely difficult to traverse, although both the Westinghouse and Oilgear systems succeeded in doing so. An 800 pound counterweight at the rear of the turret was recommended as a cure for the unbalance and it was suggested that the weight be added as a stowage box. Once balanced, any of the standard drive mechanisms could easily traverse the turret.

The second 76mm gun T1 manufactured by Watervliet Arsenal after modification by removing 15 inches from the muzzle end. This is the version standardized as the 76mm gun M1.

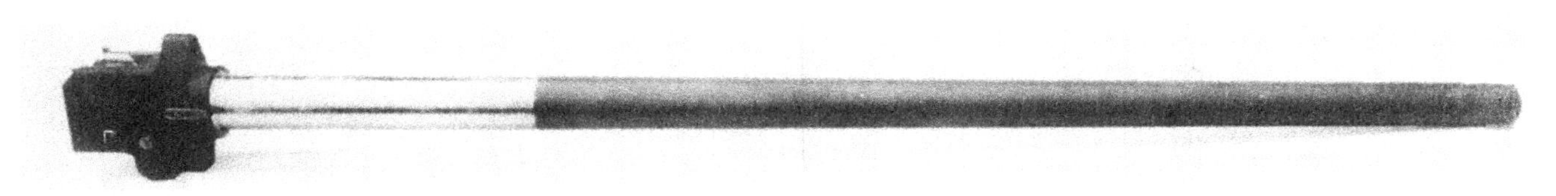

Medium tank M4A1, number 549 (above), showing the 76mm gun locked in the travel position on the rear deck.

The installation of the 76mm gun M1 in the combination gun mount M34A1 can be seen at the right. Note the weights welded into the recoil guard in an effort to balance the long cannon.

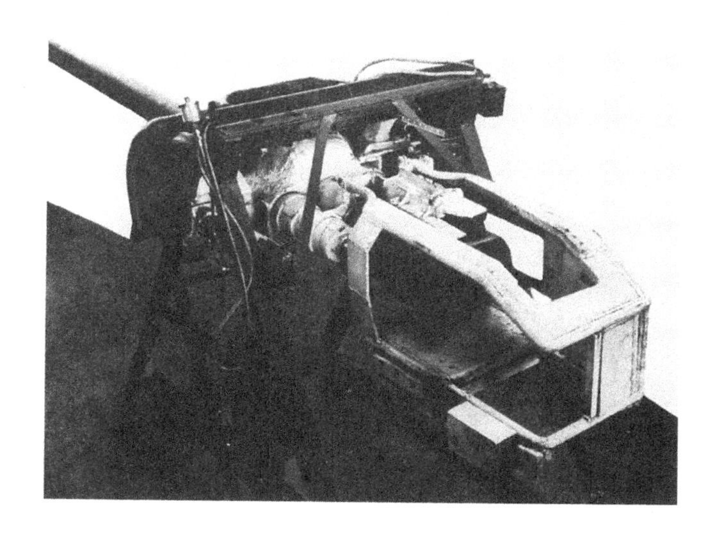

The medium tank M4A1(76M1) under test at Fort Knox during February 1943. Note the bustle extension added to balance the turret with the 76.

Twelve medium tanks M4A1(76M1) were produced at Pressed Steel Car Company for evaluation at Aberdeen, the Armored Force Board, and the Tank Destroyer Board. On 2 February 1943, one of these tanks, registration number W-3015954, arrived at Fort Knox followed later that month by number W-3016065. These tanks incorporated many of the modifications recommended by Aberdeen including the counterweight added as a turret bustle. Gun traveling locks had been installed both on the front plate and the rear deck allowing the weapon to be locked in either position. Service tests began immediately and continued on a 24 hour basis with the final report being submitted on 5 April 1943.

The Armored Force did not agree with the earlier test results. They concluded that the turret arrangement was unsatisfactory mainly because of inadequate space. They pointed out that the tank represented a "quick fix" design that was improvised from available components in order to achieve rapid production. This was, of course, true and it reflected the original intention to produce large numbers of 76mm gun tanks prior to 31 December 1942. After the rejection of the vehicle by the Armored Force, the Ordnance Committee revoked the Substitute Standard classification and cancelled the production of 17 additional tanks which had been authorized to equip a complete company. They also recommended that Aberdeen Proving Ground, the Armored Board, and the Tank Destroyer Board each retain one of the 12 tanks already manufactured. The remaining nine were to be rebuilt as standard 75mm gun vehicles.

Medium tank M4A1(76M1) during evaluation by the 7th Armored Division at the Desert Training Center in California. These photographs show the cannon locked in both the forward and rear positions. Note the special lock on the turret for the .30 caliber antiaircraft machine gun.

Medium tank M4E6 at Aberdeen Proving Ground in July 1943. A crude early model traveling lock is provided for the cannon.

The Ordnance Committee action on 3 May 1943 which ended the medium tank M4A1 (76M1) also recommended the manufacture of two pilots of an improved design mounting the 76mm gun. These vehicles, designated as the medium tank M4E6, were to be fitted with the turret and gun mount developed for the medium tank T20 series. For the first time, ammunition stowage below the sponson line was also recommended. This was a major step toward reducing the vulnerability of the Sherman to ammunition fires. The new welded hull with the cast front and larger drivers' hatches was incorporated in the design. Part of the turret basket was removed to allow access to the ammunition now stowed on the hull floor. The 76mm racks were also surrounded by water tanks to reduce the fire danger if the hull was penetrated. The additional space required by this "wet stowage" reduced the number of 76mm rounds to 71.

The new cast turret installed on the M4E6 was a preproduction version of the turret developed for the medium tank T23. The tank commander had the same rotating split circular hatch as on the 75mm gun Sherman and a double door rectangular hatch was provided in the turret roof for the loader. The 76mm gun M1A1 and a coaxial .30 caliber machine gun were carried in the combination gun mount T80. The recoil surface on the outside of the M1A1 gun was lengthened by 12 inches over that on the earlier M1. This allowed the trunnions to be moved forward improving the balance of the weapon. The T80 mount eliminated the rotor on the 75mm vehicles and covered the opening in the turret front with a gun shield 3-1/2 inches thick. The turret armor varied from 3 inches in front to 2-1/2 inches on the sides and rear. The gun mount in the M4E6 was stabilized in elevation using the Westinghouse gyrostabilizer.

A design also was proposed for a welded 76mm gun turret, but it was never used. Drawings dated 23 October 1942 show a turret assembled from rolled

The double door hatch for the loader in the M4E6 can be seen these two views. Note the similarity of the cast turret to the proposed welded design at the bottom right.

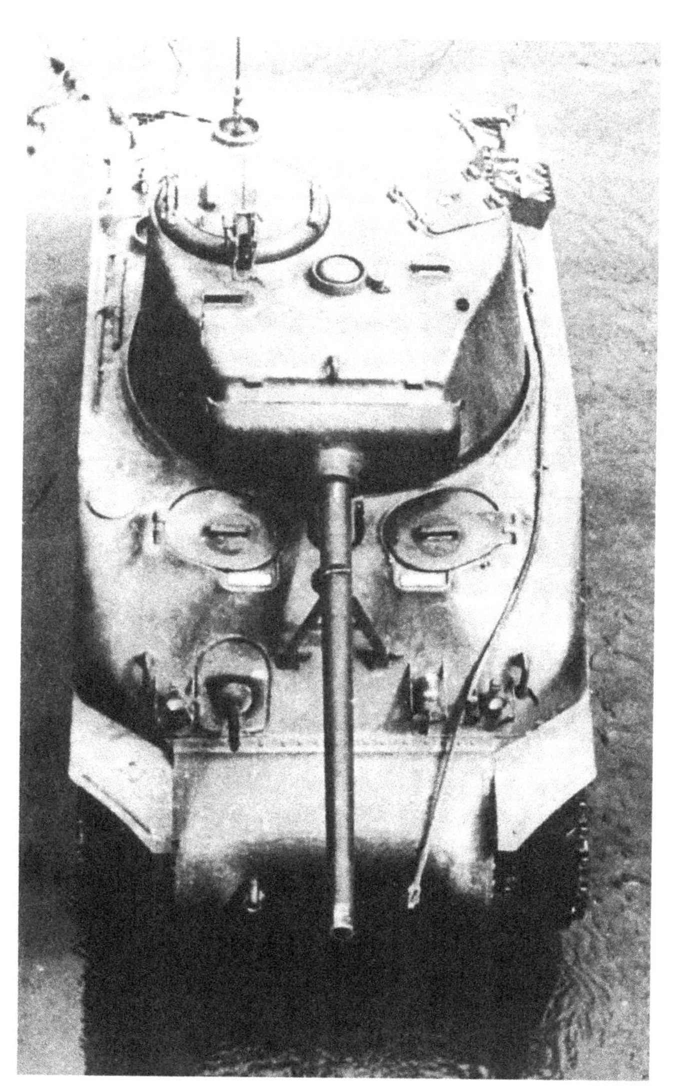

armor with the walls sloped at 30 degrees from the vertical except on the rear and right front. The vertical rear and the sloped side plates were 2 inches thick, but this was increased to 2-1/2 inches in the perpendicular area by the gunner's position. The armament was fitted in the same T80 combination mount used with the M4E6's cast turret. Like the latter, the welded design probably was intended originally for the medium tank T23.

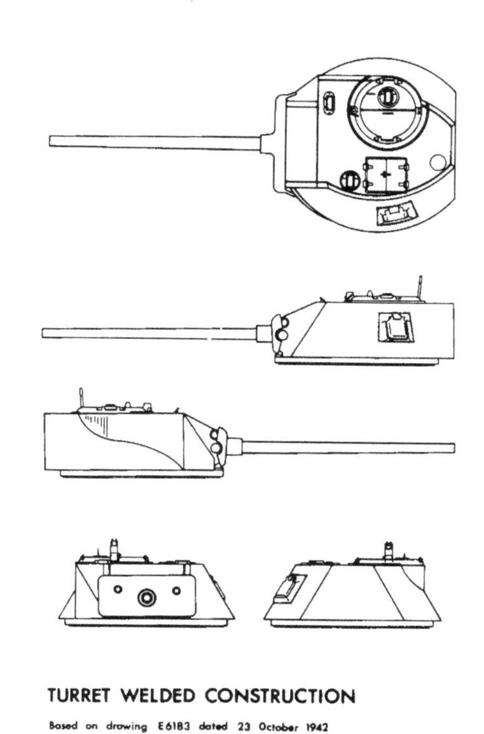

TURRET WELDED CONSTRUCTION

Based on drawing E6183 dated 23 October 1942

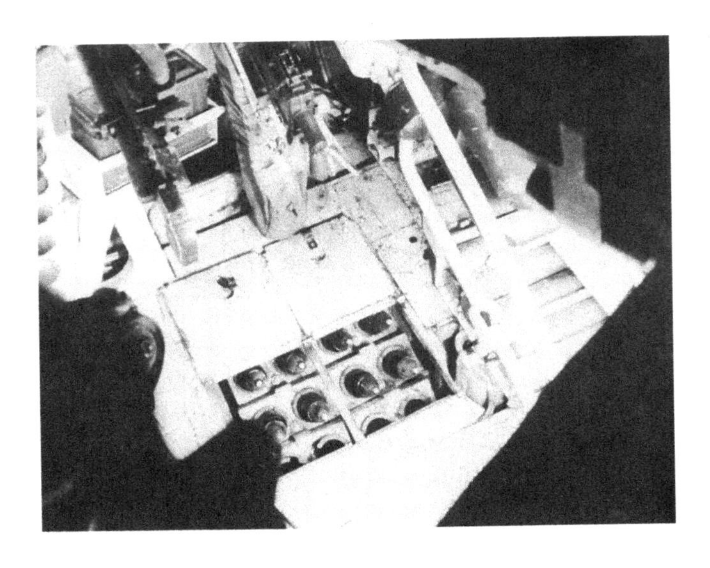

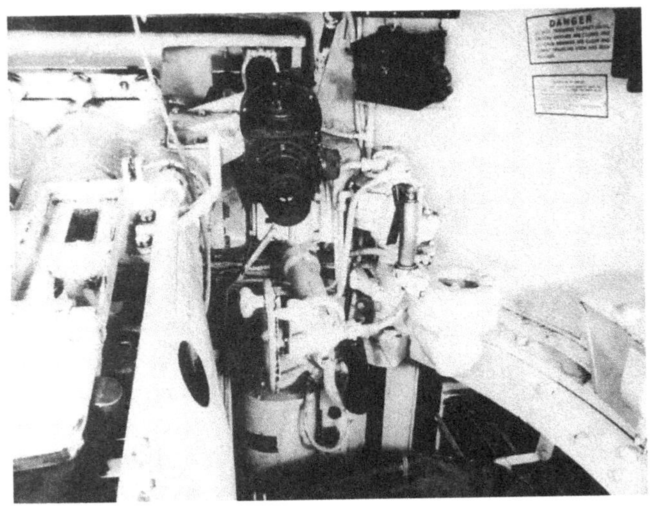

The turret interior on the M4E6 shows the loader's position (top left), the gunner's controls (top right), and the SCR 528 in the turret bustle (left below). The 76mm wet stowage ammunition racks can be seen beneath the loader's position.

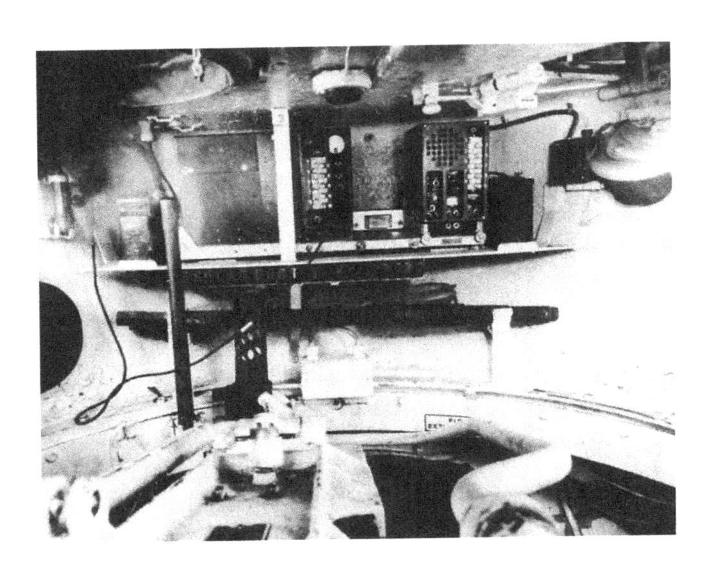

The two M4E6s were built by Chrysler at Detroit and one was retained at the Arsenal for test purposes. The other pilot, serial number 30263, was at Aberdeen Proving Ground in July 1943 and shortly thereafter was shipped to Fort Knox. Firing tests began at once and a letter report from the Armored Board dated 17 August 1943 recommended the acceptance and immediate production of tanks based on the M4E6. Numerous minor modifications were required, but none were of a serious nature. The T20 series of tanks, for which the turret was originally designed, were equipped with a hull mounted rotoclone blower. Since the Sherman did not have such a blower, additional ventilation was needed to remove the powder fumes from the turret. This and other modifications were applied to the production vehicles.

The Army Ground Forces requested 1000 M4E6s and the Chief of Ordnance was instructed to discontinue production of the 75mm gun tanks. However, the Armored Force indicated that it did not want to completely drop the 75mm gun. They pointed out that the high explosive projectile for the 75mm gun was superior to that for the 76. The M48 75mm shell weighed 14.7 pounds with an explosive charge of 1.47 pounds. This compared to only 12.9 pounds with .86 pounds of explosive for the 76. Objections were also raised to the muzzle blast of the 76 and the resulting target obscuration from smoke and dust. The larger rounds for the 76 were more difficult to handle in the turret and fewer could be carried. Against these objections, the only advantage of the 76 was its superior armor piercing performance. It would penetrate approximately 1 inch more armor than the 75mm gun M3 at the same range. In battle this would prove to be the all important factor, but that lesson had to wait until the Summer of 1944. After the Normandy fighting against the heavily armed and armored German tanks, even the 76 was considered inadequate and more powerful hole punchers were sought.

The M4E6 remained at Fort Knox and was used as a test vehicle to help solve some of the problems with the 76. Target obscuration was greatly reduced by the introduction of long primer ammunition and the installation of a muzzle brake. The long primer improved the burning of the powder, reducing the smoke and the muzzle brake deflected the gases to the side minimizing the dust kicked up by the blast. Based on the test program, it was recommended that all 76s be equipped with muzzle brakes. When the end of the barrel was threaded for a muzzle brake, the M1A1 was redesignated as the 76mm gun M1A1C. A later model, designated as the 76mm gun M1A2, differed in having

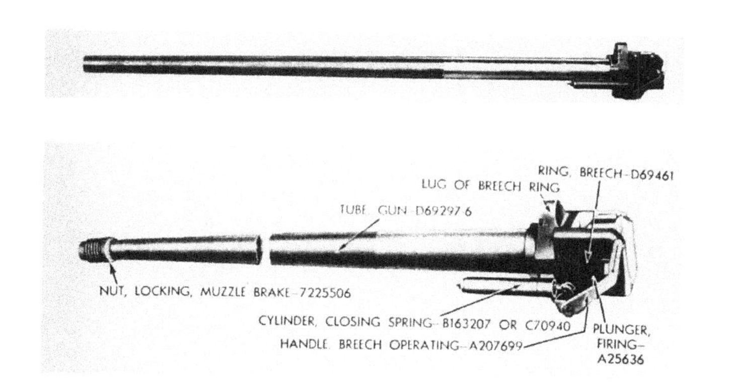

At the top left is the 76mm gun M1A1. Just below it is the 76mm gun M1A2 with the tube threaded for a muzzle brake. The M4E6 fitted with a muzzle brake by the Armored Board appears at the right above. Below are the various types of 76mm projectiles and complete rounds.

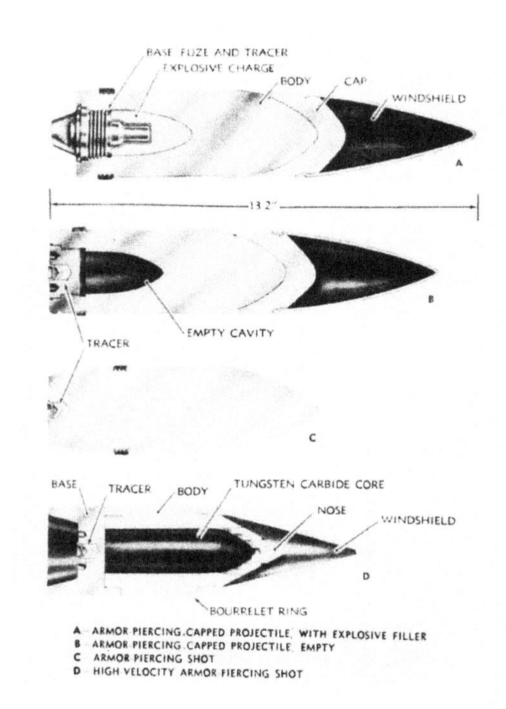

rifling with a tighter twist. Rifling in the M1A2 made one turn in 32 calibers while that in the M1A1 turned once in 40 calibers. The tighter twist improved projectile stability producing a slight increase in penetration performance at the longer ranges. All of the M1A2 guns were equipped with muzzle brakes.

The standard 76mm armor piercing round was the APC M62. This was a capped projectile fitted with a ballistic cap or windshield (APCBC) to reduce the drag and improve long range performance. Late production rounds were explosive loaded using a base detonating fuze. After the appearance of heavily armored German vehicles, a rush development program introduced the M93 hypervelocity armor piercing (HVAP) solid shot. This was a lightweight shot with an aluminum body and a tungsten carbide core. Frequently referred to as armor piercing composite rigid (APCR), the low weight resulted in a muzzle velocity of 3400 ft/sec compared to 2600 ft/sec for the APC M62. The high velocity combined with the high core density greatly increased the armor penetration. Although the velocity decreased more rapidly with the lightweight projectile, its armor piercing performance still exceeded that of the standard round at ranges greater than 2000 yards. Rushed into production for both the 76mm and 3 inch guns, the HVAP ammunition was used effectively during the final months of the war.

Medium tank M4A4E1, number 5868 (above), at Aberdeen in January 1943. Below is the breech mechanism of the 105mm howitzer M2A1. Note that it is difficult for the loader to operate from the left side.

The Sherman's original design concept included the 105mm howitzer as alternate armament and shortly after the start of production in early 1942, work began to develop a suitable mount. Two pilot mounts were completed in November and were designated as the combination mount T70. They carried the 105mm howitzer M2A1 with a coaxial .30 caliber machine gun to the left of the howitzer. Provision was made for a direct sight telescope at the right side in front of the gunner. The heavy cast shield had a maximum thickness of 3 inches. The mounts were installed in two medium tanks M4A4 at Detroit Arsenal and they were designated by Ordnance Committee action as the medium tank M4A4E1.

M4A4E1, serial number 5868, was shipped to Aberdeen Proving Ground where tests began on 7 December. The registration number of this tank was W-3057678. The other pilot, registration number W-3057717, was sent to the Armored Board at Fort Knox. Both tanks. were fitted with the Westinghouse power traverse and elevation gyrostabilizer. The range of elevation for the howitzer varied from +33 to -4 degrees. Stowage space was provided for 58 rounds of 105mm ammunition.

Tests at Aberdeen and Fort Knox showed that the 105mm howitzer M2A1 was extremely awkward to serve inside the tank turret. For example, after placing a round in the chamber, the loader had to reach across the top of the breech in order to close the breechblock. The continuous-pull type of firing mechanism proved unsatisfactory and the counterrecoil buffering was insufficient. The turret was also badly unbalanced so that the power traverse would not work properly if the tank was on a 30 per cent slope.

As a result of the test program, the howitzer was redesigned to include a constant diameter recoil slide surface on the outside of the barrel. A yoke also was added to the breech ring for the attachment of the recoil cylinders. The breechblock was shortened and its operating handle relocated for easy access by the loader. A trip-off firing mechanism replaced the continuous-pull type. These modifications were approved at a Fort Knox conference in February 1943. At the same time, it was decided to eliminate the gyrostabilizer and power traverse from the production vehicles and to use a partial turret basket with seats for the commander, gunner, and loader suspended from the turret ring. A better direct sight telescope and increased 105mm ammunition stowage were also specified.

The pilot M4A4E1 tested by the Armored Board at Fort Knox. The massive shield necessary to enclose the bulky experimental howitzer mount can be clearly seen.

Medium tank M4E5 (above and below) during tests by the Armored Board.

Two pilot tanks incorporating the required modifications were manufactured and shipped in August 1943 to Aberdeen Proving Ground for proof firing and then to Fort Knox for tests by the Armored Board. These tanks, designated as the medium tank M4E5, were powered by the Continental R975 C1 engine and used the all welded hull with the early type small drivers' hatches. The redesigned cannon, designated the 105mm howitzer T8, was lighter in weight and much easier to serve inside the tank turret. It was later standardized as the 105mm howitzer M4. The mount was redesigned to handle the new weapon with the shield modified to improve the location of the direct sight telescope. Changes to permit greater depression extended the elevation range from +35 to –10 degrees. This mount was eventually standardized as the combination mount M52 and its lighter weight did much to correct the turret unbalance of the earlier M4A4E1. The turret body casting was still the same as on the standard 75mm gun tank with the split circular hatch and rotating antiaircraft machine gun mount over the tank commander's position. A pistol port was located on the left side, but there was no roof hatch for the loader. However, one was specified for the production vehicles. The 105mm ammunition stowage was increased to 68 rounds with 45 of these located in the floor racks. Twentyone rounds were stowed in two racks in the right sponson and the remaining two rounds were in the turret ready rack.

The Armored Board concluded that the M4E5 was acceptable for issue to the troops provided a ventilating fan was installed in the turret and that the tank was equipped with the improved T93 direct sight telescope. Other modifications were considered desirable, but they would have to be added later in production since the tank was required on the battlefield at the earliest possible date.

Ammunition available for the 105mm howitzer included the 42 pound high explosive shell M1 and all other standard 105mm howitzer rounds. The hollow charge, high explosive antitank (HEAT) projectile M67 was provided for use against armored targets. It would penetrate about 4 inches of armor plate at normal impact provided a hit could be obtained. Unfortunately, with the highly curved trajectory of the low velocity howitzer, it was difficult to hit a point target except at very close range. However, the high

The M4E5 above shows the full external stowage specified by the Armored Board. Note the .50 caliber machine gun disassembled and stowed on the turret bustle.

explosive shell was extremely effective against unarmored targets and it had excellent fragmentation. With the exception of the HEAT round, all 105mm ammunition was semifixed with a variable propellant charge. Depending on the range and trajectory desired, this charge could be varied from 1 to 7 with the latter being the most powerful. The HEAT M67 was a fixed round with a propellant charge giving a muzzle velocity of 1250 ft/sec.

The photographs at the left below show the 105mm howitzer M4 with its high explosive and hollow charge ammunition. The M4E5 tested at Aberdeen during August 1943 appears below at the right. Note that the pistol port has been welded up on this tank.

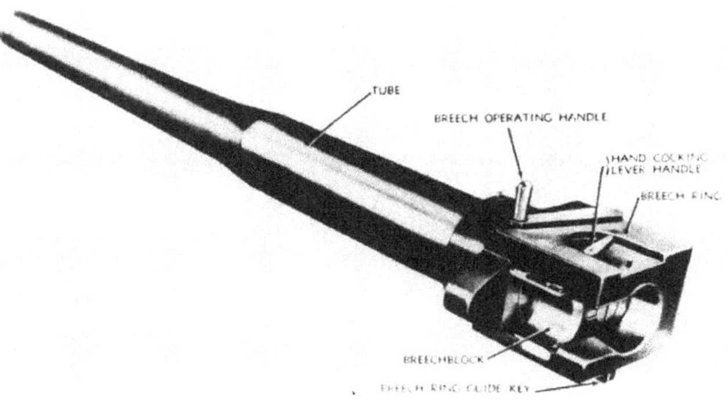

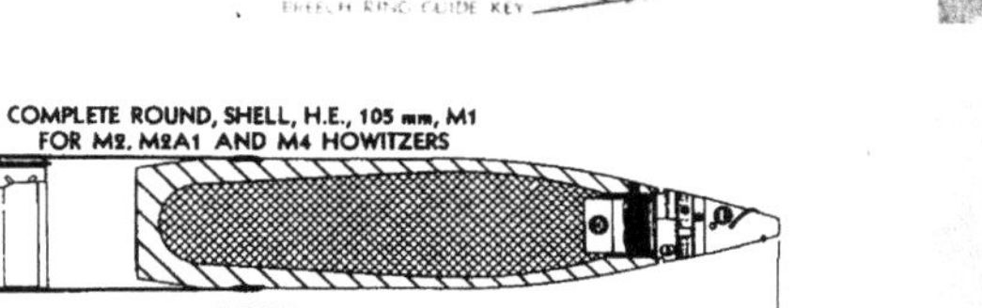

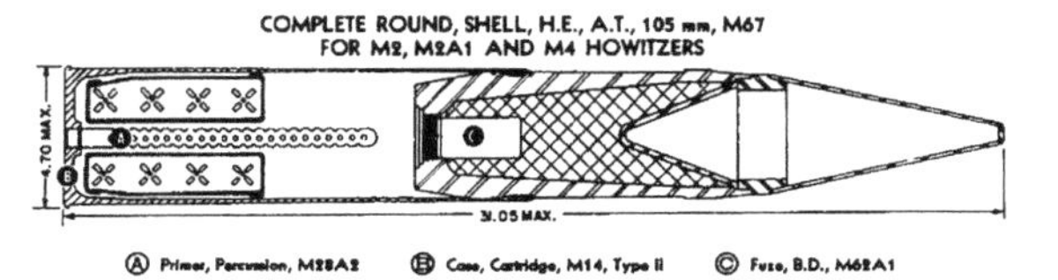

A proposal drawing for a 90mm gun Sherman. The silhouette of the tank has been lowered by reducing the height of the hull.

Long before the Normandy battles raised the cry for better armor piercing performance, Ordnance had been considering the possible use of the 90mm gun as a tank weapon. A study by the Ballistics Research Laboratory (BRL) at Aberdeen, dated 31 October 1942, reported on the feasibility of installing a 90mm gun in the Sherman turret. The report concluded that such an installation was possible, but the antiaircraft gun would have to be modified to provide a recoil slide surface on the outside of the tube. It also noted that the standard round for the 90mm gun M1 was too long for easy handling in the cramped spaced available in the 75mm gun turret. A suggested alternative was the development of a 90mm weapon with a shorter cartridge case and less chamber capacity. Such a design would, of course, reduce the attainable muzzle velocity and hence the armor penetration compared to the standard 90.

Another proposal in the same BRL study was the development of a 3 inch gun for tank use which would have a higher chamber capacity than the standard 3 inch weapon. This would raise the muzzle velocity to over 3000 ft/sec with a 15 pound projectile resulting in armor penetration comparable to the standard 90. The new gun would be designed for tank use with a light outer barrel and a heavy chamber section and breech inside the turret. Thus, when the trunnions were placed at the center of gravity, the breech would not extend very far into the turret increasing the space available. It is interesting to note that such a design closely paralleled that of the highly successful British 17 pounder just coming into service at that time as an antitank gun. Installed by the British in the modified 75mm turret, it later proved to be the most potent weapon carried by the Sherman during World War II.

By the Fall of 1943, the Armored Board had concluded that only the Sherman could be available in sufficient quantity in time for the Normandy invasion. They then requested that 90mm guns be installed in 1000 M4A3s. Ordnance did not concur, contending that the heavier weapon badly overloaded the Sherman and that the proper solution was the early production of the new T20 series with the 90mm gun. The Armored Board request was rejected by the Army Ground Forces on the grounds that the destruction of enemy tanks was a job for the artillery and the tank destroyers. It was felt that the provision of such a powerful gun would encourage tank versus tank battles thus diverting the tanks from their role as a maneuvering element and weapon of exploitation.

As a result of the crisis in Normandy, Brigadier General Joseph A. Holly returned to the United States in July 1944. As Chief of the Armor Section for the European Theater of Operations, he was directed by General Eisenhower to expedite the production and shipment of more powerfully armed tanks and tank destroyers, particularly those with 90mm guns. During his visit to Detroit Arsenal, General Holly viewed a Sherman armed with the 90mm gun M3. This was an M4 fitted with a Pershing type 90mm gun turret. Since both tanks had 69 inch turret rings, such an installation required only stowage changes and modifications to obtain adequate clearance between the turret assembly and some components on the tank hull. The experimental vehicle was fitted with the early vertical volute spring suspension and the 16-9/16 inch wide track. No doubt any production of this tank would have used the new horizontal volute spring suspension with the 23 inch tracks to reduce the ground pressure. A traveling gun lock for the 90mm gun was mounted on the front armor plate.

Although the upgunned Sherman appeared to be a good solution to the problem of increased firepower, General Holly was informed that it would be about six months before production quantities could be available. By that time the new Pershings would be coming off the assembly lines so the decision was taken to drop the 90mm gun Sherman and to concentrate all efforts to speed up the Pershing production. In retrospect, it appears that a wise course would have been to procure some of the 90mm gun Shermans as a hedge against further delays in the arrival of the Pershing. However, the real problem was the late hour when the decision was made in favor of a high powered tank gun. Production could not be turned off and on like a water faucet despite the seemingly miraculous performance that was frequently achieved. If the need for a powerful tank gun had been specified a year earlier, they certainly could have been available in time for the Normandy invasion. However, the argument over the role of the tank still raged until events on the battlefield proved conclusively that tanks had to be able to fight tanks and that the best tank destroyer was a better tank.

As late as June 1944, it was considered that the 76mm gun tank would make up only one third of the armored strength with the balance retaining the 75. Within a month, the hedgerow fighting had shown the 75 to be completely ineffective against the front armor of the German Panthers and Tigers. The combat units now wanted every 76mm gun tank available. Earlier objections to excessive muzzle blast and the long awkward rounds of ammunition were forgotten overnight, only hole punching ability was important. Even the 76 proved inadequate in this regard and the rush was on to obtain a weapon which could penetrate the front armor of the tough skinned enemy tanks.

In August a few rounds of the new 76mm HVAP (APCR) ammunition were rushed to France and tests were conducted near Isigny against six captured Panthers. The tests showed that the new ammunition was extremely accurate and a great improvement over the old APC M62, but it could not penetrate the Panther's front plate at ranges over 300 yards. Production of the new ammunition was also limited to only 10,000 rounds per month which meant that it could only be used on an emergency basis.

On 9 August, General Omar Bradley directed his Twelfth Army Group, Armor Section to request an allotment of tanks armed with the British 17 pounder. The attempt proved fruitless since the limited tank reserves were insufficient to permit the release of vehicles for the installation of the British gun. The effort to obtain 17 pounder tanks was revived later in the middle of February 1945 when the reserve tank situation had improved. At that time, the Twelfth Army Group requested an initial conversion of 160 Shermans with further conversions dependent on battle experience. Later, this was cut to 80 because of limitations in the British ammunition supply. Unfortunately, the crowded condition of the shops delayed delivery and only the first few began to arrive in mid March. These were allocated to the Ninth Army, but there is no record of their use prior to the end of the war. In fact, the Ninth Army After Action Report indicates that the delivery of 40 17 pounder tanks was expected, but it does not record their arrival.

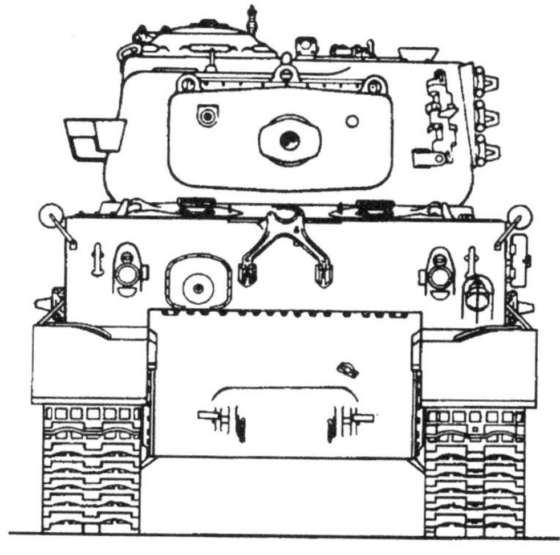

This drawing shows the Pershing's 90mm gun turret installed on a late production M4 with the horizontal volute spring suspension. Compare this vehicle with some of the postwar Israeli modifications described in Part V.

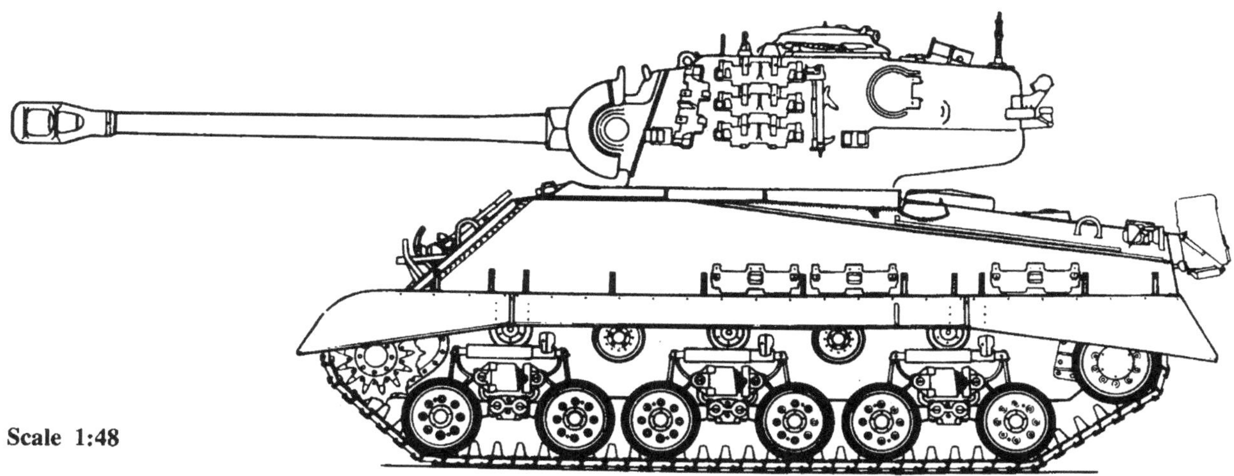

Scale 1:48

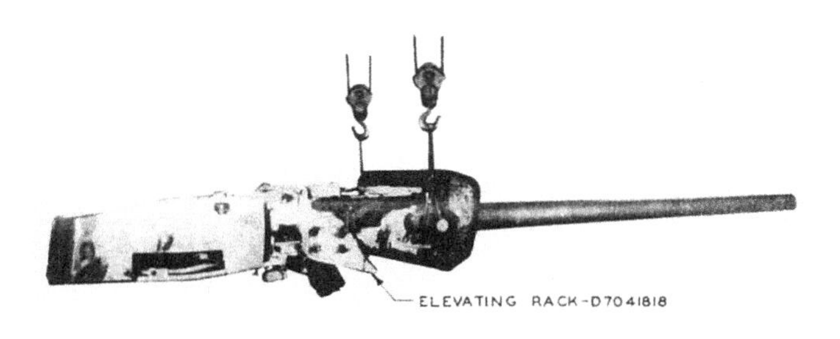

The combination gun mount T103 with the concentric recoil mechanism T42.

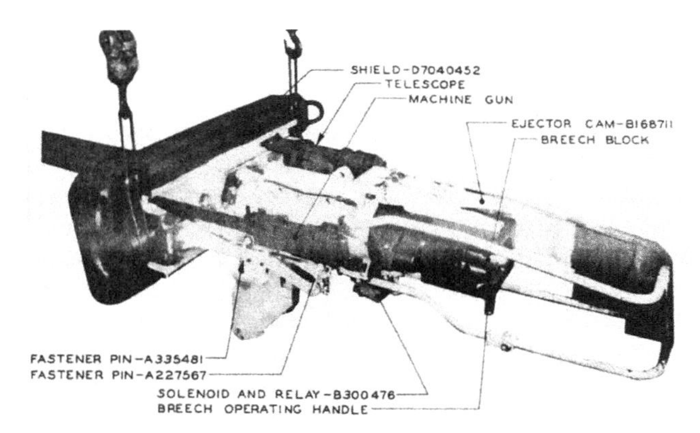

The successful introduction of the concentric recoil system for the 75mm gun M6 in the light tank M24 aroused interest in the development of similar systems for other weapons. With the concentric design, the separate recoil cylinders were replaced by a single hollow cylinder surrounding the gun barrel. Such an arrangement was lighter in weight and extremely compact permitting construction of a gun mount occupying much less space in the turret. Rock Island Arsenal designed the concentric recoil mechanism T42 for the 76mm gun and, in the Spring of 1945, it was incorporated in the combination gun mount T103. This mount carried the 76mm gun M1A2 with a coaxial .30 caliber machine gun. Except for the concentric recoil mechanism, it was similar to the standard combination gun mount M62. Installed in a Sherman turret, the new mount was tested at Aberdeen during the Summer of 1945. The tests were generally satisfactory, although some leakage problems were encountered as well as other teething problems associated with experimental equipment. With the additional space available in the turret, it would have been possible to install more powerful secondary armament or to increase the ammunition stowage for the existing weapons.

In December 1943, a study was authorized to develop a non-recoil mount for a tank gun. Such a mount would eliminate the recoil mechanism and attach the gun directly to the tank turret. The mass of the complete vehicle would then absorb the recoil energy. This arrangement would result in a roomier turret since no space would be required for gun recoil. Design work began in January 1944 on an experimental mount for installation in an armored vehicle. The 76mm gun motor carriage T72 was available at this time and it was used as the test vehicle. The mount was designed to carry either the 75 or the 76, but the major work was concentrated on the latter, although the 75 was used for the early firing tests.

Rolling contact bearings were required in the gun mount trunnions to permit the installation of an elevation stabilizer. These bearings would have been damaged if subjected to the full shock load when the gun was fired. To avoid this, the trunnions were designed to deflect elastically under the firing load until a set of false trunnions made metal to metal contact with the turret body. These false trunnions then transmitted the remainder of the load directly to the turret preventing damage to the bearings.

The installation in the T72 turret was completed on 1 July 1944 and it was test fired at Aberdeen one week later. No damage was noted on the gyrostabilizer or the turret race bearings after the firing tests. However, the turret hold down bolts were elongated and some threads were stripped. Larger bolts were expected to cure this problem. It was also noted that

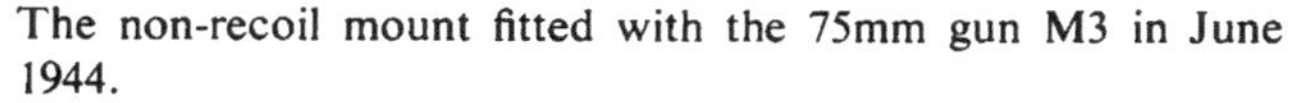

The non-recoil mount fitted with the 75mm gun M3 in June 1944.

The 75mm gun M3 in the non-recoil mount installed in the T72 motor carriage for firing tests.

the light T72 turret weighed only about 7000 pounds. With the greater inertia of the heavier tank turret, the effect of the firing shock would be less severe.

After the successful firing test of the experimental mount, OCM 25393, dated 12 August 1944, authorized the development of a complete fighting compartment using the non-recoil gun mount. Designated as the combination gun mount T116, the design was still in progress at the end of the war. On 20 August 1945, Ordnance Committee action terminated the project and the drawings were filed for future reference.

Efforts to improve the efficiency of the Sherman's main armament also involved the stabilizer system. The design of the late production stabilizer was simplified, reducing maintenance problems and improving its reliability. Battle experience showed that the stabilizer provided a definite advantage when the troops were properly trained in its use. Unfortunately, many units were not fully familiar with these advantages and disconnected their stabilizers. They did not attempt to fire on the move, preferring to stop before using the main weapon.

Experiments at Fort Knox showed that improved accuracy could be obtained with the 75 and 76mm guns by eliminating backlash from the mount. This was first achieved by adding weights to unbalance the gun and keep the breech heavy. Later, the stabilizer was modified to apply a force in the same direction with similar results.

The effectiveness of the elevation gyrostabilizer led to the consideration of an azimuth stabilization system. Experiments were conducted at both Aberdeen and Fort Knox. An elevation and azimuth stabilizer developed by the International Business Machines Corporation (IBM) was first tested at Aberdeen in December 1943. The results were unsatisfactory and

A late model 75mm gun medium tank M4A3 instrumented to measure azimuth and elevation stabilizer control at Aberdeen in March 1945.

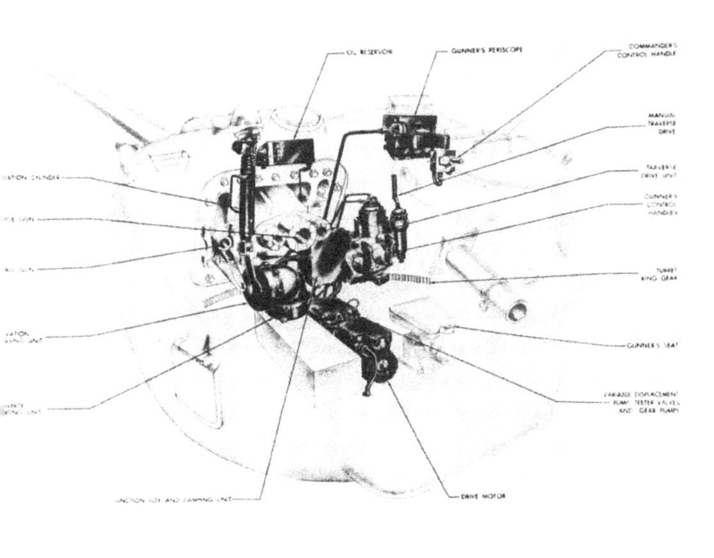

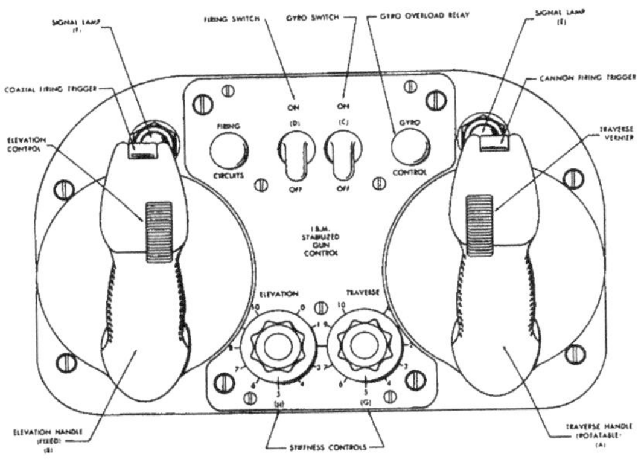

The IBM stabilizer system is shown in the phantom view at the top left. The control panel for this unit is at the left. Above is the traverse control unit which includes the gyro for azimuth stabilization on the Ordnance stabilizer.

after the equipment was modified, testing resumed in March 1944. Additional changes proved necessary and a new series of tests began in October with the equipment installed in an M4A3 armed with the 75mm gun. The IBM system was compared with an Ordnance design using standard Westinghouse components. Also installed in a 75mm gun M4A3, this azimuth stabilizer used the standard elevation gyroscopic unit with a separate auxiliary pump and motor connected to the gunner's traverse control. The unit thus gave rotation control with azimuth stabilization to the power traverse.

Both experimental systems were compared with a standard M4A3 equipped with only the elevation stabilizer. To eliminate any differences in skill, the gunners were rotated between all three vehicles. The test results indicated a definite advantage for the tanks fitted with the azimuth stabilization. The IBM equipment proved superior to the Ordnance design, but the latter was more easily adapted to tanks already in the field.

The Ordnance azimuth stabilizer was fitted to an M4A3 armed with the 76mm gun and tested at Fort Knox during June and July 1945. The test results confirmed the earlier findings, but indicated a need to make the equipment more reliable and resistant to vibration. Further experiments with azimuth stabilizers continued into the postwar period with comparative tests against the British Vickers equipment.

Battle reports indicated the need for better secondary armament. The .30 caliber machine guns in the bow and coaxial mounts were excellent against personnel, but limited in effectiveness against heavy structures or lightly armored vehicles. The only method of aiming the bow gun was by the use of tracer ammunition, hence it was relatively inaccurate particularly at the longer ranges. The .50 caliber machine gun on top of the turret was a much more powerful weapon, but its use required the exposure of a crew member in the open hatch.

To improve the sighting of the bow machine gun, linkage was attached between the weapon and the bow gunner's periscope which was now fitted with a telescopic sight. The original medium tank T6 had such a connection between the bow gun and a sight rotor in the upper front hull. Since the hull mounted auxiliary periscope did not allow rotation, it was necessary to connect the linkage to the periscope in the bow gunner's hatch. Needless to say, the linkage could be quickly disconnected to permit emergency use of the hatch. This arrangement was tested at Fort Knox on M4, registration number W-3038783. The tests showed an error of about 40 mils between the gun and sight at maximum traverse and elevation. However, all of the gunners agreed that targets could be engaged much more rapidly and accurately using the sight linkage than without it. On 19 March 1945, the Armored Board recommended that the linkage be adopted as

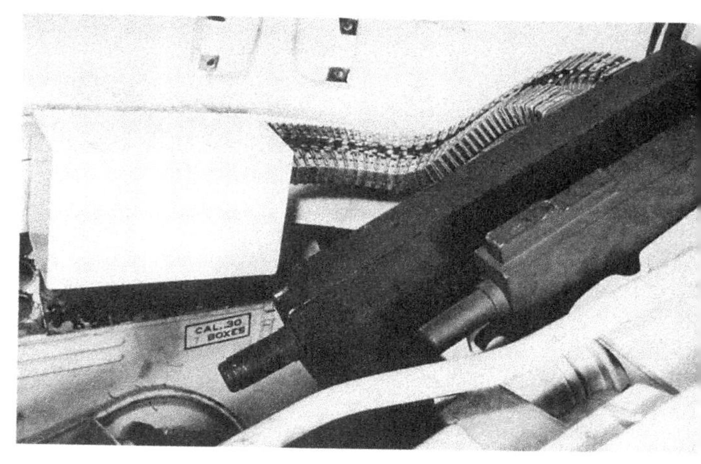

The parallelogram linkage connecting the bow machine gun and the hatch cover periscope appears at the left above. Note the telescope eyepiece in the periscope window. At the right above is the Chrysler mock-up of one .30 caliber and one .50 caliber machine gun installed coaxially with the 76mm gun.

standard for all tanks and that it be applied in production and as a field modification. However, the end of the war and the cessation of production occurred before this and many other modifications could be applied.

The need for more powerful secondary armament led to experiments at both Detroit and Aberdeen Proving Ground. In March 1945, Chrysler considered the installation of two coaxial machine guns with the 76 in the M4A3. A mock-up at the Arsenal had one .30 and one .50 caliber weapon, both located to the left of the 76mm gun. With the two machine guns plus their ammunition, the left side of the turret was extremely crowded. However, the installation would probably have been satisfactory if the more compact concentric recoil system had been used for the 76mm gun.

Other experiments continued into the postwar period with the replacement of the commander's vision cupola by the twin machine gun mount T121. This mount was fitted with either two .30 caliber, or two .50 caliber machine guns, or one of each. It was aimed and fired from inside the turret without exposing the gunner. Installed on the howitzer version of the M4A3 as well as an M26 Pershing, tests continued from April 1946 to May 1947. Aberdeen concluded that the T121 was unsatisfactory, but recommended that an improved auxiliary machine gun mount be developed for future tanks. Thus the search for effective secondary armament had followed a full circle. The removal of the M3's relatively ineffective machine gun cupola and the fixed hull machine guns on the early Shermans, did not eliminate the requirement they were intended to meet. Battle experience confirmed the need for additional automatic firepower and by the end of the war, numerous experiments were in progress with remote control guns and cupolas such as the T121.

The commander's cupola on the M4A3 below has been replaced by the twin machine gun mount T121. At the left, the mount is armed with two .30 caliber machine guns. At the right, they have been replaced by two .50 caliber weapons.

These four photographs show M4A1 "3rd Blitz" during tests by the Armored Board at Fort Knox. Note the similarity of the turret to that on the M4E6 with the rectangular double door hatch for the loader. Like the M4E6, this turret was produced during the period when pistol ports were out of favor.

After the installation of the 76 in the T20 series turret on the M4E6, consideration was given to the use of the same turret for the 75mm gun tanks. A combination mount similar to the T80 was designed for the 75mm gun. The trunnions were shifted to compensate for the lighter weight of the 75 and it was designated as the combination gun mount T94 on 21 September 1943. Two pilot mounts were constructed with one being used for firing and ballistic tests. Pressed Steel Car Company installed the other T94 mount in M4A1, registration number W-3037734. This tank, named "3rd Blitz", was shipped to the Armored Board in late 1943. The name resulted from a large number of modifications referred to as the "Blitz list" which were being evaluated on three test tanks during this period. The "1st Blitz" and "2nd Blitz" were also M4A1s with registration numbers W-3036871 and W-3036973 respectively.

The Armored Board concluded that the T20 series turret was not desirable for use with the 75mm gun. They considered the larger turret unnecessary and preferred to have the extra weight used as increased armor protection in a smaller turret designed for the 75.

The assault tank T14 after completion at the American Locomotive Works. Note the wide tracks from the heavy tank M6.

The need for more armor in assault operations had been reflected in the Aberdeen proposal for a modified Sherman. The requirement for a special assault tank was established at a conference on 30 March 1942 between representatives of the Chief of Ordnance, Aberdeen Proving Ground, and the British Tank Mission. The latter indicated an urgent requirement for such a tank, but the U.S. Armored Force had no interest at that time. It was agreed that each country would develop and manufacture two pilot assault tanks with the British vehicle based on the Mark VIII Cruiser and the U.S. tank based on the M4. After completion, one each of the pilots would be interchanged and tested simultaneously in both countries. The Ordnance Committee issued detailed military characteristics for the U.S. vehicle in May 1942, designating it the assault tank T14. Aberdeen Proving Ground was instructed to prepare preliminary layout drawings and to construct a wooden mock-up. At that time, a British requirement was established for 8500 assault tanks.

The assault tank T14 during tests at Aberdeen in August 1943. The photograph at the right shows the engine compartment door opened to expose the power plant. This view was taken from the turret looking toward the rear of the tank. In the left photograph, the 2 inch smoke mortar can be seen in the turret roof alongside the loader's periscope.

In June, Aberdeen finished the preliminary drawings and the American Locomotive Company was assigned the task of completing the design and building the two pilot tanks. Both pilots used welded armor, but a design was also prepared for a cast hull. The original concept specified the Ford GAZ V-8 engine, but provided for its future replacement by the Ford V-12 engine when it became available. The standard M4 power train was used except for changes in the final drive gear ratio. The latter was increased from 2.84:1 to 3.57:1. A leaf spring suspension design was considered, but the availability of production facilities resulted in the adoption of the horizontal volute springs and 25-3/4 inch tracks from the heavy tank M6. Three bogies were used, but unlike Aberdeen's earlier proposal, all of the wheels were 18 inches in diameter. The suspension was protected by a 1/2 inch armor skirt which combined with the 2-1/2 inch lower side armor to give protection equivalent to 3 inch plate in this area. The upper sides of the hull were 2 inches thick, but the plates were sloped 30 degrees from the vertical. The hull front ranged from 4 inches on the differential and final drive housing to 2 inches at 60 degrees in front of the drivers. The rear of the hull was 2 inches thick. The cast turret had 3 inches of armor at 30 degrees in front with 4 inch thick vertical side and rear walls.

The T14 was armed with the same 75mm gun M3 in the M34A1 mount as carried on the M4. However, Aberdeen was instructed in July to prepare layout drawings for the installation of the 105mm howitzer. Future use of the 76 or even the 90mm gun was also proposed. The inside diameter of the turret ring was 69 inches, identical to the Sherman. In addition to the gunner's coaxial .30, another machine gun was fitted on the commander's turret hatch ring for antiaircraft protection. This was originally a .50 caliber weapon, but was changed to a .30 and than back to a .50 in line with the policy changes of the time. The bow gun mount was designed to carry a .50 caliber machine gun, but an adapter was fitted to permit the later substitution of a .30 caliber weapon. Unlike the Sherman, the bow gun was equipped with a coaxial direct sight telescope. Stowage was complete on the wooden mock-up in November 1942 and the design work ended in April 1943.

Pilot number 1 was delivered to Aberdeen in July followed a month later by number 2. The tanks weighed approximately 47 tons and achieved a maximum speed of about 24 miles/hour. The tests at Aberdeen revealed the need for numerous modifications. Maintenance was difficult because of the inaccessibility of various components. The tracks were easily thrown and difficult to adjust, particularly with the armor skirts. The mobility was considered unsatisfactory and Aberdeen recommmended that no further consideration be given to the T14. The first pilot was shipped to Fort Knox in November 1943 and the second tank went to Britain where it is on display today in the Royal Armoured Corps Tank Museum at Bovington Camp in Dorset.

The Armored Force had never wanted the T14 and the Army Supply Program of 1 September 1942 made no provision for its production. The Chief of Ordnance was directed to cancel arrangements with the General American Transportation Company to build T14s at a rate of 250 per month. At the time, it was decided to continue the experimental work on the pilot tanks, but OCM 26038 of 14 December 1944 recommended complete cancellation of the T14 project.

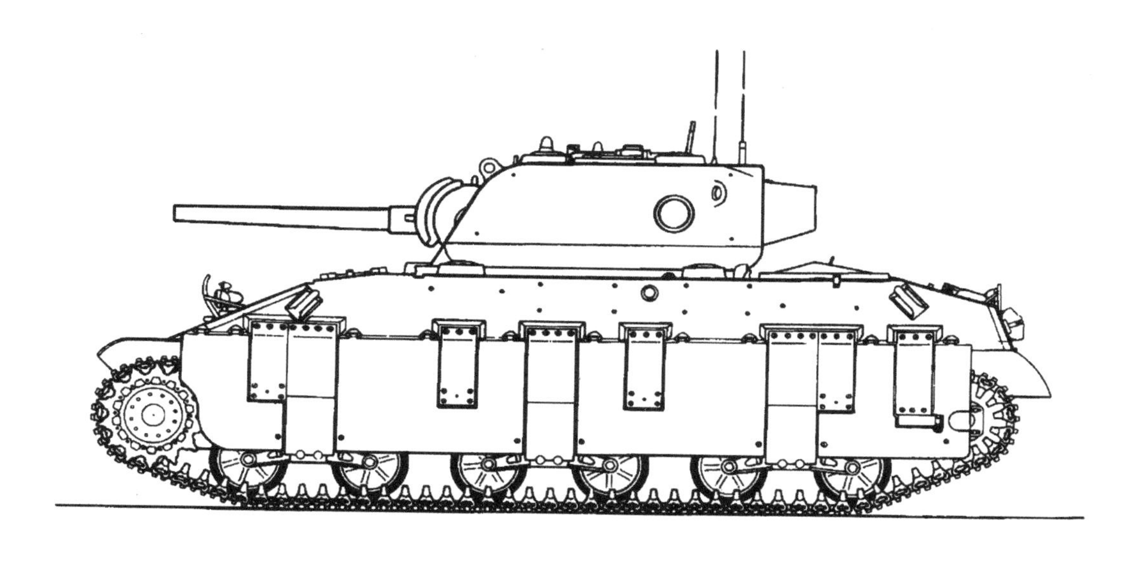

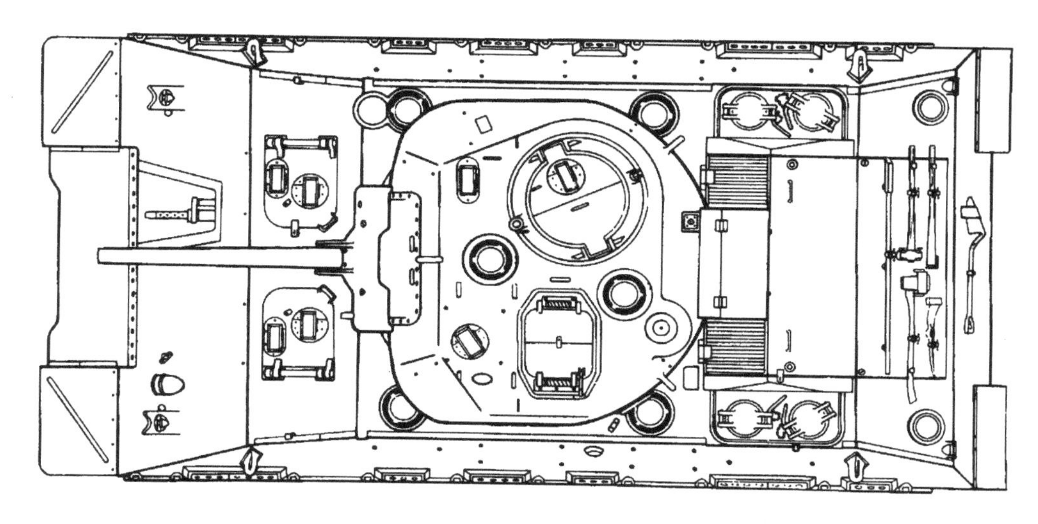

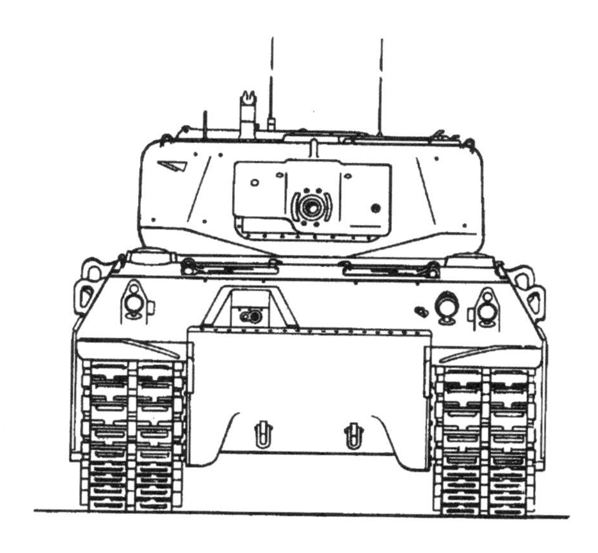

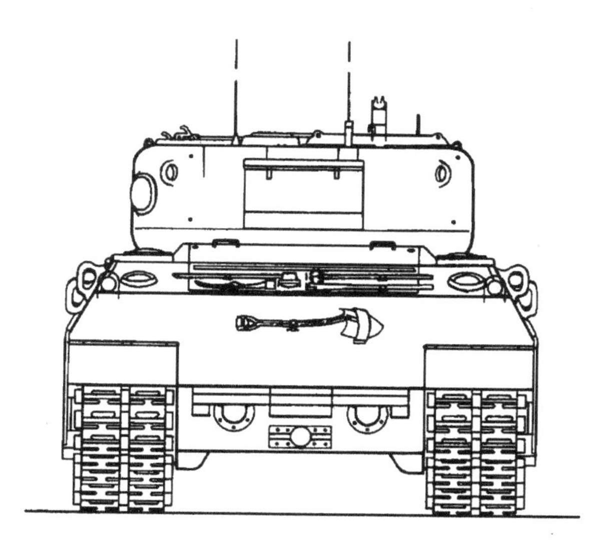

Scale 1:48

Assault Tank T14

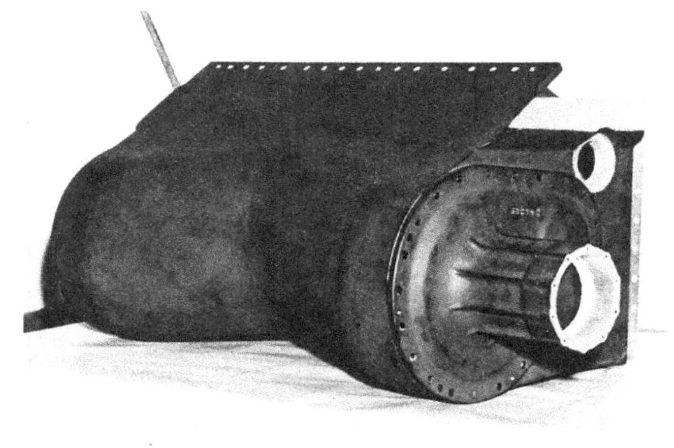

The welded differential and final drive housing installed on a tank is shown at the left above. An experimental cast housing appears above at the right.

Improvements in the armor on the standard Sherman included cleaning up the front hull thus obtaining more uniform protection in this area. These changes, plus the installation of the larger drivers' hatches, decreased the slope of the front plate from 56 to 47 degrees from the vertical. However, the single piece rolled front plate was much stronger and its thickness was increased to 2-1/2 inches to compensate for the decreased slope.

Before the improvements were introduced into production, efforts were made to increase the protection on the earlier models. Such items as the applique armor over the sponson ammunition racks, the plates welded in front of the drivers' hoods, and the armor patch on the right front of the turret have been mentioned previously. The differential and final drive housing was also a weak point on the early tanks. Both the three piece assembly and the early cast single piece housing were essentially round in profile with a constant thickness of 2 inches. Thus the vertical portion was weaker than the sloped areas on the remainder of the tank front. A number of experimental designs were evaluated before production of the new casting that was 4-1/2 inches thick in front with the sharp profile to reduce the vertical area. Concern about the shortage of foundry capacity also resulted in the design of a welded housing early in 1942, but it was never placed in production.

In May 1943, Aberdeen Proving Ground was directed to develop shields which could be attached as a field modification over the early differential and final drive housings. A previous effort to provide such a shield had been rejected since it extended beyond the front of the tank reducing its maneuverability. Two types of shield were required to fit both the three piece assembly and the single piece casting. The latter had its shield welded permanently in place since the entire housing was removed as a unit for maintenance work. However, with the three piece assembly, the shield had to be removable since the housing was disassembled to service the brakes and differential. The shields increased the housing weight by 13.5 per cent for the three piece assembly and by 20.8 per cent for the single piece unit. This was considered acceptable since ballistic tests showed the shielded housings were much stronger than the most highly sloped area on the front of the tank. Although Aberdeen recommended the shields as a satisfactory field modification, the writer finds no record of these designs being applied in service.

The first effort to improve the protection of the differential and final drive housing is shown here installed on the T6 at Aberdeen. This design was rejected because it extended beyond the front of the tank. In this photograph, the T6 has been rearmed with the 75mm gun M3.

Above are the armor shields developed for the three piece (left) and single piece (right) differential and final drive housings.

On 17 February 1944, Chrysler received instructions to develop heavy auxiliary armor which could be added in the field to the medium tank M4 and the light tank M5A1. A wooden mock-up was constructed showing heavy plate added to the front hull and all around the turret. However, the project was cancelled at the end of the same month without further work. This approach was somewhat similar to the heavy auxiliary armor designed for the medium tank M2A1 in early 1941.

Below is the wooden mock-up constructed at Chrysler of the heavy auxiliary armor which could be applied in the field to the M4.

The HCR2 plastic armor kit installed on a late model M4A3 at Aberdeen in September 1945.

The devastating effect of the lightweight German hollow charge weapons such as the Panzerfaust resulted in all sorts of field improvisations to strengthen the Sherman's armor. At the same time, Ordnance initiated several programs to develop protection against these weapons. Much of the test work extended into the postwar period. One such project evaluated the use of plastic armor added to the sides of the hull and turret. The best of these low density materials, known as HCR2, was a mixture of quartz gravel and a mastic composed of asphalt and wood flour. A kit of auxiliary plastic armor was designed by the Flintkote Company for the M4 series of tanks. The armor panels consisted of 10 inches of HCR2 faced with 1 inch aluminum plate. These panels were held in place over the sponsons and around the turret by 1/2 inch steel cables attached to brackets welded to the tank. The plastic armor kit increased the weight of the vehicle by about 8 tons. Tests at Aberdeen in the Fall of 1945 showed that the turret assembly could defeat the German Panzerfaust 100 or the 8.8cm rocket, but both weapons caused some penetrations on the sponsons. The plastic armor also increased the protection against the kinetic energy projectiles such as the 76mm HVAP, but not as much as an equivalent weight of steel. It was also noted that the attachment cables were vulnerable to attack by high explosive rounds sometimes resulting in the complete loss of an armor panel.

Another attempt to defeat the hollow charge was through the use of closely spaced steel spikes welded to the armor plate. On impact, the spikes would penetrate the hollow charge projectile breaking it up so that the jet could not form properly. The most effective arrangement tested used 1 inch diameter spikes of three different lengths. They were 7-1/2, 8, and 8-1/2 inches long and were spaced 2-1/2 inches apart. Based on the Aberdeen tests, it was estimated that the spike protection added to an M4 series tank would increase the weight by 4.1 tons or approximately half that of the plastic armor kit. Research on this type of protection against the hollow charge also continued into the postwar period.

Additional views of the HCR2 plastic armor installed on the M4A3 are above and at the right. Note that the kit does not cover the front of the vehicle or the rear of the hull.

A test of the hollow charge projectile against spike protection is shown below. The projectile is impaled on the spikes.

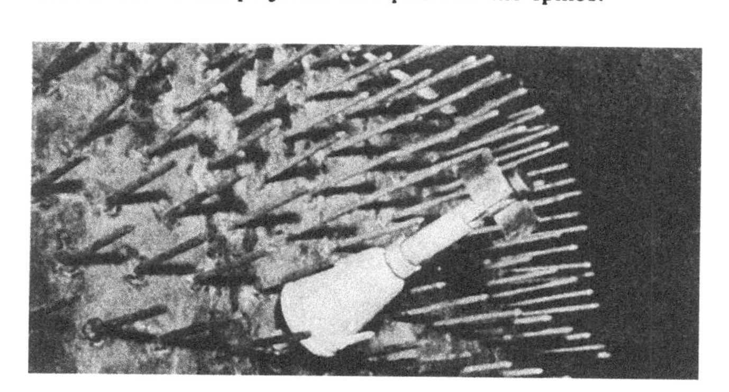

The Scorpion flame projector can be seen above installed on all four corners of the tank. Below three of the units are firing.

The problem of close-in tank defense was the subject of a number of development programs. Even when protected by accompanying infantry, the vehicles were vulnerable to attack from small groups of enemy who would remain concealed until the tank was almost upon them. With the Japanese, the attack was frequently suicidal with the enemy soldier placing a satchel charge or a magnetic mine on the hull. One suicide weapon was the lunge mine. This was a large hollow charge attached to a pole which was thrust against the hull similar to a bayonet attack. The resulting explosion was fatal to the attacker and frequently to the tank.

One weapon for combating these close-in attacks was developed by Arthur D. Little, Inc. Designated as the El antipersonnel tank projector, it was a small special purpose flame thrower mounted externally on all four corners of the tank. Containing a 1 gallon charge of an eutectic mixture of phosphorus and phosphorus sesquisulfide (EWP), each of the four flame throwers covered one quadrant of the tank. Fired from inside the vehicle, each unit could deliver 20 to 30 bursts of fire covering a fan shaped area about 15 yards from the vehicle. The four projectors could be fired either separately or together. Named the Scorpion (later changed to Skink), the antipersonnel weapon was tested at Edgewood Arsenal and Fort Knox in early 1945, but it did not see action before the end of the war.

At the left is a close-up of the El Scorpion projector.

M2A3B1 antipersonnel mines (at left) and Mk II fragmentation grenades (at right) are mounted on the outside of a tank during tests at Fort Knox.

Fort Knox and Aberdeen investigated other means of close-in protection which might be adopted as field expedients. These included the mounting of hand grenades, antipersonnel mines, and explosive loaded pipe on the outside of the tank. The Mark II grenade provided excellent fragmentation against personnel approaching the vehicle. However, the grenades had to be shielded to prevent damage to exposed components on the tank itself. Experiments replacing the Mark II hand grenade with the M3 antipersonnel mine showed the fragmentation from the latter to be much inferior and it was considered unsatisfactory. In some early tests, the standard M2A3 antipersonnel mines were attached to steel plates mounted at various locations on the outside of the tank. When fired, they ejected a modified 60mm mortar shell which exploded with a very good fragmentation effect. An installation at Aberdeen enclosed six modified M2A3 mines in a steel container located on the front hull armor. All of these devices were fired from inside the tank using a control panel mounted between the drivers' seats over the transmission.

At Aberdeen, explosive loaded pipe sections were attached along both sides of the hull and around the turret, but tests showed that the fragmentation was relatively ineffective. Fort Knox concluded that the use of externally mounted grenades and the M2A3 mine was feasible, but the protection obtained was inferior to close infantry support. They also pointed out that because of danger to friendly troops, these devices could be used only when the tanks were operating alone.

Another means of close-in tank defense was provided with the development of the bullet deflector for the .45 caliber submachine gun M3. Tested at Fort Knox during the Summer of 1945, the deflector was supplied as a kit which could be mounted in a periscope holder for use by either the tank commander or the loader. It consisted of a steel tube bent through an angle of 90 degrees which could be attached to the muzzle of the standard M3 submachine gun. The inside half of the tube wall was cut away for about 7 inches from the outer end extending past the curved portion. This prevented fouling of the .45 caliber bullets as they were deflected around the bend. The gun and deflector were designed to fit in the standard periscope holder alongside of the plastic periscope T122 which was also furnished as part of the kit. The weapon was aimed by a Polaroid infinity sight which was held in place by a bracket over the lower periscope face.

Firing tests at Fort Knox showed that the deflector could be used to effectively engage silhouette targets 100 feet from the tank. The .45 caliber bullets penetrated these 1 inch pine board targets and the dispersion was not excessive. Some breakage occurred during the tests and modifications were recommended to strengthen the deflector. The sight bracket also loosened under the vibration from firing and a better method of fixing it in place was required.

The submachine gun M3 with the bullet deflector is mounted alongside the loader's periscope below. Note the special sight fixed to the periscope window. At the right, the deflector is at maximum depression.

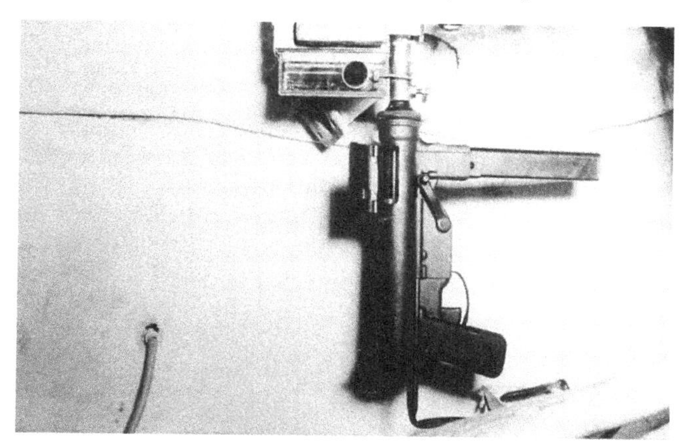

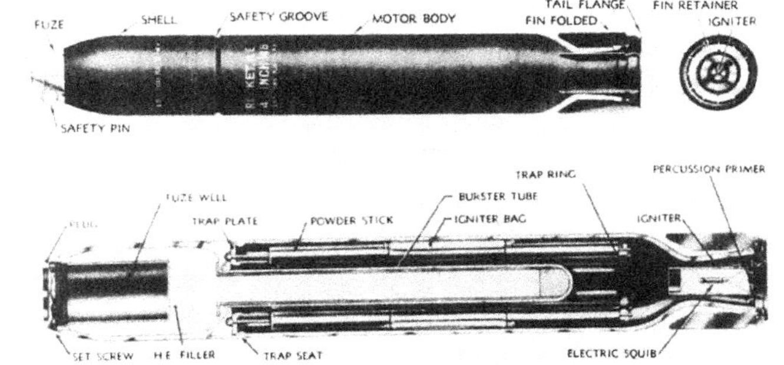

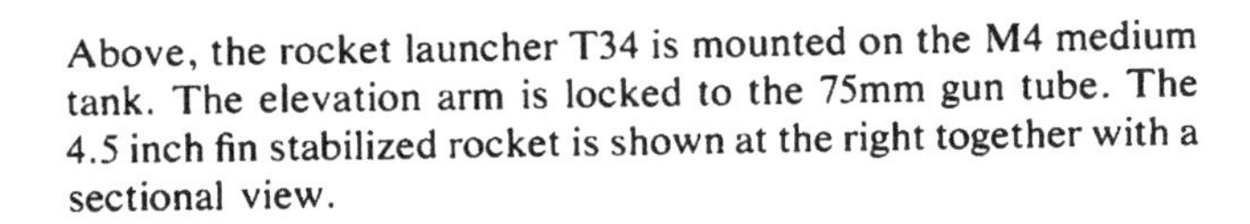
Above, the rocket launcher T34 is mounted on the M4 medium tank. The elevation arm is locked to the 75mm gun tube. The 4.5 inch fin stabilized rocket is shown at the right together with a sectional view.

To provide a high density of fire ahead of the assault troops, Ordnance developed a number of tank mounted rocket launchers. The rockets had much greater dispersion than conventional artillery, but were excellent for saturating the enemy defenses prior to an attack. The first and most widely used high explosive artillery rocket was the fin stablized 4.5 inch M8 series. Although too inaccurate for the engagement of point targets, its effect was devastating when fired into an area in large numbers. For tank use, the rocket launcher T34 was mounted on top of the turret using an arm attached to the main gun barrel for elevation and depression. Weighing 1840 pounds, the T34 carried 60 4.5 inch rockets in 90 inch long plastic tubes. These tubes were arranged with a double bank of 36 on top and two double banks of 12 below, one on each side of the elevation arm. After firing, the entire launcher could be jettisoned allowing the tank to proceed on its normal mission.

Quantities of the T34 were manufactured and shipped to Britain prior to D-day and they saw limited use during the following campaign. In the original design, the elevation arm was clamped directly to the gun barrel by a split ring and the cannon could not be fired until the launcher was jettisoned. This feature, combined with jettisoning difficulties, made the tank mounted launchers extremely unpopular with the troops. Field modifications attempted to correct this condition by removing the elevation arm from the cannon barrel and attaching it to the top of the gun shield. This permitted the cannon to be fired with the launcher in place, but the smaller movement of the gun mount limited the range of elevation.

The T34 rocket launcher installed on a Sherman in Luxembourg during February 1945. Note that the tracks on this tank are fitted with two types of extended end connectors. This is probably a mixture of standard connectors with items procured locally.

The elevation arms on the T34 launchers above have been removed from the gun tube and attached to the rotor shield. This restricts the range of elevation, but permits firing of the cannon with the launcher in place.

On the T34E1 launcher, the elevation arm was attached to extensions from the gun shield thus retaining the full elevation range and allowing the cannon to be fired without jettisoning the launcher. This model also used magnesium tubes and was equipped with an improved disconnect system for the electric and hydraulic lines to simplify jettisoning. The T34E2 launcher was similar to the T34E1, but it had an improved firing mechanism. One of these launchers in action produced an awesome sight and sound certainly justifying its nickname Calliope.

Firing at night, the T34 made an impressive sight. Below, the M8 rockets are being loaded into the launcher.

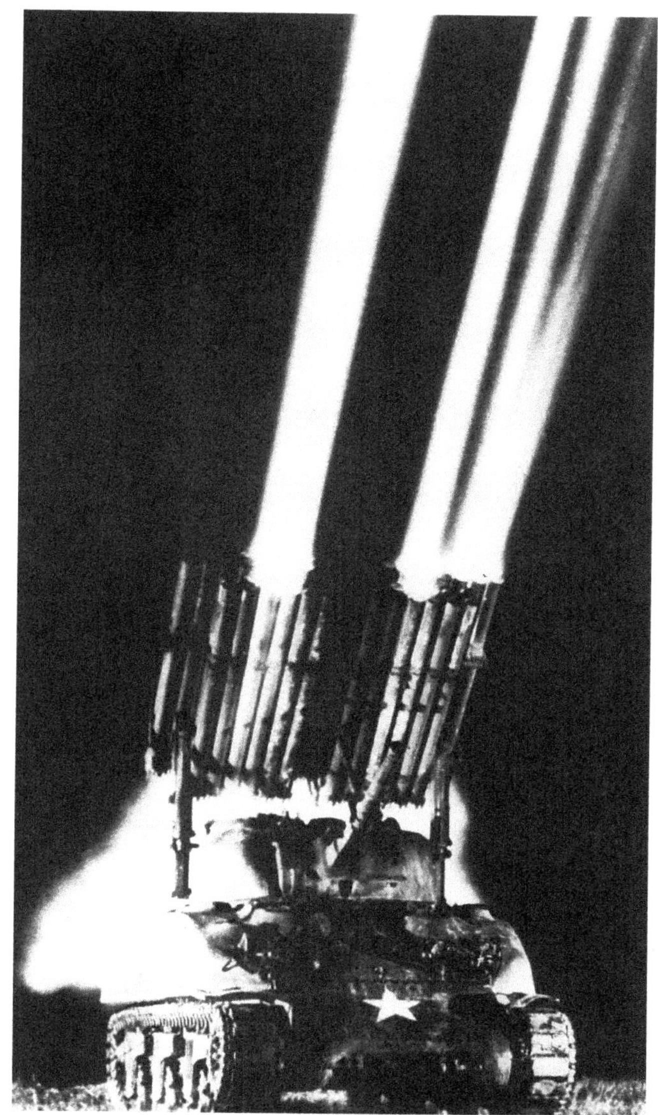

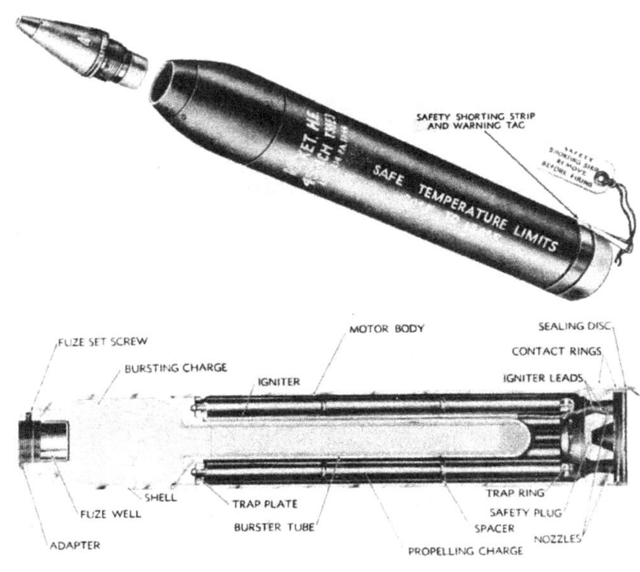

Above, the rocket launcher T72 is mounted on the Sherman (left) and the M16 spin stabilized rocket is shown to the right. Below, the T99 rocket launcher is mounted for test on the M4A3.

During the last year of the war, the 4.5 inch M16 high explosive rocket reached production status. The fins were eliminated on this round and it was spin stabilized by canted nozzles in the rocket base. Experiments showed that the dispersion was reduced compared to the fin stabilized weapons and that it could be launched from much shorter tubes without loss of accuracy. The maximum range was increased to 5250 yards compared to 4200 yards for the earlier M8 series. A new tank mounted launcher, designated the T72, was developed for the spin stabilized rockets. Like the T34 it had 60 tubes, but they were arranged with a double bank of 32 on top and two double banks of 14 each on the bottom. Unlike the T34 series, the shorter tubes of the T72 were loaded from the front. With this design, the tank gun also could be fired prior to jettisoning the launcher.

Another late development was the rocket launcher T99. Intended for use on the new M26 tank, it had four banks of launcher tubes, two on each side of the turret. Each bank carried 11 spin stabilized rockets for a total of 44. Both pairs of launcher banks could be jettisoned sideways from the vehicle by explosive charges controlled from inside the turret. Tests of the jettisoning operation were carried out at Aberdeen in June 1945 using a late model 76mm gun M4A3.

Other experiments with tank mounted rocket launchers included the use of the Navy 4.5 inch barrage rocket. This rocket had a fairly low velocity and a short range. Experiments at Aberdeen Proving Ground in March 1945 installed two T45 (Navy Mark 7) launchers on the turret of a Sherman. In this launcher, the rockets were fed to the launching rail by gravity, firing automatically as they made contact. The 12 rockets in each launcher could be fired in 4 seconds.

The 4.5 inch T45 rocket launcher is fitted to the Sherman above. Twelve barrage rockets could be loaded in each of the two racks.

The 7.2 inch rocket launcher M17 is installed above on the M4A1. The early experimental Cowcatcher launchers are shown at the left. At the left below is the 7.2 inch T 37 demolition rocket and at the bottom these rockets are being loaded into the M17 launcher.

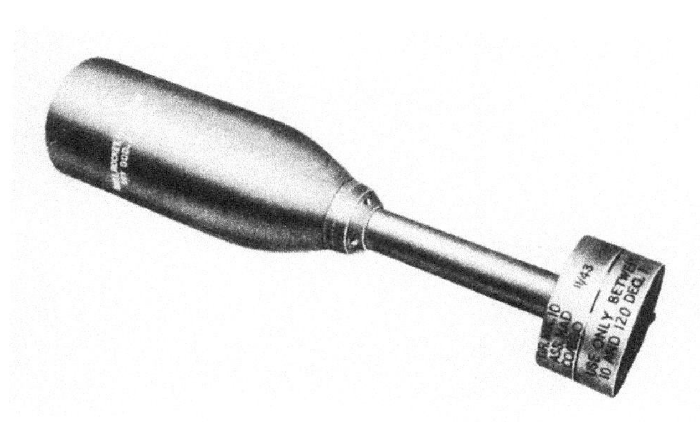

The need for a more powerful explosive charge led to the development of the 7.2 inch demolition rocket. Originally derived from a Navy antisubmarine weapon, the fin stabilized T37 round weighed 61 pounds and carried 32 pounds of plastic explosive. With a maximum velocity of 160 ft/sec, its range was limited to 230 yards. The later model T57 round was fitted with the larger 4.5 inch rocket motor increasing the range to 1200 yards.

Since it was intended to use the 7.2 inch demolition rockets against obstacles at fairly close range, armored launchers were developed for tank mounts. The T40 was the most widely used and it was later standardized as the 7.2 inch multiple rocket launcher M17. Mounted above the turret, it carried 20 7.2 inch rockets on two rows of ten 90 inch rails. The empty launcher weighed 4615 pounds and was completely enclosed in armor with a maximum thickness of 1/2 inch. An arm attached to the tank cannon controlled the elevation from +25 to -5 degrees and the rockets could be fired individually or by ripple fire at 1/2 second intervals. The front armor plate doors were operated by hydraulic controls from within the tank and the complete launcher could be jettisoned after firing. Nicknamed the Whizbang, the M17 was used in action during the invasion of southern France and in the Italian campaign.

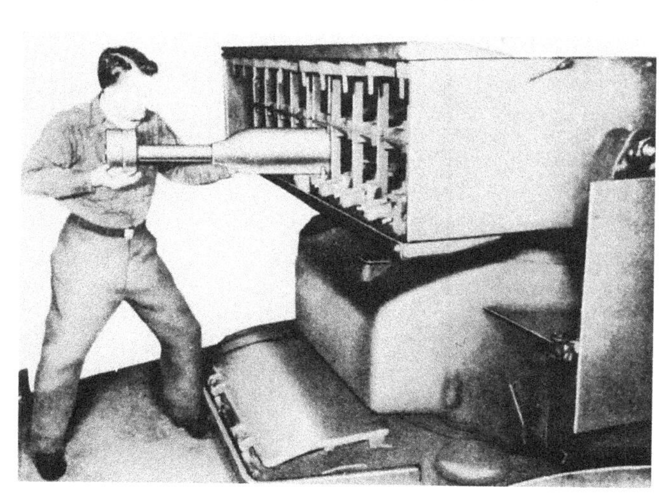

Above, the M17 launcher being loaded from the front in the field. Below is the 7.2 inch rocket launcher T73. Note the sloped side armor on the T73.

A modified version of the M17 also was placed in limited procurement. Designated as the 7.2 inch multiple rocket launcher T64, it was intended for installation on the armored engineer vehicle. It was similar to the standard model except for changes in the firing panel and other auxiliary equipment. The holding mechanism also could handle 7.2 inch rockets with 2.25 inch, 3.25 inch, and 4.5 inch motors.

The 7.2 inch multiple rocket launcher T73 was developed late in the war and differed from the earlier models in carrying only a single row of ten rockets on 50 inch rails. Protected on the front and sides by 1 inch armor, the top and bottom were covered by 1/2 inch plate. This provided protection against .50 caliber fire unlike the M17 which was only proof against .30 caliber rounds. The launcher rotated with the turret, but the elevation was independent of the gun mount. Ranging from +45 to –5 degrees, the elevation was controlled by an electric drive and the launcher was not attached to the tank cannon. When no longer required, it could be jettisoned by a manually operated hydraulic mechanism from inside the tank. The semiautomatic firing device had an average rate of 2 rounds/minute. Weighing about 4000 pounds, the T73 could handle rockets with 2.25, 3.25, or 4.5 inch motors. In addition to the high explosive rounds, 7.2 inch chemical rockets were available.

Other 7.2 inch demolition rocket launchers were developed which replaced the tank's main armament. These weapons are discussed in the section on Special Tanks and Armored Vehicles.

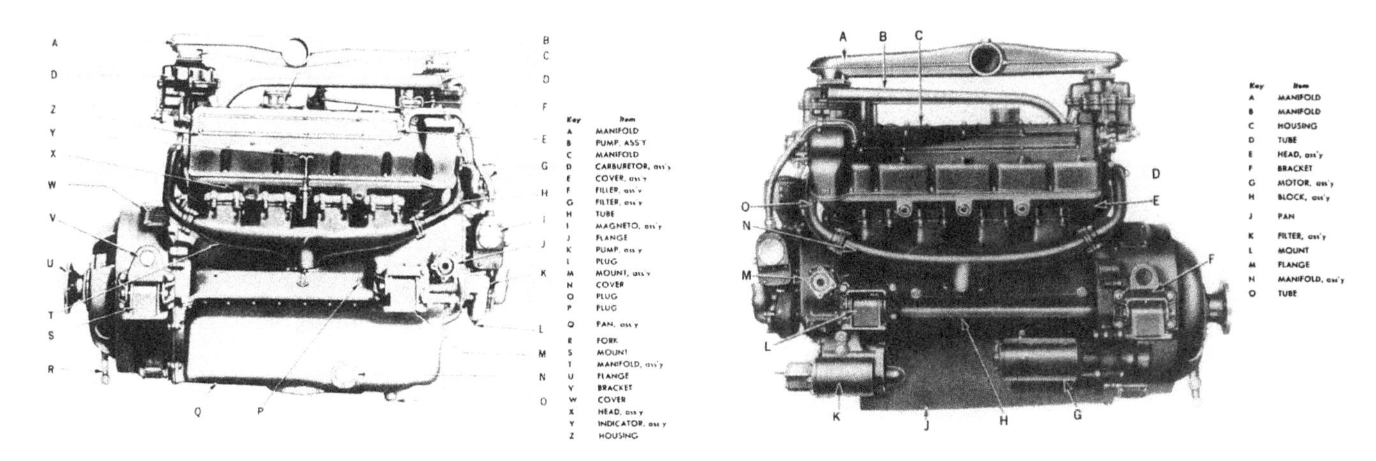

The late production Ford GAA is shown above. The oil level dip stick is marked Y on the left side of this late model engine.

INCREASING THE MOBILITY

The mobility of the tank depended ultimately on the engine available to power it and by the end of 1943, five power plants had been standardized for the Sherman. Two of these, the GM 6046 diesel and the Chrysler A57 multibank, were installed in the M4A2 and the M4A4 primarily for Lend-Lease commitments. The production of the M4A6 with the Ordnance RD1820 was stopped after completion of only 75 tanks. For service overseas, U.S. tanks were powered by either the Continental R975 or the Ford GAA. The preferred engine was the liquid-cooled Ford V-8 installed in the M4A3. If sufficient numbers had been available, it would have replaced all other types, at least in U.S. service. In fact, the Commanding General of the Armored Force recommended that it be installed in all Shermans as soon as possible. In answer to this request, layout drawings were prepared for a modified M4A1 cast hull that could accommodate either the Continental R975 or the Ford GAA. In August 1943, the Ordnance Committee authorized the construction of a cast hull pilot tank powered by the Ford engine, designating it the medium tank M4E7. It was subsequently determined that the quantity production of such a tank would further complicate an already difficult situation in the manufacture and supply of spare parts. All parties then agreed to drop the project and it was cancelled in November 1943.

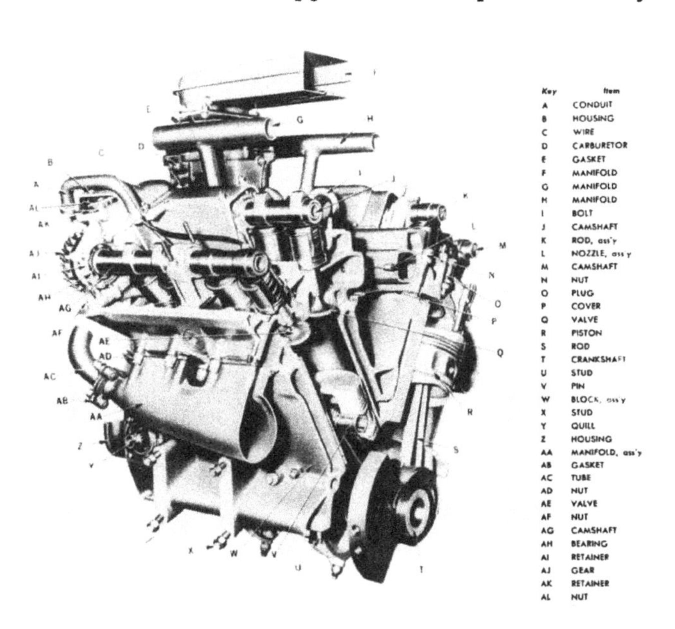

The components of the V8 GAA engine are exposed in the cutaway view at the left.

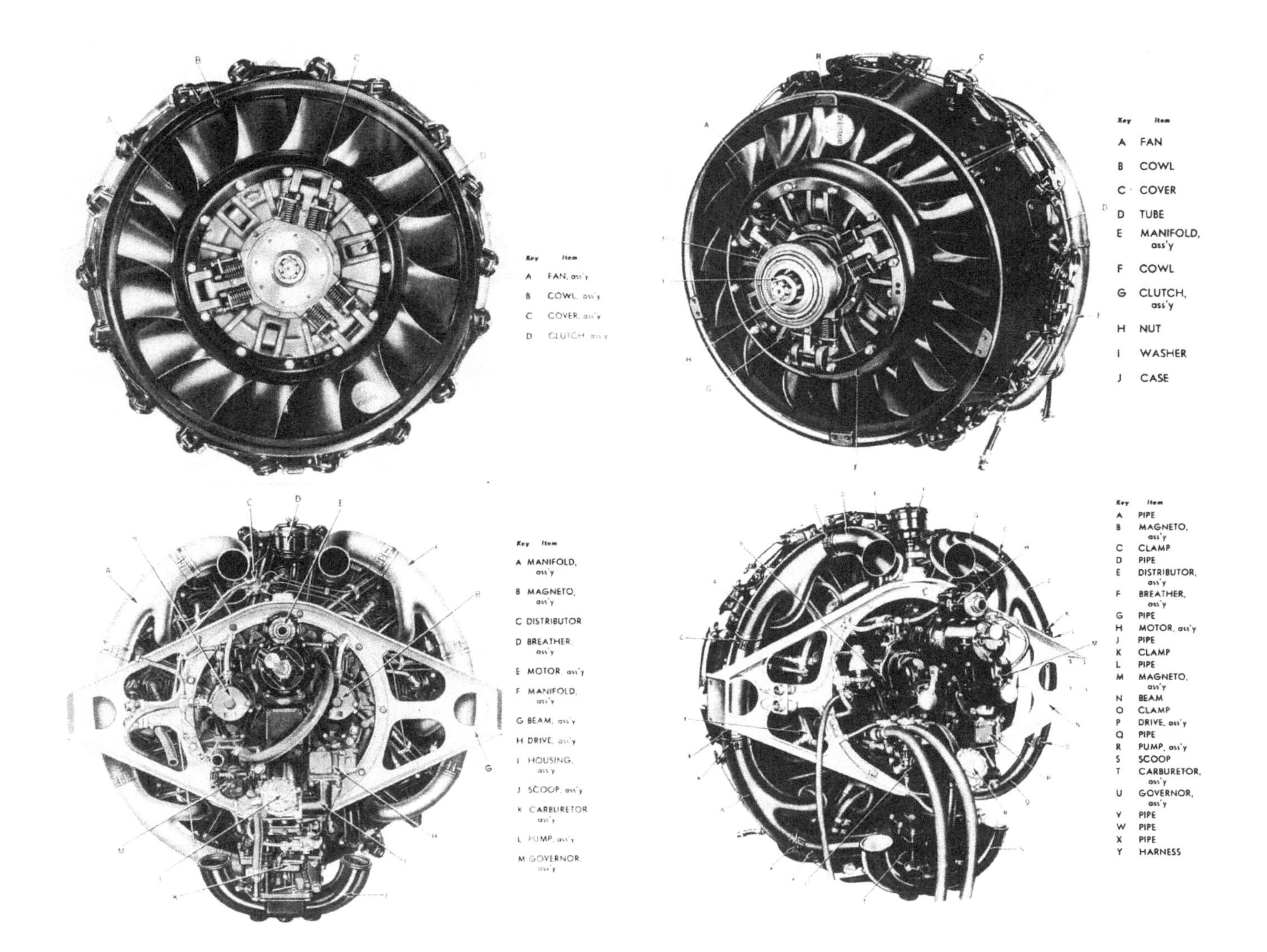

The late production Continental air-cooled radial engines can be seen above. The R975 C1 is at the left and the R975 C4 is at the right. Each engine front appears in the top photograph with the rear at the bottom.

The efficiency of the Continental R975 C1 used in the M4 and M4A1 was greatly improved by further development work. The radiation area was enlarged on the cylinder heads and the use of cast aluminum muffs increased the heat transfer from the cylinder barrels. These changes, together with a reduced supercharger ratio and a new carburetor, were incorporated in an improved version of the engine designated as the R975 C4. The modifications increased the power output to 460 gross horsepower at 2400 rpm and the maximum torque was raised to 1025 foot pounds at 1800 rpm.

In June 1943, the Ordnance Committee proposed the installation of the R975 C4 in a redesigned compartment which would have better air flow characteristics for cooling the engine and improved accessibility for routine maintenance work. Other changes increased the fuel capacity to 200 gallons and modified the engine lubrication. The Ordnance Committee recommended that the engine compartment be modified on 17 M4A1s and they were designated as the M4A1E5. It was intended to power 15 of the tanks with the new R975 C4 and the remaining two with the R975 C1.

When the proposals were made in June, it was planned to incorporate these features in future production M4A1s. Unfortunately, by the end of the year, other changes were also required that were not compatible with the M4A1E5 layout. Since they could no longer serve as production prototypes, the 17 tanks were cancelled on 2 December 1943. However, the R975 C4 was adopted as the standard engine for new production M4s and M4A1s and as a replacement for the R975 C1 as the latter wore out.

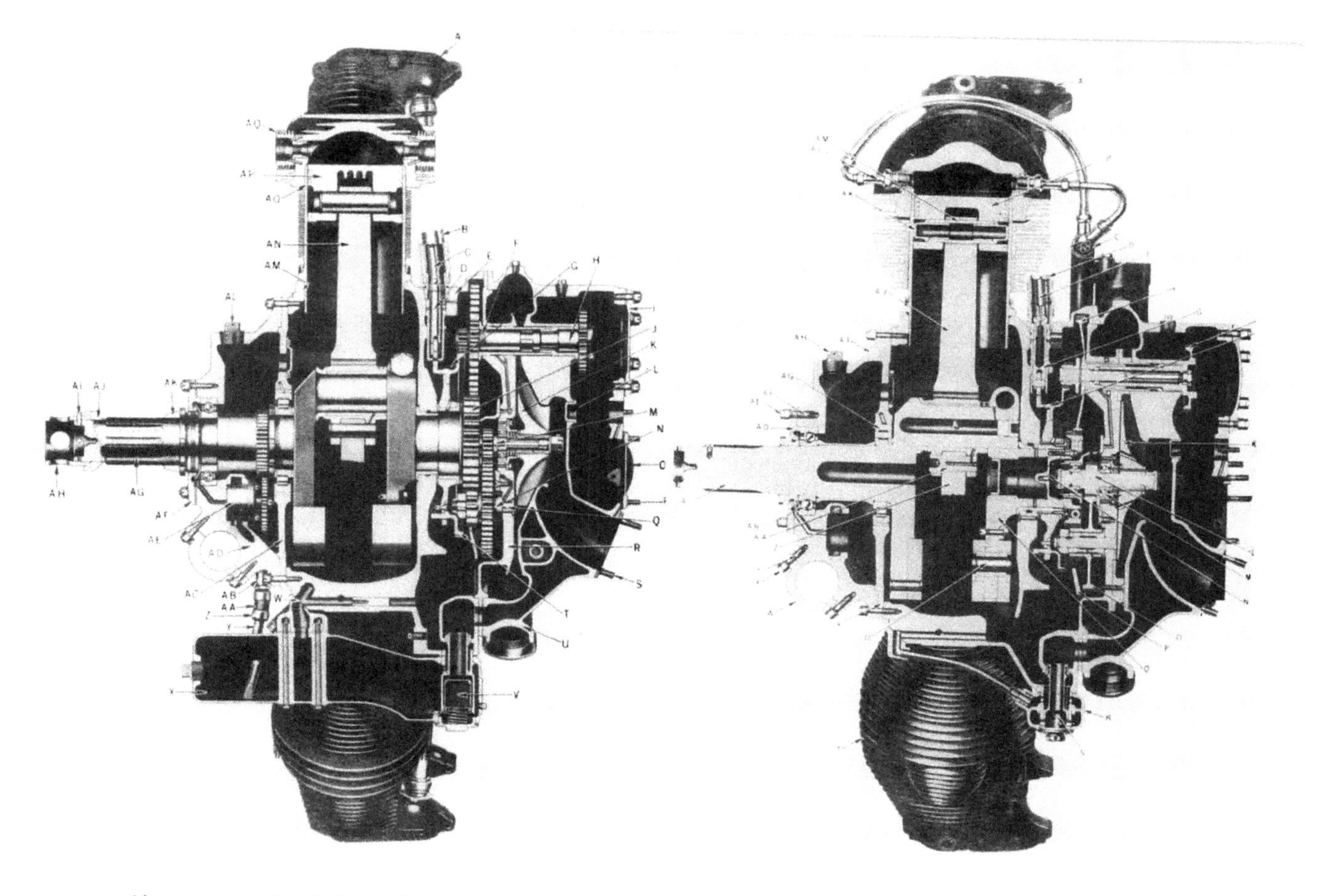

Above are sectional views of the Continental R975 C1 (left) and R975 C4 (right). The increased cooling area from the larger fins and cylinder heads on the R975 C4 is readily apparent.

On 30 January 1943, the Chrysler Engineering Division requested approval for the installation and test of the A65 gasoline engine in a medium tank. Developed by Chrysler at their own expense, the A65 was a water-cooled V-12 displacing 1568 cubic inches. Calculations indicated that the engine would develop 650 gross horsepower and 575 net horsepower when installed in a Sherman. Chrysler proposed the program to determine the feasibility of putting an engine of this size and power in a medium tank and to evaluate its performance. OCM 20010 recommended the installation on 25 March and it was approved shortly thereafter, designating the vehicle as the medium tank M4E3.

An M4A4, registration number W-3018445, was modified to accommodate the experimental power plant. The overall length of the tank had to be increased by 9-1/2 inches, but there was sufficient room in the engine compartment for a man to stand on each side of the A65. It was suggested that this space be used for additional fuel tanks. The hull modification was finished on 20 May and the engine was installed at that time. The M4E3 used the standard transmission and final drive. Comparative tests were

With the rear deck removed, the Chrysler A65 engine can be seen below installed in the medium tank M4E3. Note the extra space on each side of the engine.

The medium tank M4E3 is shown in these four projection photographs. The hull extension required to accommodate the A65 engine is easily seen.

run between the M4E3 and a production M4A4 with the tanks weighing 69,170 and 69,640 pounds respectively.

The acceleration and hill climbing ability of the M4E3 were excellent and it could be easily started in 5th gear on level concrete. As originally built, the A65 developed only 549 gross horsepower at 2400 rpm, but a change in the compression ratio from 6.3:1 to 7.1:1 increased its output to 580 horsepower. The performance was further improved by a new carburetor and a redesigned camshaft.

In its comparative tests, the experimental tank could cover the test course using two higher gears than the M4A4. To take advantage of the extra power, the bevel gear ratio was reduced from 3:53:1 to 3:05:1 and the A65 still provided faster acceleration than even an M4A3.

After 400 miles of test operation, the engine was removed for an examination which did not reveal any serious problems. Ordnance Committee action closed the project on 22 November 1943 with the recommendation that further work be done to develop engines in the 650 horsepower and greater class.

General Motors Corporation developed the V8-184 diesel engine as a company project for possible use as a tank power plant. It was based on the 16-184A vertical four bank marine diesel used by the Navy to power a 110 foot submarine chaser. Essentially, the V8-184 was half of the larger engine. OCM 21611, dated 23 September 1943, recommended the procurement of the experimental diesel and its installation in a medium tank. By February 1944, two engines were built and spare parts were on hand for a third. The V8-184 was a water-cooled, two stroke cycle, V-8 diesel displacing 1470 cubic inches with a compression ratio of 16.8:1. Rated at 600 gross horsepower at 1800 rpm, its maximum gross torque was 1910 foot pounds at 1000 rpm. With all accessories except for fans and radiators, the dry weight was 3750 pounds.

It was originally intended to install the experimental engine in an M4A2, but none were available at that time and an M4A3 hull was used instead. The installation required that the hull be lengthened by

The General Motors V8-184 diesel engine.

The medium tank M4A2E1 (above and below) at Aberdeen in May 1944. The General Motors M4Y designation is still painted on the sides of the tank. The exhaust outlet at the top center of the rear plate can be seen below at the left.

adding approximately 11 inches to the rear. General Motors referred to the test vehicle as the medium tank M4Y. When the Ordnance Department started their tests, it was designated as the medium tank M4A2 (Modified). The tank's serial number was 63999 and it carried registration number 30119820. At this later stage of the war, the W preceding the registration number was dropped. On 20 July 1944, OCM 24467 designated the vehicle as the medium tank M4A2E1.

The M4A2E1 could be indentified by the rear deck double door grill fitted on each side of the central exhaust outlet. The latter terminated at the top of the rear hull plate. The large engine also required a rectangular blister in the hull floor reducing the ground clearance to 15-1/2 inches.

Tested at Aberdeen from 10 May 1944 until 21 March 1945, the tank was driven 2914 miles. Because of its high power to weight ratio and the diesel's high torque at low engine speeds, the performance of the M4A2E1 greatly exceeded that of the standard Sherman. Although some mechanical failures occurred, they were not considered serious and corrections were possible without major design changes. The test report recommended that further study be made of two stroke cycle diesels as tank engines. It was also suggested that the original model 16-184A marine engine be considered as a power plant for heavy tanks and gun motor carriages weighing over 60 tons.

Other diesel engine experiments were initiated by OCM 20795 which recommended the procurement of two types of experimental power plants from the Guiberson Diesel Engine Company. Purchase was authorized for three each of the two proposed engines. Both designs were twin row air-cooled radials based on earlier Guiberson models. One, designated as the T-2040, was an 18 cylinder, twin row version of the 9 cylinder T-1020. The T-2800 was a double edition of the 9 cylinder T-1400. As implied by their designations, the new engines displaced 2042 and 2804 cubic inches respectively. The manufacturer's calculations estimated their respective gross output as 474 and 685 horsepower. With the low priority available, work progressed slowly and the projects were only 15 to 20 per cent complete by March 1944. The availability of more promising power plants eliminated further interest in the bulky radials for tank installation.

This is the 76mm gun medium tank M4 tested at Fort Knox with the high speed reverse transmission. Note that it is fitted with the early horizontal volute spring suspension. This tank was used to evaluate several new features.

A problem noted early in the career of the Sherman was its low speed in reverse. The gear ratio required for adequate hill climbing in reverse produced an agonizingly slow speed if the tank had to withdraw while under fire. In April 1943, the Ordnance Committee recommended the construction of six tanks with a reduced reverse gear ratio. However, the engineering tests revealed that although the reverse speed was increased, the climbing ability in that direction was unsatisfactory. The best solution was the installation of a planetary gear box which could reverse the entire transmission permitting operation at all five gear ratios. This gear box transmitted the power without any speed change in the forward direction. In reverse, the gear ratio was slightly increased. For example, if the maximum forward speed was 24 miles/hour, the reverse speed in the same gear was 21 miles/hour.

The high speed reverse transmission also included a new low level oiling system which reduced the oil capacity from 43 to 20 gallons. The operating temperature was greatly decreased and an additional 25 horsepower was transmitted to the sprockets. The new transmission used most of the parts from the standard unit and was completely interchangeable. Installation required the moving of the generator and electrical wiring. Also, the propeller shaft had to be shortened by 5 inches. The latter was an improvement since it reduced the shaft deflection and hence, the bearing loads.

On 30 April 1944, OCM 23548 recommended the use of the high speed reverse and low level oil system, but tests at Fort Knox were not complete until about a year later. In late 1944, the Armored Board received a 76mm gun M4 equipped with the new transmission. This vehicle, registration number 3038783, was one of

The shift lever used to reverse the transmission can be seen below (circled) alongside the generator. It is in the forward position for normal operation.

The medium tank M4A3E1, serial number 12729, at Aberdeen in March 1945.

the seven pilot tanks rebuilt at Detroit to serve as prototypes for the "Ultimate" Sherman. After tests, the Armored Board concluded that the high speed reverse transmission was far superior to the standard unit and recommended its adoption without delay for all tanks of the M4 series. Unfortunately, time had run out and the war was over before it could be introduced.

The M4 tested with the high speed reverse at Fort Knox also was fitted with final drives having a gear ratio of 3.36:1 compared to the standard 2.84:1. These were the final drive gears from the heavier assault tank M4A3E2. The Armored Board tests showed that although the speed on a level surface was reduced, the cross-country performance was greatly improved. Their report recommended that this final drive ratio be adopted for all production M4s, M4A1s, and M32 tank recovery vehicles. The change was not recommended for the M4A3 because of its normal higher performance. Like the high speed reverse, hostilities ended before this feature was available.

The medium tank proposal drawings, dated August 1942, showed the use of a torque converter with the R975 engine. After the successful development of the Spicer torque converter transmission for the light tank T7, it was considered for use in the medium tank. In October 1943, the Ordnance Committee directed the procurement of four Spicer Model 95 automatic torque converter transmissions. For test purposes, two were installed in M4A1s and two in M4A3s. The experimental vehicles were designated as the medium tanks M4A1E3 and M4A3E1 respectively. Tests on both types were still in progress during the Spring of 1945.

It had been originally intended to test three General Motors 3030B Torqmatic transmissions in three M4A1s. These were the same units installed in the medium tanks T20 and T20E3. However, the Model 3030B was discontinued because of production problems and replaced by the Model 900T. The latter was being used in the production of the 76mm gun motor carriage M18 which had a high priority claim on all available units. As a result, the Spicer transmissions were obtained for the original test program ending up in the M4A1E3 and the M4A3E1.

Below at the left is one of the M4A1E3s without its turret at Aberdeen during the postwar period. The armor plate was welded to the sides to simulate the weight of a fully loaded tank. At the right is M4A3, serial number 12099, which also was converted as the other M4A3E1.

The same tank often served in several experimental programs. The M4A3E8 marking indicates that this vehicle was previously used in the horizontal volute spring suspension development program. However, when these photographs were taken on 1 March 1945, it was designated as the medium tank M4A3E3.

By May 1944, the production situation had eased and General Motors was able to furnish the 900T units and install them in M4A3s. OCM 23979, dated 1 June 1944, designated the vehicles as the medium tank M4A3E3. On 10 January 1945, both tanks were under test at Aberdeen for comparison with the Spicer installation in the M4A1E3 and M4A3E1. These tests continued throughout the Spring, but with the end of the war and the appearance of the Cross Drive transmission, further work was discontinued.

On 25 February 1943, Mr. Oliver Kelley of the General Motors Transmission Division visited Lieutenant Colonel Joseph M. Colby at the Tank Automotive Center in Detroit. Mr. Kelley presented drawings for a new design combining a planetary gear transmission and an hydraulic torque converter with electric steering and braking in a single compact unit. The main speed changing mechanism was arranged along a shaft running crosswise of the tank, hence the name Cross Drive. Thus began the development which produced the standard transmission for the U.S. postwar tanks. Colonel Colby verbally requested a proposal outlining the design and development of the Cross Drive and this was provided by letter on 19 March. The Ordnance Committee on 30 April recommended the procurement of one of the new transmissions for installation in a medium tank M4A3. However, the design was to be suitable for use in later model tanks.

The first Cross Drive, the Model EX100, was installed in an M4A3 and it gave the tank a peculiar appearance. A large blister appeared in the front armor extending down into the differential housing. This was a heavy bulged steel cover bolted over a circular access hole in the front of the tank. Referred to by the engineers as the manhole cover, it gave this particular Sherman an appearance like no other.

Tests at the GM Proving Ground revealed some shortcomings in the experimental unit. The electric steering brakes failed because of a lag in the response time which made it difficult to anticipate exactly where the tank would go. On one occasion, this caused the loss of a power pole supplying the Proving Ground. Friction brakes were tried, but they suffered from overheating and excessive wear and the development of oil-cooled mechanical friction clutches was required. All of these problems were eventually solved, but by then the transmission was being installed in newer model tanks and the Sherman was no longer in the program.

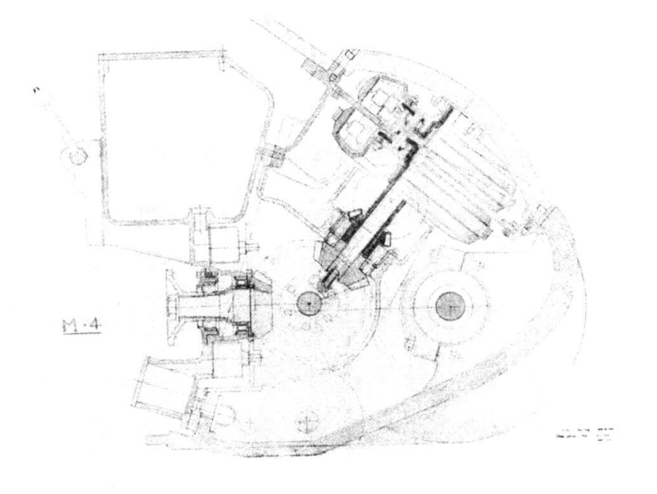

At the left is a side section drawing of the proposed EX100 Cross Drive transmission for the M4. Note the bulged cover which appeared in the front plate.

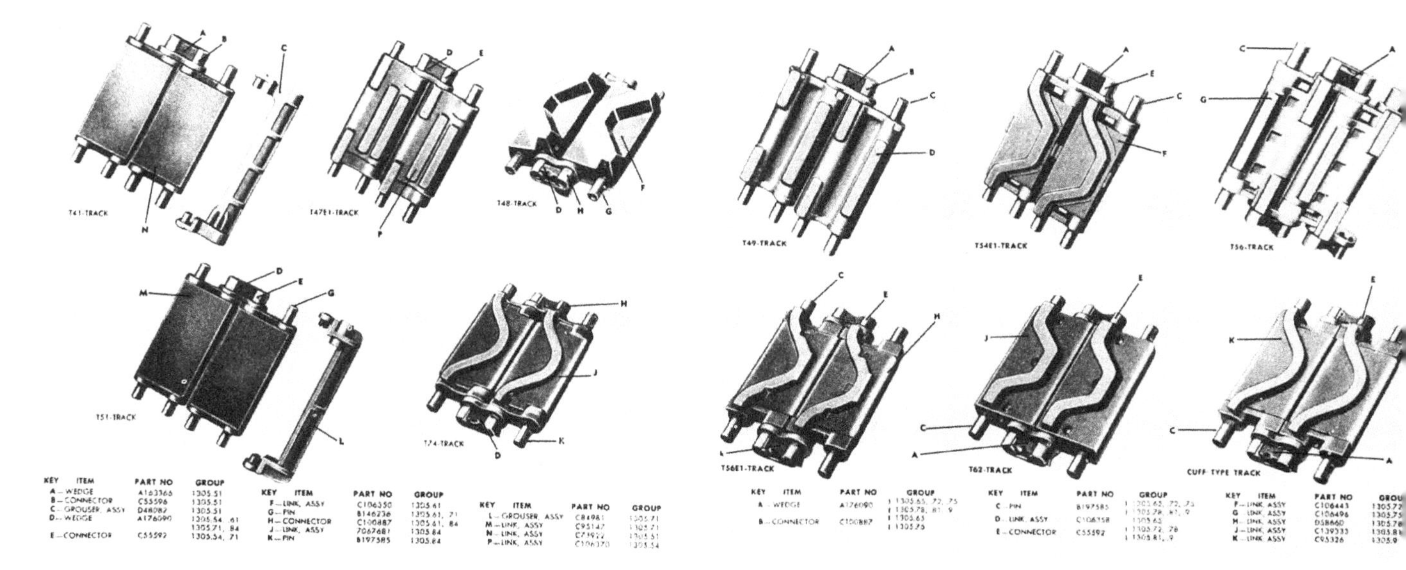

The rubber (left) and steel (right) track shoes for use with the vertical volute spring suspension are shown above.

The short life of the overloaded vertical volute spring suspension on the late model M3s and the early Shermans has been discussed earlier. The problem was actually twofold. First, the heavier weight caused permanent deformation of the volute springs as well as increased wear and second, the tank's ability to cross soft ground was limited because of the higher ground pressure. The late model vertical volute spring suspension with the larger springs provided a partial solution to the first problem, but did nothing for the second.

A study in December 1941 proposed the use of combination helical and ring spring suspension units. The suggested spring combination was designed to fit into the same space in the bogie assembly occupied by the original volute springs. However, the redesign of the bogie assembly to use the larger volute springs was the preferred solution.

Parallel with the suspension development, work continued to improve the tracks themselves. The prewar reversible flat rubber block track shoes, such as the T41, had been largely replaced by the T51 non-reversible type. Although the latter offered excellent traction on hard roads and did relatively little damage to such surfaces, it could slip easily when climbing over soft terrain. The T48 rubber block track with an integral chevron grouser was developed to improve the cross-country traction and still retain some of the advantages of the rubber shoe for road use. Detachable grousers were also developed for use with the flat tracks.

The swift advance of the Japanese during the Spring of 1942 cut off the sources of natural rubber in the Far East. The shortage soon reached crisis proportions since a single set of medium tank tracks, including spares, required 1734 pounds of rubber. With tank production rapidly increasing, it was apparent that a substitute had to be found. Synthetic rubber showed poor wear life and it was not yet available in sufficient quantities. Several designs for steel tracks were submitted to Ordnance with a double pin fabricated steel track shoe being selected for immediate production. Referred to as the "cuff" design, it was manufactured by Chrysler and later designated as the T54E2. The T54E1 was a similar track shoe produced by several other manufacturers. A number of other steel types were also introduced and, except for the Canadian dry pin design, all of the tracks for the standard suspension were 16-9/16 inches wide with a 6 inch pitch. In service, the steel shoes also proved to be less easily damaged on rocky terrain than the rubber tracks.

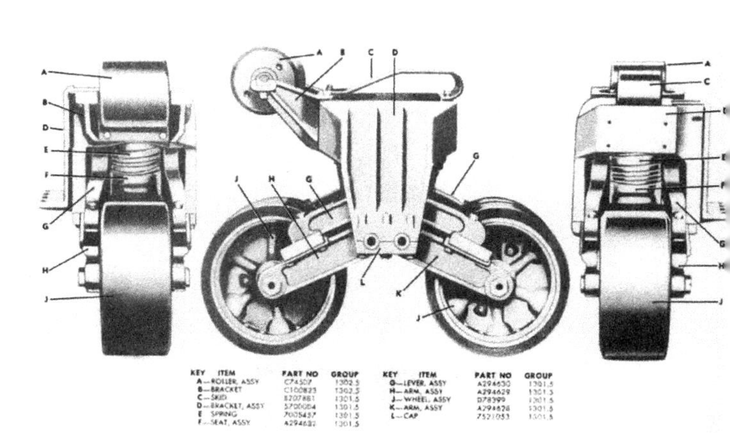

At the right are three views of the late production vertical volute spring suspension bogie with the final track skid design.

The early horizontal volute spring suspension on the medium tank M4A4 (above and below) under test at Fort Knox. This suspension used the standard 16-9/16 inch wide tracks.

Below is the M4A4 with the early horizontal volute spring suspension after assembly at Detroit Arsenal. The shock absorbers can be seen on the front and rear bogies.

A horizontal volute spring suspension (HVSS) was considered at one time for the medium tank M2 and a similar version was installed on two M3s, registration numbers W-304437 and W-305005, in early 1942. This design had the volute springs arranged to operate in the horizontal direction. One of its advantages was that when the horizontal volute springs were placed in compression by either the front or rear bogie wheel arm, the load was transmitted to the opposite arm thus keeping tension on the track. The design also permitted the installation of fluid type shock absorbers between the arms to smooth out the impact loads.

In April 1943, the Armored Board received one M4A3 and one M4A4 equipped with the early HVSS. Their registration numbers were W-3054174 and W-3019923 respectively. Both tanks had shock absorbers mounted on the front and rear bogies and three track support rollers were attached to each side of the hull just aft of the suspension units. The vehicles were fitted with the standard bogie wheels and the 16-9/16 inch wide tracks. This same suspension was installed on the medium tanks T20, T22, and T22E1. Tests continued at Fort Knox until August and the Armored Board concluded that the new suspension with the shock absorbers provided a better gun platform on rough terrain. However, the degree of improvement was insufficient to justify retooling costs since the design did nothing to correct the excessive tire loads and ground pressure. It was recommeneded that the early HVSS be dropped and work begun to design an improved suspension unit using dual bogie wheels with a 24 inch wide center guided track.

On 9 September 1943, OCM 21500 recommended the construction of pilot tanks equipped with a new HVSS. The improved design featured three rubber tired dual wheel bogies per track, each fitted with a

Above, the new horizontal volute spring suspension is installed with the T66 single pin tracks. At the right and below are details of the new suspension bogie and track shoes.

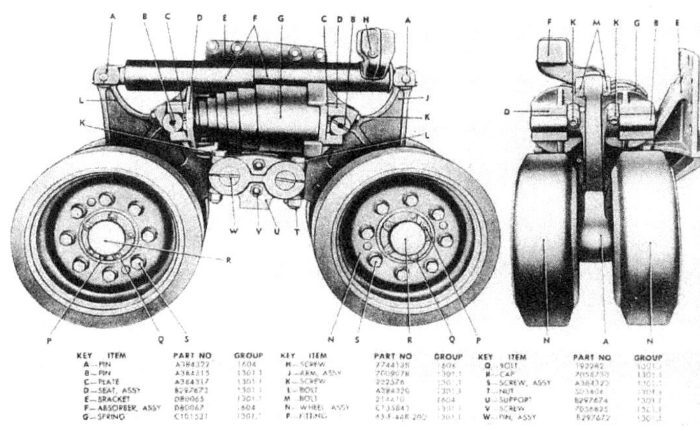

shock absorber. Two dual and three single track support rollers were attached to the hull, on each side of the tank. Rubber tires were vulcanized to the surface of all track support rollers as well as the idler wheels. The suspension was originally fitted with single pin cast steel center guided tracks that were 23 inches wide with a 6 inch pitch. The pilot vehicles were designated as the medium tank M4E8 when based on the M4. This changed to M4A1E8, M4A2E8, or M4A3E8 when other tank models were used.

Tests indicated greatly improved performance with the new running gear, but considerable modification was required to reduce excessive wear. The single pin steel track was designated as the T66 and a later 23 inch double pin track was developed which had a much greater wear life. The latter was designated as the T80 and eventually replaced the earlier model. With the HVSS installed, the weight of the tank increased by approximately 2950 pounds with the T66 track or 4780 pounds with the heavier T80. However, the large contact area with the wide tracks reduced the ground pressure to about 11 psi in both cases.

OCM 22136, dated 18 November 1943, recommended the procurement of ten additional suspensions for installation on pilot tanks. The ten vehicles, all M4A3E8s, were completed at Detroit Tank Arsenal and shipped during April and May 1944. Two were retained at the Arsenal Proving Ground, five were shipped to Fort Knox, and one each went to Aberdeen, the GM Proving Ground, and the U.S. Marines in San Diego.

During March 1944, the Ordnance Committee authorized the use of the new running gear on 500 M4A3 tanks armed with the 76mm gun. At the end of the same month, OCM 23336 recommended the release of the HVSS to production for all tanks of the M4 series.

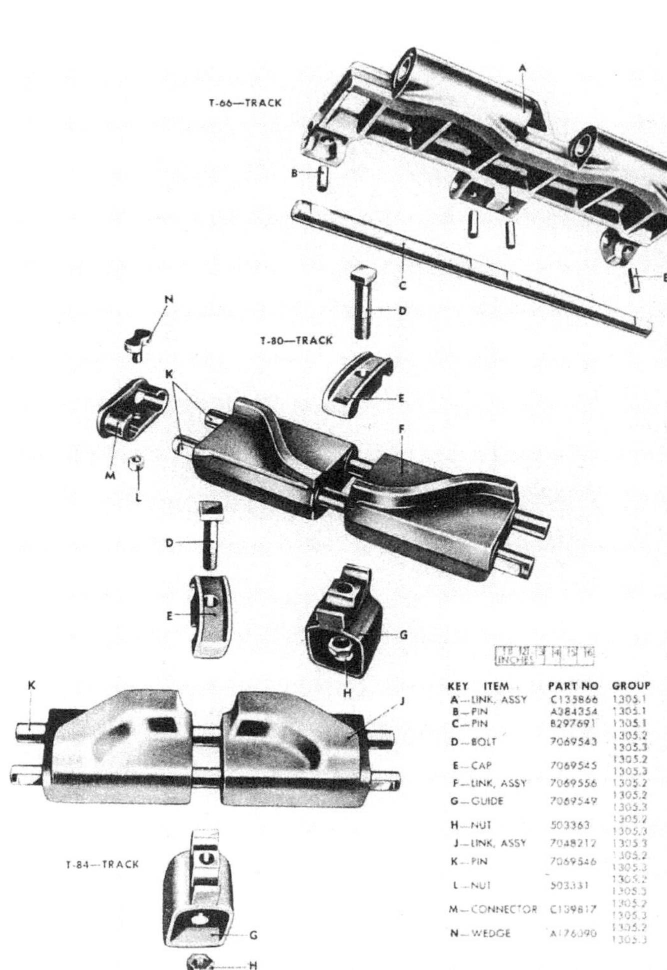

Medium tank M4E2 above is fitted with the Chrysler 24 inch wide T65 single pin steel tracks. At the top of the opposite page is the M4E2 with one T65 track and one standard track using extended end connectors on both sides. Note that the latter results in approximately the same overall width.

Near the end of 1942, Chrysler and the U.S. Rubber Company cooperated on a project to develop wide tracks for the standard vertical volute spring suspension. In February 1943, OCM 19776 approved the procurement of three tanks modified to use 24 inch wide tracks. These vehicles were designated as the medium tank M4E2. To permit the use of wide tracks, the bogie assemblies were shifted out 3-1/2 inches from the hull by the use of new castings and the rear idler bracket was widened by 3-1/2 inches. The drive sprocket attachment flange was moved toward the center of the hub thus shifting the sprocket teeth out into line with the new tracks.

Studies showed the feasibility of a 24 inch wide single pin outside guide track weighing about the same as the standard 16-9/16 inch double pin design. Chrysler manufactured such a cast steel track and it was submitted for test. After 366 miles of operation, the rubber bushings failed and it was returned to Chrysler. Redesigned to use heavier rubber bushings, this track ran for 800 miles before trouble developed with the track pin locking device. After repairs, tests continued for a total of 2200 miles of operation. OCM 19925 of 5 March 1943 designated the Chrysler track as the T65 and it later served as the basis for the design of the T66 center guided track used with the late model HVSS.

Other 24 inch outside guide tracks of both steel and rubber were submitted by U.S. Rubber, Burgess-Norton, Goodyear, Goodrich, and Ford, but none lasted as long as the T65. By this time, the superior performance of the wide track HVSS was obvious and there was no further interest in the M4E2 development.

Experiments had shown that the ground pressure of the Sherman equipped with the standard 16-9/16 inch double pin track could be reduced by using extended end connectors. These duckbill shaped devices replaced the standard end connectors on the double pin track increasing the width by 3-9/16 inches. Unfortunately, with the standard suspension, they could only be installed along the outside because of the insufficient clearance between the track and the tank hull. Even so, in soft ground the duckbills increased the contact area by over 20 per cent thus improving the tank's ability to move over muddy terrain.

Chrysler Corporation was requested in February 1944 to design spacers which could be installed between the tank hull and the components of the standard suspension. These spacers moved the entire running gear outward by 4-1/2 inches providing ample clearance for the use of extended end connectors along the inside of the tracks. The spacer brackets were welded to the tank hull and the standard suspension components were then attached to the brackets in the usual manner. If the duckbill connectors were used on both sides of the track, the total width was 23-11/16 inches reducing the ground pressure to about 10 psi. In addition, any of the experimental 24 inch outside guide tracks could be installed.

After 3000 miles of operation, the Tank Arsenal Proving Ground reported no serious difficulties and recommended the adoption of the spaced suspension and extended end connectors for use on remanufactured tanks and as a field modification. On 3 August 1944, OCM 24618 designated the pilot M4 with the spaced suspension as the medium tank M4E9. In a like manner, other tank models were designated as the M4A1E9, M4A2E9, and M4A3E9. Additional pilots were tested at Aberdeen and Fort Knox and the spaced suspension was released for the production of 1000 remanufactured tanks. Procurement of 1000 kits for field modification was also authorized.

The two views at the left show the installation of the M4E9 spaced out suspension during tests by the Armored Board. Below, the increased track width resulting from the use of extended end connectors on both sides of the tracks can be seen on this M4A3E9.

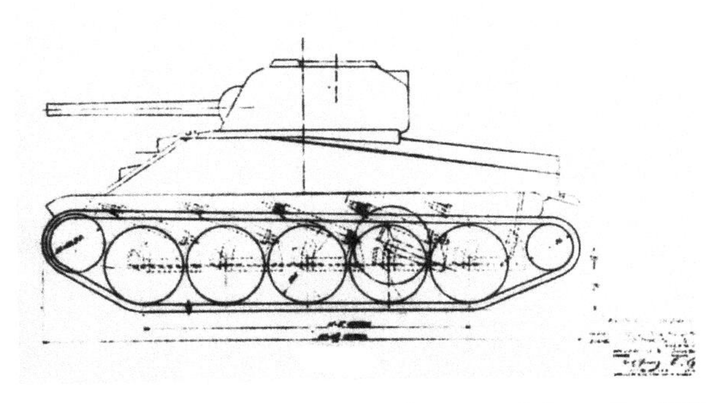

The drawing above is the original proposal from the Office, Chief of Ordnance to adapt the T4 type suspension to the Sherman.

A letter from the Office Chief of Ordnance in February 1942 requested Chrysler to study the possible application of the medium tank T4 suspension to the Sherman. This was, of course, the Christie coil spring design. Chrysler's report, dated 29 May 1942, concluded that it was practical to adapt a modified T4 type suspension to the Sherman, but since the latter weighed more than twice the T4, a number of changes would be required. Even with five large road wheels compared to four on the T4, the individual wheel loads were about twice those of the earlier tank. Because the five wheels could be more easily accommodated with the longer hull, the layout was based on the M4A4.

The T4 type spring assemblies were too long to be incorporated in the Sherman's structure. New springs were designed and mounted vertically beneath the sponsons acting directly on the road wheel arms. Each unit consisted of two concentric coil springs with shock absorbers inside the coils or adjacent to them. Armor plate covering the springs was omitted. The 18-1/2 inch wide single pin center guide tracks were based on the T4 design with a pitch of 5-3/16 inches. Using 93 shoes per track, the ground contact length was 148 inches at zero penetration. The estimated weight with the new suspension was 3080 pounds higher than the standard M4A4 mainly due to the large road wheels. However, the wider tracks held the ground pressure to about 14 psi, despite the shorter ground contact length.

Although the study showed that the T4 type suspension was adaptable to the Sherman, no pilots were constructed. Other projects were investigating torsion bar springing and interest shifted to that type of independent suspension for tank use.

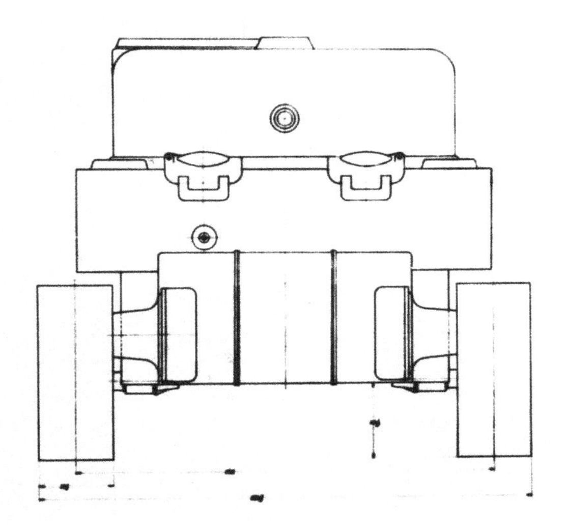

At left and below is the result of the Chrysler design study to provide a coil spring independent suspension for the M4. The original Christie arrangement has been modified and the springs are mounted vertically beneath the sponsons.

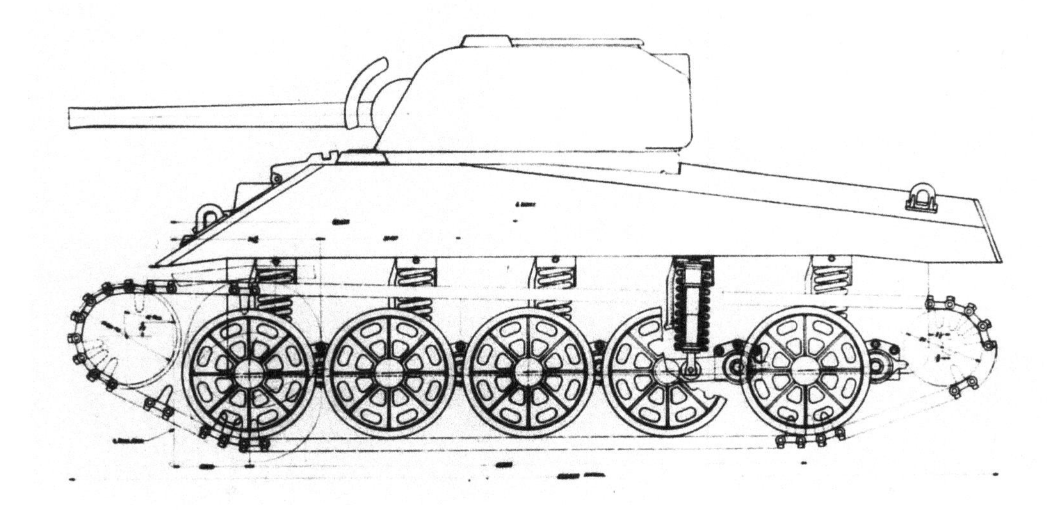

Medium tank M4A2E4 (above and below) at Aberdeen in August 1944. The welded drivers' hoods, antenna socket, and bow gun mount reflect the standard M4A2 production practice of this period.

The Ordnance Committee in March 1943 recommended the design and construction of a wide track torsion bar suspension for the M4 tank series. The designation medium tank M4E4 was assigned to this development and the procurement of two pilot tanks was approved. The two vehicles were actually M4A2s built by General Motors Corporation, thus the designation M4A2E4 was applied to the pilots. The first tank was completed on 22 July and the second on 15 August. Their registration numbers were 30104306 and 30104307.

At the time the project was initiated, work was already in progress on a similar suspension for the medium tank T20E3. The M4E4 followed the same design, but the six dual road wheels on each track were wider and the track width was increased to 24 inches. Shock absorbers were fitted on the first two and last two road wheels on each side. Three 14 inch diameter dual return rollers supported the track on each side of the tank. The single pin center guide tracks had a pitch of 6 inches and were rubber bushed cast steel construction. The 26 inch diameter road wheels were attached to arms and sprung by torsion bars mounted transversely across the floor of the vehicle. Volute bumper springs were fitted above each road wheel arm. Normal wheel movement was 5-1/2 inches for the front wheel and 5 inches for the others. All were limited to 7 inches by contact with the volute spring stops. Despite a stowed weight of about 36 tons, the wide tracks held the ground pressure to a little above 10 psi.

The original cast steel tracks failed during the preliminary tests and were replaced by a modified design. The first M4A2E4 went to the Tank Arsenal Proving Ground for further development work. The second pilot was operated for 200 miles at the GM Proving Ground and then shipped to Fort Knox for a limited test by the Armored Board. At the end of 1944, both tanks were at Aberdeen. As a result of maintenance problems, the vehicles were considered unsatisfactory, but they provided valuable data for the development of torsion bar suspensions for later tanks.

The increased track width which was so effective in reducing the ground pressure is apparent in these photographs. Wider fenders were installed to cover the 24 inch single pin tracks.

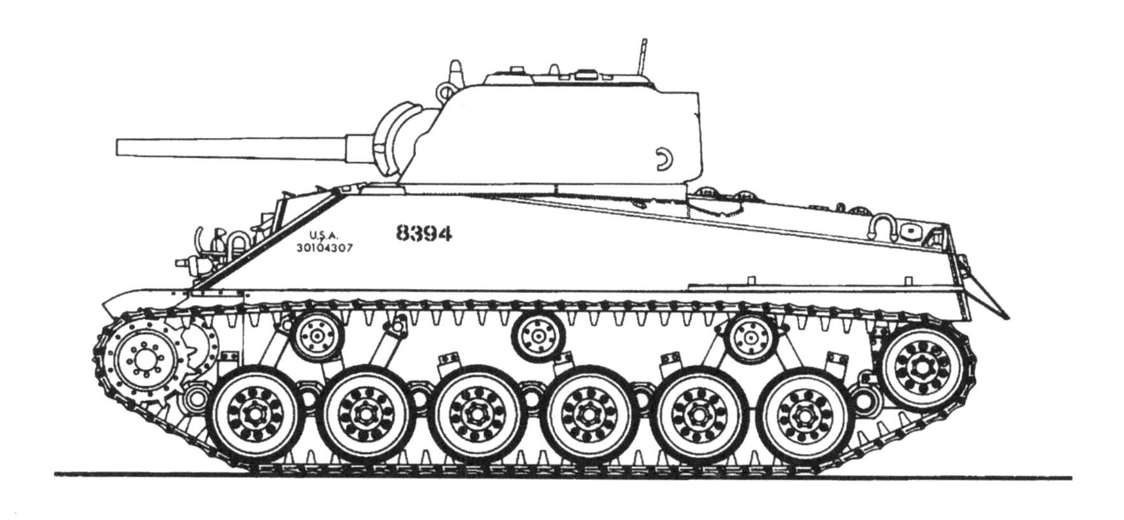

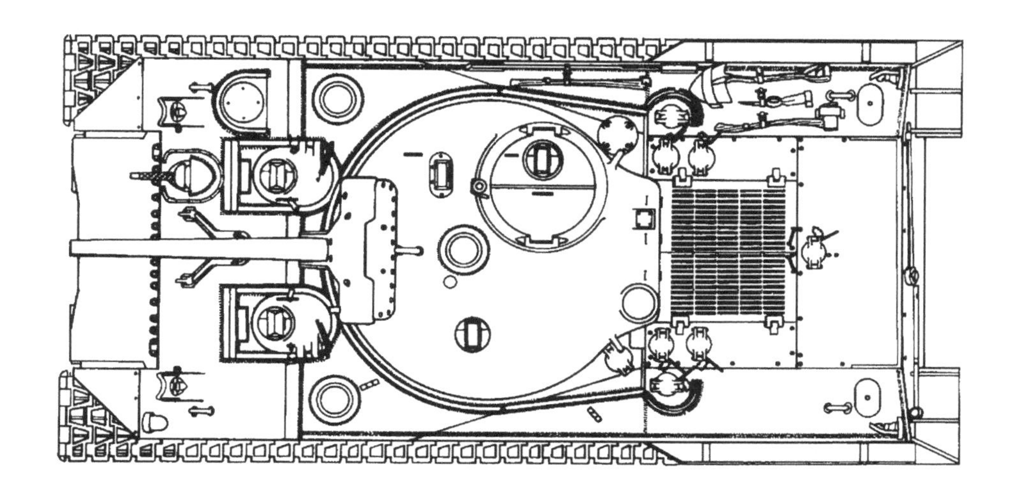

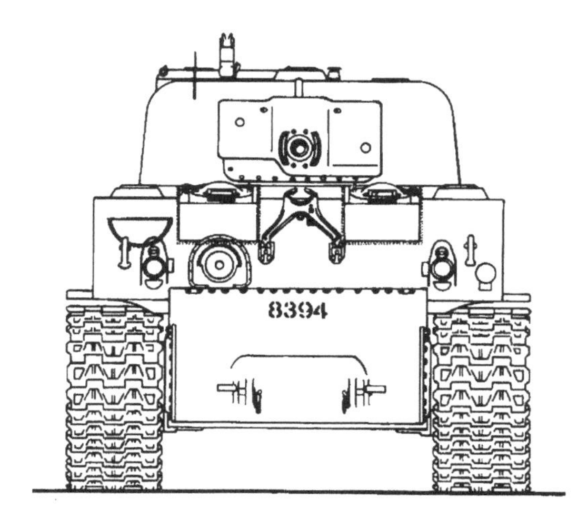

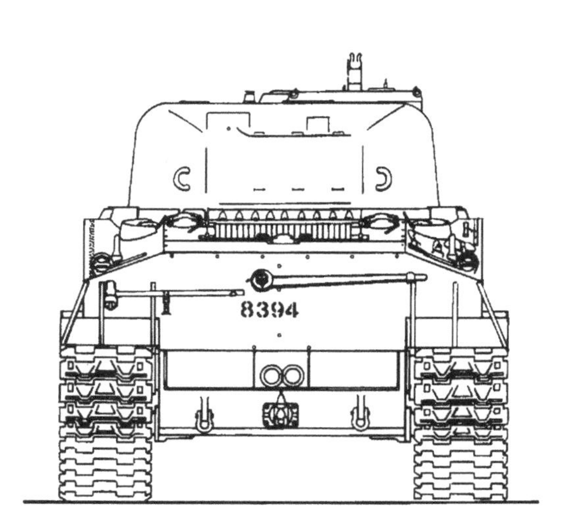

Scale 1:48

Medium Tank M4A2E4

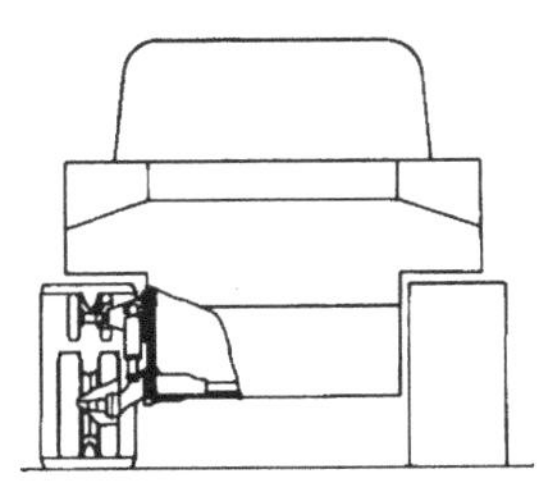

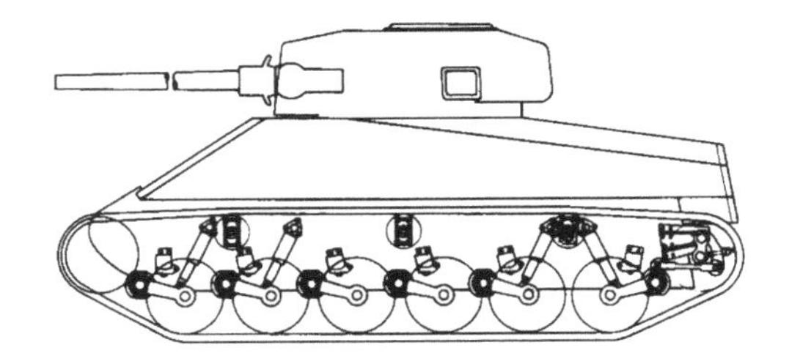

The general arrangement of the M4A2E4's torsion bars, road wheel arms, shock absorbers, and bumper springs can be seen in the sketches above.

At the left is a bottom view of the M4A2E4 hull. Note the circular escape hatch near the bow gunner's station. The torsion bars were installed inside the hull just above the floor (bottom left). With the road wheels removed, the road wheel arms, shock absorbers, and bumper springs can be clearly seen (bottom right).

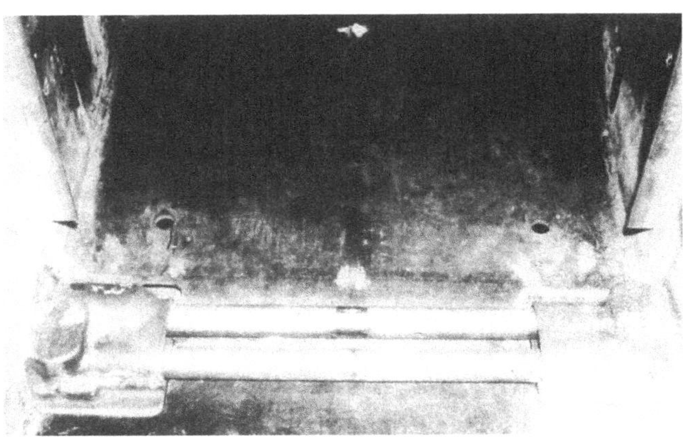

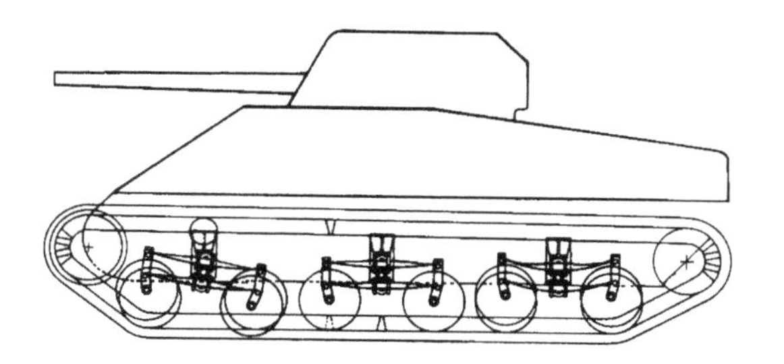

At the left is the proposed design for a leaf spring suspension to be applied to the M4.

At the request of the Office Chief of Ordnance, the Detroit Tank Automotive Center studied the feasibility of a leaf spring suspension and 24 inch track for the M4. Layout drawings showed three bogie assemblies per track with each bogie mounting a pair of dual articulated wheels 20 inches in diameter and nine inches wide. Four laminated semi-elliptic leaf springs, 36 inches in length, were fitted in each bogie. The 24 inch center guide tracks required dual support rollers or an arrangement of single rollers on each side of the guide.

A major problem with the leaf spring design was the limited wheel movement available. The 36 inch springs permitted only 2-1/2 inches of movement and the wheel articulation provided an additional 2-1/2 inches. Although the design was considered an improvement over the standard vertical volute spring suspension, it was inferior to the horizontal volute spring and torsion bar systems also under development and further work was cancelled.

A design study dated 1 May 1943 proposed the use of four volute spring bogies on each side of the tank. No shock absorbers were fitted and each bogie carried two dual wheels riding on a 21 inch wide track. An interesting feature of this design was the provision for the installation of an additional wheel on the outboard end of each bogie axle. These wheels were to be fitted with a 10 inch wide auxiliary track to decrease the ground pressure. This complicated arrangement did not survive beyond the initial proposal.

Several attempts were made to adapt suspension systems from other vehicles to the Sherman. One of these used components from the half-track truck T16 manufactured by Diamond T. Two modified half-track suspension units replaced the three standard bogies on each track. The modifications included the replacement of the half-track's double support rollers with single rollers similar to those on top of the early Sherman bogies. An additional roller was attached to the hull between the two suspension units. The standard 16-9/16 inch tracks with 79 shoes per side were used and brackets were welded between the tank hull and the rear suspension units. Installed on an M4A1 named "Centipede", this arrangement was tested at Aberdeen Proving Ground. Appearance alone should have been enough to kill the project. However, it was considered unsatisfactory mainly because of its badly overloaded condition.

Below is "Centipede" fitted with the suspension from the half-track truck T16 during its tests at Aberdeen.

A more practical substitution of another vehicle's running gear was the installation of the Allis Chalmers suspension and tracks from the heavy tractor T22. Authorized on 1 May 1943, Detroit Arsenal completed the pilot tank on 25 August. Installed on M4A4, registration number 3031035, the suspension used three bogies per side with a 22 inch wide double pin center guide track of cast steel construction. Each bogie carried two dual wheels sprung by two 7 inch horizontal volute springs. A dual track support roller was mounted at the top of each suspension unit.

From 9 September to 9 December 1943, the tank was at Allis Chalmers for engineering studies. It was then shipped to the Tank Arsenal Proving Ground for tests lasting until 14 June 1944. Numerous failures occurred and the test report concluded that the volute springs were inadequate to support the weight of the M4A4. Further work was cancelled and the tank was shipped to the Ordnance Museum at Aberdeen.

The four photographs on this page show the M4A4 equipped with the Allis Chalmers suspension from the heavy tractor T22 as completed at Detroit Arsenal. The dimensions and general arrangement of this suspension as applied to the Sherman can be seen in the sketches below.

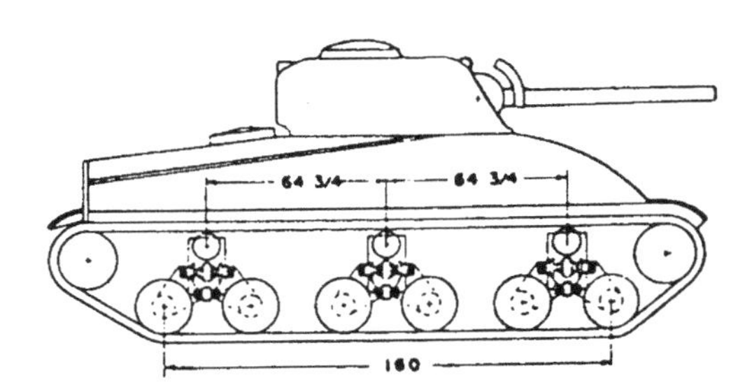

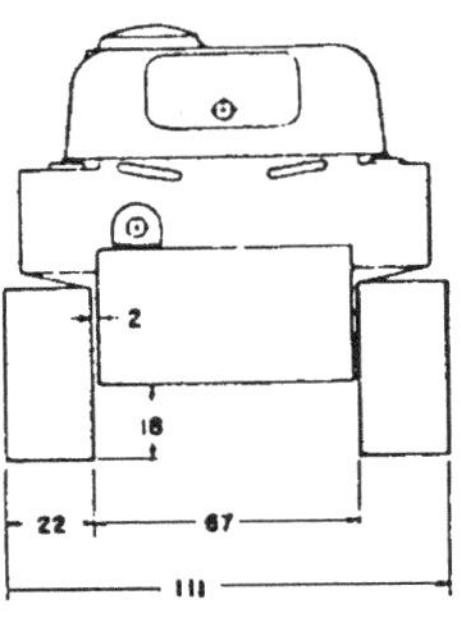

In April 1944, Ordnance requested the development of extended track grousers for use on extremely soft terrain. It was specified that they lower the ground pressure to about 7 psi. Tests at the Tank Arsenal Proving Ground showed that the limiting length for such grousers was 32-1/2 inches when installed on the standard 16-9/16 inch tracks. If the grousers were longer, the offset was too great making the tracks unstable and easily thrown. When the M4E9 spaced out suspension was used, 37 inch grousers gave satisfactory performance. The extended grousers were attached over the double pin tracks using special end

The 32-½ inch grousers are installed here on a late model M4A3. It is obvious that such grousers greatly increased the tank's ground contact area thus reducing the ground pressure.

connectors. The flat T51 rubber block shoes were used in the tests, although Fort Knox later recommended that rubber backed steel tracks be used for longer life. Heat treated for better wear resistance, the extended grousers had a life of approximately 1000 miles. Severe vibration was noted during the tests on hard roads at speeds below 6 miles/hour. However, at higher speeds above the resonant range, the vibrations decreased and the performance was satisfactory. The use of fenders and sandshields was recommended since the grousers threw mud and dirt onto the rear deck of the tank restricting the air flow and causing the engine to overheat.

A similar set of 39 inch extended grousers was developed for use with the horizontal volute spring suspension and the 23 inch T80 tracks. Also attached by special end connectors, these grousers added about 2-1/2 tons to the tank. Despite the heavier weight, the 39 inch track width lowered the ground pressure to about 7 psi.

Above, the 37 inch wide grousers are installed on an M4A3E9 with the spaced out suspension. Compare with the photographs on the previous page showing the 32-½ inch grousers used on the standard vertical volute spring suspension.

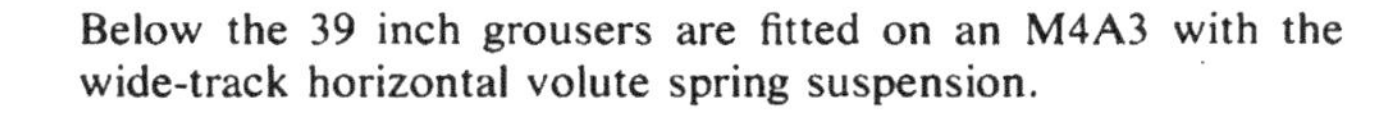

Below the 39 inch grousers are fitted on an M4A3 with the wide-track horizontal volute spring suspension.

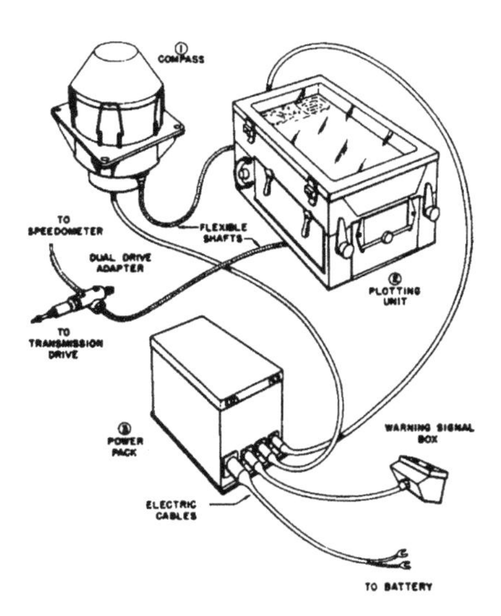

The odograph is mounted above the transmission in medium tank M4A1E2 (above left) for test during desert maneuvers. A schematic arrangement of the odograph equipment is at the right.

COMPONENT AND ACCESSORY DEVELOPMENT

During 1942, considerable development effort was devoted to the problems of desert warfare. On 6 July, OCM 18515 assigned the designation medium tank M4A1E1 to an experimental vehicle being used to evaluate the feasibility of cooling the crew compartment for hot weather operations. The tank was equipped with a Fleischer evaporative cooling unit and metal foil insulation. The latter lined the crew compartment and covered the transmission case to reduce the heat transfer. A double transmission oil cooler had to be installed to compensate for the insulation. Tests at the GM Proving Ground indicated that the cooling and ventilating systems were inadequate. The test report recommended an increase in the cooling capacity and that the layout be redesigned. However, the interest in such development had decreased. After 1942, the war moved out of the desert reducing the need for this kind of equipment and work was shifted to higher priority projects.

Another vehicle designated under OCM 18515 was the medium tank M4A1E2. It was equipped with several devices under development by Ordnance and the National Defense Research Committee (NDRC). A recording odograph was installed to permit navigation without outside aid. This equipment would have been particularly useful in featureless unmarked areas such as the desert. The odograph mapped the tank's route by means of a magnetic compass to indicate direction and a connection to the speedometer drive to show the distance traveled. Thus, as it moved, the vehicle's track was plotted continuously on a chart. The apparatus worked very well in a jeep, but the effect of the tank's armor on the magnetic compass was never fully corrected and satisfactory results could not be obtained.

Magnetic compasses were difficult to use on any armored vehicle and this particularly applied to tanks. Most U.S. vehicles were equipped with the M6 compass manufactured by the Sherrill Research Corporation, but the accuracy was limited to plus or minus 20 degrees. Some other models were also installed, but eventually all were considered unsatisfactory. Many were removed from the Shermans during the postwar period.

The M4A1E2 at the left is equipped with infrared lights and a viewing device to permit operations in total darkness.

To provide an instrument suitable for use inside a tank hull, several types of gyroscopic compasses were developed. These were unaffected by the steel armor, but they occupied more space than the magnetic instrument. A more important shortcoming was that the error in such a device was cumulative with time, hence it had to be corrected or "caged" at frequent intervals. The gyroscopic compasses were still experimental at the end of the war.

The M4A1E2 also was used to evaluate infrared equipment for night operations. Included were headlights, filtered to eliminate all visible light, and a viewing device replacing the driver's periscope. The latter permitted him to drive using the infrared lights under total blackout conditions. Experiments were also conducted with special paint which would make objects flooded with infrared light highly visible through the viewing device, but invisible in the dark to the naked eye.

The tank also was used to test special large size grease fittings in an effort to improve lubrication. The program at Aberdeen and Fort Knox showed the need for further work on various experimental items and the report concluded that they were unsatisfactory at that stage of development.

As mentioned previously, three M4A1 test tanks (1st, 2nd, and 3rd Blitz) were used to evaluate a number of proposed modifications. On "2nd Blitz" they included a mock-up installation of the commander's vision cupola and the small oval hatch for the loader in the 75mm gun turret. This arrangement proved superior to that on the early production 76mm gun turret which had the commander's cupola and a rotating split circular hatch for the loader. The high silhouette of the latter partially obscured the vision from the cupola. A new version of the circular hatch was tested which was approximately 1 inch lower in height, but when open, the double doors completely blocked the view from the cupola. In contrast, the small oval hatch could lay flat in the open position allowing a clear field of vision. Without the rotating hatch ring, a separate pedestal mount was provided for the .50 caliber antiaircraft machine gun.

Medium tank M4A1 "2nd Blitz" (below) has been fitted with a mock-up of the commander's vision cupola for evaluation at Fort Knox. Also, note the small oval hatch in the turret roof for the loader.

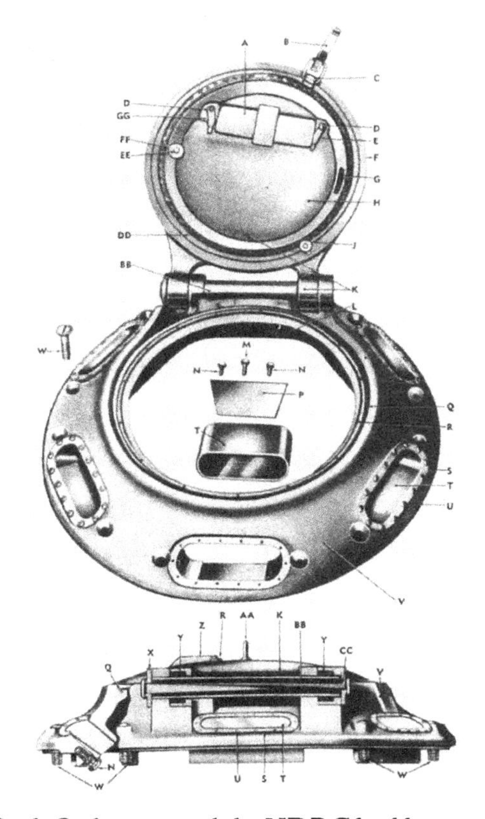

A mock-up of an early NDRC experimental vision cupola is shown above. The mirrors were replaceable from within the turret. At the left is the production model vision cupola installed in the Sherman. The vision blocks cannot be replaced from inside, but a standard periscope also is installed in the hatch cover. The letters identify the various parts from the Standard Nomenclature List (SNL).

Both Ordnance and the NDRC had been engaged in development work to produce a suitable vision cupola. The version adopted for the medium tank was fitted with six laminated glass vision blocks uniformly spaced around the central 21 inch diameter hatch. The blocks were 8 inches long and 3 inches thick and they provided protection against horizontal .50 caliber armor piercing fire at 100 yards. The six blocks gave a 360 degree field of view with vertical limits of +65 to –15 degrees. One M6 periscope was installed in a rotating mount in the central hatch cover and it could be replaced by 7x binoculars. The cupola body armor was 1-1/2 inches thick at 30 degrees on the sides with a 3/4 inch top. It was installed in the same 29-3/4 inch diameter turret roof opening as the older split circular hatch. Installation of the vision cupola required the modification of the tank commander's vane sight by reducing the height of the front element.

The vision cupola was recommended for installation on all production tanks and it was tested in comparison with the British cupola. The Armored Board preferred the U.S. design, mainly because of the larger hatch opening. They recommended that the desirable features of the British cupola be considered for future U.S. designs. These included the 360 degree rotation and the method of hatch closure without exposing the tank commander.

In addition to the cupola development, other work on vision devices covered new periscopes and sighting equipment. The M6 was the standard periscope used on the Sherman for all crew members except the gunner. It consisted of two large prisms assembled in each end of a metal shell. Frequent problems with moisture condensation resulted in the development of a new periscope consisting of a solid block of plastic with a reflecting surface at each end. Standardized near the end of the war as the periscope M13, it had a 10 inch offset and a window 1-7/8 inches high by 6 inches wide. The improvement in vision is well illustrated by comparing the M13 with the small prewar protectoscope installed on the medium tank M3. The protectoscope had a window about 3/4 inches high and 4 inches wide with an offset of only 1-1/2 inches making it impossible to install in heavy armor.

The sketch at the left shows the operation of the early protectoscope. The wartime development in periscopes can be seen at the right. Here, from left to right, are the periscope M6 (rear and front) and the late model periscope M13 (front).

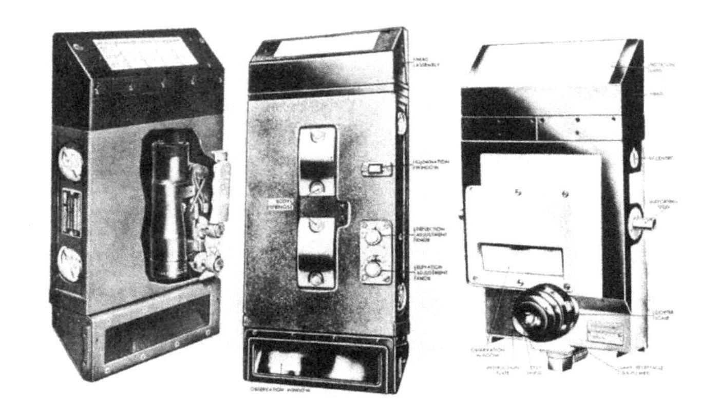

The periscopes M4, M8A1, and M10 (left to right) illustrate the development of gunner's periscopic sights during the war.

Efforts to improve the driver's vision included the experimental installation of rear view mirrors. Although some improvement was obtained when the driver's head was exposed, they only appeared on very late production tanks.

The development of fire control equipment also showed considerable progress. The standard gunner's sight on Shermans armed with the 75mm gun in the M34 mount was the periscope M4. It enclosed the telescope M38 fitted with a ballistic reticle. A later version was the M4A1 equipped with the telescope M38A2. The magnification was 1.44x with a 9 degree field of view and the later model periscope was provided with reticle lighting. For use with the 76mm gun and 105mm howitzer, the M4A1 periscope was fitted with the telescopes M47A2 or M77C respectively. The M8 and M8A1 periscopes were similar to the M4 series, but they were somewhat larger. The M8A1 was equipped with the telescope M39A2 having a 1.8x magnification with a 6 degree field. It was suitable for use with the 76mm gun as it had the same reticle as the M47A2.

Late in the war, the earlier periscopic sights were superseded by the M10 series which actually consisted of two telescopes, both linked to the gun. There was a 1x magnification system for firing at nearby targets with a horizontal field of 42 degrees, 10 minutes and a vertical field of 8 degrees, 10 minutes. For long range use, the 6x telescope had an 11 degree, 20 minute field. Fitted with an appropriate reticle, the M10s were used with the 75mm and 76mm guns and the 105mm howitzer. The periscope M16 was similar to the M10, but was equipped with a reticle adjusting mechanism. Greatly improved mounts for the periscopic sights were introduced with the M10. The sheet metal holders and inadequate linkage of the early models were replaced with cast steel cases and rigid preloaded ball bearing linkages.

The direct sight telescopes showed similar development. The original M55 and M51 telescopes were introduced for use with the 75mm and 76mm guns respectively. They only differed in the reticle and both had a 3x magnification with a 12 degree, 19 minute field of view. The M55 also was originally used with the tank mounted 105mm howitzer. These telescopes were replaced by the M70 series which were the same size and magnification, but had much superior optical quality. Later developments included the M71 with 5x magnification and a 13 degree field. With the proper reticle, it was used with the 76mm gun. The M76 series were similar in construction, but the magnification was reduced to 3x and the field was increased to 21 degrees, 30 minutes. The M76G was used with the 105mm howitzer in the M52 mount. The telescope M83 differed from the earlier models in having a variable power optical system for use under different light conditions. The magnification was 4x or 8x corresponding to 7 degrees, 40 minutes or 4 degrees, 15 minutes fields of view. The M83D had the proper reticle for use with the 76mm gun in the M62 mount.

Changes in other fire control equipment included the introduction of the azimuth indicator M20 before the end of the war. It was similar to the standard M19, but added an outer "gunner's aid" dial for laying off corrections in deflection. Along with the elevation quadrant M9, the azimuth indicators were used for indirect fire. Other efforts to improve the indirect fire control involved the experimental installation of the cant corrector T10 and periscope or turret roof mounts for an artillery type panoramic telescope.

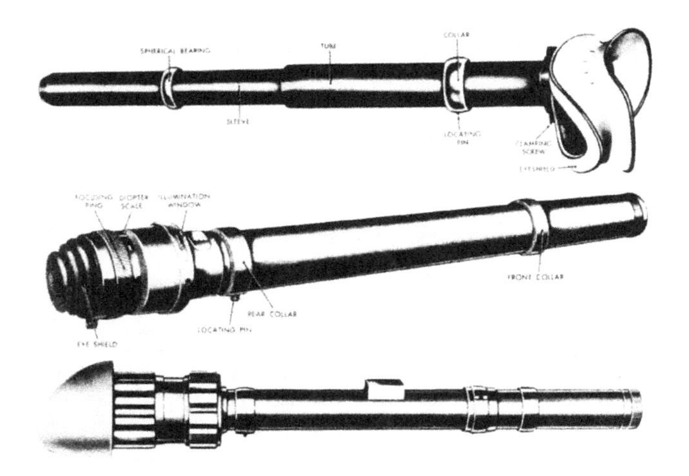

From top to bottom are the direct sight telescopes M70, M76, and M83.

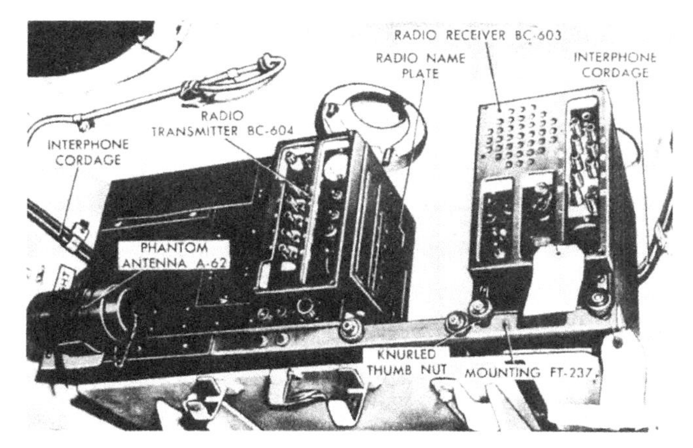

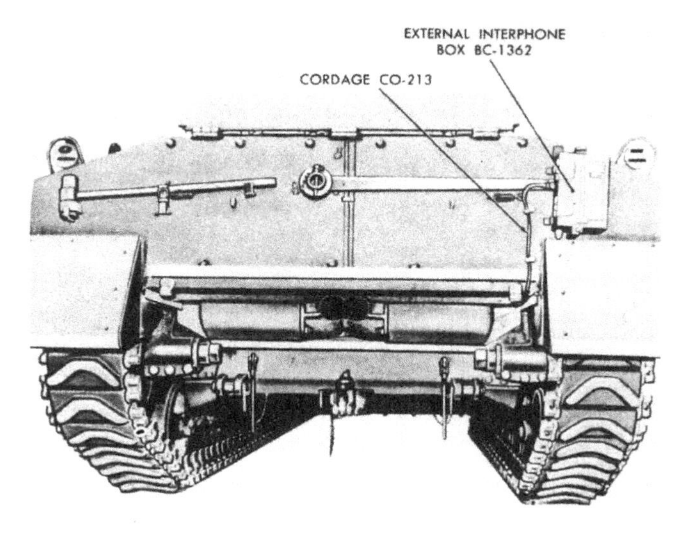

Above, the SCR 528 is installed in the turret bustle. Note the single receiver. The external interphone box is shown at the right on the rear hull plate of an M4A2.

The Signal Corps radios (SCR) 508, 528, and 538 were standard for installation in Shermans used by U.S. troops. They were frequency modulated (FM) sets with a rated voice range of 10 to 20 miles. However, depending on terrain, the actual range was often 5 to 8 miles or even less. The SCR 508 consisted of a BC 604 transmitter with an integral interphone and two BC 603 receivers, all attached to an FT 237 mounting base installed in the turret bustle. The SCR 528 was identical, but it had only one receiver. The SCR 538 had no transmitter and consisted of one BC 603 receiver with a BC 605 interphone amplifier on the same FT 237 mount.

With its two receivers, the SCR 508 was used by the tank company commander allowing him to have one receiver tuned to battalion and one to his platoons. The SCR 528 was used by platoon leaders, platoon sergeants, and other tanks that required two way communication.

In addition to its FM set, a command tank at battalion level was frequently equipped with an SCR 506. This was an amplitude modulated (AM) set with a rated range of 25 to 50 miles for voice or 75 to 100 miles for code. The equipment consisted of a BC 653 transmitter and a BC 652 receiver on a FT 253 mounting installed in the Sherman's right sponson. These command tanks could be identified by the antenna in the right sponson receptacle. When the SCR 506 was not available, the SCR 245 or the SCR 193 were often substituted. The range for both voice and code was much shorter for the older sets.

The cooperation of tanks with infantry resulted in numerous improvised methods of communication such as the exchange of radios and the installation of field telephones on the outside of the tanks. The AN/VRC 3 was an adaptation of the infantry's SCR 300 Walkie Talkie pack type radio. When carried, it was mounted on the left turret wall in front of the loader. Operated by either the loader or the tank commander, it allowed direct communication with the accompanying infantry.

The RC 298 interphone extension kit also provided a link with the infantry outside the tank. It consisted of a hand set in the external interphone box BC 1362 mounted on spacers welded to the right rear of the hull. Connected to the tank's interphone system, it permitted the infantry to talk to the crew when the tank was buttoned up.

A number of special training devices were improvised at Fort Knox to aid in tank gunnery instruction. These included a wobble plate to simulate the tank's rolling motion when demonstrating the use of the gyrostabilizer. This equipment was later replaced by the cutaway turret used to familiarize the student gunner with his future surroundings. Lima Locomotive also constructed special turret trainers equipped with the 75mm gun M3 in the combination gun mount M34A1.

The radios normally found in a medium tank company are indicated above each vehicle in the sketch below. At the right is a cutaway turret trainer in use at Fort Knox.

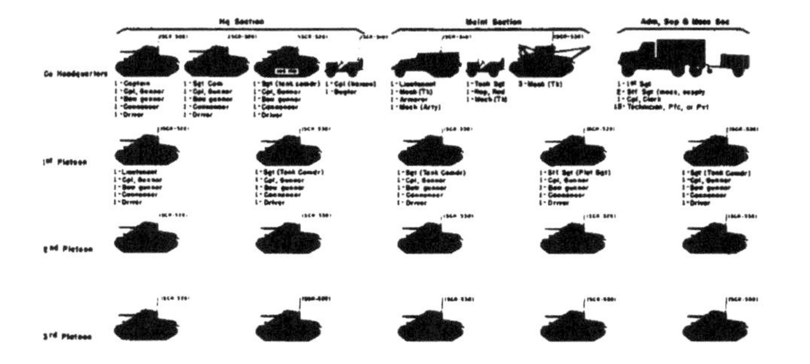

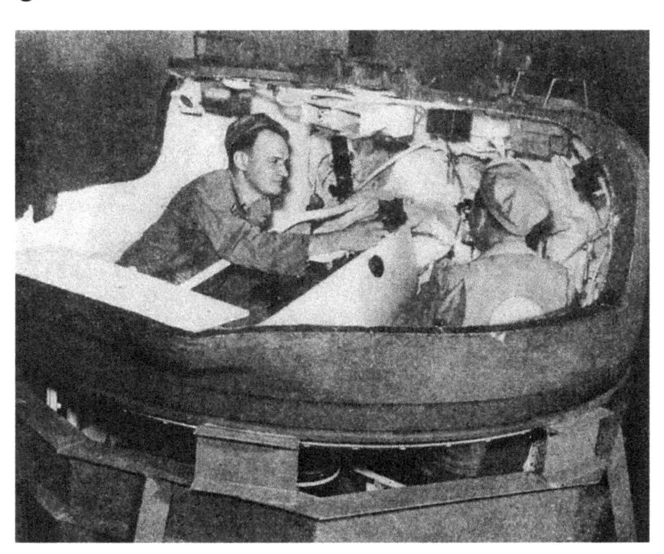

The hull for the pilot of the "Ultimate" 76mm gun medium tank M4 is shown here at Detroit Arsenal in January 1944. This is the tank that was eventually tested at Fort Knox with the high speed reverse transmission.

THE IMPROVEMENTS REACH PRODUCTION

By the Summer of 1943, the list of required modifications for the Sherman had greatly increased. These changes resulted from battle experience with the early models as well as data produced by the development and test programs. Early that year, the Armored Force had concluded that the war would be won or lost with the M4 tank series and that they should be modified to improve their combat efficiency and to incorporate a number of major changes. Among the latter, items such as the 76mm gun, the 105mm howitzer, wet stowed ammunition, and larger drivers' hatches made it necessary to rework a large part of the tank.

To insure interchangeability of parts and standardized stowage between all models, a major redesign of the Sherman began in July 1943. At that time, the new vehicles were referred to as the medium tank M4 series (ultimate design). Drawings were prepared for 76mm gun versions of the M4, M4A1, M4A2, and M4A3. Designs were also included for the M4 and M4A3 armed with the 105mm howitzer. The 75mm gun was retained only on the M4A3 and both the M4A4 and the M4A6 were dropped.

On the 75mm and 76mm gun tanks the ammunition was relocated from the sponsons to water protected racks below the turret. Ten boxes on the hull floor held 100 75mm rounds and required 37.1 gallons of water. An additional gallon protected the 4 round ready rack on the turret floor. Thus with 104 rounds stowed using 38.1 gallons of water, 0.366 gallons per round were required in the M4A3 armed with the 75. In the 76mm gun tanks, the ammunition also was located on the hull floor with 30 rounds on one side of the drive shaft and 35 on the other. These containers held a total of 34.5 gallons of water. The 6 ready rounds were carried in a box on the turret floor filled

The pilots for the 105mm howitzer armed M4 (left) and the M4A2 with the 76 (right) appear above at Detroit Arsenal in February 1944.

with another 2.1 gallons. Using 36.6 gallons for 71 rounds of ammunition, the water requirement was 0.515 gallons per round for all 76mm wet stowage vehicles.

To prevent freezing during cold weather, water solutions of ethylene glycol were frequently used in wet stowage racks. Problems with rust led to the addition of corrosion inhibitors to the water. A proprietary solution with such inhibitors was produced by the Wyandotte Chemical Company under the name Ammudamp.

Water protection was not applied to the 105mm howitzer tanks, but armored racks were installed. Sixtysix rounds of 105mm ammunition were carried. The 2 round ready rack on the M4E5 was eliminated from the production tanks to gain additional turret space.

To permit use of the floor ammunition racks, most of the turret basket was removed retaining only a partial floor suspended from the turret ring. This greatly increased the space available and permitted easy access to the driving compartment.

Other changes standardized in the "Ultimate" design included the new 2-1/2 inch thick front armor plate with the larger counter-balanced drivers' hatches and the single piece sharp nosed differential and final drive housing. New seats and improved controls reduced driver fatigue and the commander was provided with a vision cupola and a better traverse control. Components were relocated for greater efficiency in the engine compartment and provision was made for the installation of heaters for cold weather operations.

Chrysler was authorized to build a pilot tank for each of the seven new models. These were converted from older production vehicles and were intended to check out the new design and serve as production prototypes. Although the project started in September 1943, lack of drawings prevented any progress until December. All seven hulls were completed by 5 February 1944. These were as follows:

Model	Registration Number
M4 w/76mm gun	USA 3038783
M4 w/105mm howitzer	USA 30100506
M4A1 w/76mm gun	USA 3036752
M4A2 w/76mm gun	USA 3035448
M4A3 w/75mm gun	USA 3054578
M4A3 w/76mm gun	USA 3054892
M4A3 w/105mm howitzer	USA 3054283

At that time, only four turrets were completed with two 76 and one 105 turret remaining to be finished under another project.

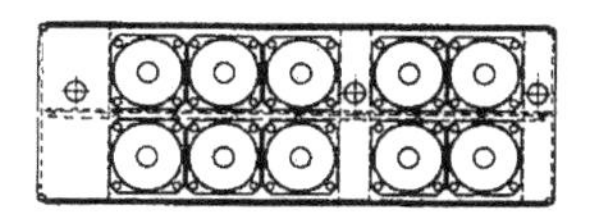

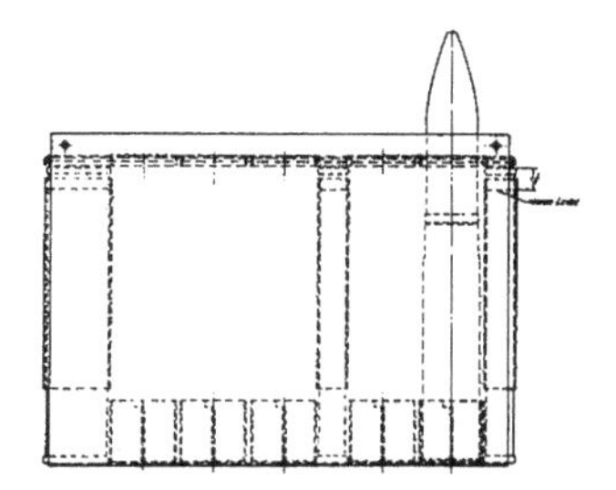

Below are the pilots for the new M4A3s armed with the 75 (left) and 76 (right). A 75mm wet stowage ammunition rack is sketched at the right.

The early production 76mm gun medium tank M4A1 is illustrated in these three photographs. Note the split circular hatch for the loader.

Production of the new tanks did not wait for the completion of the prototypes. As with the early Sherman, the M4A1 was the first model produced. The first 100 M4A1s with the 76 came off the assembly line at Pressed Steel Car Company in January 1944 beginning a run which was to build 3426 of the tanks by the end of the war. The turrets on the first vehicles were fitted with the split circular hatch for the loader and were armed with the 76mm gun M1A1 without a muzzle brake. The circular loader's hatch was replaced in M4A1 production by the later small oval design at tank number 1225 in August 1944. The 76mm gun M1A1 was superseded by the M1A1C or the M1A2, both of which were threaded for the installation of a muzzle brake. The late production tanks were equipped with the horizontal volute spring suspension and the 23 inch wide center guided track.

The M4 with the 76 was scheduled to enter production during the Summer of 1945. However, it was cancelled because of the reduced requirements for tanks following the end of the war in Europe.

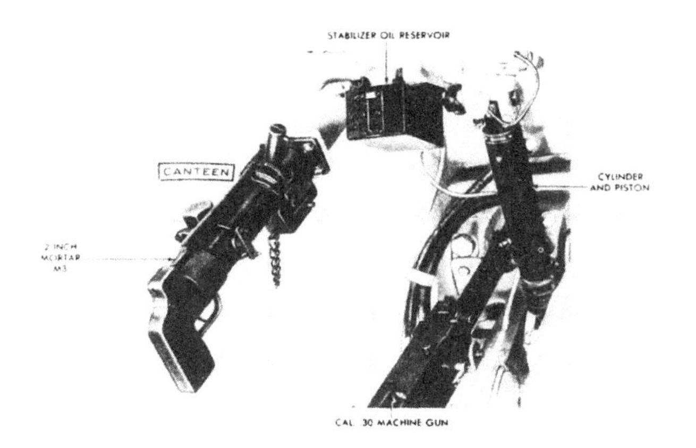

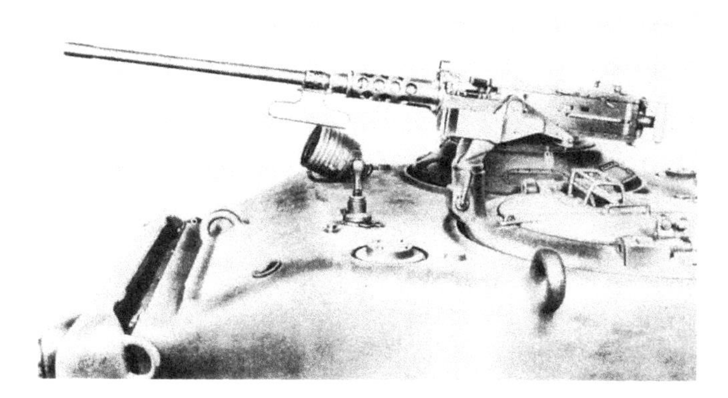

The view in the left front of the turret (top left) shows the smoke mortar in firing position and the coaxial .30 caliber machine gun. On the outside of the turret roof (top right), the smoke mortar port is in the sloped portion just forward of the loader's hatch. Note that the .50 caliber machine gun is now mounted over the loader's station.

The driving compartment is at the right. A .45 caliber M3 submachine gun is stowed on the top right of the transmission below the spare periscope heads.

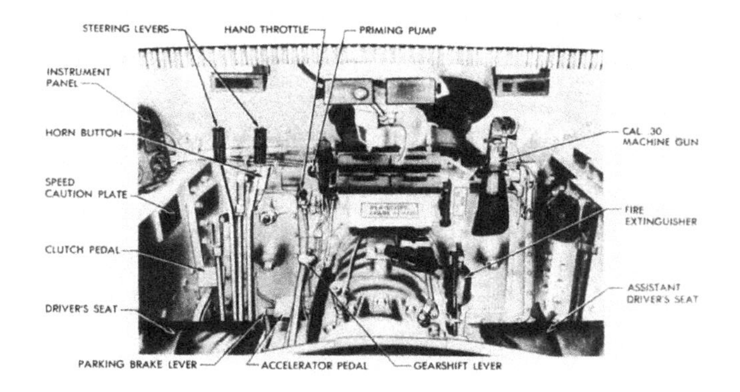

The early production M4A1 below is equipped with full stowage and all four periscopes have been mounted in the driving compartment.

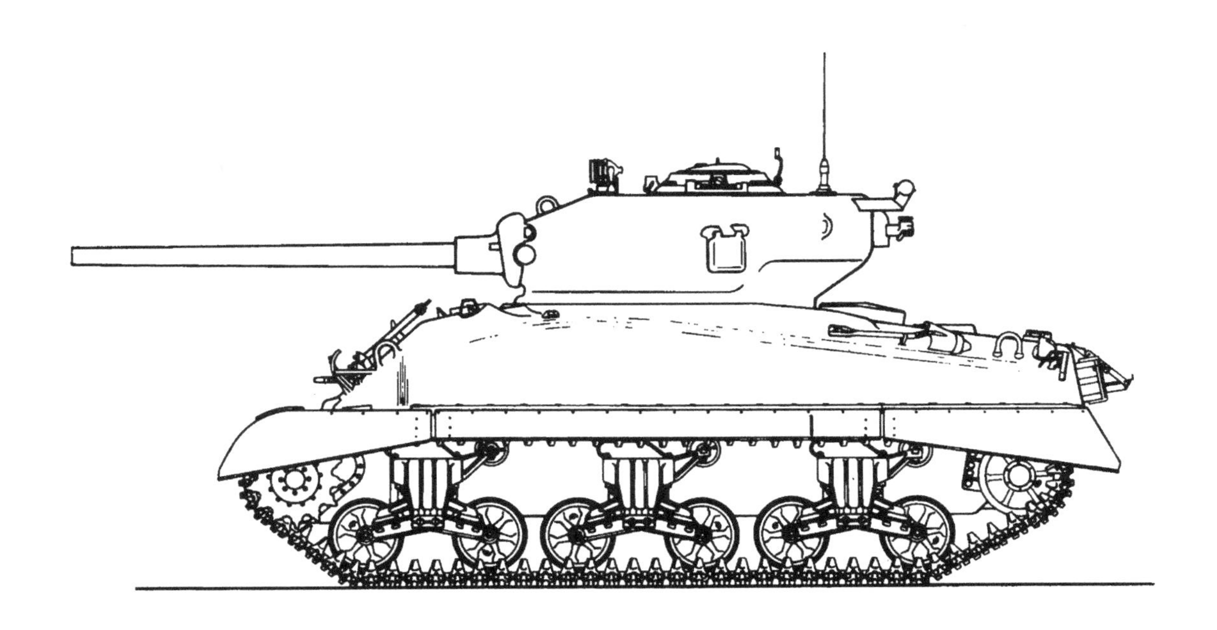

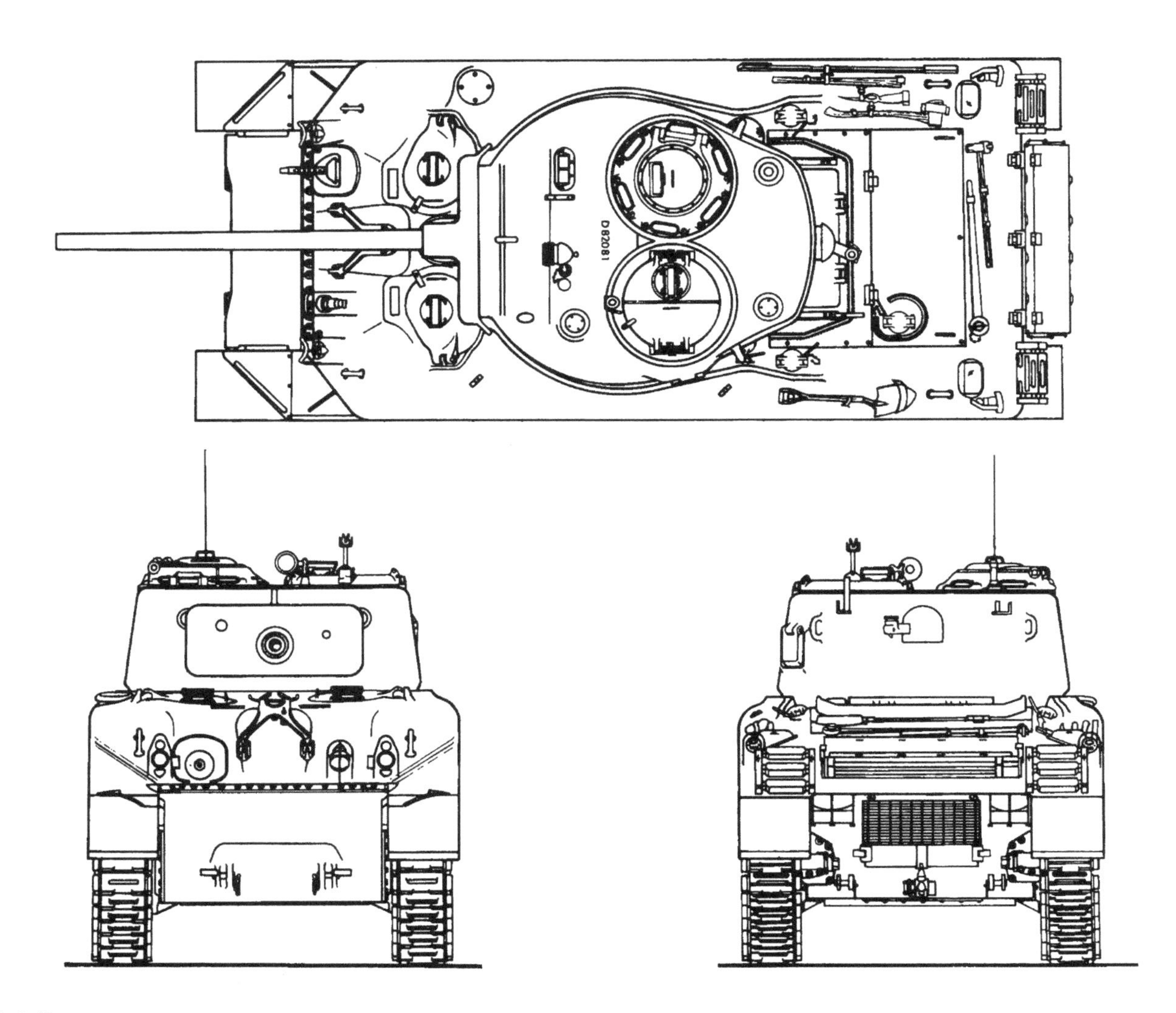

Scale 1:48

Medium Tank M4A1(76)W

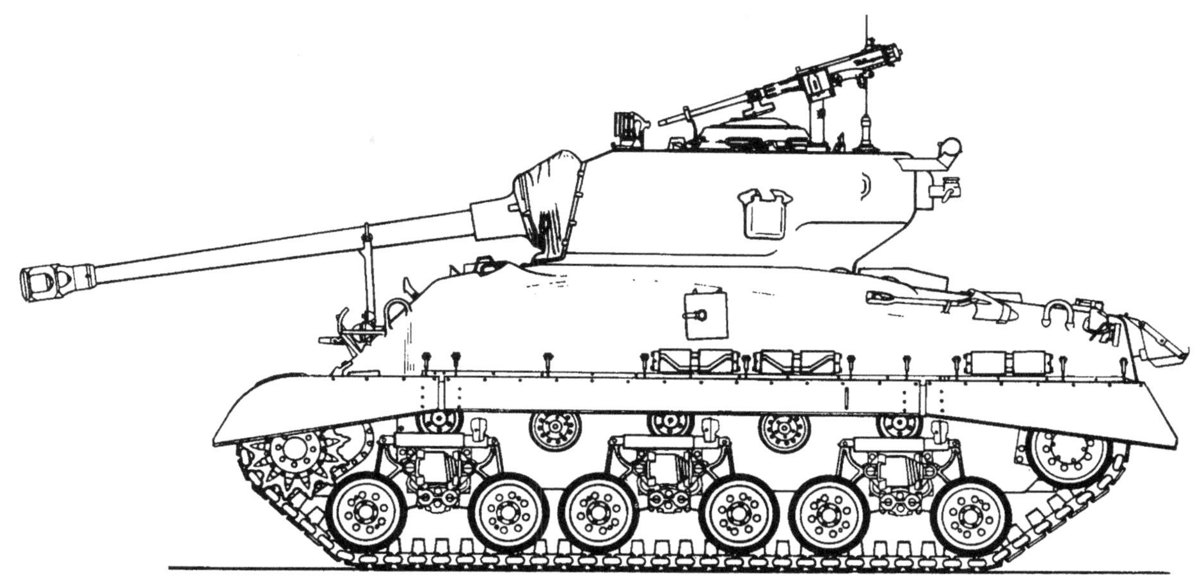

Scale 1:48

Medium Tank M4A1(76)W HVSS

The late production M4A1 armed with the 76mm gun M1A2 fitted with a muzzle brake. This tank represents the final production model of the M4A1 and it is equipped with rear view mirrors and the horizontal volute spring suspension. Note that the T66 single pin tracks are installed on the tank in the upper photograph. The lower view shows a vehicle with the later T80 double pin tracks.

A sectional view of the 76mm gun medium tank M4A1 with the horizontal volute spring suspension is shown above. The numbers refer to the part groups in the Standard Nomenclature List (SNL).

Additional details of the late production M4A1 can be seen in the four photographs below. This tank is fitted with the T66 tracks.

An early production M4 armed with the 105mm howitzer (above and below). The serial number of this particular tank was 56940.

The 105mm howitzer version of the M4 closely followed the new M4A1 into production. The first two howitzer armed vehicles were assembled at Detroit Tank Arsenal in February 1944 and a total of 1641 had been built when production stopped in March 1945. The last 841 vehicles were equipped with the horizontal volute spring suspension and the 23 inch tracks.

The early howitzer armed M4s were not fitted with the vision cupola. They retained the standard split circular hatch for the tank commander, but a small oval hatch was provided for the loader. As supplies became greater, the vision cupola was introduced on the later tanks.

The 16 inch Lipe two plate clutch used with the Continental R975 C1 engine was a constant source of trouble. The need for frequent adjustments and recurring mechanical failures made a suitable replacement highly desirable. The Borg and Beck 17-1/2 inch two plate clutch was developed to solve the problem and it proved superior during tests at Aberdeen. In April 1944, the Ordnance Committee recommended that the Borg and Beck clutch be released for production installation on all M4s and M4A1s and that it be supplied as a replacement part for overseas requirements.

All of the new tanks were fitted with a ventilating blower mounted in the hull roof between the drivers' seats. The 76mm gun turrets had another blower installed in the rear wall of the turret bustle. On the 105mm howitzer tanks, the turret blower was attached below the rear roof ventilator. On the new 75mm gun M4A3, a blower was installed below the single turret roof ventilator.

Further details of the M4 howitzer tank are shown here. Note the lack of a vision cupola for the tank commander although the small oval hatch is provided for the loader.

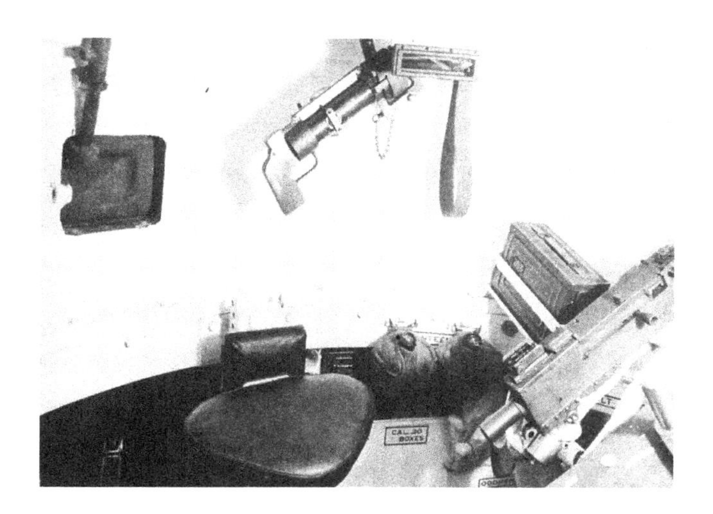

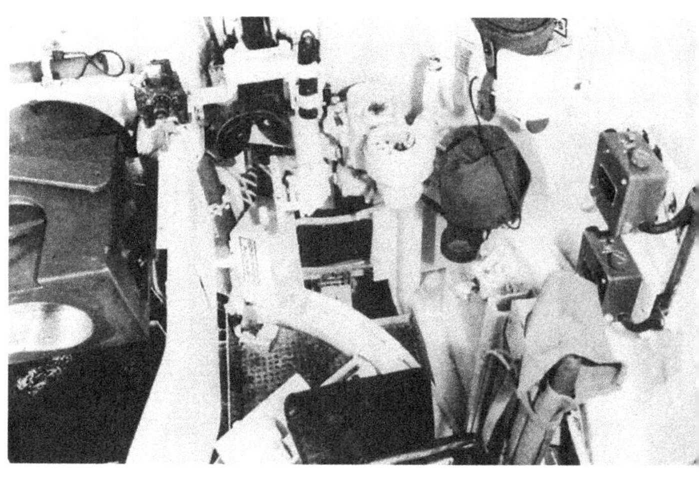

The turret interior on the M4 with the 105mm howitzer. The pistol port, smoke mortar, and coaxial machine gun can be seen at the loader's station (top left) and the gunner's telescopic sight and fire control equipment appear at the top right. An SCR 538 radio is installed in the turret bustle (at right). Note the absence of a transmitter. A .45 caliber Thompson submachine gun is stowed just below the radio.

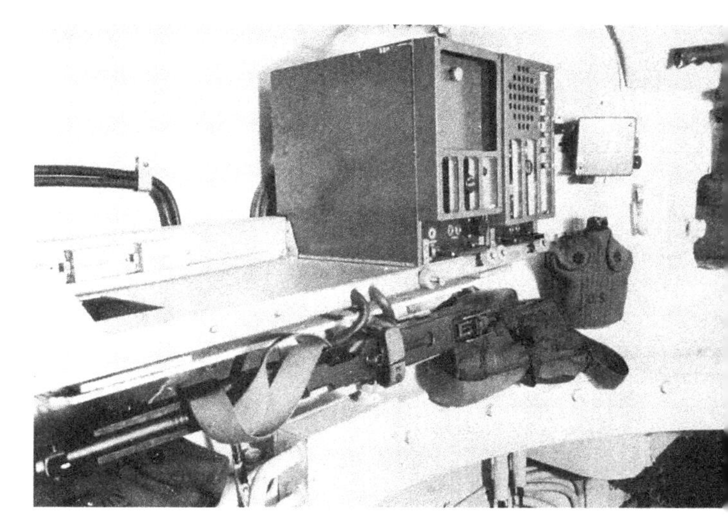

Below are the driver's controls (left) and the bow gunner's station (right). The 105mm ammunition rack can be seen in the right sponson.

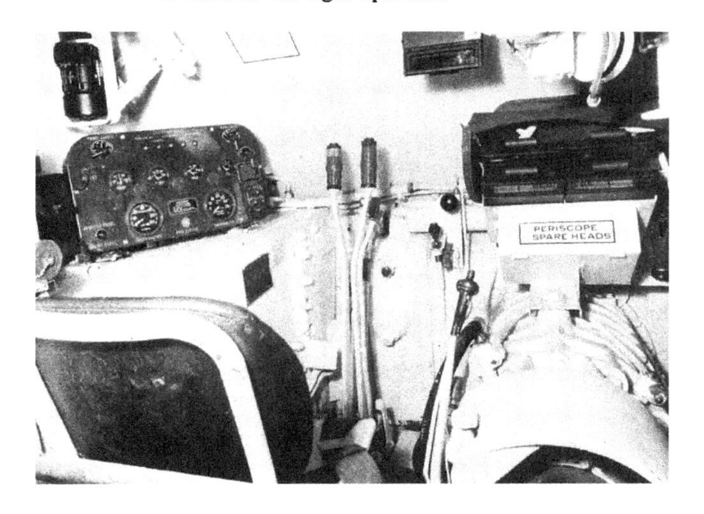

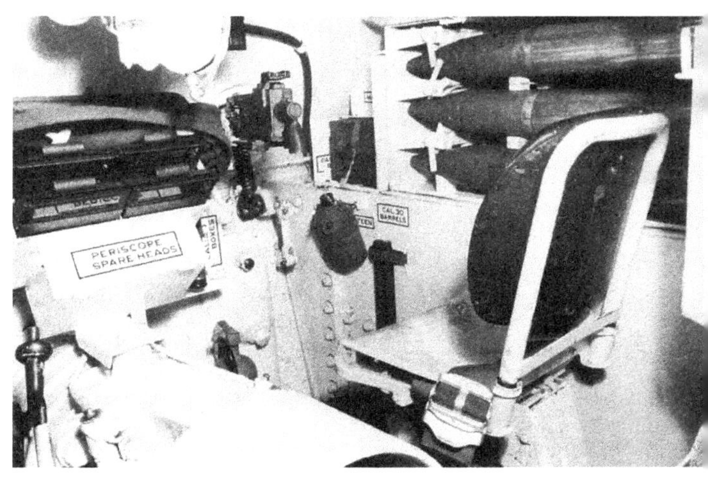

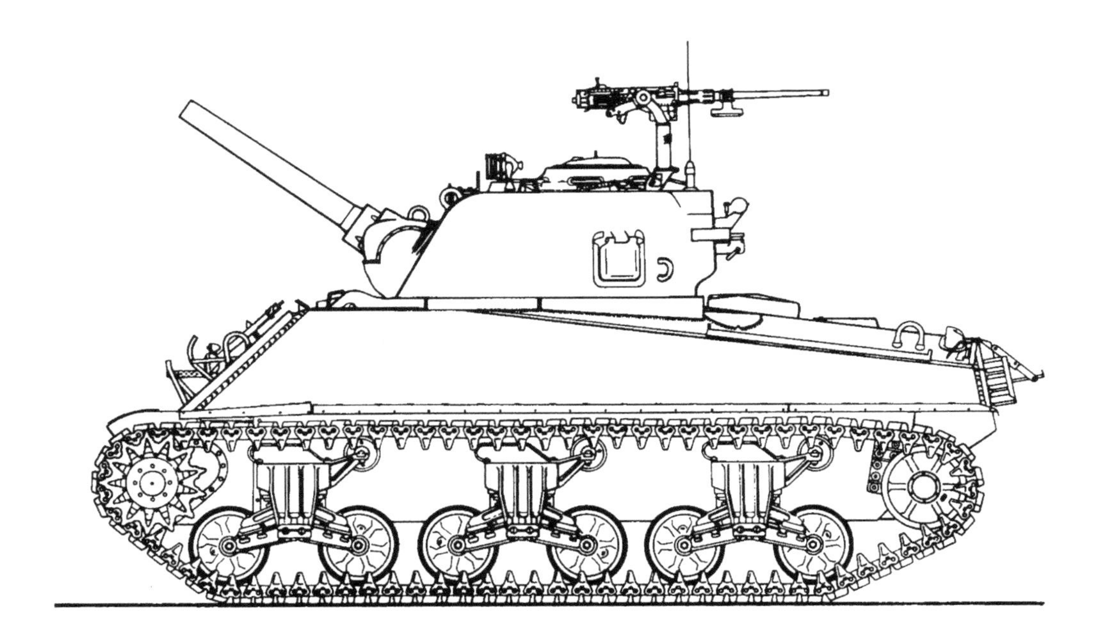

Scale 1:48

Medium Tank M4(105)

The tank at the left is equipped with a vision cupola for the commander, but it still retains the vertical volute spring suspension. The last production version of the M4 with the 105mm howitzer is shown below. It has the horizontal volute spring suspension and the power traverse for the turret.

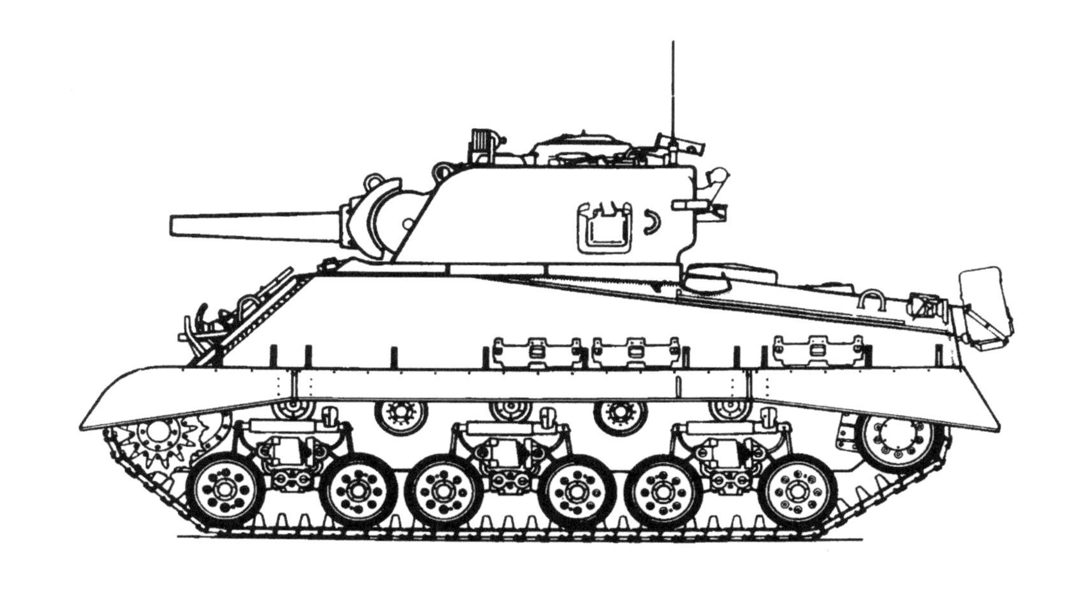

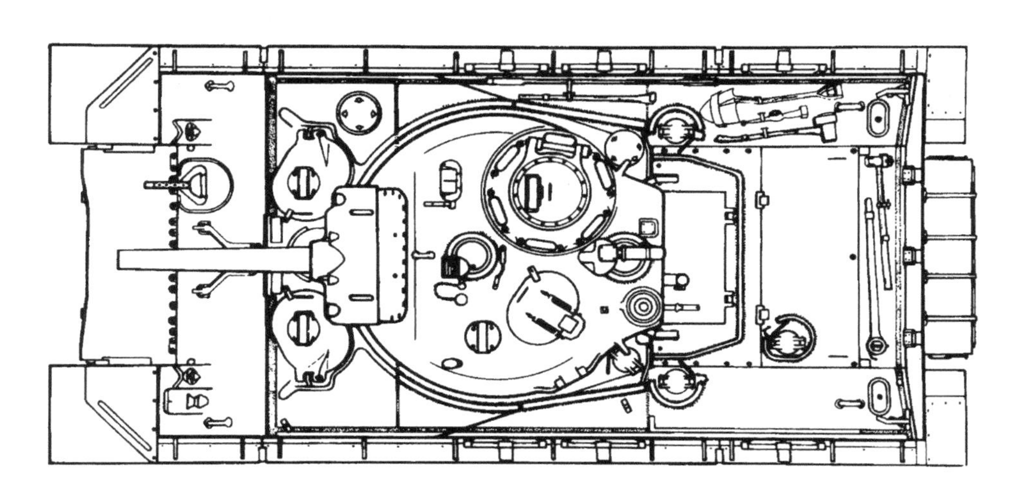

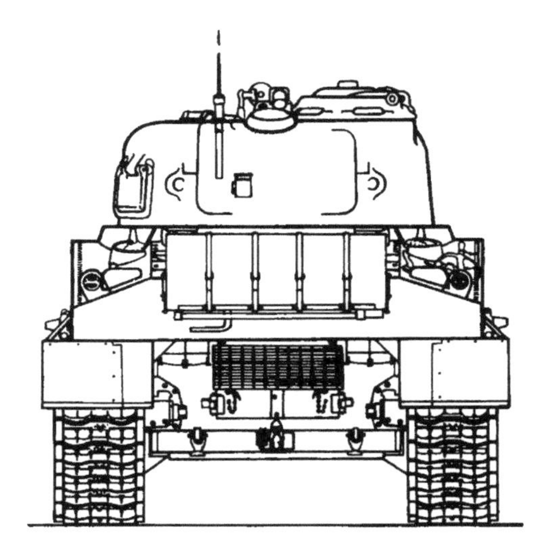

Scale 1:48

Medium Tank M4(105) HVSS

The 75mm gun M4A2 remained in production several months later than the other dry stowage vehicles. Many of these had the new heavier front armor and larger drivers' hatches as well as the turret roof escape hatch for the loader. The last 52 were delivered in May 1944 and during that same month, the first 30 M4A2s with the 76mm gun and wet stowage were completed. Production continued at Fisher until December 1944 delivering 1594 of the new tanks. During the first half of 1945, Fisher produced another 1300 of the M4A2s with the 76. Added to the 21 vehicles built at the Pressed Steel Car Company, the total production of the wet stowage 76mm gun M4A2 reached 2915 tanks. Like the other models, some of the late production vehicles were equipped with the horizontal volute spring suspension. Intended primarily for foreign aid, most of the new M4A2s were supplied to the Soviet Union.

An early production medium tank M4A2 armed with the 76mm gun is shown in these three photographs. This vehicle, serial number 47856, still has the split circular hatch for the loader and the 76mm gun M1A1.

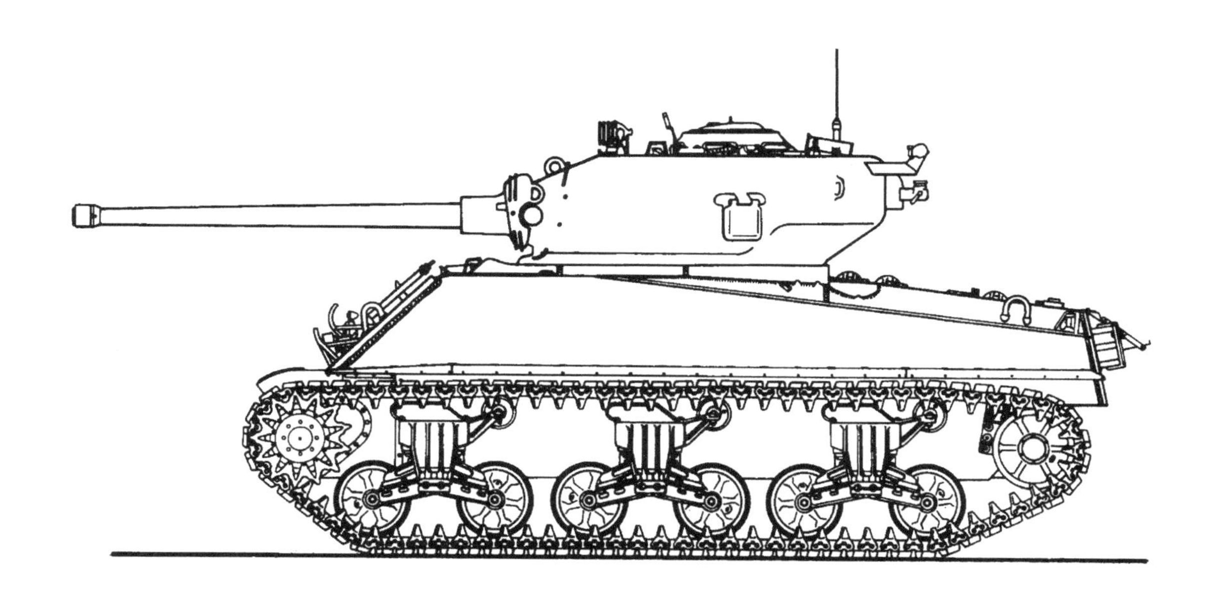

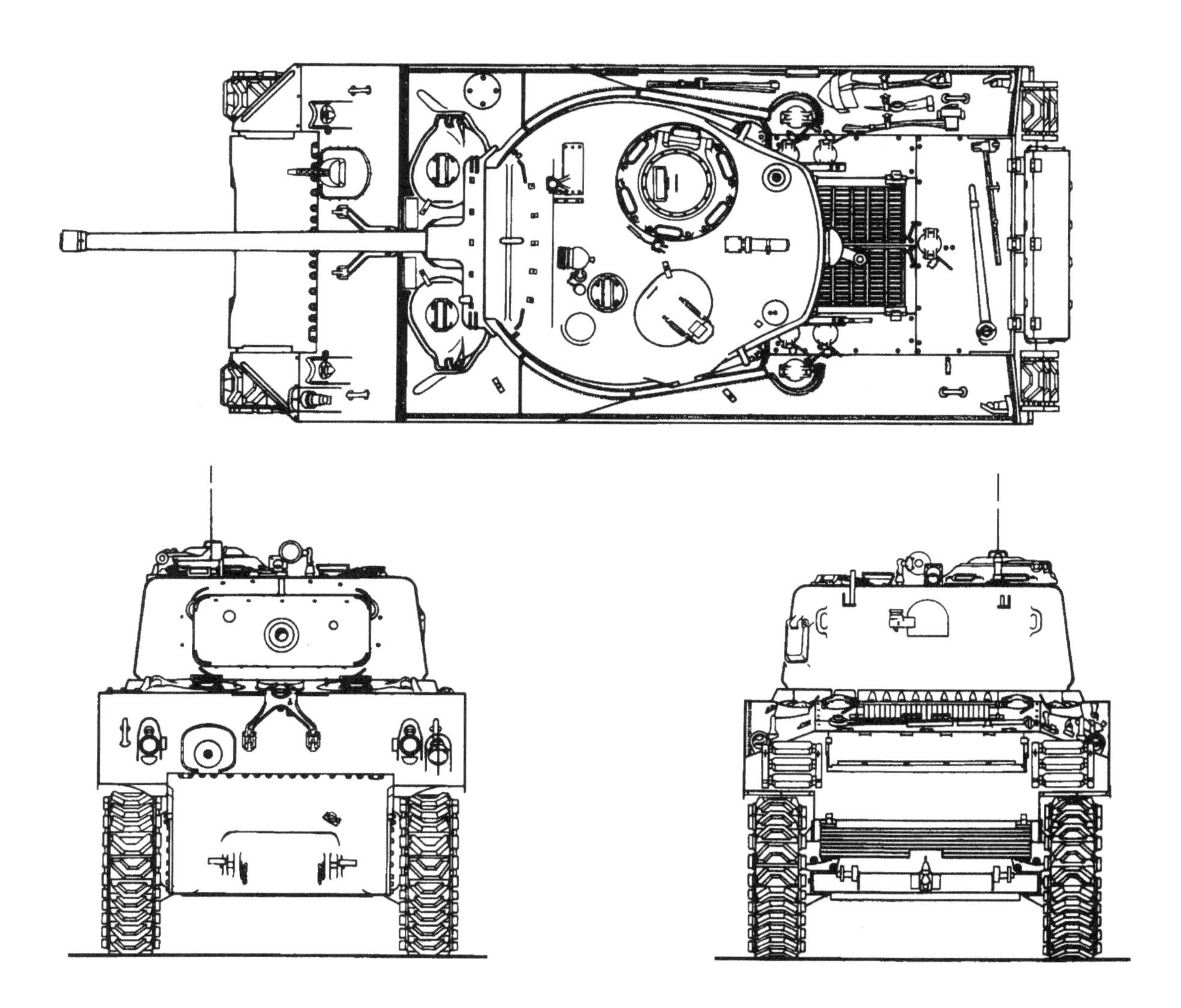

Scale 1:48

Medium Tank M4A2(76) W

Above and at the left are additional views of the 76mm gun medium tank M4A2. Below is the final version equipped with the horizontal volute spring suspension and the 23 inch wide tracks. The cannon also is fitted with a muzzle brake. Note the rare example of rear view mirrors for the driver.

These three photographs show the early production 75mm gun medium tank M4A3 with wet stowage. Although a small oval hatch has been provided for the loader, the original split circular hatch has been retained for the tank commander.

The modernized version of the M4A3 was placed in production with all three types of armament. The Fisher Tank Arsenal manufactured the wet stowage vehicles with the 75mm and 76mm guns. At Detroit Tank Arsenal, Chrysler also produced the 76mm wet stowage tank as well as the 105mm howitzer vehicle.

The 75mm gun wet stowage tank, designated as the M4A3W, first came off the assembly line in February 1944. Production continued until March 1945 with a total run of 3071 tanks. Vision cupola shortages resulted in the assembly of the early production vehicles with the original split circular hatch for the tank commander. Other features of the turret were up to the new standard including the oval loader's hatch. As supplies became available, the vision cupola became standard equipment. Since it was interchangeable with the split circular hatch, the cupola could be installed in the field. When this was done, a pedestal mount for the .50 caliber machine gun was welded to the turret roof to replace the ring mount on the circular hatch.

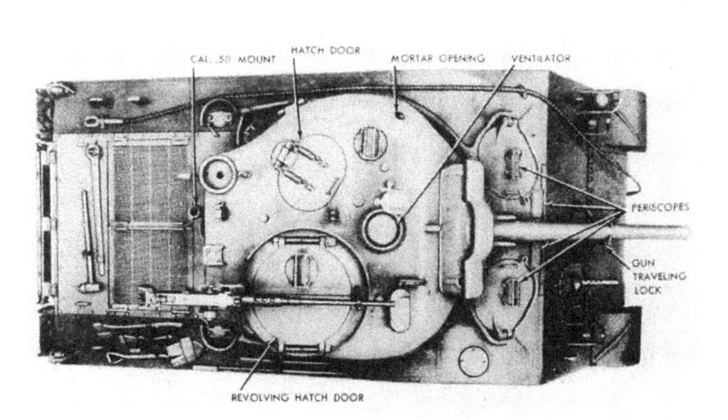

Details on top of the tank can be seen at the right.

The wet stowage M4A3 with the 75mm gun under test at Fort Knox. Note the interference between the .50 caliber machine gun and the radio antenna (below).

The gunner's controls are shown above. Below are the driving compartment (left) and the bow machine gun (right).

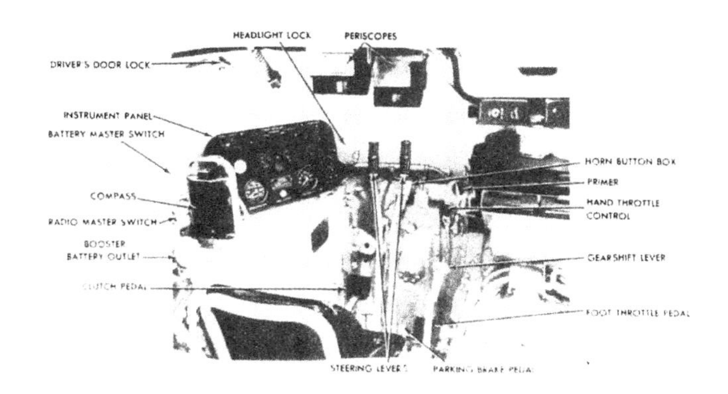

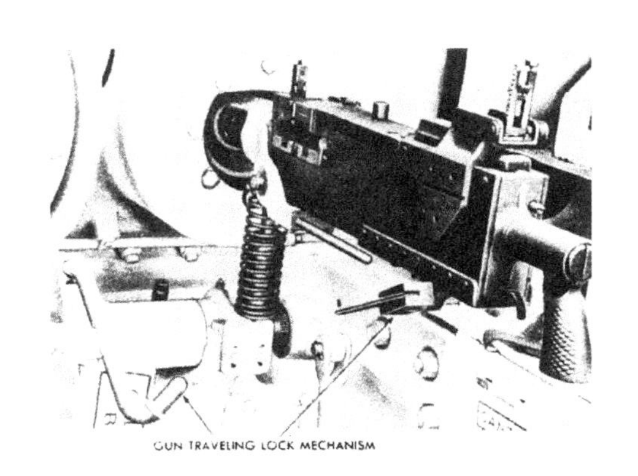

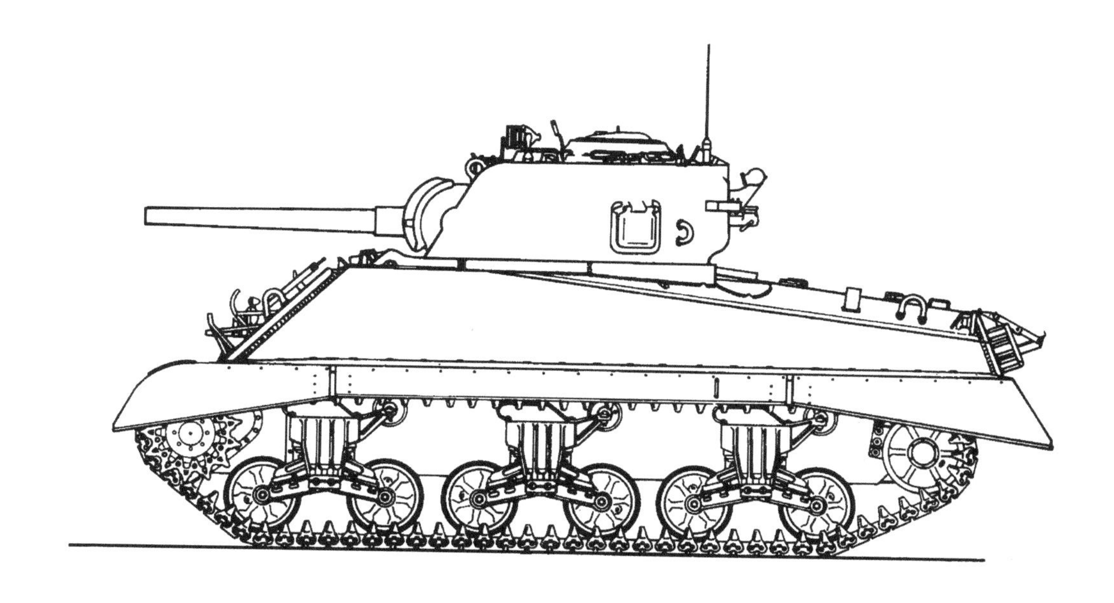

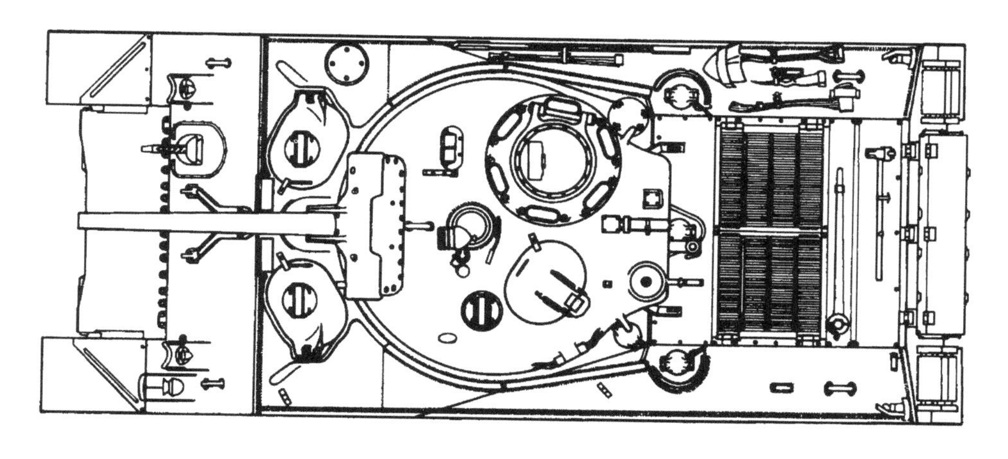

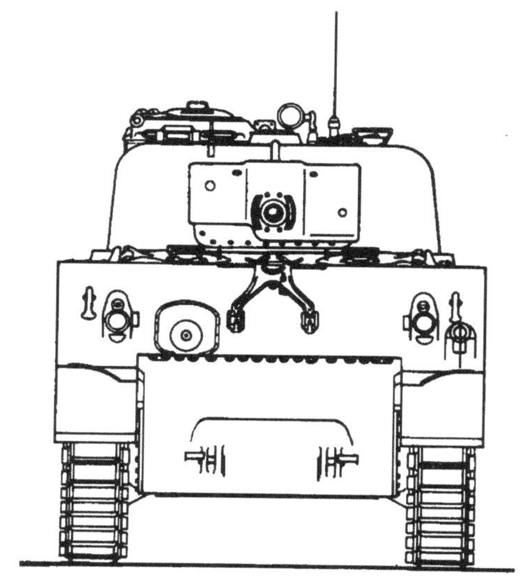

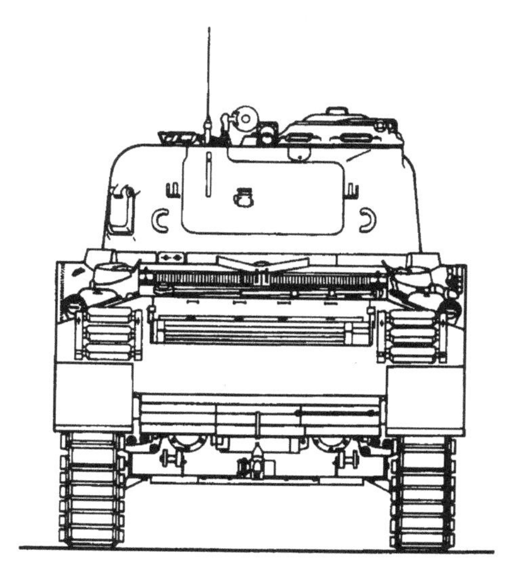

Scale 1:48

Medium Tank M4A3(75) W

The early production medium tank M4A3 armed with the 76mm gun. The vehicle above is fitted with the later model 76mm gun M1A1C or M1A2 threaded for a muzzle brake. The tank below mounts the earlier M1A1 cannon.

As mentioned previously, the M4A3 was the preferred type of Sherman in the U.S. Army and its ultimate production model was the version armed with the 76mm gun. Chrysler began the first production of this new model at Detroit in March 1944 and 1400 vehicles were delivered by the end of August. These tanks were still equipped with the vertical volute spring suspension and the 16-9/16 inch wide tracks. During August, Chrysler shifted to the horizontal volute spring suspension and the 23 inch center guided tracks building ten such tanks before the end of the month. This was the tank that was to serve the U.S. Army for a decade after World War II. Chrysler had completed a total of 2617 wide-track M4A3s with the 76mm gun when production stopped in April 1945. From September through December 1944, Fisher delivered 525 of the new vehicles raising the overall production of the 76mm gun M4A3 to 4542.

Like the other 76mm gun tanks, the early production M4A3s provided a vision cupola for the tank commander and a split circular hatch for the loader. The latter was superseded on later vehicles by the small oval hatch in the turret roof. The first tanks also were armed with the 76mm gun M1A1 which was soon replaced by the M1A1C or the M1A2 with the muzzle brake. A new design floor escape hatch was introduced in the later vehicles. Its location remained the same in the bottom of the hull just behind the assistant driver's seat.

Other changes during the production of the 76mm gun tanks included modification of the gun barrel traveling lock. The double pronged jaws on the early design were replaced by a single locking arm hinged at one side. The first production 76mm gun turrets retained a partial basket under the gunner and tank commander. Although only about one third the size of the original basket, it was eliminated completely from the later vehicles to increase the space available and improve access to the ammunition stowage. On these tanks, the seats for the turret crew were suspended on brackets from the turret ring.

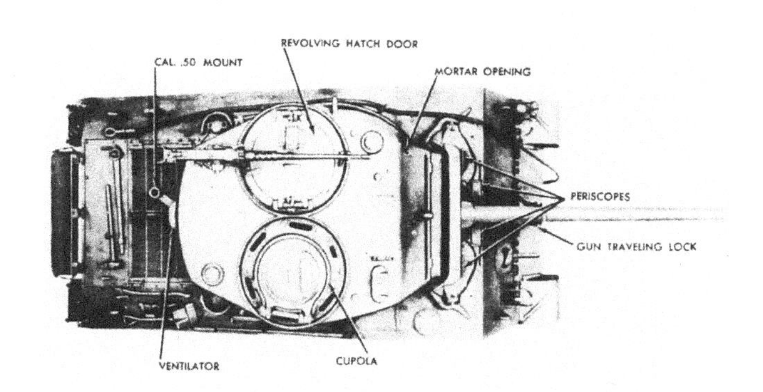

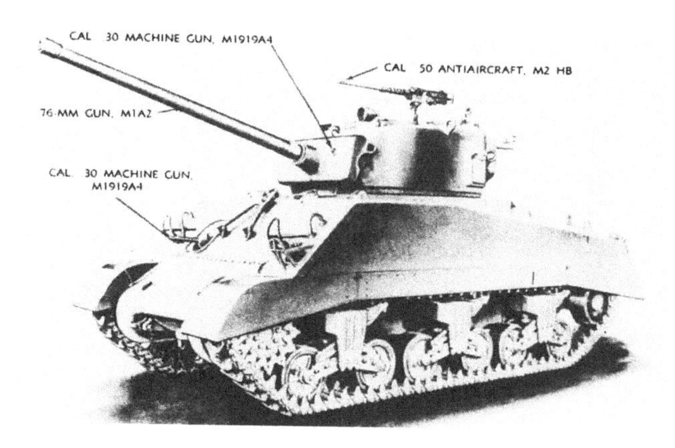

Further details of the early production 76mm gun medium tank M4A3. Note that the tank at the top right is fitted with the 76mm gun M1A2.

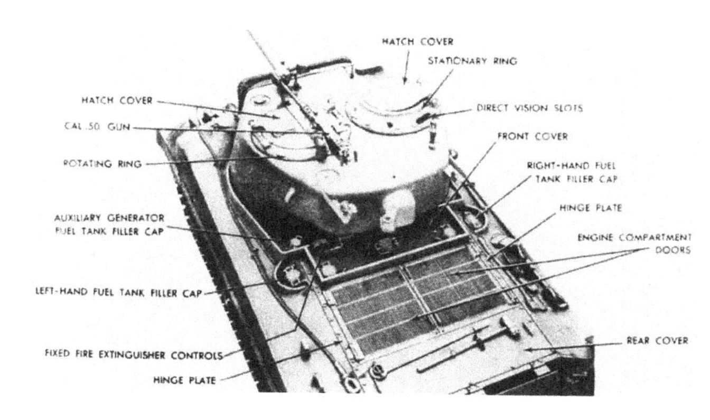

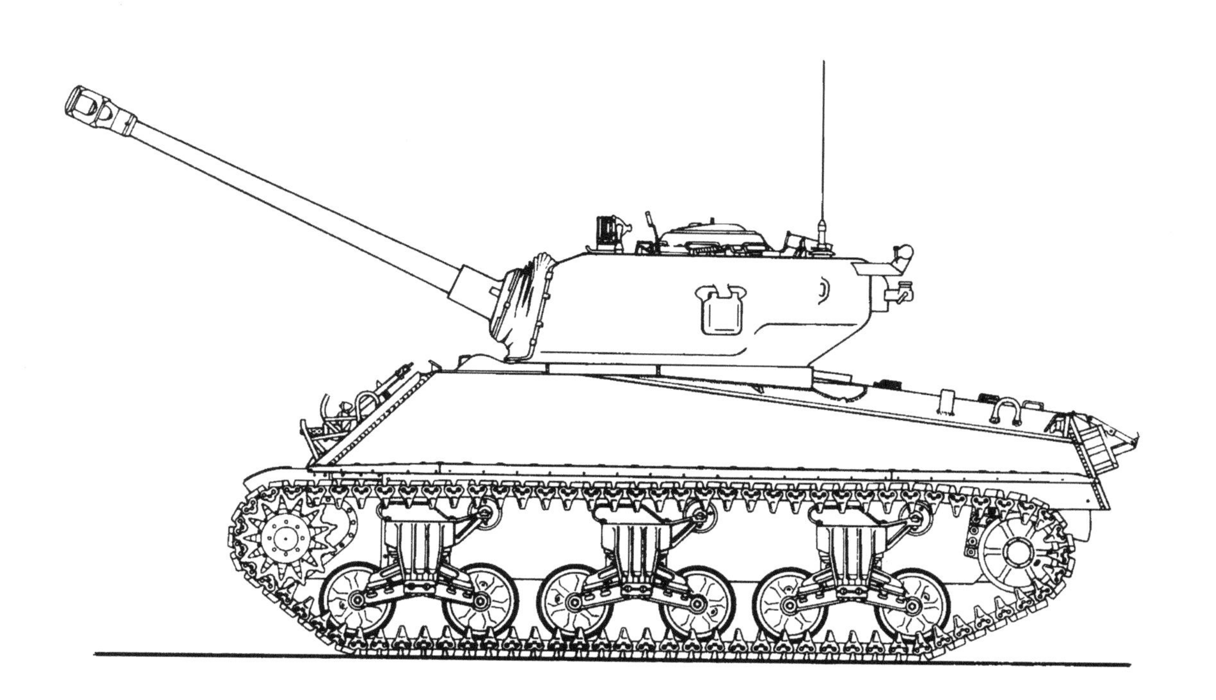

Scale 1:48

Medium Tank M4A3(76) W

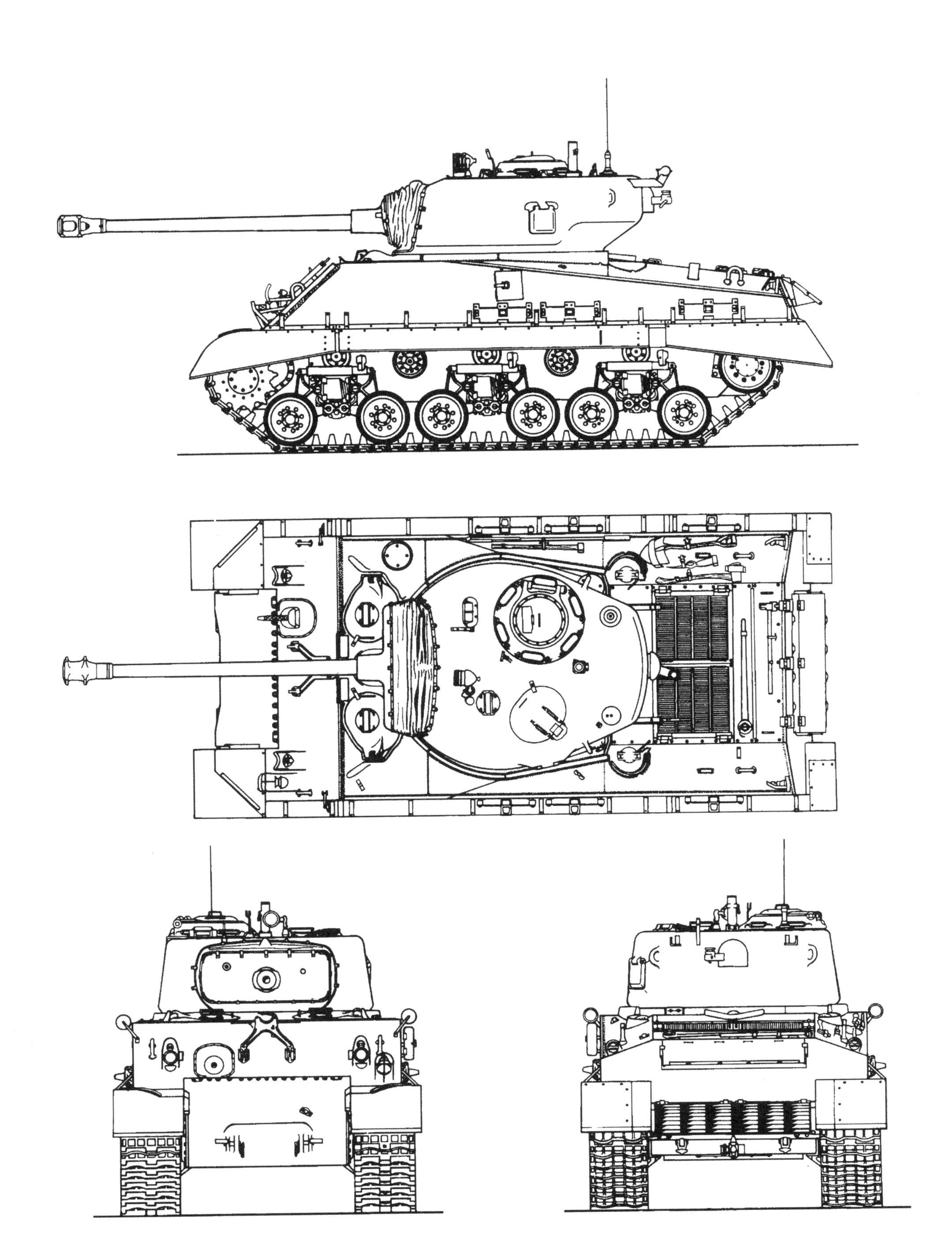

Scale 1:48

Medium Tank M4A3(76)W HVSS

The M4A3 above has the horizontal volute spring suspension, but it retains the split circular hatch for the loader. In the later production tank at the left and below the loader has the small oval hatch.

Late production M4A3s equipped with the horizontal volute spring suspension during assembly at Detroit Arsenal. Both 76mm gun and 105mm howitzer tanks can be seen here.

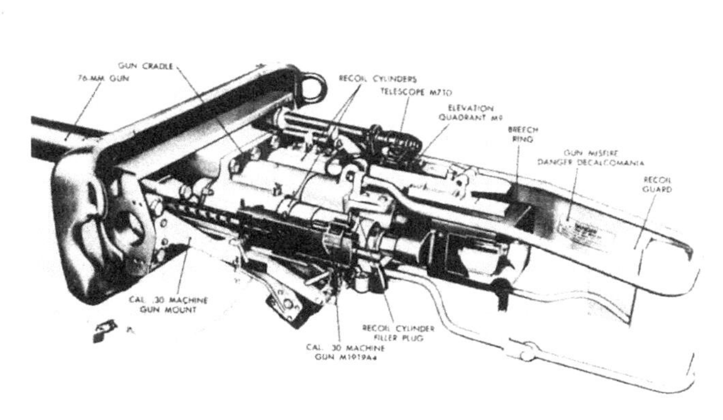

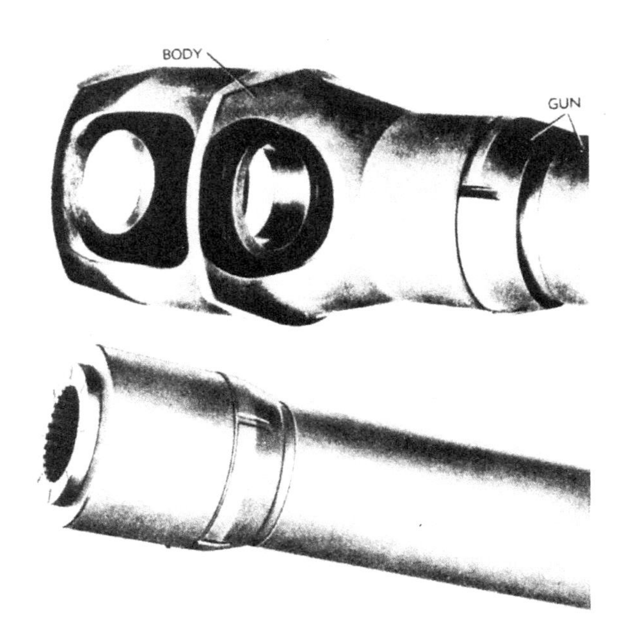

The 76mm gun M1A2 in mount M62 is shown above. At the right is the muzzle brake and the thread protector used when it was not installed.

Below, the installed M62 mount can be seen from the bottom left (left) and top rear (right) in the M4A3.

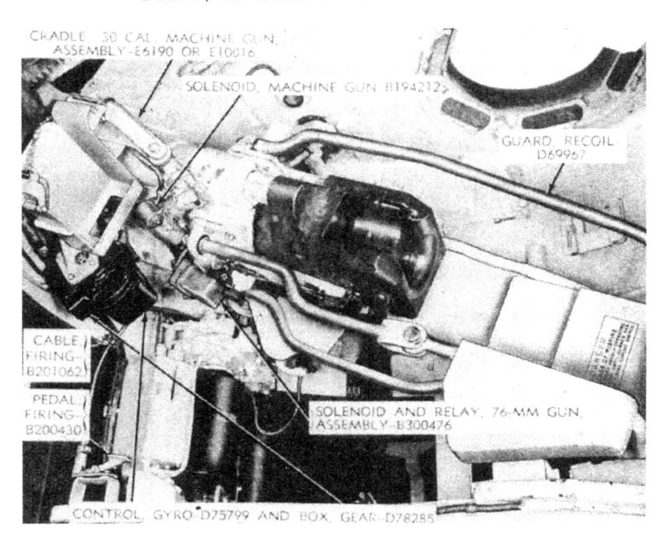

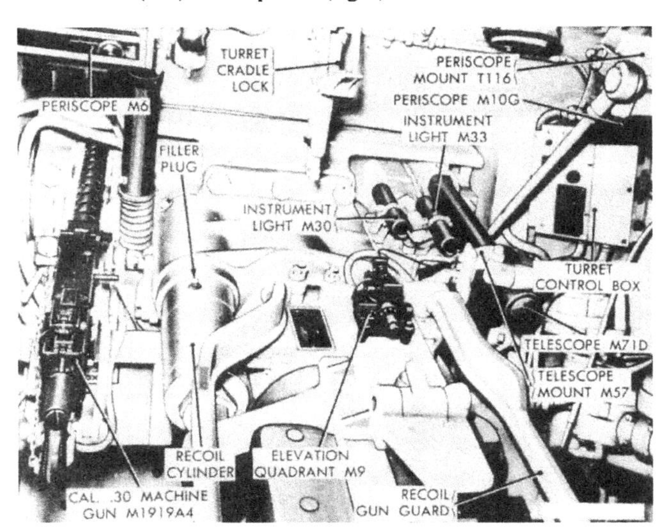

Below, the gunner's controls are shown at the left and the removal of the gun mount is illustrated at the right.

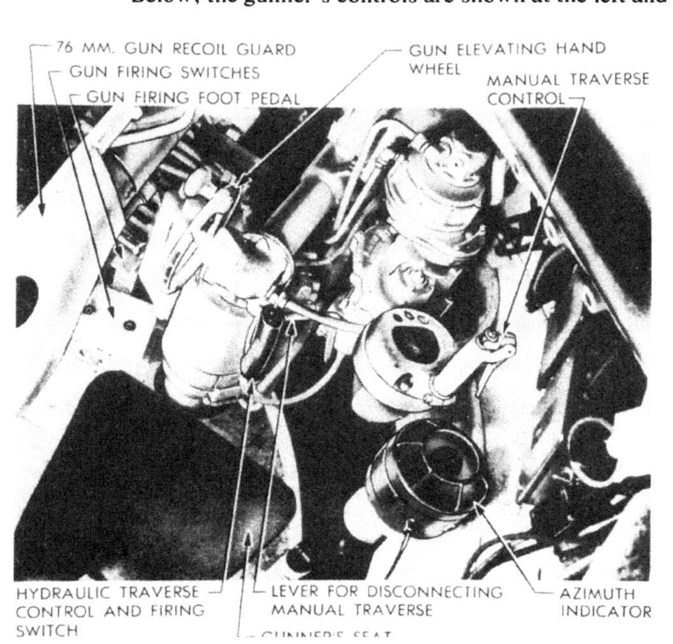

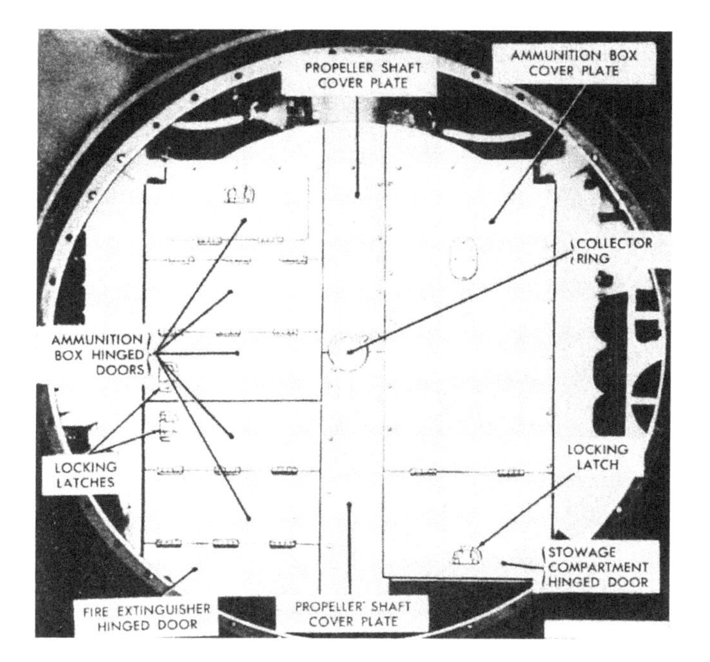

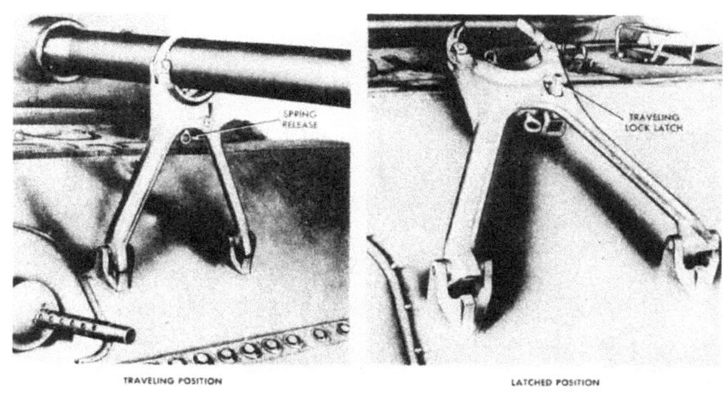

TRAVELING POSITION LATCHED POSITION

The covers for the wet stowage ammunition racks can be seen in the floor under the turret (top left). The gun travel lock on the front plate is shown above in the traveling and latched positions.

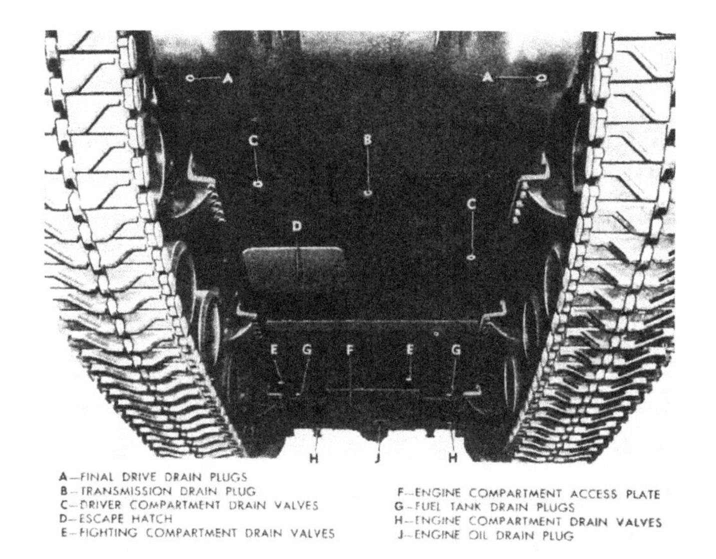

A—FINAL DRIVE DRAIN PLUGS
B—TRANSMISSION DRAIN PLUG
C—DRIVER COMPARTMENT DRAIN VALVES
D—ESCAPE HATCH
E—FIGHTING COMPARTMENT DRAIN VALVES
F—ENGINE COMPARTMENT ACCESS PLATE
G—FUEL TANK DRAIN PLUGS
H—ENGINE COMPARTMENT DRAIN VALVES
J—ENGINE OIL DRAIN PLUG

The bottom front of the hull appears above at the left and at the right, a 14th Armored Division sergeant emerges from the floor escape hatch during a training exercise. Below is a diagram of the fuel system in the late model M4A3 (left) and the auxiliary generator (right) installed in these tanks.

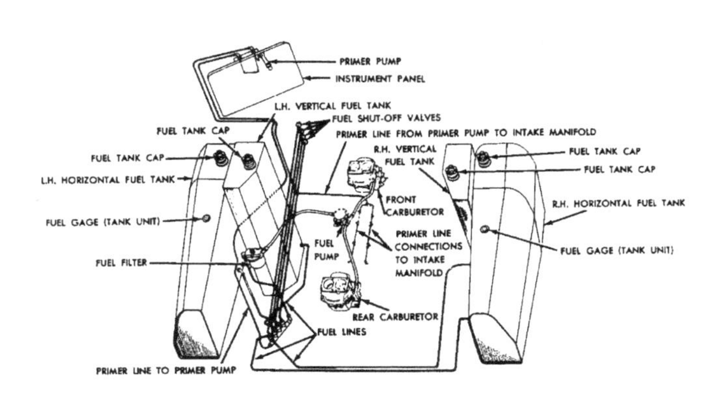

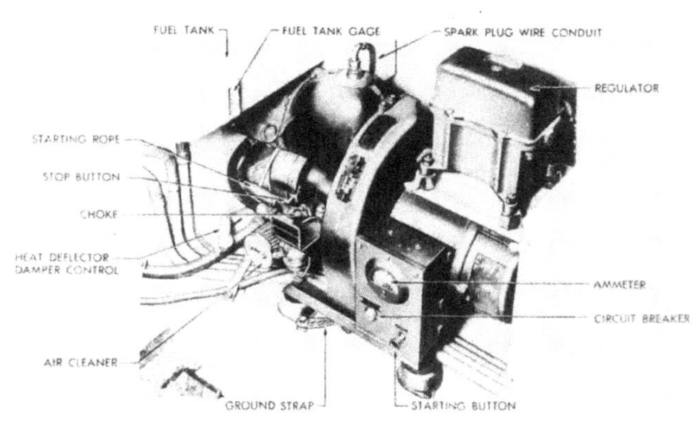

A new M4A3 armed with the 105mm howitzer awaits shipment outside Detroit Arsenal. This tank is fitted with the vision cupola for tank commander.

All of the tanks armed with the 105mm howitzer were manufactured by Chrysler at Detroit Tank Arsenal. Production of the M4A3 fitted with that weapon began in May 1944 and 500 vehicles with the vertical volute spring suspension were delivered by September. During that month, the change was made to the wide-tracked horizontal volute spring suspension and an additional 2539 tanks were produced by June 1945. This brought the total production of M4A3s with the 105mm howitzer to 3039. Like the howitzer armed M4, the first M4A3s with that weapon did not have a vision cupola. It appears that the limited quantities available during the Spring of 1944 were reserved for the 76mm gun tanks.

As mentioned before, the power traverse was originally considered unnecessary and was dropped from the production howitzer tanks. However, further tests had shown that it was required to permit rapid engagement of widely separated targets. Experiments on the M4E5 using the Oilgear system proved successful, but some turret rearrangement was necessary and it was omitted in order not to delay production. However, it was quickly introduced after the first tanks reached the combat troops and the complaints began to pour in. As the first howitzer tanks with the power traverse were being shipped overseas, the war in Europe ended.

The noise from the unmuffled Ford and Continental engines was easily detected by enemy listening posts. Artillery barrages or low flying aircraft were frequently used to cover the sound of tank movements. To correct this problem, outside mounted exhaust mufflers were designed for the Sherman and released to production in April 1945. Like many other innovations, the war ended before they could be of any use.

The M4A3 howitzer tank at the left is an early production vehicle without the vision cupola for the tank commander.

The M4A3 105mm howitzer tank fitted with the commander's vision cupola is shown in the views above and below. Note that pistol ports have reappeared on these late model tanks.

Concern was expressed over the large port for the direct sight telescope in the shield for the 105mm howitzer. In close combat, this opening made the turret vulnerable to small arms fire. The Armored Board requested that the size of the opening be reduced and that a moveable cover be provided which could be operated from within the turret. Such a cover was designed and released for production.

Among the stowage changes on the new series of tanks was the replacement of the .45 caliber submachine gun M1928A1 with five of the new .45 caliber submachine gun M3. Thus each member of the crew was provided with a weapon.

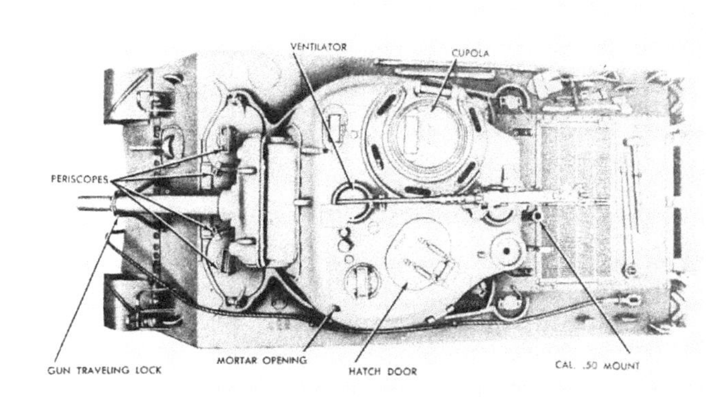

The M4A3 howitzer tank below at the right does not have a vision cupola. It retains the original split circular hatch incorporating the .50 caliber machine gun mount. A close-up of this mount appears below at the left. Also, note the late model vane sight alongside the gunner's periscope.

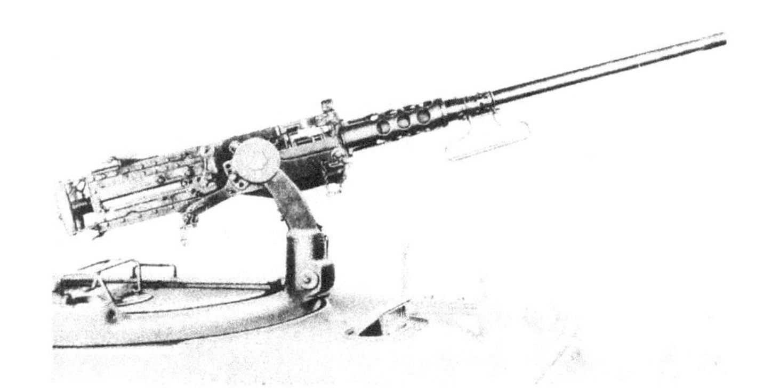

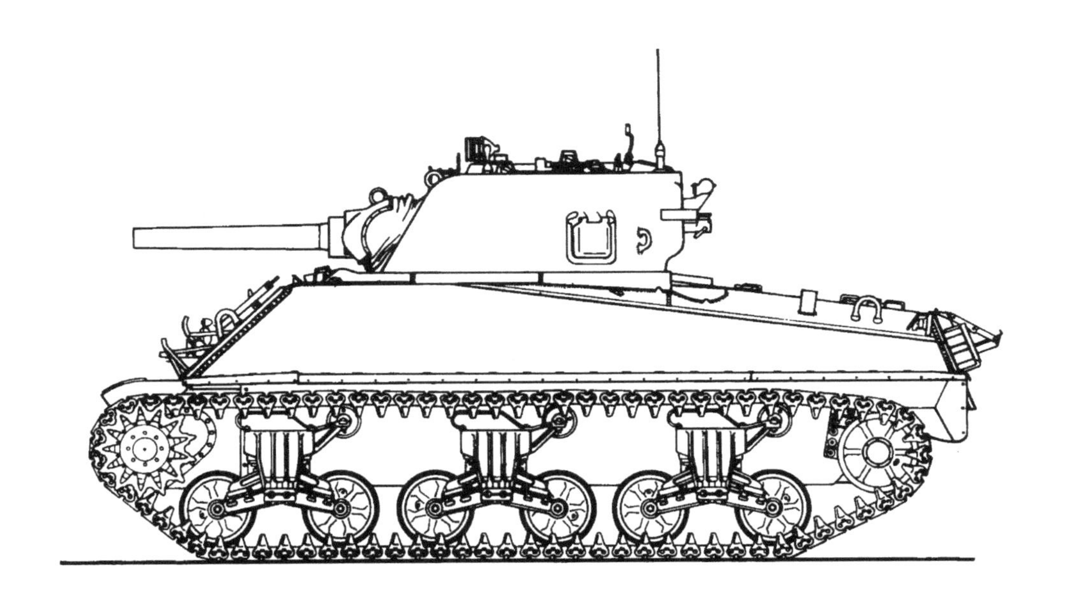

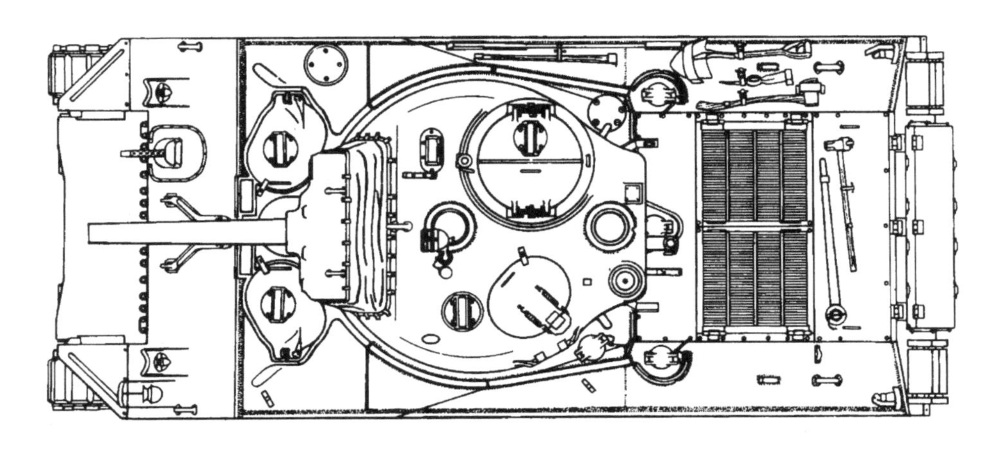

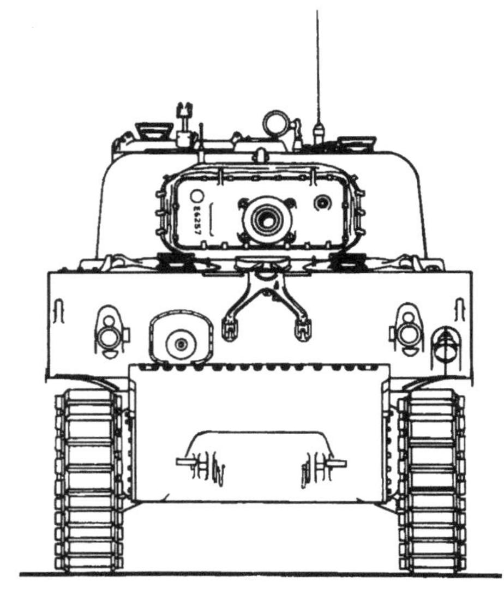

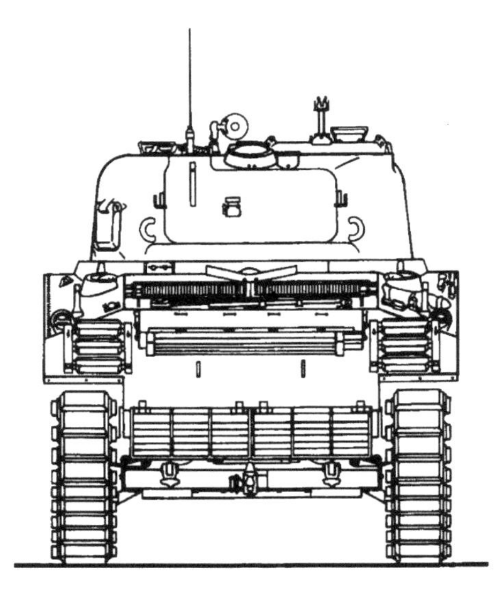

An early production howitzer tank without the vision cupola.

Scale 1:48

Medium Tank M4A3(105)

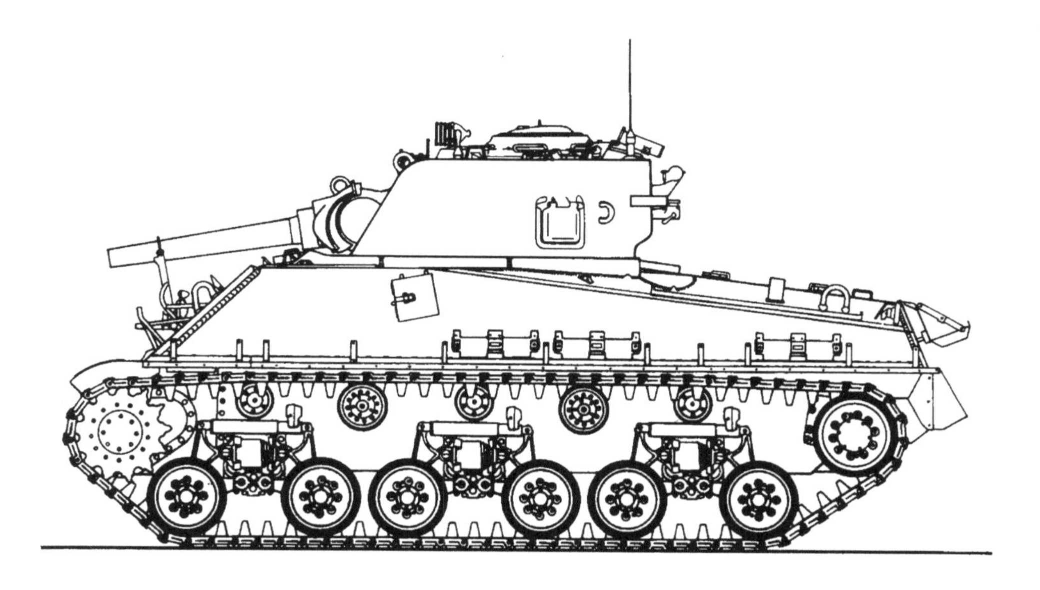

Scale 1:48

Medium Tank M4A3(105) HVSS

A very late production M4A3 with the 105mm howitzer appears below. This tank is equipped with the wide-tracked horizontal volute spring suspension and even has rear view mirrors for the driver.

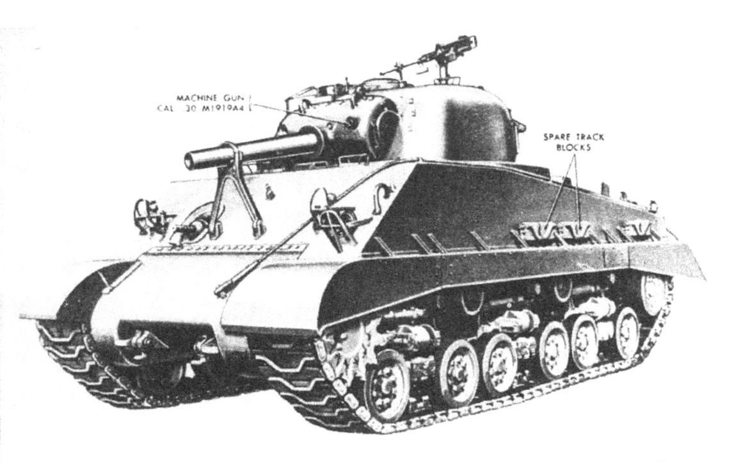

Above are two views of a 105mm howitzer medium tank M4A3. This late production tank has the T80 double pin tracks installed on the horizontal volute spring suspension.

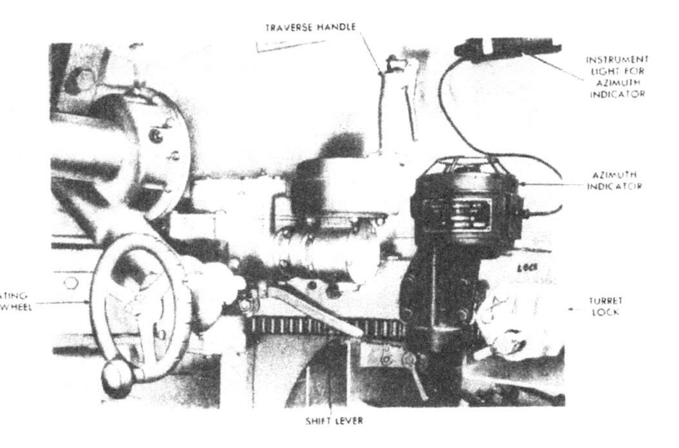

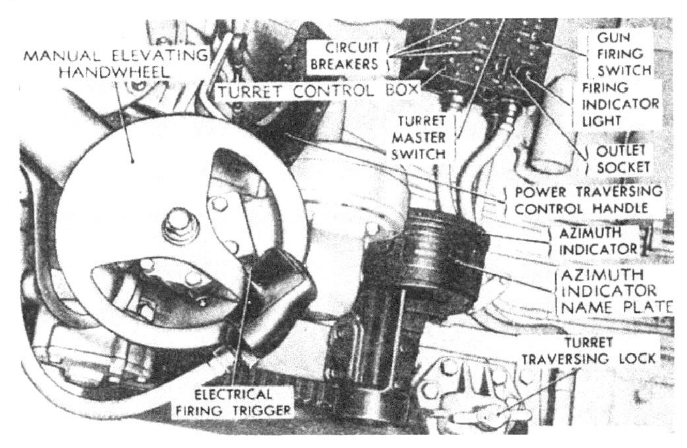

The gunner's controls on the early howitzer tanks with only manual turret rotation can be compared above (left) with the later models having hydraulic power traverse (right).

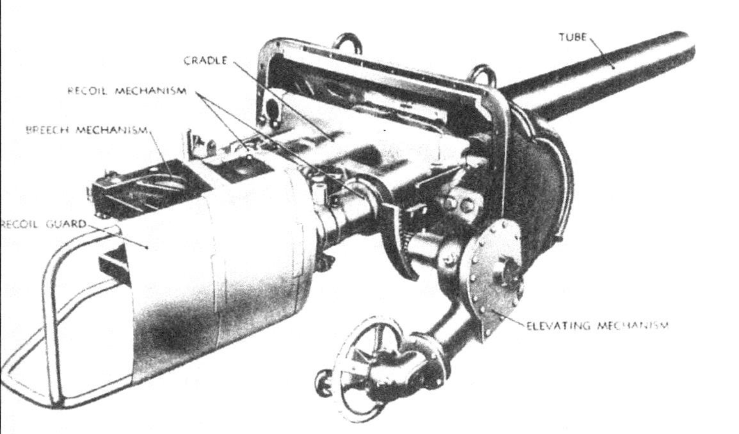

At the left is the combination mount M52 fitted with the 105mm howitzer M4. The views at the bottom left show the old (left) and new (right) design traveling locks for the howitzer.

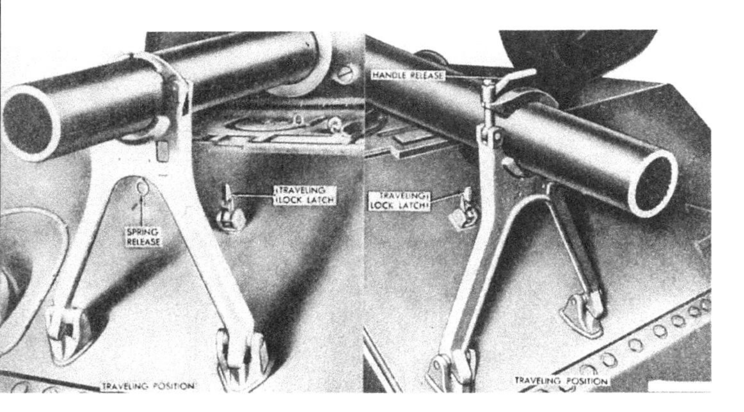

A new M4A3E2 assault tank is shown above and below. In the lower photograph the .50 caliber machine gun has been disassembled and stowed on the turret bustle.

During early 1944, preparations were intensified for the impending attack on the continent of Europe. It was apparent that a heavily armored assault tank would be required for infantry support during the coming battles. The T14 was no longer in the picture and it was obvious that the new T26E1 would not be available in time. In February, the Army Ground Forces suggested that the standard light and medium tanks be modified for the assault role by the use of auxiliary armor added in the field. As mentioned before, wooden mock-ups were constructed, but the project was dropped in light of later developments. Further study had concluded that the M4A3 could be converted to a satisfactory assault tank by increasing the armor and modifying the tracks and power train. Procurement of 254 such vehicles was authorized and it was designated as the assault tank M4A3E2 by Ordnance Committee action in March 1944.

The protection was improved by welding an additional 1-1/2 inches of rolled armor over the hull front and on the sides of the sponsons. This increased the total thickness in these areas to 4 inches and 3 inches respectively. A heavier differential and final drive housing was cast with a maximum thickness of 5-1/2 inches. The remaining parts of the hull retained the standard M4A3 armor.

A new turret was cast with walls 6 inches thick on the front, sides, and rear. A vision cupola and an oval hatch were provided for the tank commander and the

The extra armor plate is obvious around the bow gun mount. The extended end connectors on the outside of the tracks were necessary to reduce the ground pressure of the heavy vehicle.

loader, but the pistol port was eliminated. The T110 combination gun mount was a modified version of the M62 used in the standard 76mm gun tanks. In fact, the new gun shield was fabricated by welding a heavy plate to the front of the M62 shield increasing the total thickness to 7 inches. It was originally intended to mount the 76mm gun, but the 75 was preferred for infantry support so the latter weapon was installed in all 254 tanks. Since the mount was almost identical with the standard M62, it was relatively easy to replace the 75 with the higher powered weapon. The normal Sherman secondary armament was carried including the 2 inch smoke mortar in the left front of the turret roof. Other equipment also corresponded to that for a wet stowage M4A3 armed with the 75, except that the headlights and siren were omitted.

The thick armor increased the combat weight of the M4A3E2 to about 84,000 pounds. To insure adequate performance with that weight, the final drive ratio was increased from 2.84:1 to 3.36:1 reducing the maximum speed to around 22 miles/hour. The standard M4A3 power train was used except for the final drive. To reduce the ground pressure, the double pin tracks were assembled using duckbill extended end connectors on the outside. The increased contact area held the ground pressure to approximately 14 psi.

Production of the M4A3E2 began at the Fisher Tank Arsenal in May 1944 with the last of the 254 tanks being delivered in July. Tested at both Aberdeen and Fort Knox, the M4A3E2s were shipped to Europe arriving in the Fall of 1944. Employed throughout the remainder of the fighting, they were considered highly successful.

In early 1945, additional production was requested for the heavily armored M4A3E2 which was to be equipped with the horizontal volute spring suspension and the 76mm gun. A later request changed the armament to the 90mm gun using the turret from the M26 General Pershing. However, since the Pershing itself was already in full production, interest shifted to the design of an assault version of the newer tank. Designated as the T26E5, its frontal armor had a maximum thickness of 11 inches.

The thick turret walls can be seen in the top view below as well as the extra plate welded to the front of the gun shield. Note the absence of the headlights and siren.

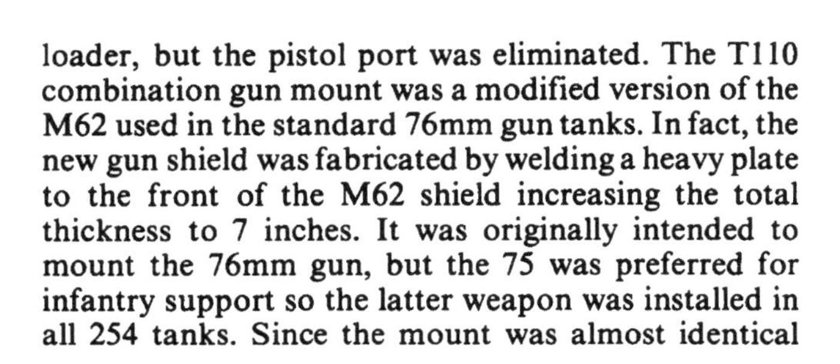

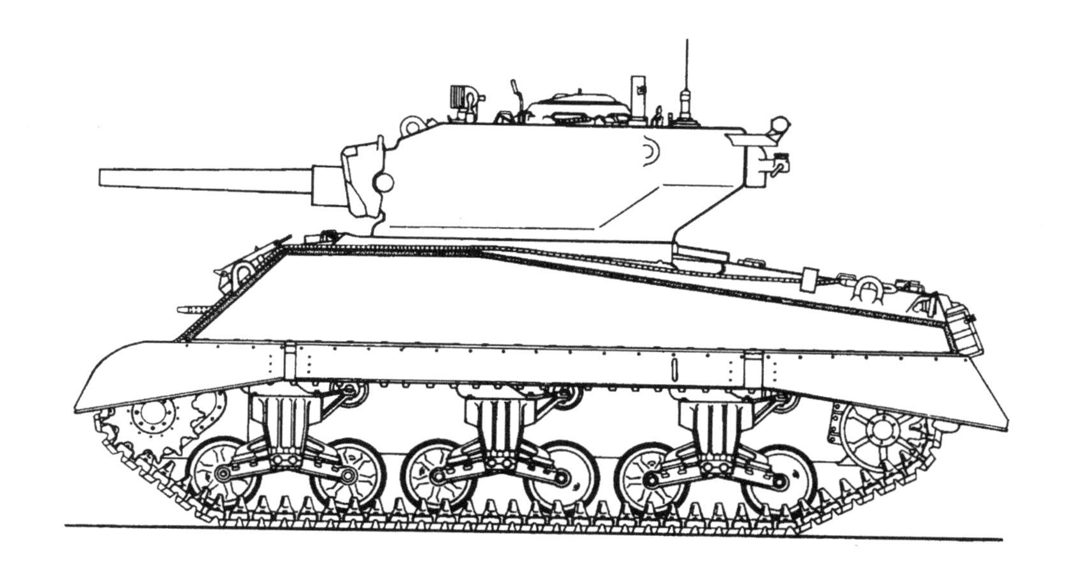

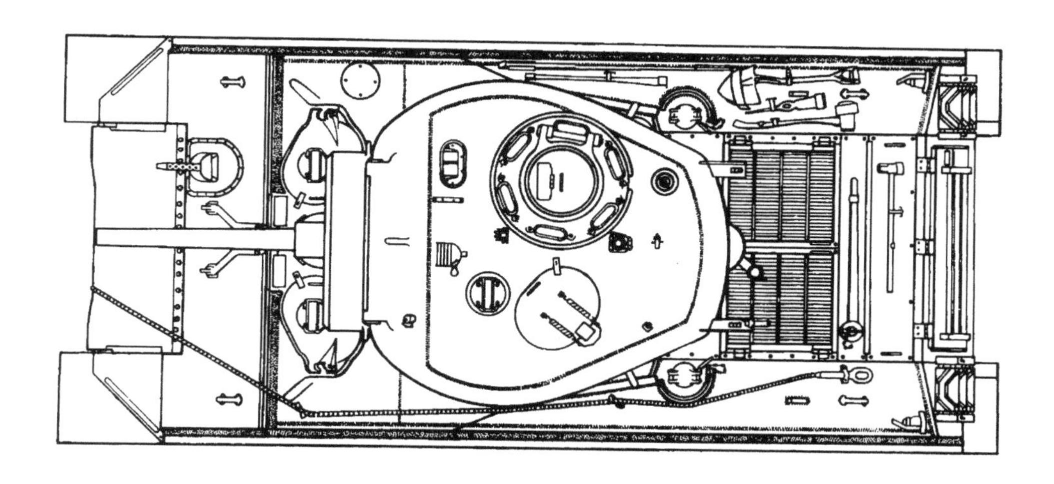

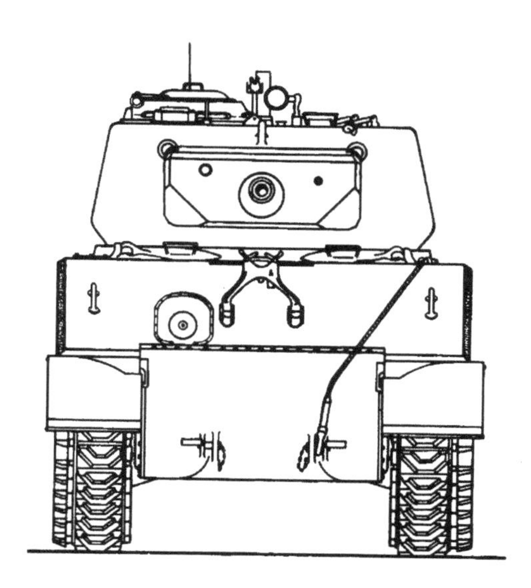

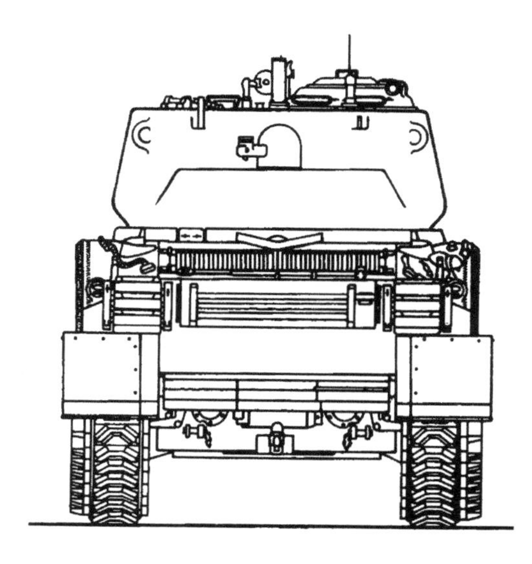

Scale 1:48

Medium Tank M4A3E2

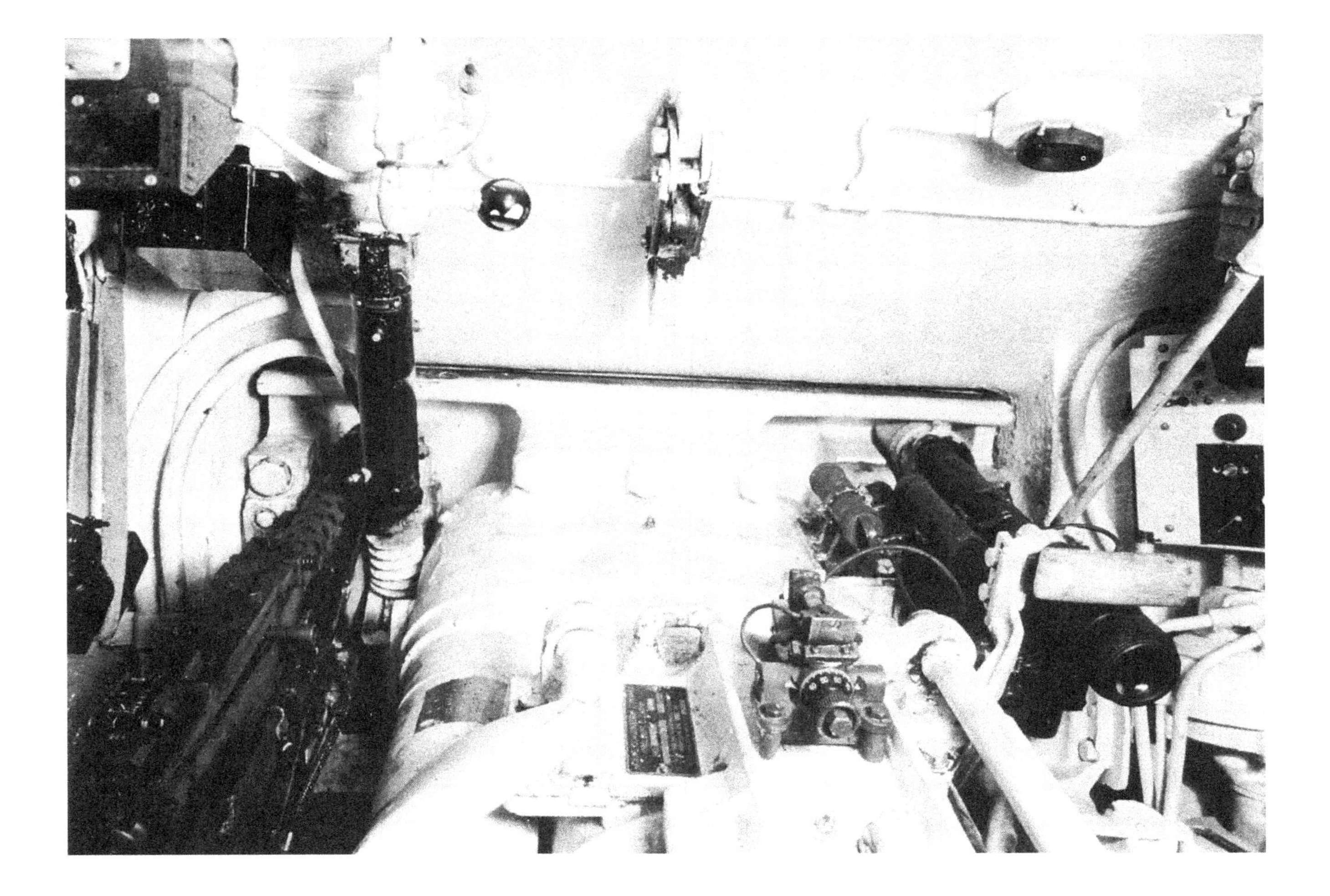

The inside front of the M4A3E2 turret is shown above. The coaxial machine gun is at the left of the gun mount and the gunner's telescope appears at the right. The small instrument with the graduated knob on top of the mount is the elevation quadrant M9.

The SCR 508 is installed in the turret bustle (at right). Note the two receivers. In the bottom photograph, the radio is covered and the spotlight and two M3 submachine guns are stowed below it.

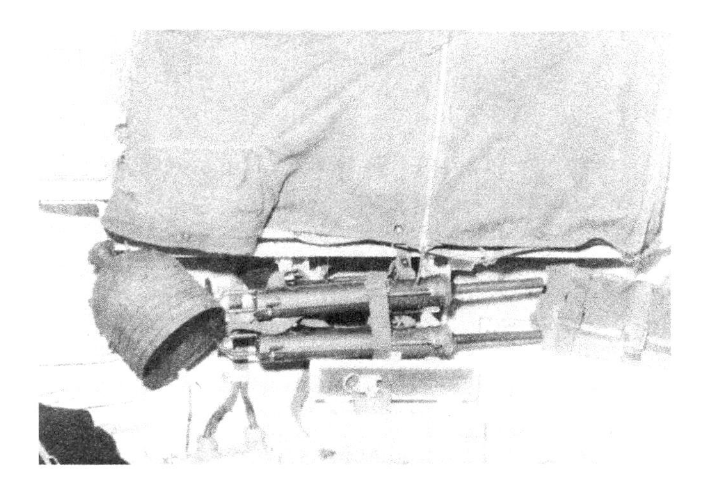

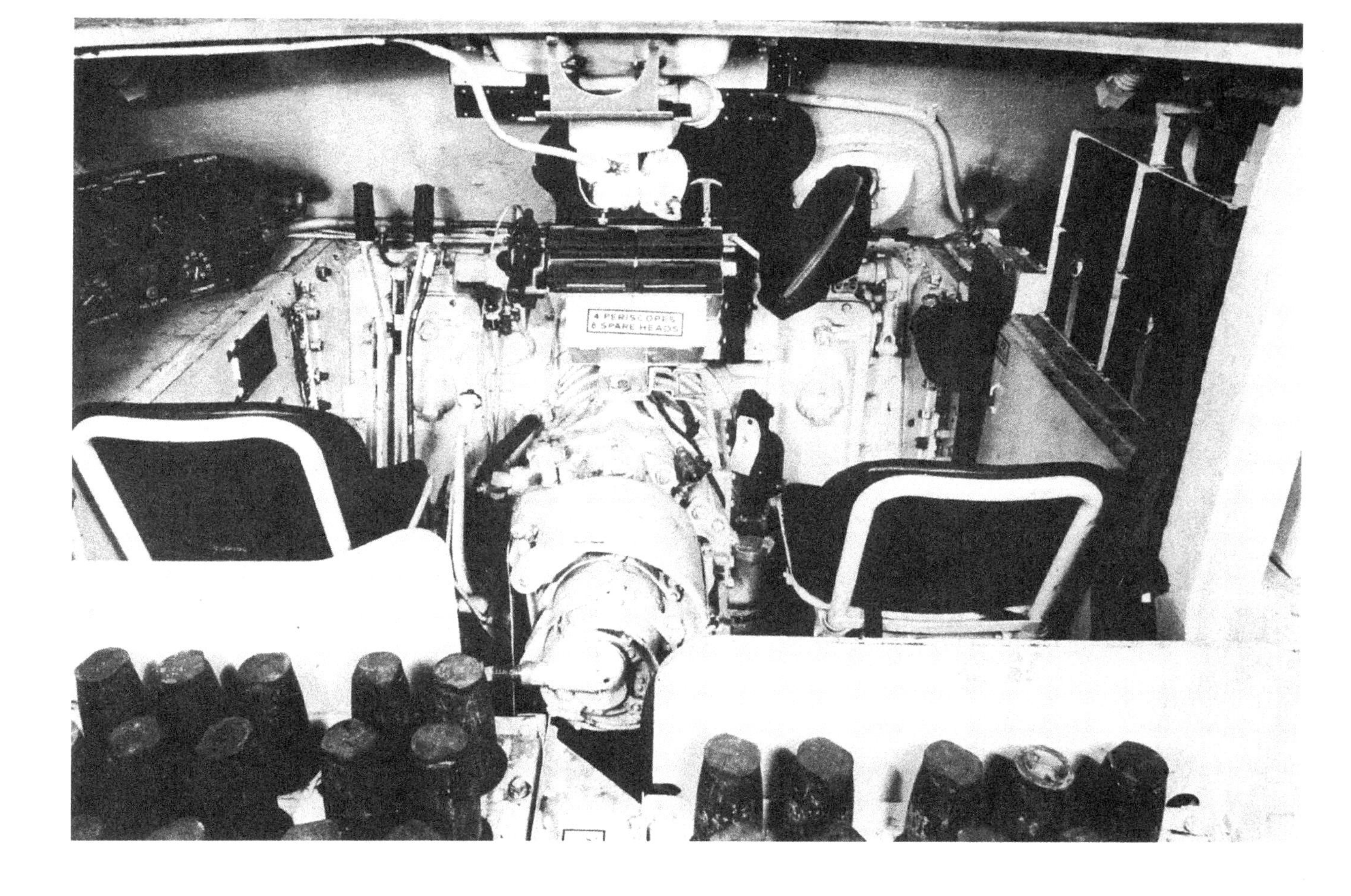

Additional interior details of the M4A3E2. The view at the top is looking forward into the driving compartment. At the right is the rear wall of the fighting compartment. Below, the auxiliary generator can be seen in the rear of the left sponson (left). The stowage in the right sponson appears below at the right.

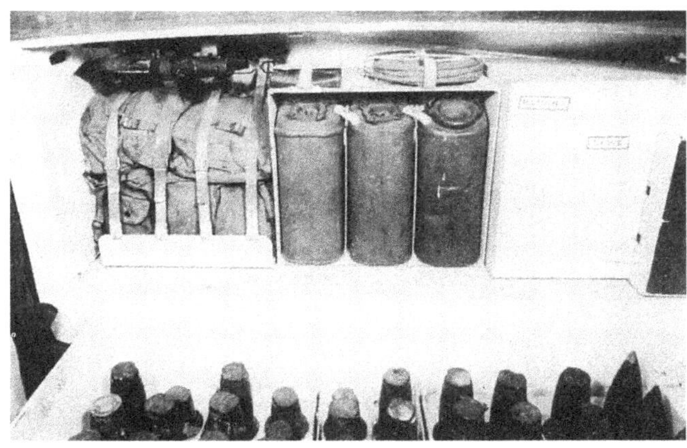

The M4A1 above might be considered the ultimate remanufactured tank. It includes just about every feature introduced in the modernization program. Note the commander's vision cupola, applique armor, and the M34 gun mount modified to include a direct sight telescope. Also, the tank has been fitted with the spaced out suspension and extended end connectors are installed on both sides of the tracks.

By the end of 1943, many of the U.S. armored units had completed their training and received new tanks prior to shipment overseas. This resulted in a large accumulation of early production Shermans which had been badly worn during the training program. With worldwide operations producing an increasing demand for tanks, a remanufacturing program was set up to rebuild and modernize these training vehicles. Chrysler began the work at Detroit Tank Arsenal in December 1943 and a total of 1610 M4A4s were rebuilt by October 1944 and then shipped to Britain under the Lend-Lease program. Also destined for foreign aid, the M4A2s were refurbished at the Fisher Tank Arsenal and at Federal Machine and Welder Company starting in April 1944. Fisher rebuilt 218 tanks by July and Federal Machine and Welder finished their run of 317 in November.

The M4s, M4A1s, and M4A3s entered the remanufacturing program in August 1944. The major work on the M4s was done at Chrysler's Evansville plant and by International Harvester at the Quad Cities Tank Arsenal. Four hundred and fortysix M4s were reworked at Evansville, 289 at International Harvester, and 60 more at the Chester and Lima Tank Depots. The work was completed at all four locations by April 1945. Evansville and International Harvester also performed most of the work on the M4A1s, rebuilding 1216 and 737 tanks respectively. Another 306 M4A1s were reworked at the Chester, Lima, and Richmond Tank Depots with the program being completed in May 1945. The same three tank depots remanufactured 281 M4A3s in addition to the 400 rebuilt at the Montreal Locomotive Works. All 681 M4A3s were delivered by April 1945. The program thus provided an additional 5880 tanks which could be shipped to U.S. and Allied troops around the world.

During remanufacturing, the tanks were completely stripped down and reassembled using new parts to replace any worn components. They were also modernized by incorporating as many late production

Medium tank M4A1, registration number W-3038692, remanufactured by Chrysler at Evansville. The suspension is spaced out and the extended end connectors are installed on both sides of the tracks. It also has been fitted with a vision cupola.

features as possible without excessive rebuilding. The original vertical volute spring suspensions were retained, but extended end connectors were fitted to the outside of the 16-9/16 inch wide tracks to reduce the ground pressure. About 1000 M4s and M4A1s were rebuilt at Evansville with the spaced out suspension developed on the M4E9. These tanks were equipped with extended end connectors on both sides of the tracks further reducing the ground pressure.

When available, new components such as the commander's vision cupola brought the rebuilt tanks close to the late production standard. Other new features included applique armor, the oval loader's hatch in the turret roof, and the gun barrel traveling lock on the front hull plate. In new condition with these improvements, the remanufactured tanks helped to relieve the tank shortage in all theaters of operation.

Medium tank M4, registration number W-3015195, remanufactured by the International Harvester Company. Applique armor has been added to the turret, the hull sponsons, and in front of the drivers' hoods.

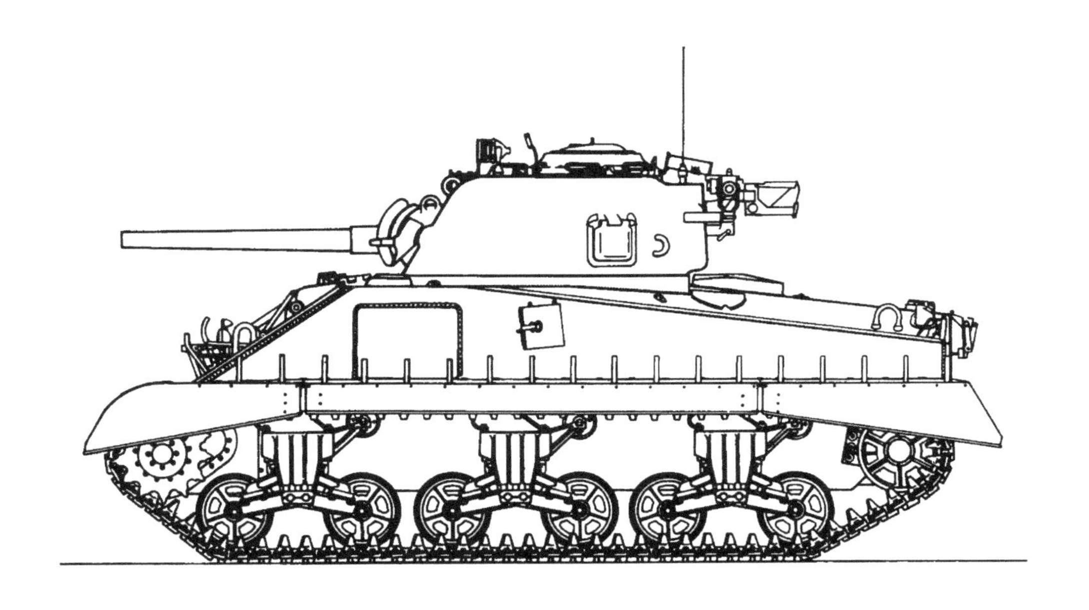

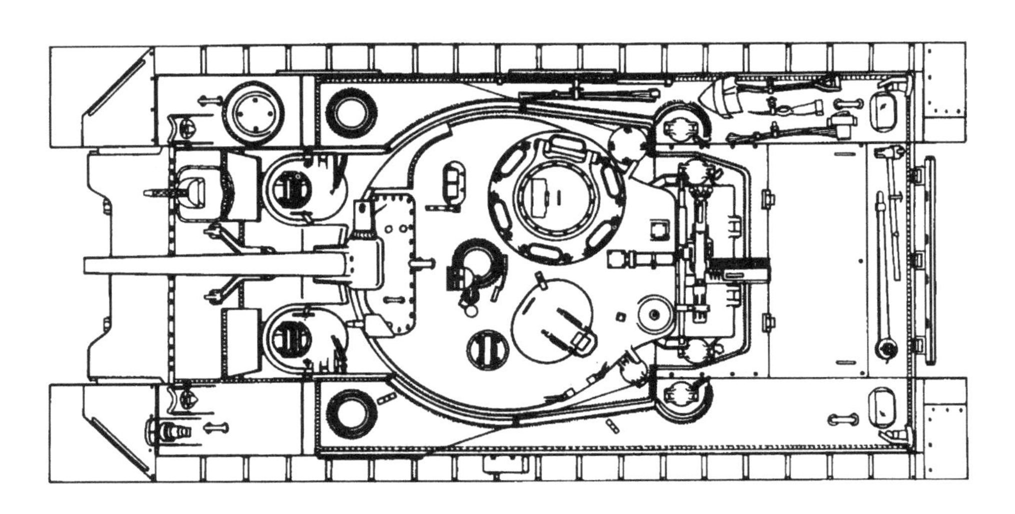

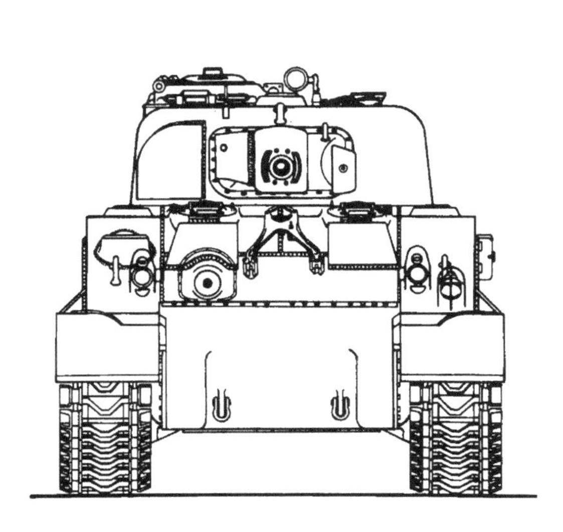

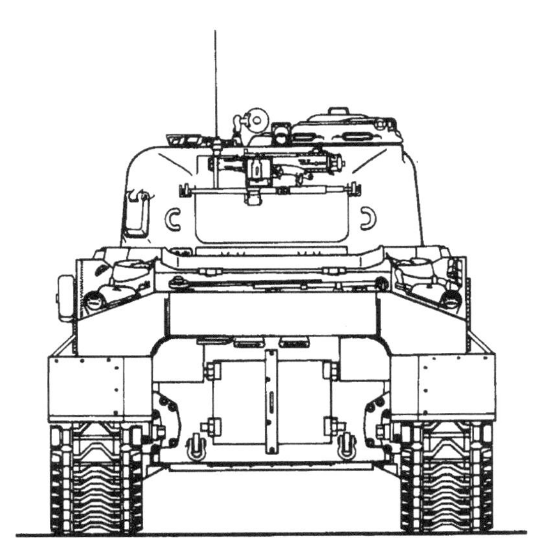

Scale 1:48

Medium Tank M4, Remanufactured and Modernized

The great contribution the modernization program made to the tank supply can be seen in these long lines of Shermans assembled in Britain during March 1944. Although these tanks were not part of the remanufacturing program, they incorporated many of the same improvements such as applique armor to upgrade the older production standard.

Views of two British Sherman Is appear above. These vehicles are fitted with the later production features such as the gun traveling lock and applique armor.

THE BRITISH SHERMANS

Unlike the General Grant with its special turret, the British Shermans were almost identical in appearance to their U.S. counterparts. Differing only in the installation of British equipment and stowage, they were often difficult to distinguish from the U.S. tanks. One obvious exception was the version fitted with the British high velocity 17 pounder cannon. Installation of this long barreled 3 inch gun with its double baffle muzzle brake made a drastic change in the appearance of the Sherman.

The British designated the medium tanks M4 through M4A4 as the Shermans I through V respectively. The late production M4 with the cast upper front hull was termed the Sherman Hybrid I. If the armament of the tank was other than the standard 75mm gun, it was signified by the letter A, B, or C added to the designation. This A, B, or C indicated the main armament to be the 76mm gun, the 105mm howitzer, or the British 17 pounder, respectively. Thus the M4A4 fitted with the 17 pounder became the Sherman VC. When the horizontal volute spring suspension and 23 inch tracks were introduced late in the war, the letter Y was added to the designation of any tank so equipped. An M4A2 with the 76mm gun and the horizontal volute spring suspension was then the Sherman IIIAY.

External differences which identified the British tanks included stowage bins installed on the turret bustle and the rear hull plate. Several arrangements of these were shown on the standard stowage charts and many further modifications were made in the field. For example, the rear hull stowage bin specified for the Sherman V was sometimes relocated on the front plate above the differential housing. The stowage charts showed six track shoes on brackets welded to the right front hull. In the field, many additional track shoes were tack welded to both hull and turret to improve the armor protection.

British tanks were equipped with the Number 19 radio set mounted in the turret bustle. This was actually two radios in one with each requiring its own antenna or aerial. The "A" aerial was installed in the standard antenna socket at the left rear of the turret bustle. The "B" aerial was fitted in a small socket just to the right of center in the turret bustle roof. The "A" set operated at a frequency of 2 to 8 hertz with a voice range of 10 to 15 miles. The "B" equipment worked at 230 to 240 hertz with a voice range of 1 to 5 miles. Both were amplitude modulated and the equipment included intercommunication apparatus for the tank crew.

Tanks which did not have the 2 inch smoke bomb thrower in the left turret roof were sometimes fitted with two 4 inch smoke generator dischargers. These were mounted at a fixed elevation on the right side of the turret. Six additional smoke generators were stowed inside the tank.

British tanks carried two methyl bromide fire extinguishers in addition to the standard carbon dioxide equipment. One was mounted at the top rear on each side of the hull. A small external first aid kit was specified for attachment to the rear hull plate.

British charts also showed a rear view mirror mounted on the right front edge of the hull for use by the driver. These were often omitted in service or were buried in unofficial stowage.

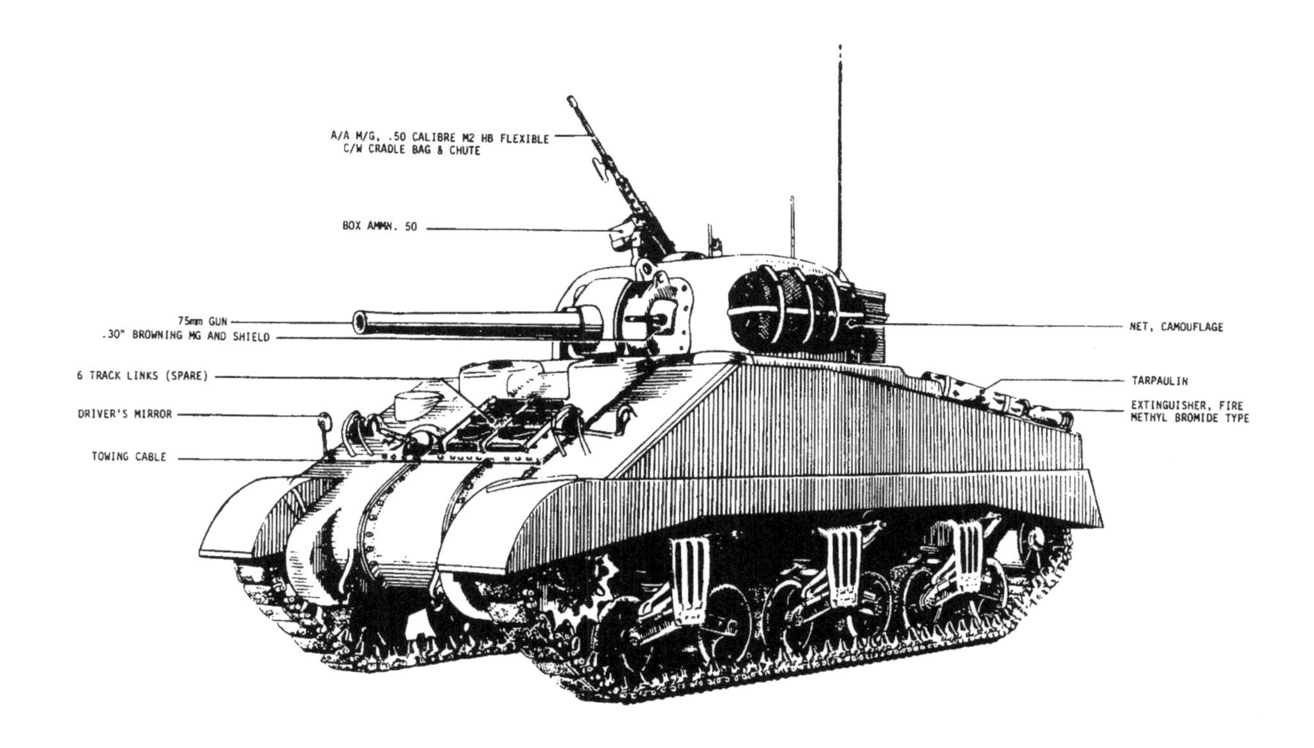

The external stowage arrangement on the British tanks is illustrated here on the Sherman V. Note the methyl bromide fire extinguishers on the top rear hull and the stowage boxes installed on the turret bustle and rear hull plate.

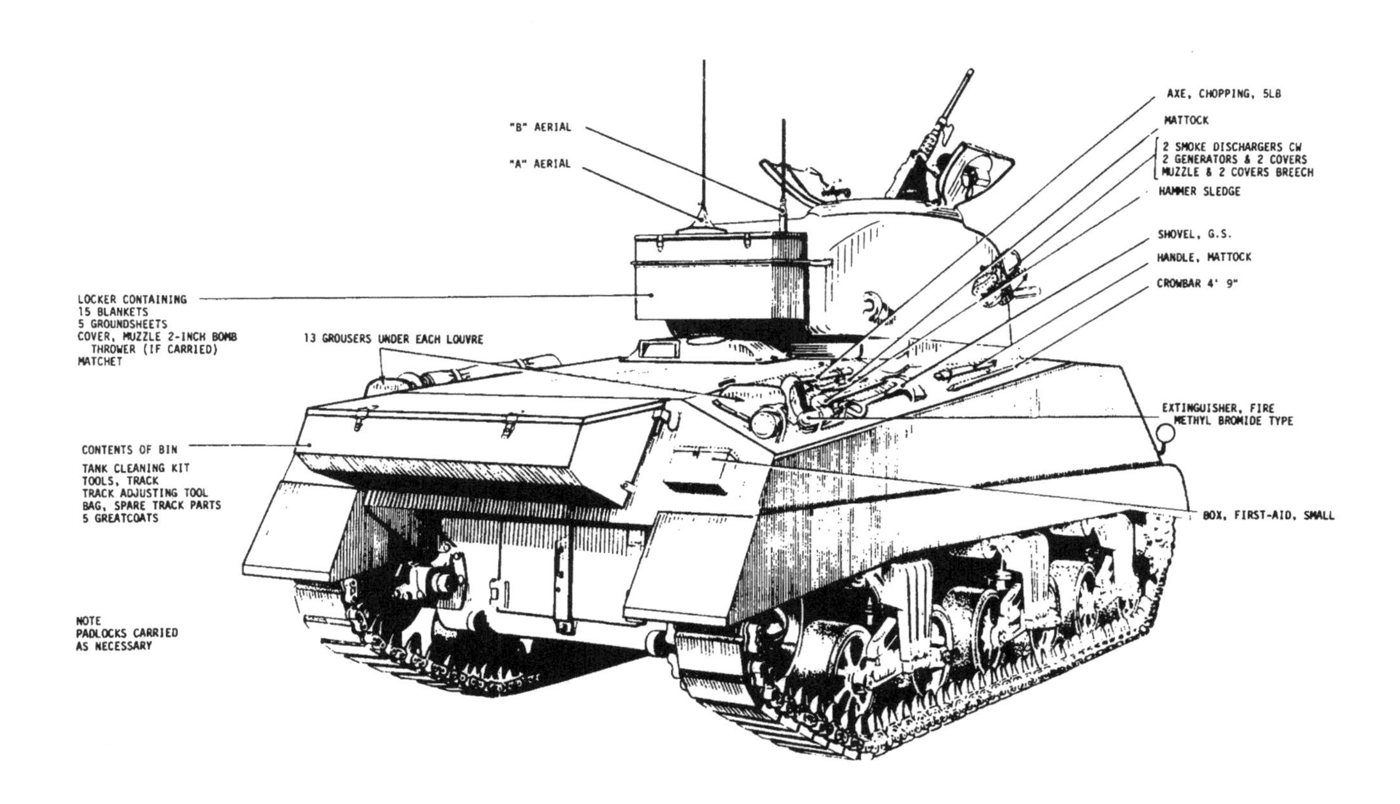

The only type of 76mm gun tank to see combat service with the British was the Sherman IIA (above and below). This is an early production vehicle with the split circular hatch for the loader. The cannon is the 76mm gun M1A1 without the muzzle brake.

Two photographs of the Sherman IB armed with the 105mm howitzer are shown above. This is the later production tank with the vision cupola for the tank commander. At the left, a crew member loads rounds of the 105mm explosive shell M1.

At the right, a wide-tracked Sherman IIIAY is under test. On this late production tank, the 76 is fitted with a muzzle brake.

The British Mk II vision cupola is mounted on the Sherman above by means of an adapter ring.

Experimental work continued in Britain in an effort to improve the combat efficiency of the Sherman. The Mk I and Mk II vision cupolas designed for British tanks were adapted for use replacing the standard circular turret hatch. This greatly improved the tank commander's range of view when the tank was closed up.

To protect the suspension from shell fragments and small arms fire, armor plate skirts were developed. Three sections of 6mm armor plate were suspended from the sponsons on each side of the tank. They were approved for use, but like the vision cupolas, they did not reach the troops in time to be of effective service.

Another British development was the design of a suspension by Horstmann of Bath. The Canadian AFV User Committee authorized its installation on a Ram tank and it was submitted for test in early 1943. After about 2000 miles of operation and a number of changes, the new design was judged superior to the standard vertical volute spring suspension in cross-country performance. It offered a more stable gun platform and an improved ride. It was recommended that a modified version of this design be adapted to the Sherman. The Canadians accepted this recommendation and a Horstmann suspension was fitted on Sherman V number T-148350.

As installed, three 2-wheel bogies using coil springs replaced the standard suspension units on each side of the tank. Each bogie was fitted with two large coil springs mounted concentrically with two smaller diameter coil springs. A single track return roller was located at the top of each bogie. Standard Sherman V wheels, idlers, sprockets, and tracks were used with the normal 83 track shoes per side.

Tests of the Horstmann design were suspended and the work was concluded in early 1945 after 340 miles of operation. The tank was then refitted with a standard suspension. Although the riding qualities were superior with the Horstmann, it was considered unsatisfactory on the Sherman because of excessive wear and poor reliability during the test run.

The Horstmann suspension is shown below installed on the Sherman V. Details of the Horstmann bogie can be seen at the right.

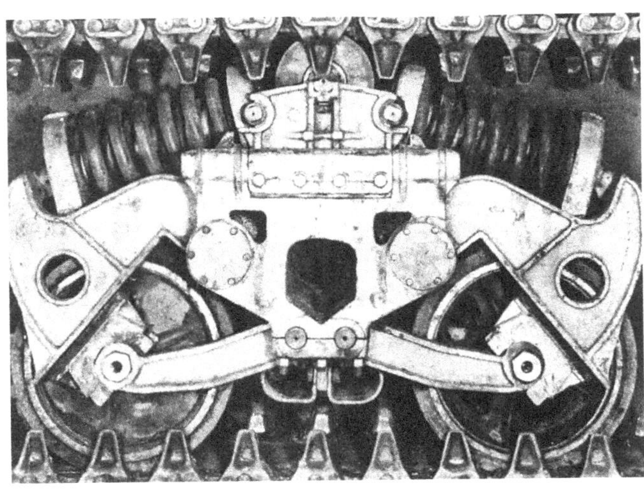

The British Sherman VC armed with the powerful 17 pounder gun. Note the hatch added in the turret roof for the loader.

The most important British modification to the Sherman was, undoubtedly, the installation of the 17 pounder high velocity gun. This weapon corrected the major weakness of the M4 series by providing firepower comparable to that in the best of the German tanks. Although the improvised installation in the original 75mm gun turret was cramped and inconvenient to use, it gave the Sherman its most powerful armament installed during the war.

Authorized in March 1941, the first 17 pounder antitank gun on a towed carriage was delivered 18 months later in August 1942. Arriving in the Middle East in December, the first 17 pounders reached Tunisia in January 1943. Most of these early guns were fitted on 25 pounder carriages because of delays in the production of their own mounts.

Intended from the beginning for use as both a tank and antitank gun, the weapon was an excellent design for installation in a turret mount. Its comparatively heavy breech ring and lightweight barrel kept the center of gravity near the breech end. This allowed the mount to be easily balanced on its trunnions without the breech extending very far into the already crowded turret. With a chamber capacity of 300 cubic inches, the large propellant charge produced a muzzle velocity of 2980 ft/sec using the standard 17 pound APCBC projectile. At 1000 yards range, such a round would penetrate 5.1 inches of homogeneous armor at 30 degrees obliquity.

The appearance of increasingly heavy German armor made it obvious that the 17 pounder had to be installed in a tank. Originally, it was intended to base such a vehicle on the Cromwell and designs were prepared for a version with a lengthened chassis. Designated as the Challenger, it suffered numerous development problems and by the Summer of 1943, it was apparent that it would not be available in sufficient quantity in time for the invasion of Europe. However, there were ample numbers of Shermans available and efforts began to install the 17 pounder in the standard 75mm gun turret. The Tank Division of the Ministry of Supply at first rejected such a conversion as impossible, but this decision was reversed after the successful demonstration of an experimental installation. This success was due, in no small part, to the Sherman's 69 inch diameter turret ring which was 3 inches larger than that in the Challenger itself. The short distance from the trunnions to the rear face of the 17 pounder's breech ring also helped. In the Sherman mount, this was only 37.75 inches compared to 43.5 inches and 52 inches for the U.S. 76mm gun M1A2 and 90mm gun M3 respectively.

The Sherman VC Firefly with the 17 pounder in the forward firing position (left) and stowed in the traveling lock on the rear deck (right).

The 17 pounder Mk IV or Mk VII was installed in the Sherman. Outwardly identical, they differed only in the spring case. In the Mk VII, a buffer sleeve and spring were added to cushion the effect of opening the breech. Both guns were fitted with a lightweight double baffle muzzle brake and a semiautomatic horizontal sliding breechblock. The powerful weapon required a new mount and recoil system, but the installation retained the original trunnions used with the 75mm gun. A new elevating mechanism was fitted with a range of +20 to –5 degrees. Both manual and power traverse equipment were provided. Linkage attached to the turret roof could be locked to the breech ring when the gun was depressed. On the rear deck, a support and traveling lock secured the barrel during movement.

A coaxial .30 caliber Browning machine gun was mounted to the left of the 17 pounder and a direct sight telescope was located on the right for the gunner. The telescope was provided with interchangeable heads having 3x or 6x magnification. The gunner's M4A1 periscope coupled to the mount also was retained.

The Number 19 radio set was moved into an armored box welded to the back of the turret bustle.

A Sherman IC in Normandy. Note that the stowage box normally attached to the rear of the hull is installed on the front plate.

The sketches at the right show details of the shield and mantlet used with the 17 pounder installation.

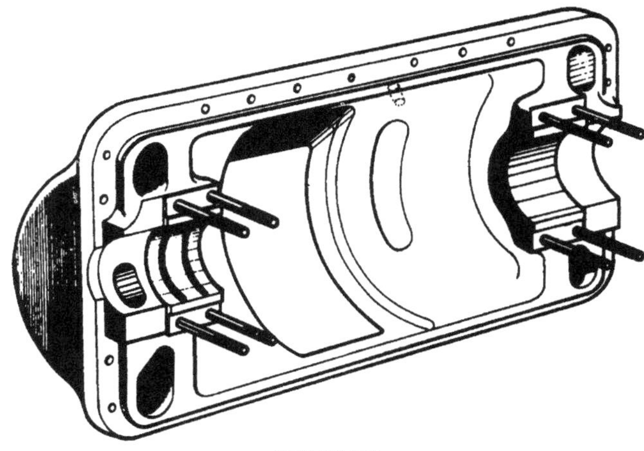

Assembled from plates 2-1/2 inches thick in the rear, 2 inches on the sides, and 1 inch top and bottom, this box helped balance the long cannon and freed additional space inside the turret. A hole cut through the original rear wall of the turret bustle provided access to the radio. The crew was reduced to four by eliminating the assistant driver and his space was used for ammunition stowage. The bow machine gun was removed and the hole was covered with an armored plug. The original stowage layout provided space for 78 rounds of 17 pounder ammunition with 5 ready rounds in two bins on the turret basket floor, 14 rounds in the assistant driver's space, and 59 rounds in three bins under the turret floor. Some charts show 58 rounds beneath the turret reducing the total ammunition stowage to 77 rounds.

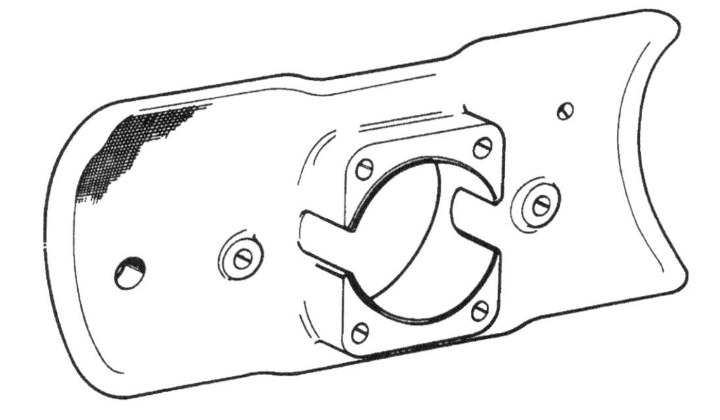

The side view of the Sherman IC below shows one method of camouflaging the long 17 pounder barrel. A metal can was fitted on the barrel a little over halfway to the end. The barrel outboard of the can was then painted with a pattern which would break up its outline giving the impression of a much shorter gun.

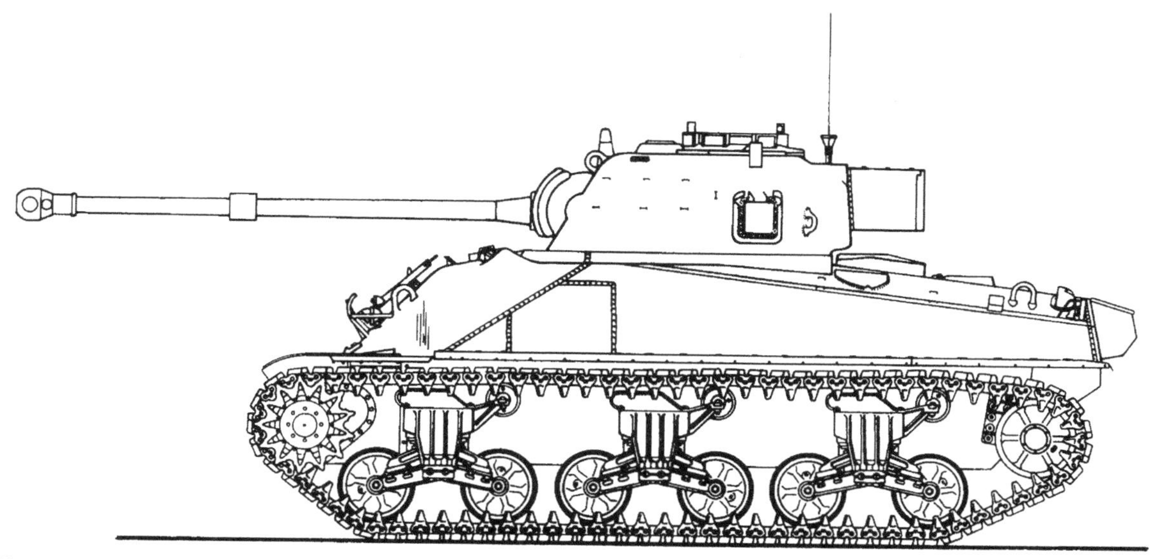

Scale 1:48

Cruiser Tank Sherman IC

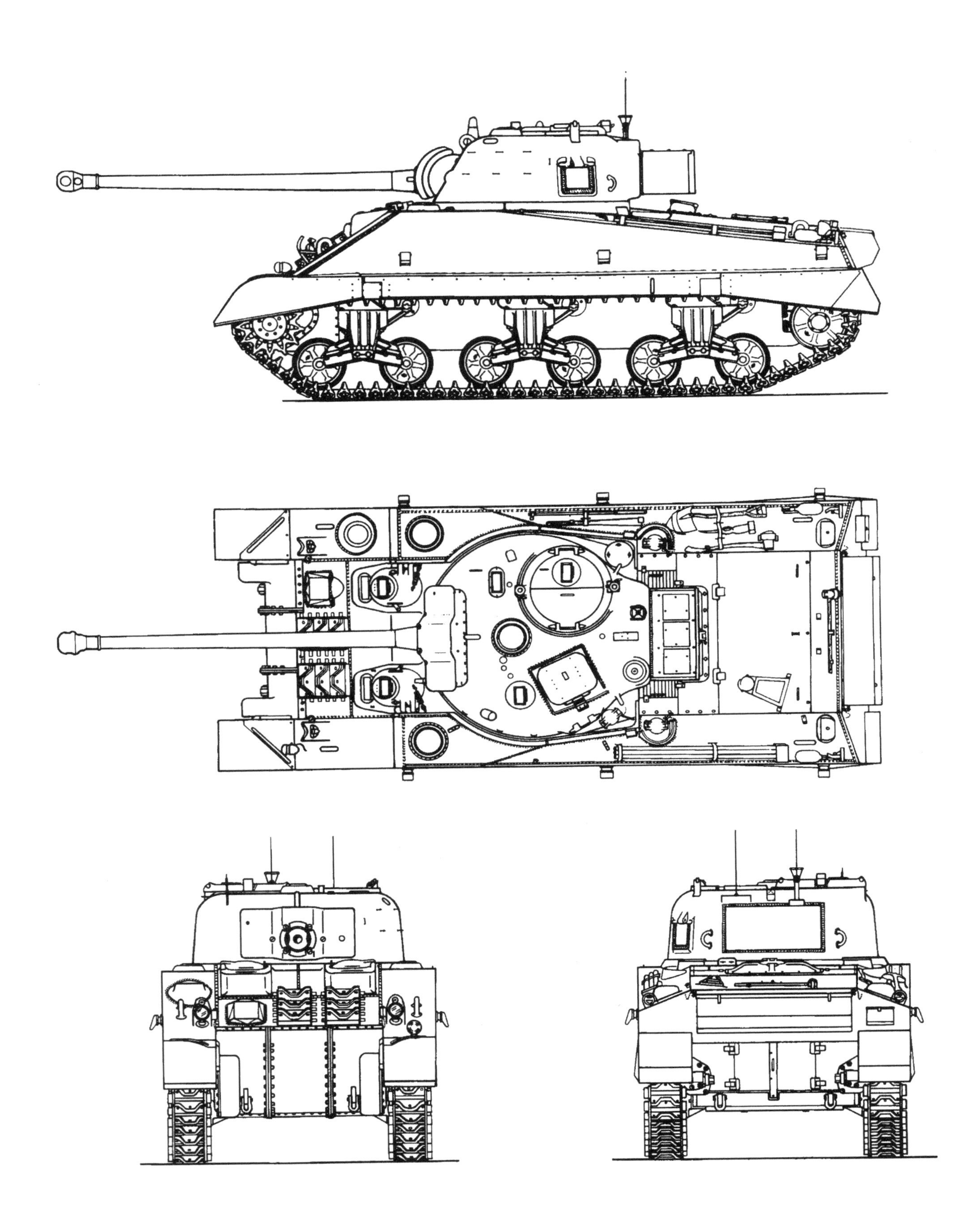

Scale 1:48

Cruiser Tank Sherman VC

The Sherman VCs above show relatively slight additions to the standard stowage. No attempt has been made to camouflage the long 17 pounder barrel.

On the Firefly at the right, the rear hull stowage box has been moved once again to the front plate.

Below, Canadian Shermans including some 17 pounder tanks line up to fire near Veen, Germany.

At the left, the ammunition for the 17 pounder is compared with that for the U.S. 76mm and 90mm guns. Rounds 1, 2, and 3 are the 76mm HVAP (APCR), HE M42, and APC M62 (APCBC) respectively. The numbers 4, 5, 6, and 7 indicate the 17 pounder SVDS (APDS), APC, HE, and APCBC. The 90mm rounds, 8 through 10, are the HVAP M304 (APCR), HE M71, and APC M82 (APCBC). Note that despite its large chamber size, the 17 pounder round is relatively short and thus easier to handle in the turret.

A rush conversion program at the Royal Ordnance Factories produced enough 17 pounder tanks by D-day to provide 12 for each British armored regiment. Nicknamed the Firefly they went into action in Normandy. At that time, the most effective 17 pounder armor piercing ammunition was the APCBC solid shot. By August 1944, a few rounds of a new type became available. These were designated as super velocity discarding sabot or SVDS (also referred to as armor piercing discarding sabot or APDS) and consisted of a high density tungsten carbide core in a lightweight carrier. The total projectile weight was only 7.91 pounds of which 5.5 pounds was the core. With such a light projectile, the muzzle velocity increased to 3950 ft/sec and the carrier separated from the core after leaving the muzzle. This reduced the drag of the small high density projectile allowing it to retain its high velocity to a greater range. The high velocity and density dramatically increased the penetration performance to 7.6 inches of homogeneous armor at 1000 yards range and 30 degrees obliquity. Unfortunately, the new shot was less accurate than the APCBC and some of the early production were particularly erratic, limiting their use to targets at fairly close range. However, they did provide a round capable of penetrating the heavy German armor then appearing on the battlefield.

In the reverse of the usual practice, a standard 75mm gun Sherman V (below) is disguised as a Firefly.

Below are two examples of camouflage applied to the Firefly. Note the paint job on the outer end of the gun barrel.

Two widely used British and Canadian modifications of the Sherman were the Command or Control tanks. Similar except for minor details, both served the same purpose. The Command tanks were assigned to armored divisions or brigades as battle headquarters and the Control tanks performed the same function in armored regiments or armored reconnaissance regiments. Equipped with two Number 19 radio sets, the stowage was arranged to permit retention of the tank's full armament. These tanks also served as rear link vehicles to maintain communication between forward and rear command echelons.

The Sherman Observation Post tank was developed to provide an armored mobile observation post for controlling artillery fire. In most of these vehicles, the 75mm cannon was replaced by a dummy to allow more space inside the tank. One Number 18 and two Number 19 radio sets were carried as well as two portable Number 38 sets for use outside the tank. Folding map boards were installed in the front center of the turret replacing the gun mount. The .30 caliber coaxial and bow machine guns were retained as well as the .50 caliber weapon on the commander's hatch. Stowage also included artillery fire control and wire communication equipment.

Two Sherman Command tanks appear above at the left. The antenna for the extra radio is installed in the sponson socket. The sketch below shows the stowage arrangement for the Sherman Observation Post tank.

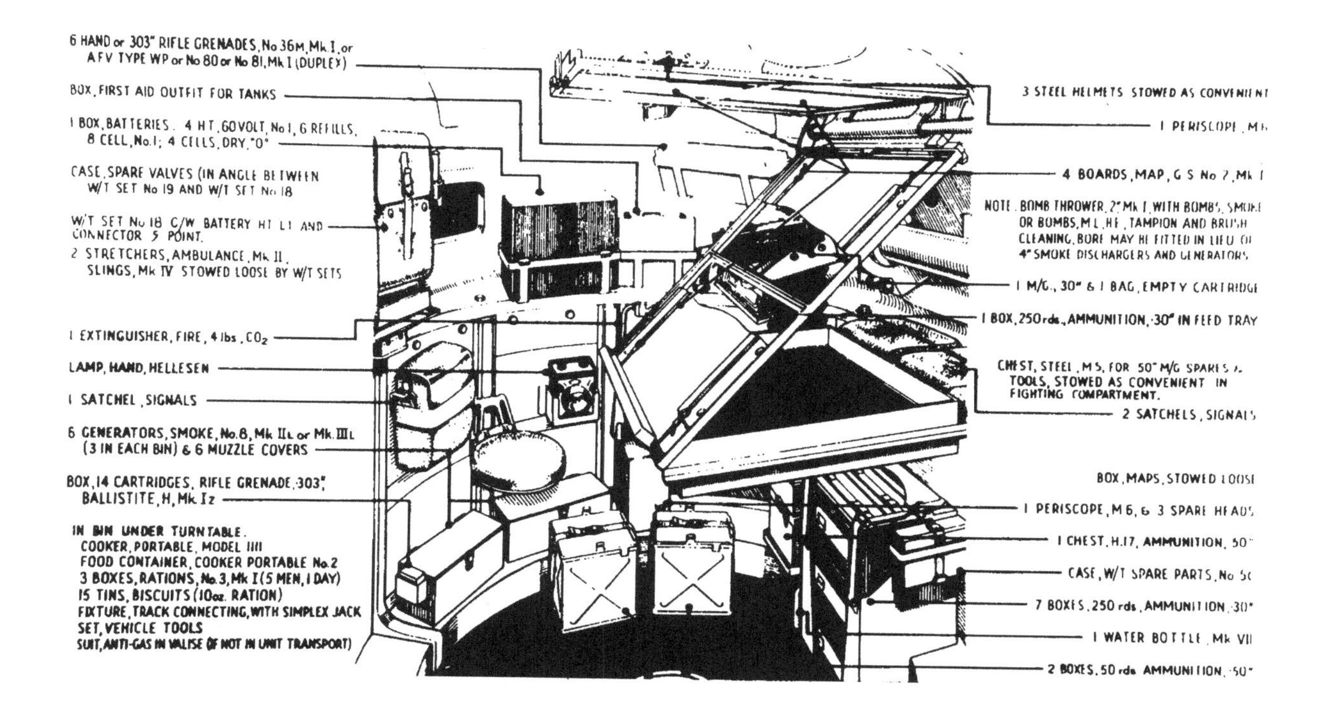

M4s armed with the 105mm howitzer firing from a French wheat field on 13 July 1944. The air inlet cover is open on the first tank.

THE NEW TANK GOES TO BATTLE

The improved models of the Sherman began to come off the production lines as the buildup of troops and equipment for the invasion of Europe was reaching its peak. The more powerful armament was of the greatest importance to the combat troops and the tanks fitted with the 76mm gun and the 105mm howitzer were rushed to Britain during the late Spring of 1944. Demonstrations were arranged prior to D-day to introduce the new weapons to the troops. The howitzer tank was readily accepted, but this was not true for the 76. It was immediately apparent that although the armored commanders were interested in the increased firepower, they were reluctant to replace the familiar 75 on the eve of battle. Of all of the armored divisions scheduled for the invasion, only the 2nd had been previously in action and that was a year earlier in Sicily. This early experience and the training program had instilled confidence in the 75 and there was insufficient time to properly familiarize the troops with the 76 before D-day on 6 June. A similar situation existed with the separate tank battalions. Here the prime mission was infantry support for which the 75 with its superior high explosive shell seemed better suited. Thus the armored units went into action on 6 June with the old familiar 75mm gun Sherman already fighting in other theaters around the world.

A final demonstration of the Sherman armed with the 76mm gun was held in England at the Imber firing range on 12 June. Shipments of the new tanks indicated that about 300 would soon be available in the theater. George S. Patton, Jr., then a Lieutenant General, was in the audience along with Major Generals Oliver and Grow commanding the 5th and 6th Armored Divisions respectively. All of the commanders were impressed by the performance of the 76, but were unwilling to see it replace most of the 75s. In fact, General Patton agreed to accept the 76 only if it was first placed in separate tank battalions for a combat test.

This plan was soon dropped because of the increasing demand for the more heavily armed tank. The early hedgerow fighting quickly revealed the weakness of the 75 against the thick armor of the German Panthers and Tigers. The combat troops now wanted every 76mm gun tank they could get and a clamor was raised for even more powerful armament to defeat the heavy German armor. The original plan was to arm one third of the tanks in a unit with the

An M4A1 of the 3rd Armored Division's 33rd Armored Regiment awaits orders to move forward near Reffuveille, France on 8 July 1944. This early production 76mm gun tank is fitted with a Rhinoceros hedgerow cutter.

76mm gun. However, by the end of the European campaign in the Spring of 1945, well over half of the Shermans in the U.S. units were equipped with the new weapon.

The hedgerow or Bocage country of Normandy greatly limited tank movement. They were confined to narrow roads or were dangerously exposed when climbing over the hedgerows. This situation resulted in the development known as the Rhinoceros. The idea was credited to Sergeant Curtis G. Culin of the 102nd Cavalry Reconnaissance Squadron for which he was later awarded the Legion of Merit. The device was an arrangement of steel angles welded to the front of the tank. Forming a tusklike structure, it cut into the base of the hedgerow preventing the vehicle from climbing. The tank then pushed a complete hedgerow section ahead of it into the next field burying any enemy troops dug in on the opposite side.

After a demonstration for General Omar Bradley, Ordnance started a crash production program. Using steel from the German beach obstacles, 500 tanks were fitted with the Rhinoceros in time for Operation Cobra. This was the breakout from Normandy beginning on 25 July 1944.

At the left, a welder assembles a Rhinoceros for installation on another M4A1.

An M4A1 of D Company, 32nd Armored Regiment, 3rd Armored Division operating in Normandy during August 1944. Note the Rhinoceros.

By 28 July, four U.S. armored divisions were in action as the drive gained momentum. The 4th pushed south into Avranches with the 2nd and 3rd fighting to the east. The 6th moved along the coast to the west. The fierce nature of the fighting which raged all along the front might be best characterized by a brief action described in the 4th Armored Division history.

> "A medium tank commandeered by Captain Murray W. Farmer, commanding the 25th's F Company (25th Cavalry Reconnaissance Squadron), encountered a German Mark V only 30 yards down an Avranches street. Captain Farmer ordered the Sherman's driver to ram the Panther before the German tank could bring its high velocity gun to bear. The two armor plated giants crashed together with a metallic clangor. The Sherman struck the Panther full in the flank and the muzzle of the medium's 75 almost touched the German turret. The Panther's crew tried vainly to swing their tank gun against the Sherman, but the long barrel would not clear the medium. Sergeant Edward A. Rejrat ... fired four 75mm HE and AP shells pointblank into the Panther. The explosions rocked the men in the Sherman, but as the dazed survivors of the Panther's crew tried to climb out of their tank, Captain Farmer shot them with a submachine gun. With one last heave, the Sherman tried to push the heavier Panther over and knock it completely out of the fight. Instead, the straining Sherman overturned into a ditch with its tracks in the air. The medium began burning, but the crew wriggled away from the two tanks and dodged safely through scattered German infantrymen."

M4s of the 4th Armored Division move past the remains of a German horse drawn column on the Avranches road.

An M4A1 and a howitzer armed M4 are shown here near Chartres, France on 16 August 1944. These tanks belong to the 4th Armored Division's 31st Tank Battalion. Note the spare bogie wheel stowed on the front of the howitzer tank.

After the breakout from Normandy, fast moving armored columns fanned out westward into Brittany and swung southeast into the heart of France. During this drive, close air support was of major importance. Tank mounted forward air controllers accompanied the leading columns. Frequently pilots themselves, they were in direct radio contact with the fighter bombers above the spearhead. With the U.S. troops, the air support usually consisted of P47 Thunderbolts heavily armed with bombs and rockets and easily able to deal with enemy armored vehicles or antitank guns. For the British forces, the Hawker Typhoons provided a similar service. These were ideal conditions for the reliable Shermans allowing them to cut rapidly into the enemy rear areas. With the fighters covering the advance, they were usually able to avoid a head to head duel with the powerful German tanks. The aggressive tactics of the armored divisions aimed to destroy or

The 3rd Armored Division crosses the Seine River on a floating bridge at Port Seine, France on 26 August 1944. The design of the Rhinoceros on this tank is somewhat different from those previously illustrated.

Shermans of the 8th Tank Battalion, 4th Armored Division crossing the National Canal near Bayon.

bypass centers of enemy resistance and allowed him little time to organize his defenses. During this rapid advance, the tankers often improvised methods of crossing obstacles without waiting for supporting troops. Once again, an example is provided by the 4th Armored Division history.

> "On the 11th (September 1944), mediums of the 8th Tank Battalion, commanded by Lieutenant Colonel Edgar T. Conley, rumbled into the Moselle valley at Bayon, 20 miles southeast of Nancy. Moving from bivouac south of Vaucouleurs, CCB's troops were to make a crossing with the 35th Infantry Division.
>
> Bridges over the Moselle and the canal paralleling it on the west had been blown. First Lieutenant William C. Marshall ... didn't wait for treadway spans. He wheeled his medium tank platoon to the edge of the canal, fired 75s into the opposite bank to break it down and threw logs into the mud and water at the bottom of the drained waterway.
>
> Gunning his tank, Marshall roared down the 20 foot canal and labored triumphantly through the muck up the bank. He towed the rest of his platoon over when they bogged down. The five tanks raced downstream between the canal and the river until the Moselle split into three fordable channels. Water surged to the turrets as the M4s plunged across. They climbed the east bank and went on to shoot up German infantry and guns that were pressing back the infantry's thin bridgehead. Half-tracks, tanks and towed peeps surged through the current as engineers labored until late next afternoon to complete 168 feet of floating bridge over the channels."

Although the Sherman served all over the world, its greatest concentration was in northwest Europe. By the end of the war, the United States alone had deployed 15 armored divisions and 37 separate tank battalions in that theater. When added to the British units, the combined force contained almost every production model and quite a few variants that were improvised in the field.

Towing bogged tanks across the canal at Bayon.

Above, a 17 pounder Sherman moves up in France, August–September 1944.

Below, a Canadian Sherman passes through the ruined streets of Caen (left). At the right, a Sherman of the 13/18 Royal Hussars by the Waal River, October 1944.

A heavy 48 hour rainstorm flooded this area in France where these Seventh Army howitzer tanks were operating, 8 November 1944.

Faced by tanks with superior armament and protection, the tactical employment of the Sherman required flanking attacks to hit the enemy in the sides and rear. Superior numbers usually permitted such tactics, although frequently at considerable cost.

The onset of Winter changed the situation. Lack of supplies slowed the attacking armies giving the enemy time to reorganize and strengthen his defenses. Wet weather frequently grounded the air support and soft terrain restricted the Shermans to the roads limiting their ability to outflank the enemy strongpoints. Things became particularly serious during the fighting in the Ardennes when the Shermans often were forced to engage in tank versus tank combat.

Although at a grave disadvantage against the powerful enemy tanks, there were occasions when the Sherman won such contests. Often expensive in casualties, these victories frequently required great skill and considerable heroism to offset the advantage of the heavily armed and armored enemy. Both were provided in ample quantity during the 740th Tank Battalion's introduction into combat.

A former CDL unit converted to a standard tank battalion, the 740th arrived in Belgium on the eve of the Ardennes offensive. Commanded by Lieutenant Colonel George K. Rubel, the battalion had an

A crew from C Company, 42nd Tank Battalion, 11th Armored Division loads 75mm ammunition into their Sherman near Jodenville, Belgium on 5 January 1945.

Identified by members of the battalion as the tank commanded by First Lieutenant Charles Powers, this Sherman of the 740th Tank Battalion was operating with the 82nd Airborne Division near Herresbach, Belgium.

excellent record in training and was particularly outstanding in gunnery. Unfortunately, they had received no tanks since converting from a CDL unit. By 18 December, the situation in the Ardennes was rapidly deteriorating and the battalion moved to the Ordnance Depot at Sprimont, Belgium to draw combat vehicles. They found that very little was available and much of that was not in operating condition. Working all night, the battalion repaired 15 tanks although they were still missing radios and other items of equipment. These tanks were manned by C Company commanded by Captain James D. Berry and the remaining gaps were filled with whatever vehicles were available. Sergeant Charlie Loopey and his crew took over an M36 tank destroyer and others manned M10 and M7 motor carriages.

On the afternoon of the 19th, C Company was ordered forward to support the 119th Infantry which was being overrun by elements of Kampfgruppe Peiper from the 1st SS Panzer Division. The ensuing action described in the following excerpt from the 740th Tank Battalion history earned C Company and its attached troops a Distinguished Unit Citation for their first battle.

> "Captain Berry, leading his tanks in a peep, arrived at 1530 hours and we outlined the situation. He was ordered to attack at once before the Infantry were overrun completely . . .
> Lieutenant (Charles B.) Powers spearheaded the attack. He had gone scarcely 800 yards when he saw a Panther tank about 150 yards ahead at a curve in the road. His first shot hit the gun mantlet, ricocheted downward, killed the enemy driver and bow gunner and set the tank on fire. Powers kept on moving and about a 100 yards further on came upon a second tank. He fired one round which hit the Panther's front slope plate and ricocheted off. His gun jammed and he signaled Lieutenant Loopey (then Sergeant Loopey) to move in quickly with his TD. Loopey's first round with his 90mm gun set the tank on fire, but he put in two or three more shots for good measure. By this time, Lieutenant Powers had cleared his gun and resumed his advance. About 150 yards further on he came upon a third Panther. His first shot blew the muzzle brake off the Panther's gun and two more shots set the tank on fire.
> All during this action, which occurred within 30 minutes after the attack had started, a slow drizzling rain was falling and a blanket-like fog covered the whole area. It was difficult to see an object 400 yards away. Lieutenant Powers' platoon had not only knocked out three tanks that had been raising hell with the Infantry, but his machine guns had sprayed the roadsides as well as the sides of the hills and quite a number of enemy soldiers were killed."

Such an outcome to a contest between Shermans and Panthers was, of course, the exception rather than the rule. Although the tankers continued to attack aggressively, the costs were extremely high and the crews were losing confidence in their tank. This was particularly true of the vehicles armed with the 75mm gun.

A photograph testifying to some accurate shooting, this view shows Sergeant Floyd of C Company, 740th Tank Battalion. Count the kill marks on the barrel of the 76.

The Sherman above has been driven onto a ramp to increase the elevation angle and thus the range of its 75. This practice was frequently used when the tanks were firing as artillery. This Sherman and the 76mm gun tank below both have sandbags on the front armor to increase the protection against the Panzerfaust. Note that both tanks are fitted with extended end connectors on the tracks.

As losses mounted, extra protection was added to the tanks by a variety of methods. After the success of the heavily armored M4A3E2 assault tanks, many units welded additional armor plate to the front and sides of the standard Sherman. Ordnance units obtained the necessary steel by cutting up disabled tanks or even captured enemy vehicles.

Protection against the German shaped charge weapons such as the Panzerfaust posed a particular problem. Layers of sandbags, rocks, logs, and even cement were sometimes applied to the vulnerable areas of the tank by the troops in the field. The added weight from all this extra protection increased the ground pressure reducing the mobility even further. Partial compensation was obtained by fitting the duckbill extended end connectors on the outside of the tracks. To meet the demand, large quantities of these connectors were manufactured by local contractors in Europe.

The 7th Armored Division tank above used logs, sandbags, and spare bogie wheels to increase the armor protection.

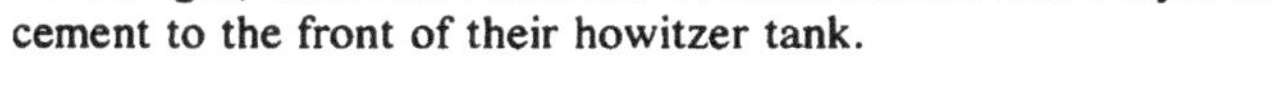

At the right, these 2nd Armored Division tankers add a layer of cement to the front of their howitzer tank.

The 8th Armored Division tanks (below) pause in Bergerhausen, Germany during the drive to Cologne. Note the variety of extra protection improvised in the field.

Above are the 3 inch 60 pound high explosive aircraft rockets installed on the tanks of the Coldstream Guards. Note that standard aircraft launchers are attached to the tank turrets.

Many unofficial additions were applied to the Sherman in the field by British as well as U.S. troops. One exclusively British modification was the attachment of aircraft rocket launchers to each side of the turret. Installed by the 1st Armoured Battalion of the Coldstream Guards just before the Rhine river crossing, they were in use until the end of the European war. The launchers were aircraft equipment normally used on the Typhoon and Tempest fighters. Each carried the standard 3 inch rocket with a 60 pound high explosive head. The launchers were usually fixed at an angle which would insure a hit on a target ahead of the tank up to either 400 or 800 yards. Since they were relatively inaccurate, a target as small as a tank could not be effectively engaged. However, the rockets were extremely useful against roadblocks and large wooden structures. The powerful high explosive warheads also often were effective in suppressing enemy fire and inducing him to surrender.

A less successful field addition to the tank's armament was applied to Sherman V, number T-232270, by the 2nd Canadian Armoured Brigade workshop. A 3 inch infantry mortar was mounted on the turret bustle aimed forward in line with the cannon. Fired by the tank commander, the muzzle loading weapon used a recoil system fitted with standard 8 inch vehicle shock absorbers. Unfortunately, the recoil system proved inadequate during trials by the 6th Canadian Armoured Regiment. Cracks appeared in the mount after firing two rounds and further tests were discontinued.

At the left is the Canadian experiment with the 3 inch mortar on the Sherman turret. At the upper left is a similar postwar installation in Britain which, although it operated without failure, was considered unsatisfactory as a support weapon.

The top and bottom photographs show M4A3E2 assault tanks after rearming with the 76mm gun. Note the nonstandard traveling lock in the bottom view. Both of these 4th Armored Division tanks have an extra .30 caliber machine gun on the turret top. At the right below is a standard 75mm gun tank after rearming with the 76.

It was proposed in early 1945 that a large number of 75mm gun tanks be rearmed with the 76. Such a modified tank was demonstrated at the Paris Ordnance Depot on 24 February. The project was approved, but later was limited to the M4A3E2 assault tanks. The latter were relatively simple to convert. They only required minor modifications and stowage changes since the gun mount was originally designed for the 76. The smaller turret on the standard 75mm gun tank made the change much less desirable as had been revealed during the 1942 tests at Fort Knox. Increased supplies of new 76mm gun tanks and a declining loss rate resulted in the cancellation of this makeshift conversion. However, the fact that it was originally approved illustrated the overriding importance of firepower when the chips were down.

Throughout the campaign, the high powered enemy guns continued to take a heavy toll. Since victory usually went to the tank which shot first, many gunners developed a "quick draw" technique reminiscent of the old west. This fast response is well illustrated by an incident described in the history of the 5th Armored Division. It occurred on the afternoon of 22 April 1945 during the final drive toward the Elbe river.

> "Corporal James E. Mathies, tank gunner of A Company, 34th Tank Battalion, was all set for anything as his tank rounded a corner and he saw an unfamiliar vehicle 400 yards away, its gun pointed straight at Mathies' tank. Mathies' 76 roared twice in rapid succession and the rear of the strange vehicle disappeared. It was a British scout car. The British soldiers manning it piled out and were recognized before further damage was done.
>
> The British commander of the car afterwards came up looking for Mathies. 'That was fast shooting, old chap.' he told the 34th Tank Battalion gunner. 'We had been there an hour, waiting to shoot anything that moved around that corner, and when you came around it you hit me twice before I could lay my hand on the trigger.' With that he patted the startled Mathies on the back and went to see what he could salvage out of his scout car"

Above, a 3rd Armored Division 76mm gun Sherman burns near Bergerhausen on the road to Cologne, 1 March 1945.

The numbers of 76mm gun tanks continued to increase until the close of the European war in May. Near the end, large numbers of tanks with the wide-track horizontal volute spring suspension became available reducing the maintenance requirements and improving the mobility of the armored units.

The end of the long drive as a 7th Armored Division Sherman reaches the Baltic at Rehna, Germany on 3 May 1945. These were the first U.S. troops to reach the Baltic.

The 76mm gun medium tank M4A3 with the horizontal volute spring suspension which appeared in large numbers near the end of the war in Europe. The tank at the right is from the 66th Armored Regiment, 2nd Armored Division at Tueven, Holland on 22 February 1945. Below, a new tank of the 4th Armored Division covers highway H-4 near Bastogne, Belgium on 8 January 1945.

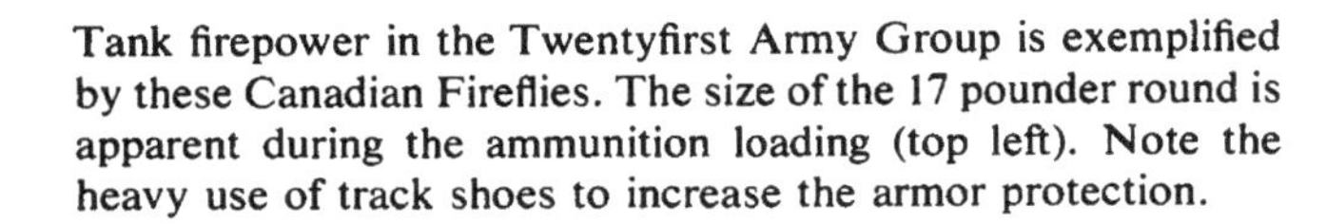

Tank firepower in the Twentyfirst Army Group is exemplified by these Canadian Fireflies. The size of the 17 pounder round is apparent during the ammunition loading (top left). Note the heavy use of track shoes to increase the armor protection.

Field Marshal Montgomery indicated that he did not want the 76mm gun in his Twentyfirst Army Group, preferring to rely on the Firefly armed with the more powerful 17 pounder. The latter had been in action since the invasion and was an extremely effective hole puncher despite its cramped quarters in the 75mm gun turret. Originally issued for the Normandy landings on a basis of one 17 pounder tank per troop, its numbers had greatly increased by the end of the war. Roughly equivalent to the Panther's 7.5cm KwK 42, the 17 pounder was slightly superior in penetration performance to both the Tiger I's 8.8cm KwK 36 and the U.S. 90mm gun. As a tank weapon on the western front, it was outclassed only by the 8.8cm KwK 43 on the Tiger II.

Wide grousers are installed on the Firefly at the left above. At the top right, a 17 pounder tank of the 4th County of London Yeomanry, 7th Armoured Division wades ashore from an LST in Normandy.

Below, the 5th Canadian Armoured Division is massed at Eelde Airport, Holland on 23 May 1945. Note the extensive use of track shoes as extra armor.

Above, 76mm ammunition is loaded into an M4A3 on the firing range near Pisa, Italy on 19 August 1944. The markings indicate that this is tank number 14 of A Company, 13th Tank Battalion, 1st Armored Division. This was after the 1st Armored Division had been reorganized dropping the regimental structure.

The late model Shermans were also supplied to U.S. and Allied forces in other theaters. In Italy, the U.S. 1st Armored Division received M4A3s during the Fall of 1944 and, unlike northwest Europe, the British were issued the 76mm gun Sherman IIA. Both armies made use of the 105mm howitzer tanks. Large numbers of M4A2s armed with the 76 were supplied to the Soviet Union, but little is known regarding their employment.

Another tank from A Company, 13th Tank Battalion returns to the bivouac area near Pisa (at left). Note that this M4A3 is an early production 76mm gun tank with the split circular hatch for the loader.

Above is a British Sherman IIA. The tanks at the top left belong to Snake Troop (Asp, Anaconda, and Adder), B Squadron, 2nd RTR at the Po River crossing on 27 April 1945. Lieutenant Colonel P.H. Hordern (with pipe) commanding the 2nd RTR is at the left with the RHQ Troop on 9 May 1945.

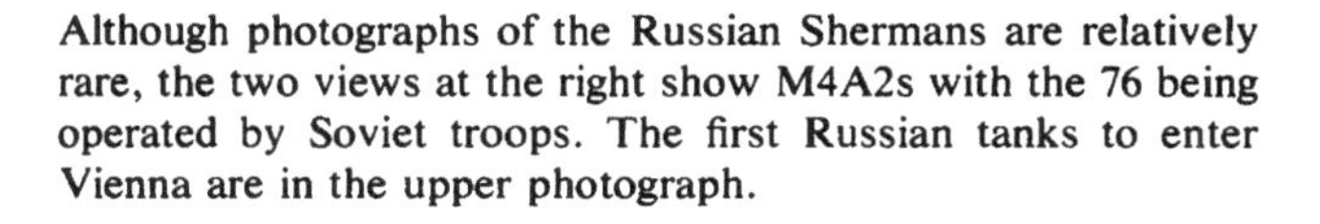

Although photographs of the Russian Shermans are relatively rare, the two views at the right show M4A2s with the 76 being operated by Soviet troops. The first Russian tanks to enter Vienna are in the upper photograph.

U.S. Marine Corps Shermans in action on Iwo Jima, February 1945. The tank above is still fitted with its deep water fording equipment. Note the wooden planking added to the sides for extra protection. The tank below had a track blown off by a land mine and was hit five times by artillery fire without any casualties to the crew.

Shermans of the 6th Marine Division on Okinawa during June 1945. Note the use of track shoes for extra protection. The tank at the right in the top photograph is a command tank fitted with a sponson radio.

Against the Japanese in the Pacific, the original 75mm gun was completely satisfactory and many of the late production 75mm M4A3 wet stowage tanks were supplied to that area. They were in action during the final battles on Okinawa and in the Philippines. Large numbers were also received during the buildup for the invasion of Japan scheduled for the Fall of 1945.

The commander of the Japanese Army on Okinawa testified to the effectiveness of the Sherman in the Pacific operations. In a battle lesson to his Thirtysecond Army, Lieutenant General Mitsuru Ushijima stated that "the enemy's power lies in his tanks. It has become obvious that our general battle against the American forces is a battle against their . . . M4 tanks".

An extreme example of extra protection applied to the Sherman in the field (above). This is a flame thrower tank of the 713th Tank Battalion modified at Okinawa. Those are light tank tracks on the turret.

Below, tanks are stockpiled at the Manila Ordnance Depot on Luzon in preparation for the invasion of Japan, 1 August 1945. These appear to be 75mm gun wet stowage M4A3s. Note the tanks with the horizontal volute spring suspension.

PART IV

SPECIAL TANKS AND ARMORED VEHICLES BASED ON THE SHERMAN

The first pilot 105mm howitzer motor carriage T32 during tests at Fort Knox.

SELF-PROPELLED ARTILLERY

Battle reports early in World War II indicated the need for highly mobile artillery to accompany the fast moving armored columns. Such a requirement could be met best by self-propelled artillery mounted on a full-track chassis. This view was forcefully expressed by Major General Jacob L. Devers, Chief of the Armored Force, in the Fall of 1941. As an artilleryman commanding an organization formed originally from the infantry and cavalry tank elements, General Devers was particularly suited to supervise the development of artillery as part of the armored striking force.

In October 1941, General Devers recommended the manufacture of two 105mm howitzer motor carriages based on the chassis of the medium tank M3. The two pilot vehicles were constructed at the Baldwin Locomotive Works and shipped to Aberdeen Proving Ground for proof tests. Designated as the 105mm howitzer motor carriage T32, they were armed with the M2A1 howitzer using the top part of the standard field carriage. The weapon was mounted in the right front of a boxlike open top hull on the tank chassis. At Aberdeen, a door was cut in the rear superstructure armor on the first pilot to provide more clearance for cleaning the howitzer and changing the tube.

After preliminary tests, pilot number 1, registration number W-6010106, was shipped to the Armored Force Board at Fort Knox. Beginning on 5 February 1942, testing continued around the clock for three days. The Board concluded that with a few modifications, the T32 was a suitable artillery weapon for the armored division. It was recommended that the superstructure armor be decreased in thickness from 3/4 to 1/2 inches and that the sides and rear walls be lowered by 11 inches. The front armor superstructure was to be raised by 3 inches. As originally designed, the howitzer on the T32 had a traverse of 15 degrees left and 23 degrees right. However, as constructed, a total of only 31 degrees was available. The Board requested that the mount be rotated to the right to utilize the full 45 degree range available in the standard M2 field

The first pilot T32 during the Fort Knox tests (top left) can be compared with the second pilot after modification at Aberdeen (top right). Note the cut down rear and side walls as well as the addition of the machine gun ring mount.

carriage. This allowed a traverse of 15 degrees left and 30 degrees right. Elevation ranged from +35 to -5 degrees. The former was reduced from a maximum of +65 degrees originally specified by the Armored Force in order to preserve the low silhouette of the vehicle. This limitation on maximum elevation was to prove a disadvantage in combat, frequently requiring that the vehicle be parked on a steep ramp to obtain high angle fire.

The Armored Force also requested that a .50 caliber antiaircraft machine gun be installed. It was to be fitted to a folding pedestal located on the rear deck or on a ring mount over one front corner of the vehicle. An access door was also considered necessary in the front hull plate to permit servicing of the transmission. The ammunition stowage was rearranged and increased from 44 to 57 rounds and seats were provided for a crew of seven.

The various modifications were incorporated in the second pilot, registration number W-6010107, which had been retained at Aberdeen. The result was a considerable change in the vehicle's appearance with the front armor being reshaped to provide more interior space and to permit mounting the .50 caliber antiaircraft machine gun. The modified T32 was then shipped to the American Locomotive Company to serve as a production prototype.

Standardized as the 105mm howitzer motor carriage M7 in April 1942, the first vehicles came off the assembly line that same month, starting a production run that was to last until August 1943. Except for a gap during March 1943, deliveries continued every month totaling 2814 vehicles. The first two production carriages arrived at Aberdeen on 6 April 1942. After proof firing, one was used for automotive tests and the other was turned over to the Design Section for a

Below is the first production 105mm howitzer motor carriage M7 at Aberdeen in April 1942. Additional armor has been added around the machine gun mount compared to the modified T32.

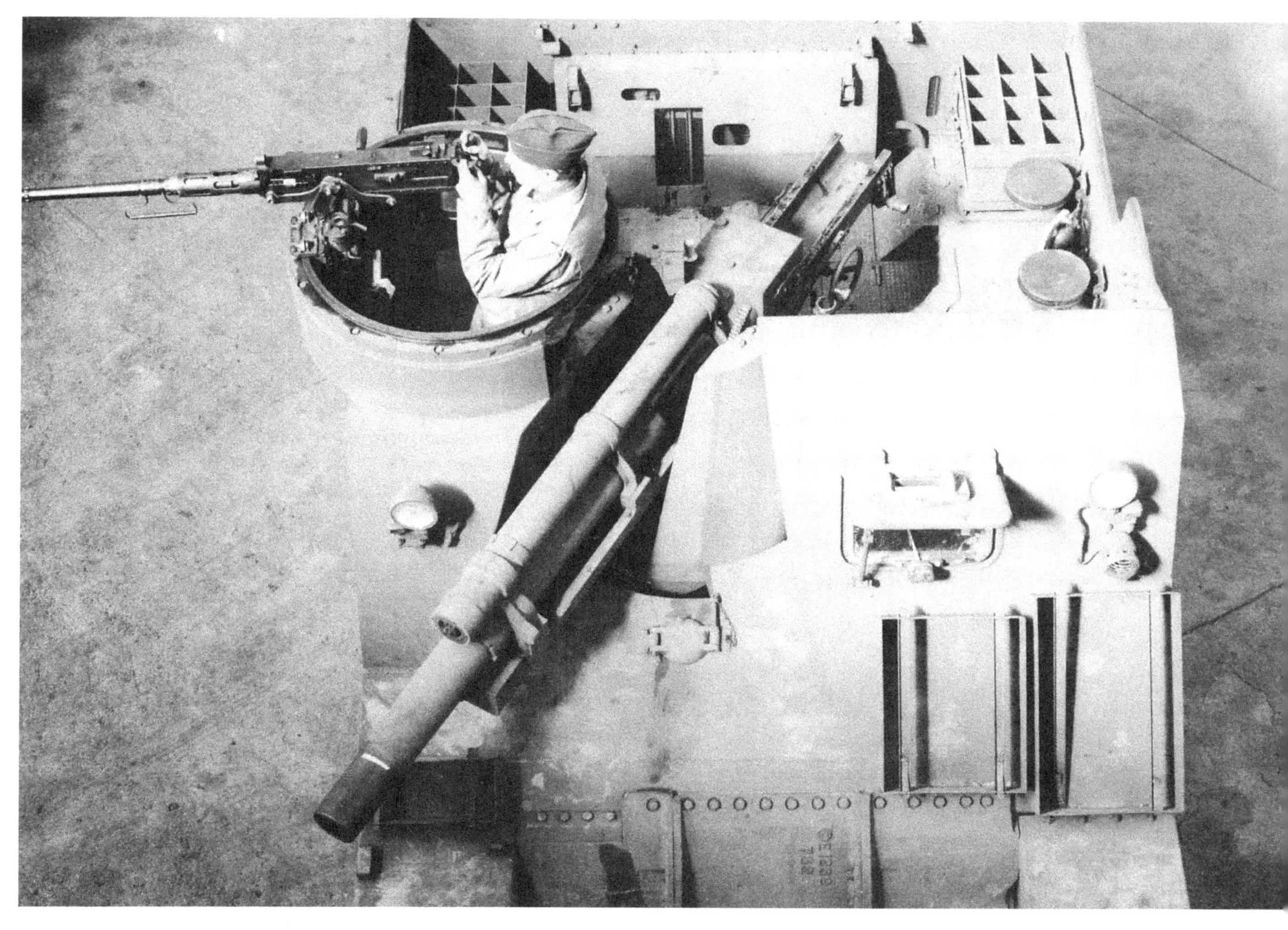

The first production M7 (above) with the 105mm howitzer at maximum right traverse. It is fitted with the differential housing from the medium tank M3 with the cut-out at the top of the right-hand section.

stowage study. This program resulted in additional changes which were approved on 5 May, provided they did not interrupt production. The ammunition stowage was increased to 69 rounds by adding 7 rounds along the left side wall of the hull and 5 along the right. To provide the required space, four of the folding crew seats were eliminated. The curved armor plate below the .50 caliber machine gun ring was extended farther down the side of the vehicle increasing the interior space and providing a seat for the machine gunner.

The prototypes and early production vehicles used the three piece differential and final drive housing from the medium tank M3. These could be readily identified by the rectangular cut-out at the top right of the right-hand section. This was to provide clearance for the sponson gun mount on the M3. Later vehicles used the three piece housing from the M4 tank series as well as the single piece casting. Both prototypes and early production vehicles used the riveted lower hull and early vertical volute spring suspension of the M3. They were superseded by the welded M4 type lower hull and the later heavy duty suspension bogies.

At the right is 105mm howitzer motor carriage M7, serial number 1850, during acceptance tests at Aberdeen. The ammunition containers can be seen extending above the side armor. This vehicle is equipped with the late type suspension bogies.

At the left is an M7 Priest in British service at El Alamein. Note all of the extra stowage.

At the left below is another British Priest during landing operations.

The driver was seated at the left front of the vehicle alongside the transmission. Direct vision was provided by a door in the front plate. When open, it could be fitted with a removable windshield. In the closed position, the driver had a protectoscope in the door itself for indirect vision. The remainder of the crew had direct vision over the sides of the open top hull. A canvas cover was provided for shelter from the weather.

First introduced into action by the British at El Alamein, the M7 was named the Priest because of the pulpit appearance of the .50 caliber antiaircraft mount. Rapidly replacing the half-track 105mm howitzer motor carriage T19, it served with U.S. troops in Tunisia and became the standard light artillery weapon for the U.S. armored divisions.

Below, a 105mm howitzer motor carriage is firing on enemy positions at Anzio, Italy on 6 March 1944. This is an early production carriage fitted with the original suspension bogies.

Details of the late production M7 can be seen in these photographs. Folding side armor has been added to protect the ammunition stowage and late model components such as the single piece differential and final drive housing have been incorporated.

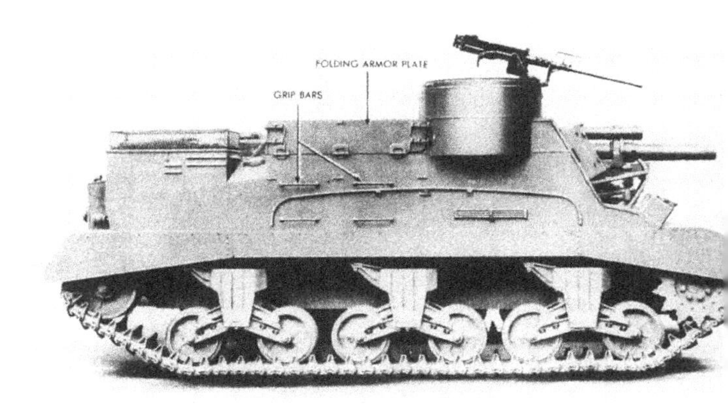

The stowage arrangement is clearly visible in the view below. Note how the howitzer field mount was adapted to the vehicle.

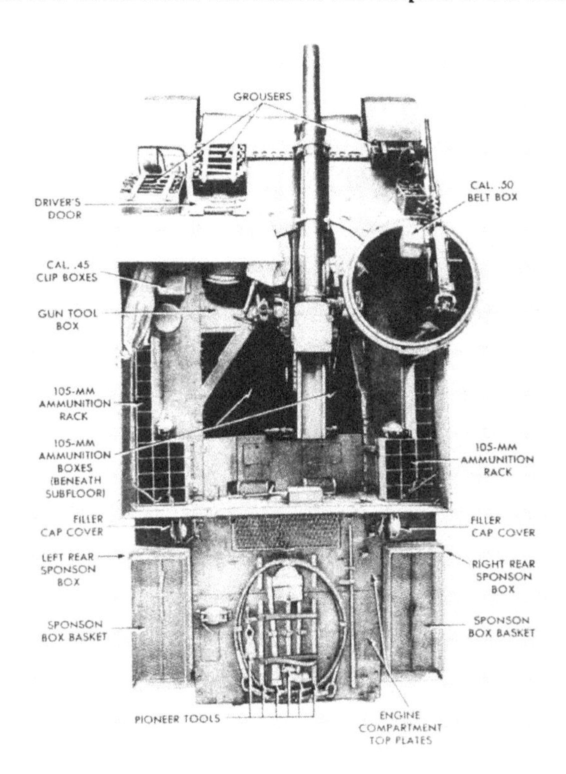

By the end of 1943, battle experience as well as data from the test programs indicated the need for further modification of the M7. It was noted that the ammunition stowed vertically in the cellular racks was partially exposed above the side armor. Hinged armor plates were designed which could be raised on the sides and rear of the fighting compartment to protect the ammunition. A new traveling lock was developed for the howitzer which was much more convenient to use and did not interfere with the floor ammunition racks. Other features of the late model M4 tanks were also applied to the new M7s. These included such items as double anchor brakes, disc type idler wheels, sand-shields, and the single piece sharp nosed differential and final drive housing. The upper armor on all of these vehicles was 1/2 inch thick homogeneous plate. However, the lower hull was assembled from 1-1/2 inch thick soft carbon steel.

Five hundred of the improved M7s were produced at American Locomotive between March and October 1944. Starting in March 1945, another 176 M7s were built at Federal Machine and Welder Company bringing the total M7 production to 3490.

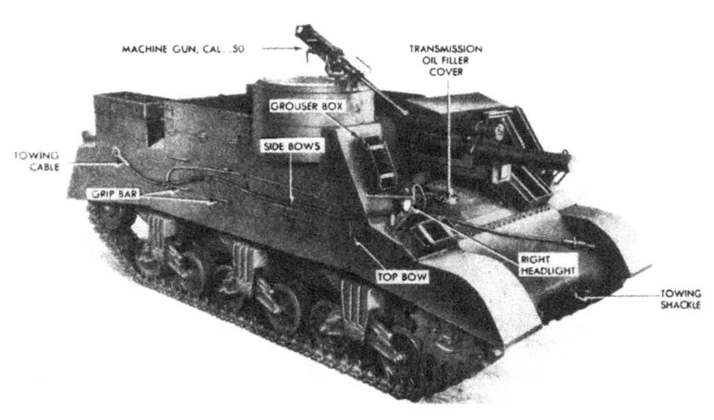

The 105mm howitzer motor carriage M7B1 is shown in these photographs. Except for the rear deck, this vehicle is quite similar to the late production M7. The wide grill type engine compartment doors provide the main point of identification for the M7B1.

Parallel with the production of the late model M7s, 826 vehicles were constructed at Pressed Steel Car Company using the Ford tank engine. Based on the M4A3, they were designated as the 105mm howitzer motor carriage M7B1. Except for the power plant, they were similar to the late model M7s with the lower hull also fabricated from 1-1/2 inch thick soft steel plate. The last M7B1 was completed in February 1945.

Below is a side sectional view of the 105mm howitzer motor carriage M7B1.

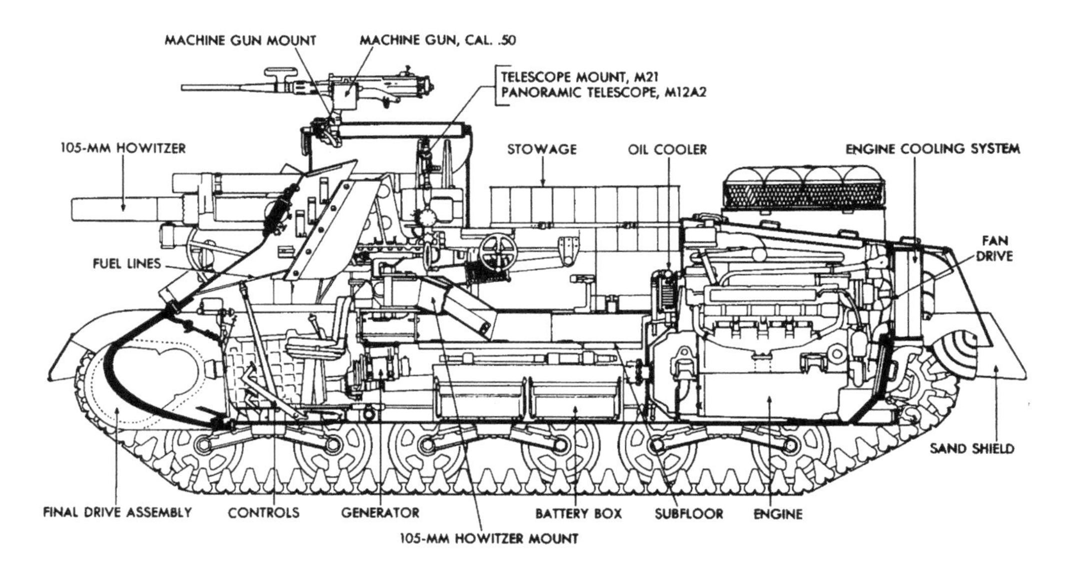

Above is 105mm howitzer motor carriage M7B1, serial number 4366, at Aberdeen Proving Ground on 28 December 1944. Below, a late production howitzer motor carriage is firing from an improvised ramp to increase the maximum elevation. This vehicle is from the 231st Armored Field Artillery Battalion of the 6th Armored Divison. It is in action near Kleinblittersdorf, Germany on 7 December 1944.

Above is a 1st Armored Division M7 in Italy at the moment of firing. The howitzer is in full recoil. This photograph was dated 29 August 1944.

Below, M7s of the 1st Marine Division in action on Okinawa on 12 May 1945. Note the track shoes added to reinforce the thin armor.

The 105mm howitzer motor carriage M7B2 (above and below). The increased height of the howitzer and machine gun mount is obvious when compared with the M7B1 on page 339. The motor carriage in the bottom photograph served in the Austrian Army during the postwar period.

Both the M7 and the M7B1 served the U.S. Army long after World War II. During the Korean War in the early 1950s, the limitations imposed by the 35 degrees maximum elevation were once again apparent. The rugged Korean terrain required higher angles of elevation to place fire on the reverse slopes. The solution in the Italian mountains almost ten years before had been to drive the vehicle onto a steep ramp to obtain the necessary angle. Now a better fix was considered. The M7B1 was modified increasing the maximum elevation to the +65 degrees found on the standard field carriage. Designated as the 105mm howitzer motor carriage M7B2, the howitzer mount was raised increasing the height of the vehicle. The circular machine gun mount was also raised to maintain a clear field of fire in all directions.

The 25 pounder gun motor carriage T51 at Aberdeen on 7 December 1942. Note the registration number, W-6010107, which indicates that this vehicle was converted from the second pilot 105mm howitzer motor carriage T32.

A project was started in June 1942 to adapt the British 25 pounder Mk II gun to a self-propelled carriage. The second pilot T32 was reworked to mount the British weapon and it was designated as the 25 pounder gun motor carriage T51 on 11 June. The 25 pounder replaced the 105 using its own upper carriage with adapters to fit the howitzer mount. The pulpit type antiaircraft machine gun mount was retained similar to that on the M7 Priest.

After assembly at Aberdeen, the weapon was proof fired resulting in a cradle failure. Repairs were delayed since the original cradle was an early riveted design which was no longer in production. The mount was reworked to accept a later model welded cradle and proof firing was resumed with satisfactory results. As designed, the elevation range of the 25 pounder was +40 to -5 degrees, slightly exceeding that for the 105 on the M7. However, the traverse totaled only 24 degrees (7 degrees left, 17 degrees right). As frequently happened, things changed during construction and as completed, the elevation ranged from +34 to -6 degrees with the traverse increased to a total of about 39 degrees.

By the time the new gun mount was proof fired, the successful development of the Canadian Sexton killed further interest in the project. The T51 was cancelled in March 1943.

The 25 pounder and its mount are clearly visible in this view of the T51.

An early production Sexton I (above) with the three piece differential and final drive housing. Also, note the early suspension bogies.

To meet British Army requirements for self-propelled light artillery, the Canadian Department of National Defense requested the development of a 25 pounder mount on the Ram tank chassis. The pilot was completed in late 1942. After successful tests and some modification, production began at the Montreal Locomotive Works in early 1943. Originally known as the 25 pounder Ram Carrier, it was later designated as the tracked self-propelled 25 pounder, Sexton, thus continuing the clerical name tradition established by the earlier Bishop and Priest.

The 25 pounder was mounted to the left of center in the front of the open top vehicle. The driver was located on the right front as in the Ram tank. The boxlike superstructure was assembled by welding homogeneous armor plate 1/2 inch thick on the sides and rear and 3/4 inches in front. Unlike the Priest, there was no ring mount for an antiaircraft machine gun. However, starting with vehicle number 147, brackets were provided for two Bren light machine guns. Numerous other changes were made during the production run reflecting mainly the improvements in the basic tank chassis. Thus the single piece differential and final drive housing replaced the three piece version on the later models. The suspension showed similar development with the heavy duty bogies and trailing

On this view of the Sexton I, the absence of the battery and auxiliary generator boxes on the rear deck is obvious.

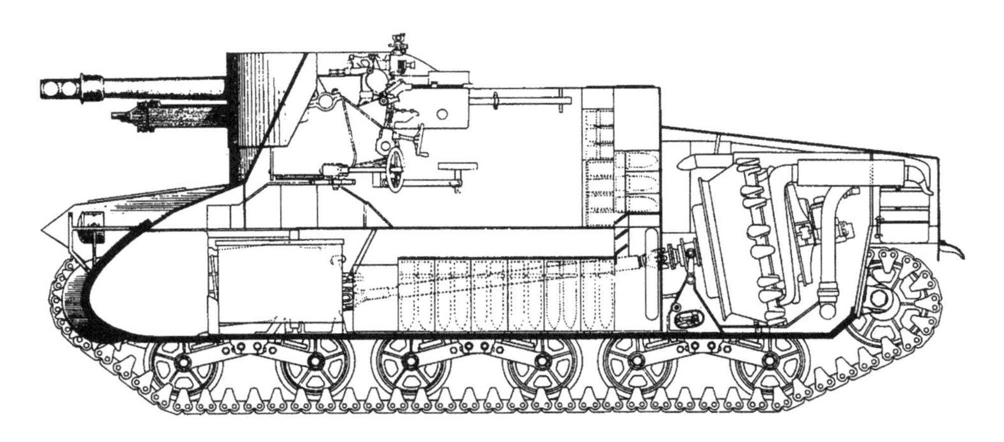

Above is a side section drawing of the Sexton I.

track return rollers appearing on the later vehicles. Except for the early production, all of the Sextons were equipped with the Canadian dry pin tracks and 17 tooth sprockets.

As mounted in the Sexton, the 25 pounder could be traversed 25 degrees left and 15 degrees right. The elevation ranged from +40 to –9 degrees requiring that the recoil travel be limited to 20 inches instead of the normal 36. Ammunition stowage consisted of 112 25 pounder cartridges with an assortment of high explosive, smoke, and armor piercing projectiles. Manned by a crew of six, the Sexton was widely used by the British Army in Italy and northwest Europe. It soon became the standard self-propelled artillery weapon in British service replacing the Priest which was converted to other uses. The first 124 vehicles were designated as the Sexton I. They could be easily identified by the absence of the battery and auxiliary generator boxes on the rear deck. Later vehicles were designated as the Sexton II. Total production reached 2150 by the end of the war and they remained in British and Canadian service long into the postwar period.

Details of the gun mount and stowage can be seen in this view of the Sexton I.

The late production Sexton II shown in these photographs is fitted with the heavy duty suspension bogies and the single piece differential and final drive housing. These vehicles are equipped with the Canadian dry pin track and the 17 tooth sprockets. The battery and auxiliary generator boxes can be seen at the rear corners of the hull.

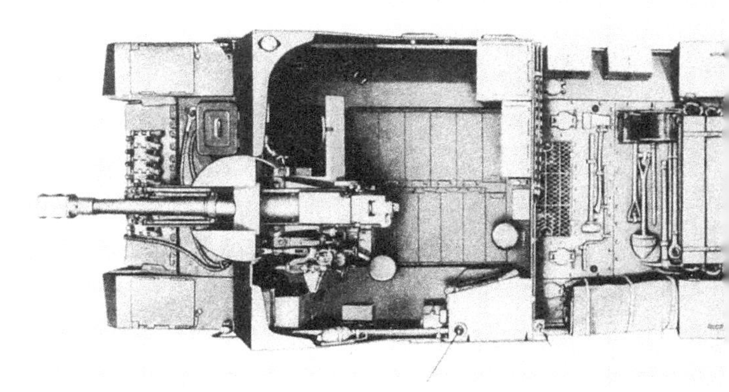

Above, a Sexton II is fitted for deep water fording.

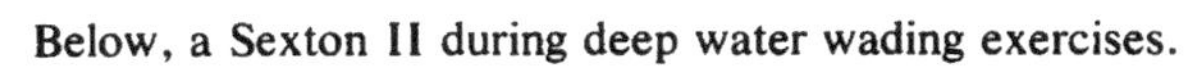
Below, a Sexton II during deep water wading exercises.

The 9.75 inch mortar installed on an M7 chassis being demonstrated to the U.S. Seventh Army at Benny, France on 28 February 1945.

After being replaced by the Sexton, the British Priests were converted to various uses. One interesting experiment was the mounting of a 9.75 inch mortar. Developed by the British Petroleum Warfare Department, it fired a very large incendiary shell. Examples of this self-propelled mortar were demonstrated to the U.S. Seventh Army at Benny, France in February 1945, but they were not accepted for service.

Two of the 9.75 inch mortar motor carriages. Note the size of the white phosphorus incendiary shells.

The 155mm gun motor carriage T6 in its original configuration at Aberdeen (above and below) in February 1942. The hydraulic actuated spade can be seen in the bottom photograph.

The Ordnance Department commenced studies on a self-propelled 155mm gun using the M3 tank chassis in June 1941. At that time, artillery doctrine envisaged the use of tractor towed guns and there was little interest in a self-propelled weapon. After discussions between Ordnance and the Artillery, an agreement was reached to construct a pilot vehicle. The 155mm gun M1918M1 with its recoil mechanism and top and bottom carriages was mounted on the M3 tank chassis. OCM 16912 approved this development and designated the new vehicle as the 155mm gun motor carriage T6. The pilot was built at Rock Island Arsenal and delivered to Aberdeen Proving Ground on 12 February 1942.

Firing tests showed the T6 to be a stable firing platform for the 155mm gun. However, the hydraulically actuated spade was damaged and failed to retract after firing. Even in the retracted position, this protruding spade was a limiting factor to cross-country

Production 155mm gun motor carriage M12 number 35 with a cargo carrier T14. The production vehicles have the later type of suspension bogies.

mobility and a redesign was required. It was also necessary to provide a suitable dust seal for the gun mount traversing mechanism.

After modification, the T6 was shipped to Fort Bragg, North Carolina for service tests by the Field Artillery Board. These tests showed the superiority of the self-propelled mount in supporting rapidly moving formations. During one exercise, the T6 moved 6 miles to a new firing position in 35 minutes compared to about 3 hours for a towed gun. On 17 July, the Board recommended that the T6 be adopted after a few interior and stowage changes. They also requested that a similar companion vehicle be procured as a personnel and ammunition carrier. The latter development was already in progress and was designated as the cargo carrier T14.

The success of the T6 led to the consideration of self-propelled mounts for even heavier weapons. After World War I, 330 240mm howitzers based on the French design had been manufactured at Watervliet Arsenal and many of these weapons were available. The feasibility of mounting such howitzers on the T6 chassis was studied by the Franklin Institute. Proposal drawings dated October 1942 show the 240mm howitzer M1918 installed on a modified T6 chassis. The three bogies on each side were moved toward the rear, but their spacing remained the same. A trailing idler was added increasing the ground contact length to reduce the ground pressure. An interesting feature of the design was the use of both the howitzer motor carriage and a T14 type of ammunition carrier to absorb the recoil during firing. Spades were installed only on the ammunition carrier and the two vehicles were coupled back to back so that when the howitzer fired, the motor carriage recoiled against the ammunition carrier. This arrangement placed the rear bogie of the motor carriage on top of the buried spade assembly attached to the ammunition carrier holding it firmly in the ground. With the two vehicles so closely connected, the howitzer crew used the platform on the ammunition carrier to serve the piece. This double vehicle recoiling concept was rather complicated and required the use of both vehicles during firing. It did not progress beyond the study stage.

OCM 18584 recommended standardization of the T6 as the 155mm gun motor carriage M12 and procurement was authorized for 50 vehicles. This was increased to 100 on 10 August 1942. The original T6 was shipped to Pressed Steel Car Company as a prototype and they completed the first production vehicle in September. Deliveries continued until March 1943 when the last five of the 100 M12s were received.

The first production M12 was shipped to the Erie Proving Ground where stowage arrangements were worked out and approved by representatives of the Armored and Field Artillery Boards. It was then sent

A model of the proposed motor carriage for the 240mm howitzer M1918.

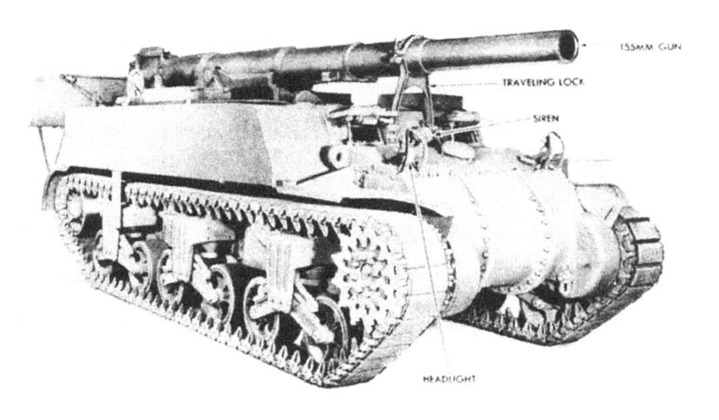

Details of the remanufactured and modernized 155mm gun motor carriage M12 can be seen in these views. Note the holders for the ten 155mm projectiles alongside the gun mount (below).

to Fort Bragg for additional tests. Modifications required on the production model included the correction of the old vapor lock problem inherent in the M3 tank and changes in the flame arrester and exhaust pipes.

Headquarters, Army Ground Forces indicated that the 100 M12s available would meet all known requirements and the vehicles were either stored or assigned to training units. The tests and training program revealed the need for even further changes. With the buildup for the Normandy invasion starting, plans were made in December 1943 for the remanufacture and modernization of 74 M12s. A similar number of T14 cargo carriers, now standardized as the M30, also were to be rebuilt. The work began at the Baldwin Locomotive Works in February 1944 and was completed in May.

Even with the many modifications, the production M12s retained the same general arrangement as the original T6. The 155mm gun was carried at the rear of the vehicle on the M4 pedestal mount. The weapon itself was the 155mm gun M1917, M1917A1, or M1918M1 depending upon availability. These guns used the same ammunition and differed only in minor details. They all dated from World War I and the M1917 was of French manufacture and still retained the original French breech ring. The M1918M1 was manufactured in the United States and when its breech ring was fitted to the M1917 gun, the latter was redesignated as the M1917A1.

The M4 gun mount could be traversed 14 degrees to the right or left and its elevation ranged from +30 to -3 degrees. Ten 155mm projectiles were located on the carriage floor with 6 to the left of the gun mount and 4 to the right. Six propelling charges were stowed below the left rear seat. Two others were in wells in the lower carriage support and the remaining 2 were carried on the center of the rear floor compartment cover. Seats were provided for six men, with two in the driving compartment, two at the left side of the gun mount,

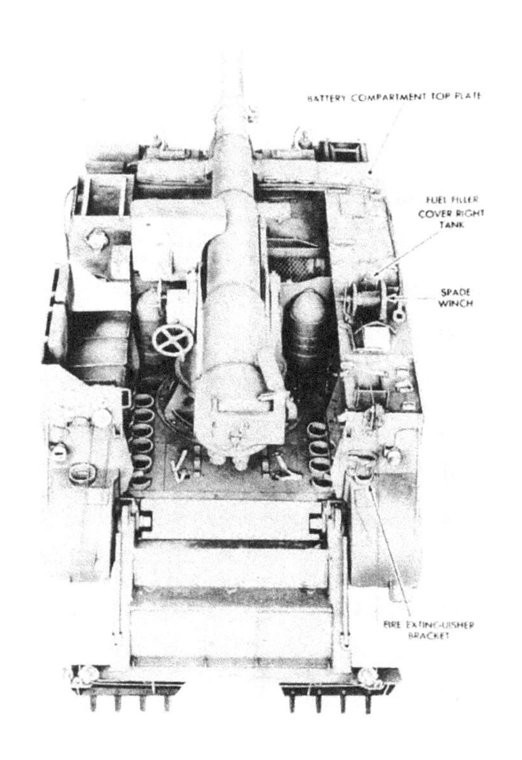

and two on the spade when it was in the retracted position.

To leave the rear of the tank chassis clear for the gun mount, the Continental R975 C1 engine was moved forward to just behind the driving compartment. The exhaust pipes extended out through each side of the vehicle between the center and rear bogies. Two fuel tanks with a combined capacity of 200 gallons were mounted horizontally in the sponsons, one on each side of the engine compartment. The hull was constructed of welded homogeneous armor plate with the sides 1/2 inch thick above the fenders and 3/4 inches below. The lower hull front consisted of the standard three piece differential and final drive housing.

These two photographs show the M12 with the spade retracted in the traveling position. Below, the gun barrel is stowed in the traveling lock.

Above, a battery of M12s attached to the 11th Armored Division open fire near Budssheim, Germany on 10 March 1945. At the left, an M12 of the 988th Field Artillery Battalion is in full recoil while firing into a Siegfried Line pillbox near Seelbach, Germany on 18 March 1945.

In action in Europe, the M12 fully justified the effort that went into its development. It was particularly effective in supporting the fast moving columns after the breakout from Normandy. On a number of occasions these self-propelled guns were the only heavy artillery within a days march of the front and they successfully performed all of the normal missions for such weapons.

When the attacking armies came up against the heavy fortifications of the Siegfried Line in the Fall of 1944, the M12 proved to be an effective means for their destruction. Using direct fire at ranges of 1000 to 2000 yards, the 155mm shells were deadly to the pillboxes. With concrete piercing fuses, the high explosive rounds could penetrate up to 7 feet of reinforced concrete. Frequently, only one or two shots were required to cause the pillbox crew to surrender.

At the left, the M12s are firing from ramps to obtain the maximum elevation.

The 155mm gun motor carriage T83 is shown above with the weapon in the traveling position. At the left below, the carriage is ready for firing.

After the successful introduction of the M12, the Artillery requested additional 155mm gun motor carriages. By this time, the supply of the M1918 type gun had been exhausted and studies indicated that the M12 chassis was unsuitable for the more powerful 155mm gun M1.

Further study showed that a satisfactory chassis for the new weapon could be provided using late model Sherman components. This vehicle was designed with a wider hull and used the new horizontal volute spring suspension with the 23 inch tracks. The general arrangement followed that of the M12 with the engine moved forward behind the drivers and the cannon mounted at the rear. The hull was open on top except for the driving compartment where access was provided by two vision cupolas in the roof. A floor mounted escape hatch was located just behind the assistant driver's seat. The upper hull was constructed of 1/2 inch thick welded homogeneous armor plate. The lower sides were 1 inch thick and the lower front consisted of the standard single piece sharp nosed differential and final drive housing.

Special castings were welded to the floor and the front of each hull side plate to adapt the standard differential housing to the wider hull. These castings also provided the forward tilt necessary to align the transmission with the increased angle of the propeller shaft. This increased angle resulted, of course, from moving the engine forward to just behind the driving compartment and a similar modification had been required on the M12.

OCM 23279 on 18 March 1944 authorized the procurement of five pilot vehicles designated as the 155mm gun motor carriage T83. Pressed Steel Car Company received the contract and pilot number 1 was completed on 28 July 1944. At Aberdeen, tests of the T83 proved extremely satisfactory. Proof firing showed good stability at all ranges of elevation and traverse, both with and without the use of the spade. After firing 200 rounds of 155mm ammunition, the gun was replaced by the 8 inch howitzer M1 to evaluate this weapon on the vehicle mount. These tests were considered equally satisfactory after firing 75 rounds. Based on these results, OCM 25754 in November 1944 approved the arming of the last two pilots with the howitzer. They were then redesignated as the 8 inch howitzer motor carriage T89.

The second and third T83 pilots were completed in October and shipped to the Field Artillery Board at Fort Bragg. After a month of intensive testing, a number of modifications were introduced. These included changes to increase the working space inside the hull and on the rear platform as well as some rearrangement of the stowage. The manually operated spade winch was relocated from the right to the left side of the hull and the rear vertical sections of the fighting compartment were separated from the hull and attached to the platform. Pilot number 2 was then

At the left is the 8 inch howitzer motor carriage T89. The upper photograph shows the carriage in firing position. Details of the vehicle in travel order can be seen in the lower view.

shipped to Aberdeen and number 3 went to the Lima Tank Depot where it was processed for overseas shipment.

Production of the T83 began in February 1945 and a total of 418 vehicles were delivered before the end of the year. During the latter half of 1945, 24 of these were converted to 8 inch howitzer motor carriages T89. The T83 was standardized as the 155mm gun motor carriage M40 in May 1945.

Both pilot T89s were completed in early January 1945. After tests at the General Motors Proving Ground, one vehicle was shipped to the Field Artillery Board and the other was processed for overseas shipment along with the third pilot T83.

The T89 pilots were designed as a universal chassis which could mount either the 8 inch howitzer or the 155mm gun. The ammunition racks could carry either 8 inch or 155mm rounds and the travel lock was reversible so that it could fit the tube of either weapon. All other components were designed to handle either type of armament or they were interchangeable. Although 576 T89s were requested, the end of the war reduced the total production at Pressed Steel Car to 48. All of these were completed by September, 1945 and 24 of them were converted from the 155mm gun motor carriage M40. The T89 was standardized as the 8 inch howitzer motor carriage M43 in November 1945.

Below are the production 8 inch howitzer motor carriage M43 (left) and the 155mm gun motor carriage M40 (right). Note that the mounts and carriages are identical. Both vehicles are shown with the weapon locked in the travel position.

Although the production T83s and T89s were too late for the war, two pilot vehicles saw action in early 1945. They were included with the Pershing tank and other new ordnance equipment introduced by the Zebra mission in February 1945. Led by Major General Gladeon M. Barnes, Chief of Research and Development for the Ordnance Department, the objective of this mission was to introduce newly developed weapons to the troops and to evaluate them under combat conditions.

The T83 and T89 were assigned to the 991st Field Artillery Battalion which was then equipped with M12s. The 991st promptly removed the howitzer from the T89 and replaced it with a 155 for uniformity. During the attack on Cologne, it became the first artillery piece to open fire on the German positions in the city. Later, the 8 inch howitzer was reinstalled and it too was used in action.

In their second war for the U.S. Army (below), the M40s fire their 155s against Chinese positions on the central Korean front.

The M40 with .30 caliber machine guns fitted for close-in protection. These mounts could be used only when the crew floor was raised into the vertical traveling position. A 57mm recoilless rifle is mounted experimentally on the left sponson.

The excellent mobility of the self-propelled artillery frequently resulted in their use as close support weapons. On a number of occasions the M12s were under fire from enemy artillery and small arms. The open topped carriage left the crews exposed to air bursts and only their personal weapons were available for defense against enemy infantry.

After his return from the Zebra mission, General Barnes verbally directed Aberdeen to study the installation of additional armor protection as well as secondary armament. T83 pilot number 2 was used for these experiments. A ball mount carrying a .30 caliber machine gun was fitted into the right front hull as on the standard tank and two other .30 caliber machine guns were installed, one at each rear corner of the vehicle. Alternate mounts for the latter two guns were welded to the rear platform which when raised formed the rear wall of the fighting compartment. Tests indicated that these guns provided excellent coverage around the vehicle. Additional .30 caliber machine guns were installed in the gun shield on both sides of the cannon, but this location proved unsatisfactory because of the limited traverse. The 57mm and 75mm recoilless rifles were also tested as secondary armament. However, the powerful backblast from these weapons made them very difficult and dangerous to fire from the vehicle. Aberdeen considered the recoilless rifles unsatisfactory and recommended the .50 caliber machine gun if additional armament was required beyond the .30 caliber weapons.

To provide overhead protection, an armored cab was designed to fit over the rear of the carriage. The original intent was to assemble this cab from many small pieces so that it could be installed or removed by the crew. This did not prove feasible since such an arrangement greatly weakened the structure. The final design was fabricated from large sections requiring an overhead lifting device for installation or removal. The side walls of the cab could be extended to the rear when in the firing position, providing protection for the crew while ramming the projectile. These extensions folded forward when the spade and rear platform were retracted keeping the structure fairly compact during movement.

A 1/8 scale model was constructed for detailed examination and a full scale wooden mock-up was installed on the T83. The small model had additional plates attached to the bottoms of the side extensions. These were omitted from the full size mock-up since it was determined that the weapon could be loaded and fired without any crew member dismounting.

Weights were calculated for cabs constructed of 7/8 inch thick aluminum alloy as well as 1/2 or 3/4 inch thick steel. These were 3151, 5134, and 7712 pounds respectively. Since the original side walls were only 1/2 inch steel, the 3/4 inch thickness was considered unnecessary. Further study indicated that although the cab provided some protection for the crew, many parts of the recoil mechanism and equilibrator were still exposed and vulnerable. Aberdeen recommended that the cab be considered unsatisfactory and that the motor carriage be redesigned to give adequate protection to both crew and mount.

The ⅛ scale model of the M40 with the additional armor. Note the skirts on the bottom rear of the side extensions.

The full scale mock-up of the extra armor protection installed on the 155mm gun motor carriage T83. Here it has been labeled M40 after standardization. The bottom skirts on the model have been eliminated from the side extensions.

Above is the 250mm mortar motor carriage T94 in the traveling position.

It is apparent in the view above that a wooden mock-up has been installed to simulate the 250mm mortar.

The successful employment of heavy self-propelled artillery indicated the possible requirement for even larger such weapons capable of high angle fire. On 15 March 1945, the Ordnance Committee approved a feasibility study for a heavy self-propelled mortar based on the chassis of the T83. Armed with the 10 inch mortar T5E2, the vehicle was designated as the 10 inch mortar motor carriage T94. A test vehicle was converted from a T83 and fitted with a wooden mock-up of the heavy piece. The latter replaced the 155mm gun and the stowage was rearranged to handle 20 rounds of mortar ammunition. A crane and ammunition handling equipment were installed to service the muzzle loading smooth bore mortar. A .50 caliber machine gun was specified on a ring mount over the assistant driver's cupola, but this was not installed on the test vehicle. A 2 inch smoke mortar also was to be fitted in the front hull plate.

In line with the policy of designating mobile artillery in millimeters instead of inches, the designation was changed to the 250mm mortar motor carriage T94 by OCM 30524 on 2 May 1946. With the end of the war, interest shifted to improved weapons and vehicles for heavy self-propelled artillery and cancellation of the T94 project was recommended in January 1946.

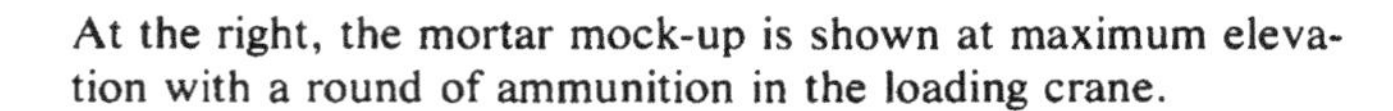

At the right, the mortar mock-up is shown at maximum elevation with a round of ammunition in the loading crane.

At the right is an artist's concept of the 155mm mortar motor carriage T90 with the mortar at maximum elevation. In line with the policy in effect at that time, the concept shows the pilot based on an early model tank chassis. If the carriage had reached production, it would, no doubt, have incorporated all of the late development features.

Research at the Franklin Institute developed several types of 155mm mortars for use against light and medium field fortifications. These weapons were muzzle loaders except for the 155mm mortar T9. The latter was a rifled breech loading design making it suitable for turret installation. It was originally proposed to mount the mortar in a thin walled turret on the light tank T24E1. However, the close support role required heavier armor protection and more stowage space for the large mortar rounds.

On 4 January 1945, OCM 26281 approved the development of a self-propelled mortar based on the M4 medium tank and designated the new vehicle as the 155mm mortar motor carriage T90. Construction of two pilots was authorized. The heavy work load in early 1945 resulted in some delay, but in March, the Birdsboro Steel Foundry and Machine Company received a contract to design and build a mock-up of the turret and mount.

To conserve space in the tank turret, the T9 mortar was modified to use a concentric recoil system and redesignated as the 155mm mortar T36. The high angles of fire necessary for its effective use required that the elevation mechanism be designed with three overlapping stages giving a total range of +70 to -10 degrees. The appropriate stage could be rapidly selected and locked by means of a spring loaded plunger. A quick release mechanism also allowed the mortar to be lowered to the horizontal position for loading and then returned to the original setting. Since the projectile weighed about 60 pounds, this was an important feature.

Thanks to the space saved by the concentric recoil mechanism, the mount, designated as the T28, carried two machine guns and a direct sight telescope along with the mortar. One .30 and one .50 caliber gun were specified. In addition, the tank carried its normal .30 caliber bow machine gun and the .50 caliber anti-aircraft weapon on the turret roof. The turret itself was similar to the standard 75mm gun model except for changes required to accommodate the mortar mount. The Ordnance Committee directed that M4 tanks unsuitable for overseas shipment be used to construct all pilot models. It was estimated that the space available would permit the stowage of 26 rounds of mortar ammunition.

The design and construction of the mock-up was completed at Birdsboro. However, with the end of the war, there was no further interest in heavy self-propelled mortars and OCM 28848 terminated the project on 23 August 1945.

Below, the 155mm breech loading mortar T36 is installed in the concentric recoil system.

The 3 inch gun motor carriage T24 (above and below) at Aberdeen Proving Ground in November 1941. Note the extremely high silhouette of the gun mount.

TANK DESTROYERS

The employment of the German panzer troops in the Blitzkrieg campaigns of 1939-40 forced a major reappraisal of tank defense tactics throughout the armies of the world. Opinion in the United States followed two major lines. The first was to meet fire with fire by drastically reorganizing the army replacing the traditional infantry-artillery team with tanks using close air support. The second approach retained the older arms in addition to an armored force, but delegated tank defense to specially organized antitank units. Lieutenant General Lesley J. McNair, at that time General Headquarters Chief of Staff, strongly favored the latter concept. On his recommendation, the Tank Destroyer Center was established at Fort Meade, Maryland on 1 December 1941. The mission of the new organization was to engage and destroy enemy armor thus permitting U.S. tanks to concentrate on what General McNair considered their primary role. This was the exploitation of breakthroughs and the destruction of the enemy rear areas.

The tactical doctrine developed for the tank destroyers required the use of a powerfully armed highly mobile motor carriage as a primary weapon. Work began immediately to develop such a vehicle, but the inevitable problems indicated that there would be a long delay before it could reach the troops.

Ordnance had proposed an interim full-track self-propelled weapon as early as September 1941. This would mount the M3 3 inch antiaircraft gun on the chassis of the M3 medium tank which was already in production. OCM 17358 approved the project on 23 October and the vehicle was designated as the 3 inch gun motor carriage T24.

The pilot T24 was built by the Baldwin Locomotive Works and delivered to Aberdeen in early November. The 3 inch gun was mounted in the open top tank hull using parts from the standard M2A2 antiaircraft

The 3 inch gun motor carriage T 40 (M9) at Aberdeen (above and below) in March 1942. It is obvious that the height of the gun mount has been reduced compared to the T24.

mount. It was aimed forward and located sightly to the left of the hull center line with a total traverse of 33 degrees. The elevation ranged from +15 to -2 degrees.

Firing tests showed the carriage was stable at all points of elevation and traverse. However, the range of both was considered inadequate and the silhouette of the carriage and mount was much too high and conspicuous for use as an antitank weapon. In January 1942, the gun was removed and the vehicle returned to Baldwin for conversion to the 3 inch gun motor carriage T40. The T24 project was cancelled by OCM 18061 in April 1942.

After the attack on Pearl Harbor in December 1941, the need for an expedient tank destroyer became so urgent that Ordnance was authorized to mount 50 of the early M1918 3 inch antiaircraft guns which were available on the M3 tank chassis. The proposed vehicle was designated as the 3 inch gun motor carriage T40. Baldwin Locomotive modified the front hull of the T24 to provide for a lower gun mount and to increase the traverse. The 3 inch gun M1918 was mounted by installing its traversing base ring on a firing platform just above the propeller shaft. The trunnion mount was cut down by about 1 foot to lower the gun.

Tests began at Aberdeen in March 1942 and modifications were authorized to permit loading the gun at all elevations up to 20 degrees. The elevating handwheel was relocated to allow one man operation and the ammunition racks were redesigned. OCM 18143 recommended that the T40 be adopted as Substitute Standard on 30 April. This was approved and it was designated as the 3 inch gun motor carriage M9.

The approval was short-lived. The Tank Destroyer Board indicated that the M9 did not meet the requirements of speed and mobility which were essential in tank destroyer operations. Other difficulties arose when efforts were made to start production. It turned out that only 27 of the M1918 guns were available and there was no assurance that even these were all serviceable. With such a limited number, manufacturing costs were excessive and there were no facilities immediately available to take on the project. Since the greatly superior 3 inch gun motor carriage M10 would reach production at almost the same time, the M9 was cancelled on 20 August 1942.

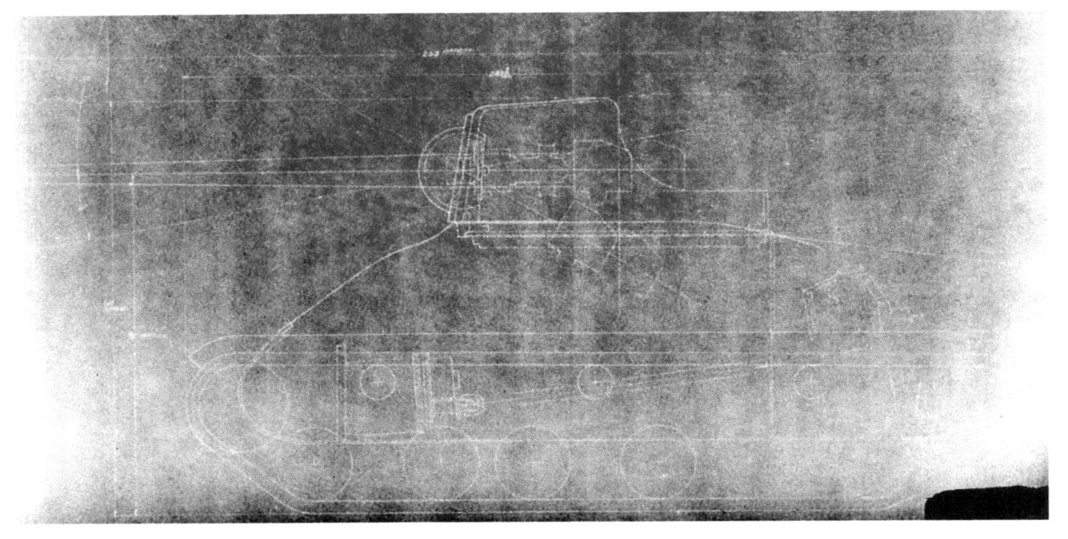

Above is the original specification drawing of the 3 inch gun motor carriage T35 as submitted by the Office, Chief of Ordnance. As can be seen, it was based on the chassis powered by the Continental R975 engine.

The advantages of using the medium tank chassis as the basis for a tank destroyer were apparent from the tests on the T24. They also showed the importance of a lower silhouette, better protection, and a 360 degree traverse for the gun. The Office Chief of Ordnance submitted proposal drawings for a tank destroyer based on the medium tank M4A1 which was about to enter production. These drawings designated the vehicle as the 3 inch gun motor carriage T35 and were dated 12 November 1941. In December, Aberdeen prepared a revised design for the T35 based on the diesel powered M4A2 and a wooden mock-up was constructed in January 1942. At this stage, the 3 inch gun T12 was mounted in a turret open at the top and rear. This weapon was also the main armament of the heavy tank M6 and it used the same trunnion assembly and bearings. The gun rotor was similar to that in the heavy tank, but it was shortened by 7 inches. Elevation ranged from +30 to -10 degrees and a direct sight telescope was fitted to the right of the cannon. There was no coaxial machine gun, but the mock-up retained the .30 caliber bow mount of the medium tank. The hull was similar to that of the M4A2, but the armor was reduced to 1 inch in thickness on the sides and rear. The full 2 inches were retained on the front plate.

While the design work was in progress, early reports from the fighting in the Philippines emphasized the advantages of sloped armor in deflecting projectiles. The Tank Destroyer Board then requested that the new motor carriage have the lowest possible silhouette and make use of sloped armor plate. Ordnance sketched out three possible designs differing mainly in silhouette. The first of these, with a 94 inch overall height, was selected and later designated as the 3 inch gun motor carriage T35E1. It still retained the turret open at the top and rear as on the T35. However, the height of the hull was decreased and its upper front was a single highly sloped 2 inch plate without the drivers' hoods or vision slots. A hatch for the driver, fitted with a single periscope, was installed in the top deck just back of the front plate. The bow machine gun was omitted from the T35E1 design. The 1 inch thick upper hull sides were angled at 38 degrees from the vertical and 1/2 inch skirts were attached to the edge of the sponsons. The latter sloped inward providing some protection for the tracks and lower hull.

The Aberdeen proposal drawing for the 3 inch gun motor carriage T35 appears below. Note that this design is based on the diesel powered tank.

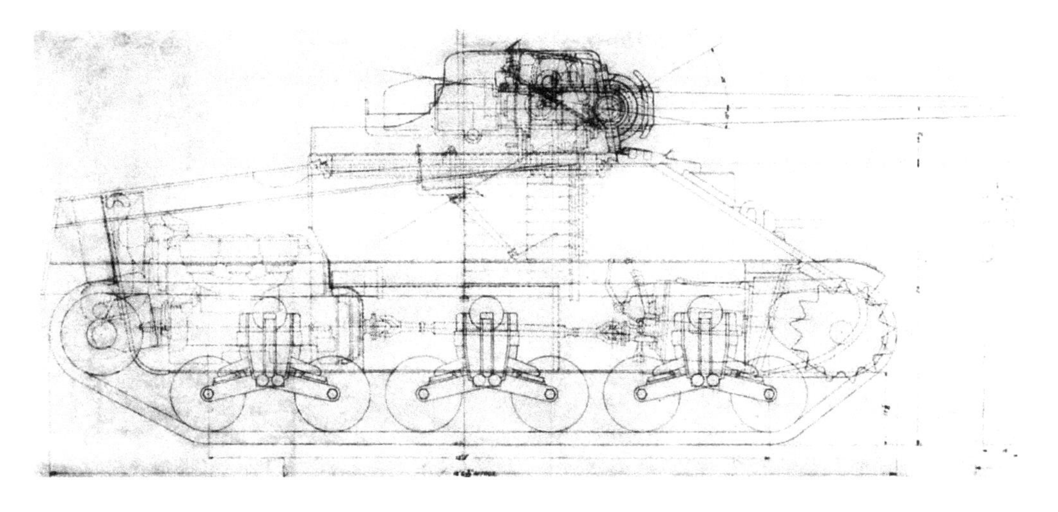

Close-up views of the turret on the T35 wooden mock-up are shown above. The gun mount is similar to that in the heavy tank M6 and the turret is open at the top rear.

Below is the T35 as completed with the redesigned turret and without the bow machine gun. An auxiliary armor shield has been added over the differential and final drive housing.

The Fisher Tank Division started detail design work in January 1942 and by April had completed a pilot model of both the T35 and T35E1. Each was manned by a crew of five with two men in the front hull and three in the turret. Both vehicles differed somewhat from the original drawings by being fitted with a cast circular, partially open top, turret of equal height on the sides and rear. The turret walls sloped inward at 33 degrees toward the top and 31 degrees toward the bottom from a point about halfway up the sides. A partial roof containing two periscopes extended back from the front. The turret armor was 2 inches thick in front and 1 inch thick on the sides and rear. Both vehicles followed their preliminary hull designs except that the bow machine gun was eliminated from the T35 at the request of the Tank Destroyer Board. Each was fitted with the three piece differential and final drive housing. The vertical part of the housing was reinforced by a right angle section of auxiliary armor plate bolted on to provide a 45 degree angle of obliquity to horizontal attack.

The simple design of the circular welded turret on the T35 can be seen at the right.

These views of the 3 inch gun motor carriage T35E1 (above and below) show the sloped armor on both hull and turret. The latter was the same design as on the T35 with a partial roof in front.

Tests at Aberdeen showed that the sloped armor of the T35E1 provided much superior protection to that on the T35. They also revealed that the ballistic properties of the cast turret were considerably inferior to rolled armor plate. After a demonstration on 2 May 1942, a decision was made to standardize the T35E1 with a number of modifications. To lower the weight, the armor thickness was reduced to 1-1/2 inches on the upper front plate and to 3/4 inches on the upper sides. The vertical lower sides remained at 1 inch, but the skirt thickness was reduced to 1/4 inches. The cast turret was replaced by a welded model for the production vehicles. A single piece cast differential and final drive housing was specified and the auxiliary armor was omitted. A hatch was provided for the assistant driver similar to that for the driver with a single periscope in each. In addition, the driver now had an auxiliary periscope in the hull roof to the left of his hatch. Concern at Aberdeen over the decreased protection offered by the thinner armor led to the installation of bosses on the hull front and on the sides of the turret and hull. They permitted the fitting of auxiliary armor plate when additional protection was required.

OCM 18313 recommended standardization of the T35E1 as the 3 inch gun motor carriage M10 on 4 June 1942. This was approved and the T35 project was cancelled although the vehicle was retained for experimental and training purposes.

Details of the early production 3 inch gun motor carriage M10 can be seen here. The bosses for the installation of auxiliary armor plate appear on the front and sides of the hull and the sides of the turret.

A new and greatly simplified gun mount was designed for the production vehicles. The rotor and the turret front plate were eliminated and a gun shield attached to the mount covered the opening in the front. Reversing the usual practice, the trunnion pins were fixed in the turret with the bearings on the gun yoke. This arrangement allowed easy removal in the field. The trunnion pins were removable as it was originally intended to provide for interchanging the 3 inch gun with the 105mm howitzer or the British 17 pounder. This was never done in U.S. service, but the British later installed the 17 pounder with great success. Bronze sleeve bearings replaced the usual roller bearings on the trunnions. They introduced enough friction to damp out the bobbing action resulting from the unbalanced gun. Standardized in June 1942, the weapon was designated as the 3 inch gun M7 in mount M5. Fiftyfour rounds of 3 inch ammunition were carried with 6 ready rounds in the turret and the remaining 48 stowed in the sponson racks.

The original welded turret proposed at Aberdeen was hexagonal in shape with five sides and the gun shield. Some design problems resulted in the adoption of a pentagonal turret with four welded sides and the gun shield as a temporary expedient. When the problems with the hexagonal design were solved in June, jigs and fixtures already had been ordered for the pentagonal model and any further changes would have delayed production. Thus the pentagonal welded turret became the production standard. The turret sides were 1 inch thick with a 2-3/4 inch thick gun shield. The area of the partial roof was reduced and the turret periscopes on the T35E1 were eliminated.

Production of the M10 began at Fisher in September 1942 with 105 vehicles delivered during that month. This started a run which lasted through December 1943 for a total of 4993 motor carriages.

The stowage on the early M10 is shown below. Note the attempt to balance the turret by attaching the grousers to the top rear.

The pilot 3 inch gun motor carriage M10A1 (above) at Aberdeen. Like the first M10s, grousers are stowed on the rear of the turret. Below is a later production motor carriage with the triangular turret counterweight.

The wide grill type rear deck doors characteristic of the M10A1 can be seen below.

To meet the urgent need for tank destroyers, a contract was let to the Ford Motor company to produce a vehicle similar to the M10, but based on the medium tank M4A3. Identical to the M10 except for the Ford gasoline engine, the new vehicle was designated as the 3 inch gun motor carriage M10A1. They could be identified most easily by the larger grill type doors on the rear deck. The M10A1s began to come off the assembly line in October 1942 and continued until September 1943 for a total of 1038 vehicles. Production shifted that same month to Fisher where the M10A1 was built alongside the diesel powered M10. Fisher produced 375 M10A1s by the end of November and in January 1944, an additional 300 were delivered without turrets. These were completed later as the 90mm gun motor carriage M36. Counting the latter 300, a total of 1713 M10A1s were built.

After test of the first production vehicles, Aberdeen reported that they had few mechanical problems. As on the prototype, the installation of the heavy 3 inch gun in the unbalanced turret made traversing difficult when the carriage was on a slope. The gun lock also was frequently damaged during cross-country movement. In an attempt to balance the turret on the early production vehicles, track grousers were stowed on the back and the .50 caliber machine gun was mounted on the rear corner. This proved insufficient and counterweights were improvised and installed by many units in the field. The situation was finally corrected by the introduction of two standard counterweights weighing a total of about 3600 pounds. Triangular in cross section, they soon appeared attached to the top rear of the turret on all new production vehicles.

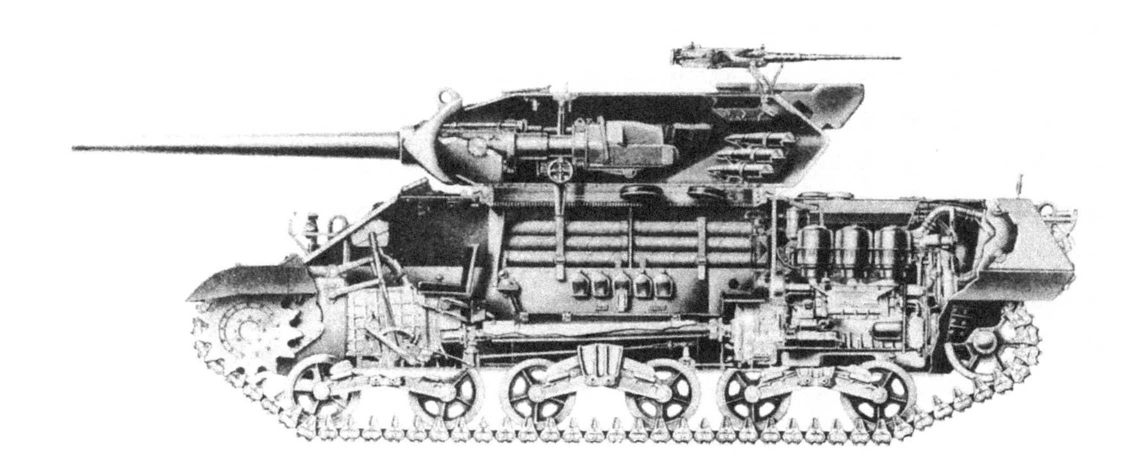

3 inch Gun Motor Carriage M10

Details of the M10 (above) and the M10A1 (below) can be compared in these sectional views. On both vehicles, the fiber containers for the 3 inch ammunition are stowed in the sponsons with bare ready rounds on the rear turret wall.

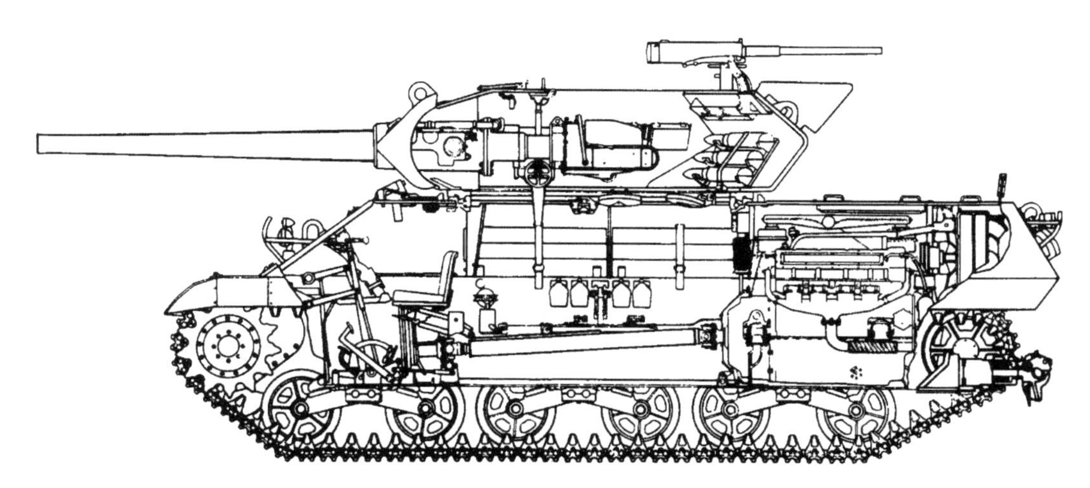

3 inch Gun Motor Carriage M10A1

Above is an M10 during training exercises at Camp Hood, Texas on 16 October 1943. Painted on the rear of the turret is the black panther emblem of the Tank Destroyers. Below is a close-up view of the turret on an M10 of the 811th Tank Destroyer Battalion at Camp Carson, Colorado on 1 May 1943. Note the track grousers stowed on the front armor plate.

The turret on the M10 and M10A1 used a worm gear manual traverse mechanism. In the late Spring of 1943, a program began to develop a spur gear system which would have greater efficiency and permit the use of one man or two man operation as required. During this same period, the Oilgear hydraulic power traverse unit, which had proven so successful on the medium tanks, was installed in one of the carriages. Tested by the Tank Destroyer Board, it was reported in December 1943, to be far superior to the manual traverse mechanism. However, by now the M10 and M10A1 were going out of production and this and other projects were cancelled.

Early vehicles of the M10 series carried sights for direct fire only, but this was later modified to include equipment for indirect fire. In March 1943, the Ordnance Committee recommended that the fire control equipment include a telescope M51, a telescope M44, an open sight, an azimuth indicator M18, and a gunner's quadrant M1.

The late production M10 with the redesigned turret and new counterweights. The 3 inch gun mount can be seen at the left.

Other changes were made during the production run. The rear of the late model turret was modified to increase the working space and a new design counterweight was installed. The auxiliary armor bosses were omitted from the sides of the late production hull and turret, but they were retained on the upper front hull plate.

Below is the late production M10A1, serial number 7994, with the new turret and counterweights.

Above, an early M10 in North Africa on 13 March 1943. Note the improvised counterweights installed on the rear of the turret.

Rushed to Africa in early 1943, the M10s rapidly replaced the half-track 75mm gun motor carriage M3 as the main weapon in the tank destroyer battalions. First committed to battle during the middle of March near Maknassy, Tunisia, the M10 soon proved the worth of its powerful gun. Serving throughout the remainder of the war, it was widely used during the Italian campaign and in northwest Europe. It also appeared in the Pacific, where its high velocity gun was effective in knocking out Japanese fortified positions. Approximately 3600 M10s were shipped overseas for use by U.S. and Allied troops.

Thirty M10s were modified for a special Signal Corps project during the Fall of 1944. Highly classified at the time, this project involved the installation of powerful sound systems to deceive the enemy. Using wire recordings played through loudspeakers, the equipment could simulate the sound of many kinds of military activity such as construction projects or tank and troop movements. The sound equipment was installed in 24 M10s after replacement of the 3 inch gun with a dummy and some rearrangement of the interior. For security purposes, these vehicles were designated as "Special Cars". The remaining six M10s were called "Control Cars" and they retained their armament. Some programing equipment was installed in the latter vehicles replacing part of the 3 inch ammunition stowage.

The 30 M10s were modified at the York Safe and Lock Company and shipped to the Army Experimental Station at Pine Camp, New York during September 1944. The sound equipment was installed at Pine Camp and the vehicles were taken overseas by the 3133rd Signal Service Company. They were in operation in northern Italy early in 1945.

Since the M10 production was sufficient to meet troop requirements, the M10A1s were retained in the United States. Here they were used for training purposes and some were converted to tank recovery vehicles or prime movers. However, when the need arose for a tank destroyer with increased firepower, most of the M10A1s were rebuilt as the 90mm gun motor carriage M36. A later similar modification to the M10 was designated as the 90mm gun motor carriage M36B2.

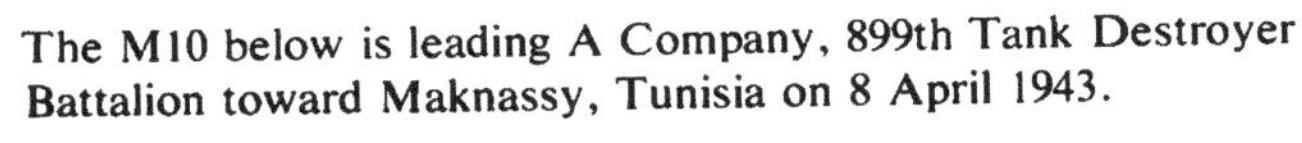

The M10 below is leading A Company, 899th Tank Destroyer Battalion toward Maknassy, Tunisia on 8 April 1943.

M10s are in action above on Kwajalein supporting the 7th Infantry Division on 3 February 1944.

Below is a late production M10 with the newer turret supporting the 77th Infantry Division on the beach at Ormoc, Leyte, 16 December 1944. A Japanese barge is burning on the shore. The M10 is still fitted for deep water fording.

Enemy observation posts are under fire from these M10s (above) of A Company, 634th Tank Destroyer Battalion in Aachen, Germany, 14 October 1944.

An M10 (below) attached to the 8th Infantry Division enters Düren, Germany on 24 February 1945. This vehicle is still fitted with a Rhinoceros hedgerow cutter.

An M10 tank destroyer (above) firing at night on enemy positions in the Mount Belvedere area of Italy on 20 February 1945.

The armored top below was improvised for the M10 by the 536th Ordnance Heavy Maintenance Company at Luneville, France, 13 February 1945. This is a late production M10 with the redesigned turret.

The 1/11 Antitank Regiment of the 6th South African Armoured Division fires at German positions near Bologna, Italy on 17 November 1944. These are standard M10s with British stowage.

Seeing the need for a more powerful antitank gun than the 3 inch M7, the British rearmed many of their late model M10s with the 17 pounder Mk V. This was a modified version of the 17 pounder Mk II gun which was already in production. Two lugs added to the breech permitted its installation in the standard 3 inch mount. Since the 17 pounder barrel was smaller in diameter than the original 3 inch tube, a special casting was welded over the gun shield to reduce the hole to the proper size. It also served as a counterweight to help balance the gun. An additional counterweight was fitted on the end of the barrel just back of the muzzle brake. An elongated hole was cut in the gun shield for a new direct sight telescope. The stowage was rearranged to accommodate the new weapon. Fifty rounds of 17 pounder ammunition were carried with 6 in the turret ready racks and 44 stowed in the sponsons. With the new gun, elevation ranged from +20 to –5 degrees.

Designated as the Achilles IIC, the self-propelled 17 pounder was a deadly antitank weapon. Used by the British in northwest Europe and Italy, it was still in service at the end of the war.

Below is the late production M10 rearmed with the British 17 pounder. Note the counterweight back of the muzzle brake necessary to balance the 17 pounder in the M10's 3 inch gun mount.

The two views of the Achilles IIC at the right show the special casting welded on the gun shield to fit the 17 pounder. Also, the elongated hole can be seen in the shield for the new direct sight telescope.

Below, an Achilles IIC is firing. Note the muzzle blast from the 17 pounder.

The 76mm gun motor carriage T72. Except for the new turret and stowage, the vehicle is the same as the 3 inch gun motor carriage M10A1.

On 18 March 1943, OCM 19953 recommended the development of a turret mounting the 76mm gun for installation on the M10 chassis. It was expected that a considerable weight reduction could be achieved compared to the heavy 3 inch turret with its counterweights. Although its armor piercing performance was identical to the 3 inch gun, the 76 was a much lighter weapon. With a properly designed turret, it was originally hoped that the overall vehicle weight might be reduced by three tons. Ordnance Committee action in May designated the new vehicle as the 76mm gun motor carriage T72.

The new turret was a lightweight version of the design used on the medium tank T23. The gun mount also was similar to the T80, but the coaxial .30 caliber machine gun was eliminated and the gun shield was thinned down to 1-1/2 inches. Since there was no stabilizer, its brackets were removed and the direct sight telescope was relocated. The revised design was designated as the 76mm gun mount T2. The turret armor was reduced to 1-1/8 inches on the sides and rear and the top was left open. The bustle which balanced the lightweight turret provided space for 27 rounds of ammunition. Improved stowage allowed 72 of the smaller 76mm rounds to be carried in the sponson racks. Thus 99 rounds were available, an increase of 45 over the amount of 3 inch ammunition in the M10.

Two pilot turrets were manufactured and installed on M10A1 chassis. The first vehicle arrived at Aberdeen in March 1943 and the second followed in April. Obviously the work did not wait for Ordnance Committee action. Tests showed an actual weight saving of about 4350 pounds over the M10. The traversing and elevating handwheels were much more conveniently located and the narrower gun mount and bulged turret walls provided additional space for the gun crew. However, it was noted that less protection was afforded by the thinner gun shield compared to the M10.

Parallel with the T72, development work was in progress on the 76mm gun motor carriage T70. The latter vehicle with its torsion bar suspension was considered far superior to the M10 chassis and Aberdeen recommended in February 1944 that work on the T72 be halted. They also suggested that the T70 turret be used if a 76mm gun was required for the M10. Since the project was cancelled, neither of the T72s were sent to the Tank Destroyer Board, but one was subsequently used at Aberdeen for experiments with the rigid gun mount.

Details of the new lightweight 76mm gun turret installed on the T72 can be seen at the right. A dummy .50 caliber antiaircraft machine gun is fitted to the pedestal mount. Note that the gunner is located on the right side of the cannon, unlike the arrangement on the M10 and M10A1.

The profile of the new turret is clearly visible in the side view of the T72 below. The welded assembly gives a sharp cornered angular appearance to this turret.

Gun motor carriage M10 number 1 (above and below) fitted with the 90mm gun T7. These photographs were taken during the tests at Aberdeen in November 1942.

By 1942, the appearance of increasingly heavy armor on the battlefield strongly indicated a future requirement for an antitank gun superior to the 3 inch M7. The British had an excellent weapon in the new 17 pounder for both towed and self-propelled mounts. In the United States, the 90mm antiaircraft gun was considered for a similar role and proposal drawings dated 17 April 1942 show this weapon mounted in an open top turret on an M4 chassis. Ordnance Committee action in October approved the modification of two 90mm M1 guns for use in tank mounts. The changes included the removal of the side rails and their replacement by a cylindrical slide surface on the outside of the tube. A manual breechblock operating handle also was provided. Designated as the 90mm gun T7, the modified weapons were installed in the heavy tank T1E1 and the first pilot M10, replacing the 3 inch gun in both vehicles. The mount for the latter weapon was used with modifications to handle the recoil of the heavier gun. Fortytwo rounds of 90mm ammunition were stowed in the M10 with 6 of these in the usual location on the rear turret wall. The fatter 90mm rounds reduced the sponson stowage to 36.

Tests at Aberdeen in late 1942 showed no problems with the M10 installation that did not already exist when using the 3 inch gun. The 90 weighed 290 pounds more than the 3 inch weapon it replaced thus aggravating the turret unbalance. This increased the traversing hand wheel effort by approximately 7 per cent. This was, of course, on the M10 pilot which did not have turret counterweights. The firing tests were successful and Aberdeen concluded that the 90 could replace the 3 inch gun in the M10 and that such a change could be made in the Ordnance base shops. However, the preferable solution was the design of a new turret which would correct many of the problems with the M10. Such a turret would be balanced and equipped with a power traverse mechanism. The elevation and traverse controls and the direct sight telescope would be relocated for easier use.

The pilot 90mm gun motor carriage T71 as originally constructed with the ring mount for the .50 caliber machine gun over the left rear of the turret.

Chevrolet started work on the design and construction of a wooden mock-up for the new turret on 3 March 1943. After completion, the project was transferred to Ford with an order to build two soft steel pilot vehicles based on the M10A1 chassis. Completed during September, one pilot was shipped to Aberdeen for proof tests and then to Fort Knox. On 9 December, OCM 22336 approved the designation of the new vehicle as the 90mm gun motor carriage T71 when based on the M10A1 or as the T71E1 when based on the M10. Under the same OCM, the mount for both vehicles became the 90mm gun mount T8.

The new turret arrangement was similar to that in the medium tank. The gunner was seated at the right front with the direct sight telescope and the elevation and traverse controls. An hydraulic power traverse mechanism was installed in addition to the manual system. The vehicle commander was behind the gunner and the loader was located to the left of the gun. As originally constructed, a .50 caliber antiaircraft machine gun was fitted on a ring mount over the left rear of the open top turret. A 3 inch cast gun shield covered the opening in the turret front and the side walls were 1-1/4 inches thick. The heavy gun mount was balanced by a large bustle at the rear having a maximum thickness of 4 inches. This bustle also provided stowage space for 11 ready rounds of 90mm ammunition increasing the total in the vehicle to 47.

Tests at Aberdeen and Fort Knox resulted in the usual changes. The ring mount for the .50 caliber machine gun was replaced by a pedestal to permit easier use of the gun from both inside and outside the turret. It was requested that the sponson ammunition racks be increased in height from 39 to 39-1/2 inches to better accommodate the 90mm rounds in their fiber containers and that the manual traversing mechanism be shifted 1-1/2 inches to the right of its original position. The second T71 was modified to include the recommended changes and then shipped first to Fort Knox and then to Camp Hood for service tests. The Tank Destroyer Board concluded that the T71 was a satisfactory vehicle, but the Armored Board recommended that a muzzle brake and long primer ammunition be required to reduce the target obscuration caused by the flash and muzzle blast from the 90mm gun. They also recommended the installation of an improved type T92 direct sight.

Production drawings for the T71 had been released in November and Fisher was requested to build 500 by converting M10A1s then on the assembly lines. How-

Above is the 90mm gun motor carriage M36 (T71) with the early type gun rest on the rear deck.

ever, most of the latter were too near completion and only 300 could be made available without turrets for conversion. These were completed as T71s starting in April 1944 and finishing in July. To meet the requirement for additional carriages, M10A1s were returned from the field and Ordnance depots for conversion. Because of the heavy work load at Fisher, this job was assigned to the Massey Harris Company although the new turret assemblies were manufactured by Fisher. Starting in June, Massey Harris completed their order of 500 vehicles by the end of 1944.

The M36s at the left below are fitted with the later model traveling lock on the rear hull plate. Like the M10s, these vehicles carry grouser racks on both hull side plates.

Below is a top view of the 90mm gun turret on the M36. The arrangement is similar to that in the medium tank with the gunner to the right and the loader to the left of the cannon.

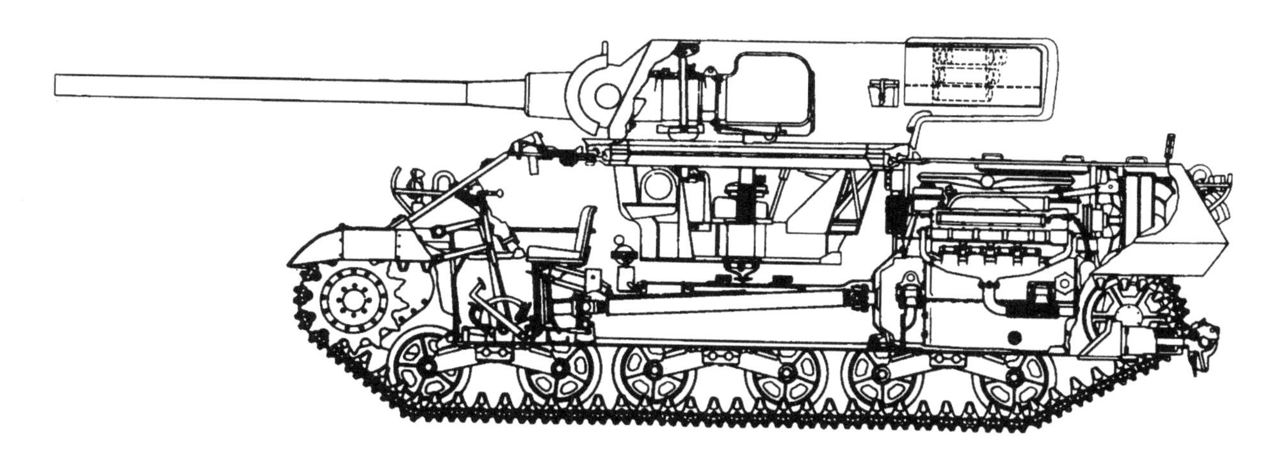

A sectional view of the 90mm gun motor carriage M36 is shown above.

Standardized in July 1944 as the 90mm gun motor carriage M36, the demand for the new tank destroyer increased greatly soon after D-day. The Normandy battles showed the 90mm gun to be the only U.S. weapon capable of dealing with the heavy German armor. In the last three months of 1944, the American Locomotive Company converted another 413 M10A1s to M36s. During this same period, Fisher built 187 tank destroyers by installing the M36's 90mm gun turret on the hull of the M4A3 medium tank. With its stowage rearranged to accommodate the larger ammunition, the vehicle was designated as the 90mm gun motor carriage M36B1 and classified as Substitute Standard in October 1944. This brought the total production of 90mm gun tank destroyers to 1400 when production stopped at the end of the year.

Changes resulting from the service tests were applied to the production vehicles. The addition of a muzzle brake required the design of a new equilibrator, a stronger elevating mechanism, and a heavier gun traveling lock. All three were installed after the first 600, but the equilibrator was not connected since none of the first 1400 carriages were fitted with muzzle brakes. However, muzzle brakes could be installed in the field on any vehicle after the first 600 since they were equipped with all of the necessary items. Actually, this was not done because of the large number of man hours required.

The 90mm gun motor carriage M36B1 appears at the right and below. Note the standard M4A3 tank hull. The 90mm gun tube is threaded for a muzzle brake and a thread protector is installed. A spare barrel for the .50 caliber machine gun is stowed on the left side of the turret bustle roof.

The first M36s arrived in Europe in August 1944 and were immediately committed to action in France. Battle experience brought out the need for additional changes. Because of its heavy firepower, the M36 was frequently used as a tank rather than in its original role as a tank destroyer or self-propelled gun. Under these conditions, it was vulnerable with its thin armor and open top turret. Because of the latter, artillery air bursts and small arms fire often caused casualties to the crew. In August, the Army Ground Forces directed the development of an overhead cover kit to provide protection for the turret crew. These covers were folding armor tops designed to protect against small arms fire and shell fragments without completely sacrificing the all round vision of the open top turret.

Another problem arose from the new waterproof steel containers being developed for the 90mm rounds. Since they were too large to fit in the sponsons, new ammunition racks were designed to permit stowage of the bare rounds. The new racks were released to production along with the armored turret tops for all vehicles produced during 1945.

The continuing demand for 90mm gun motor carriages resulted in additional production starting in May 1945. Montreal Locomotive converted 200 M10A1s to M36s during the remainder of the year. This exhausted the supply of M10A1s requiring the use of the diesel powered M10. Originally designated as the T71E1, it was classified as the Substitute Standard 90mm gun motor carriage M36B2 in March 1945. Starting in May, American Locomotive produced 672 M36B2s by the end of 1945. An additional 52 were converted at the Montreal Locomotive Works by the end of the year. This brought the total production of the M36 series to 2324.

In April of 1945 the development of fording equipment was completed for the M36 and in June standardization was approved for the new M83 direct sight telescope. Battle reports from Europe indicated that the M36 was being employed more and more in the role of a tank, a task for which it was not properly designed. Requests were received for both a coaxial and a bow machine gun. The latter was already provided in the M36B1 since it used the standard tank hull. Complaints about the high ground pressure resulted in the application of the M4E9 spaced out suspension and extended end connectors to the late production vehicles. All of these factors foreshadowed the demise of the tank destroyer in the postwar army. It was too much to expect a vehicle originally designed as a highly mobile self-propelled gun to perform the role of a tank. All of the modifications such as the auxiliary armor and folding turret top only served to underline its deficiencies when compared to a properly designed tank. Nevertheless, the M36s continued to serve during the postwar period and were furnished as foreign aid to a number of Allied nations. They were still in service in Korea during the mid 1950s.

The 90mm gun motor carriage M36B2 is shown here with features adopted for the late production tank destroyers. A folding armor turret top is installed and the gun is fitted with a muzzle brake. Also, note the spaced out suspension with extended end connectors on both sides of the tracks.

The letters in the photograph at the right indicate the following:

A—SPARE MACHINE GUN BARRELS
B—MACHINE GUN PEDESTAL
C—LIFTING EYES
D—DRIVER'S DOOR
E—TOWING CABLE
F—FENDERS
G—ASSISTANT DRIVER'S DOOR
H—ANTENNA
J—MACHINE GUN
K—TURRET DOORS' LATCH
L—TURRET TOP
M—LIFTING EYES
N—PICK MATTOCK
P—PICK MATTOCK HANDLE
Q—CROW BAR
R—TRACK ADJUSTING WRENCH
S—SHOVEL
T—AX
U—EXTERIOR FIRE EXTINGUISHER PULL HANDLES
V—SLEDGE

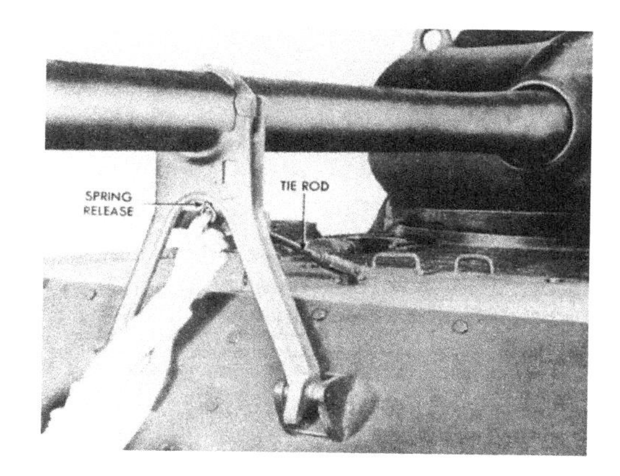

At the left is the traveling lock for the 90mm gun as installed on the late model M36 and M36B2.

Below, the 90mm gun motor carriage M36 can be compared with its predecessor the M10. The major identification features of the M36 are the long thin cannon barrel, the massive round gun shield, and the large turret bustle.

The 90mm gun in the M36 above has been threaded for a muzzle brake and it has been fitted with a thread protector. This M36 from the 702nd Tank Destroyer Battalion, 2nd Armored Division is dug in on a ramp to fire across the Roer River on 16 December 1944. The size of the 90mm APC M82 round is readily apparent.

Below, M36s attached to the 82nd Airborne Division move forward near Werbomont, Belgium to engage the spearhead of the German attack in the Ardennes on 20 December 1944.

The 628th Tank Destroyer Battalion (above) attached to the 5th Armored Division, is in Rheydt, Germany. Note the armored tops with vision slots added to the turrets of these vehicles. An extra .30 caliber machine gun is mounted on the left front of the turret.

Below, a 90mm gun motor carriage M36B1 of the 654th Tank Destroyer Battalion is in Rheinberg, Germany on 6 March 1945. The kill marks on the gun shield represent two Tigers and two Panzer IVs.

Above is a postwar M36 in Korea. It has been modernized by the installation of the 90mm gun M3A1 with the single baffle muzzle brake and a bore evacuator. This vehicle is manned by the 53rd Republic of Korea Tank Company. The photograph was dated 12 July 1952.

Two more postwar tank destroyers are shown below. The vehicle at the left served with the French and the one at the right is in Pakistan. Both have armored tops and spaced out suspensions with extended end connectors on both sides of the tracks. The Pakistani vehicle is armed with a later model 90mm gun fitted with a bore evacuator and a blast deflector.

The pilot 40mm gun motor carriage T36 at Aberdeen Proving Ground in December 1942. The 40mm gun is at maximum elevation.

SELF-PROPELLED ANTIAIRCRAFT GUNS

Ground attack aircraft developed rapidly during the 1930s and the early campaigns of World War II saw them used with a decisive effect. The development of a defense against this form of attack was considered essential to Armored Force operations. Self-propelled antiaircraft guns were an obvious choice to accompany the fast moving armored columns and a program was started to develop such weapons.

The Ordnance Committee initiated a project in October 1941 to mount a low velocity 75mm antiaircraft gun on the chassis of the medium tank M3. This was the 75mm gun T6 which was standardized in modified form as the M2 tank gun. It also was expected to be effective against ground targets thus providing a useful dual purpose weapon. Designated as the 75mm gun motor carriage T26, the vehicle was designed to carry the cannon in a special antiaircraft turret with 360 degree power traverse. Fire control equipment included the computer T9, remote control system T8, fuze setter T30, telescopes T27 and T28, and the generating unit T12. This permitted remote control operation of the gun. To conserve space, it was proposed to modify the fuze setter to include a rack for 20 to 25 rounds of ammunition.

OCM 17470 in November approved the diversion of one medium tank M3 for the manufacture of a pilot T26. The work began, but tests during the same period showed that the T6 was unsuitable as an antiaircraft gun. Its low velocity also made it relatively ineffective as a tank destroyer thus limiting its secondary role. Work was stopped in March 1942 and the pilot was set aside for completion as the 40mm gun motor carriage T36. The Ordnance Committee cancelled the project for the T26 and its fire control equipment in April.

Shortly after the start of the T26 project, a similar vehicle was proposed mounting the 40mm gun M1. Approved in December 1941, it was designated as the 40mm gun motor carriage T36. Like the T26, the gun

The high position of the driver located over the transmission is apparent in the front view of the T36.

was carried in a power operated turret with 360 degree traverse. The walls and top of this cast steel turret were 2 inches thick. When the vehicle was stationary, a T10 computer operated by a three man crew provided azimuth and elevation data. This information was fed to the T9 remote control system which traversed the turret and elevated the gun. The T27 (azimuth) and T28(elevation) telescopes were used as on the T26. Power also was supplied by the T12 generating unit. The latter consisted of an engine driven alternator with a 15 kva capacity furnishing 110 volt, 60 cycle, 3 phase power.

The development of the T36 was given precedence over the T26 and in March 1942, the turret and hull components of the latter were used to expedite completion of the pilot. When the T26 was subsequently cancelled, its chassis was used to construct a second pilot T36. The first carriage was shipped to Frankford Arsenal in June for installation of the fire control equipment. Pilot number 2 followed in August. Problems in completing the fire control apparatus delayed delivery of the first T36 to Aberdeen until December. When it arrived, tests began immediately and continued through January 1943. The vehicle was then shipped to Camp Davis, North Carolina for firing tests against towed sleeve targets.

The 40mm gun mount T4 was originally intended to have an elevation range of +80 to -10 degrees. However, as installed, the depression was limited to -2 degrees because of interference with the turret roof and it was impossible to load a 4 round ammunition clip at elevations below +10 degrees. Because of heavy powder fumes during automatic firing, the installation of a forced ventilation system was recommended. As an interim measure, a rectangular pattern of holes was drilled in the turret roof and it was proposed that this area be completely cut out to increase air circulation and to provide clearance for the loading rack at low elevations. For future production, a change was recommended in the turret contour to allow adequate clearance at all elevations.

The T36 was manned by a crew of five. The azimuth tracker was located at the left side of the turret with the elevation tracker on the right. The range setter was in the center. He was also the gun commander and controlled the slewing lever which placed the weapon roughly on target. The loader's station was at the bottom of the turret and he both loaded and fired the gun. The driver sat in the front center of the hull in the usual position for the medium tank M3. The clearance above his seat was inadequate for a normal size man and Aberdeen recommended an increase of 4-1/2 inches to permit a comfortable sitting position. They also pointed out the need for additional escape hatches in the hull floor and the rear of the turret.

Other recommendations from the test program included the provision of a suitable deflector for the ejected cartridge cases, installation of lighting system inside the turret, and the design of an electric solenoid trigger to permit the trackers or range setter to fire the gun. The Antiaircraft Artillery Board found other objections. These included the poor access to the gun for maintenance, complexity of the fire control system and insufficient mobility. The limited stowage space also was considered a problem as the 100 rounds of 40mm ammunition were considered inadequate. In July 1943, the Ordnance Committee recommended that the project be discontinued and the pilot vehicles be salvaged.

Note the ventilation holes in the T36 turret roof at the left.

At the left is the Firestone turret installed on the multiple gun motor carriage T52. The cramped quarters for the two man turret crew are obvious.

The military characteristics of a self-propelled weapon for the antiaircraft automatic weapons battery were outlined at a conference in May 1942. Representatives of the Army Ground Forces, the Antiaircraft Artillery Board, and the Ordnance Department agreed that such a vehicle should be armed with either two 40mm guns or one 40 and two .50 caliber machine guns. The proposed fire control equipment included the computing sight T4. This was a gyroscopic sight similar to the General Electric T3, but was modified for turret mounting. Movement in azimuth and elevation was to be provided by the T7 and T8 power drives respectively.

During this same period, Firestone Tire and Rubber Company had proposed a preliminary design for such a gun mount fitted with one 40mm gun and two .50 caliber machine guns. The Artillery and Automotive Subcommittee believed that this mount would meet the requirement. Designated as the combination gun mount T62, it was recommended for installation on two pilot motor carriages based on the medium tank M4. The same OCM, dated 30 July 1942, designated the complete vehicle as the multiple gun motor carriage T52.

The first turret was completed at Firestone in October, but difficulties in obtaining parts and materials delayed the delivery of the first vehicle to Aberdeen until March 1943. Preliminary tests were completed in July, but work continued on both pilots through the end of the year.

The T52 carried a crew of four with two men in a ball type turret having an armor thickness of 1-1/2 inches. The gunner was located at the right side of the 40mm gun M1 and was responsible for sighting and firing all three weapons. He also had to reload the right-hand machine gun. The loader at the left side of the turret was an extremely busy man. He had to load the 40mm gun, set the range indicator, cock and clear both machine guns, reload the left machine gun, and locate new targets. The Proving Ground concluded that he had insufficient space to perform his duties. Perhaps they meant that two men were required for the job.

Like the earlier T36, the T52 did not carry enough ammunition with only 64 rounds for the 40mm gun. A total of 1000 rounds were provided for the two .50 caliber machine guns. Lack of access to the guns made servicing difficult and some redesign was required to prevent the empty .50 caliber shell cases from jamming the turret in traverse. A redesign also was recommended for the turret openings to provide a better escape route for the turret crew and to improve the access to the machine guns. Since the 40mm gun breech was close to the rear turret wall, a hole was needed to permit boresighting the weapon.

The tests also showed that the tracking rates were inadequate for column defense against low flying aircraft and Ordnance considered the vehicle much too heavy for its caliber of armament. Cancellation of the project was recommended in October 1944 and approved the following month.

At the right is the multiple gun motor carriage T52 with the turret in the traveling position. Note that this pilot is based on the medium tank M4A2.

The 90mm gun motor carriage T53 at Aberdeen on 13 August 1942. In this view, the firing platform is folded up into the travel position and the cannon is stowed in the traveling lock.

The effective use of the German 8.8cm antiaircraft gun in the antitank role raised the possibility of similar employment for the U.S. 90mm weapon. Proposal drawings dated 29 June 1942 showed the 90mm gun M1 on a self-propelled carriage based on the chassis of the medium tank M4. On these drawings, the hull was cut down to the sponson line ahead of the engine compartment and the 90mm gun was mounted at approximately the center of the vehicle. Ordnance Committee action in July recommended the development of such a vehicle designating it the 90mm gun motor carriage T53.

A number of changes were incorporated and the construction of a pilot was rushed through at Chrysler using the hull of the medium tank M4A4. The multibank engine was replaced by a Continental R975 EC2 which was installed just behind the driving compartment. With the engine closer to the front, it was necessary to tilt the transmission and final drive forward to maintain the alignment with the drive shaft. This required the insertion of an armor plate transition section between the top of the differential housing and the upper front of the hull. The bow machine gun was eliminated and the mount for it was partially masked. The 90mm gun M1 was fitted on a modified M1A1 mount at the rear of the chassis. Plates at the sides and rear folded down to the sponson line forming a firing platform.

The T53 was shipped to Aberdeen in early August and firing tests showed that the carriage was too unstable to be effective against high flying aircraft. It also was apparent that the gun mount should be located over the vehicle center of gravity for tank destroyer use. Modifications were required to reduce the handwheel effort when elevating or traversing the gun on a slope and a shield which could be removed in the field was considered desirable.

After tests at Aberdeen, the T53 was shipped to the Tank Destroyer Board at Camp Hood for evaluation as a self-propelled gun. The Board reported that it was completely unsatisfactory as a tank destroyer because of its high silhouette, inadequate mobility, lack of armor protection, and insufficient ammunition stowage. They recommended that efforts to develop a dual purpose tank destroyer and self-propelled antiaircraft gun be abandoned.

Following the initial tests of the T53, the design was modified to incorporate the recommended changes. OCM 18726 designated the redesigned vehicle as the 90mm gun motor carriage T53E1 on 27 October 1942 and two new pilots were built by Chrysler. At this time, procurement was authorized for 500 T53E1s during 1942 and an additional 3500 were planned.

The 90mm gun motor carriage T53 is shown below after the installation of the shield. The folding side plates have been removed from the hull and the crew is protected by the semicircular shield rotating with the mount. This shield was completely open at the rear.

Above is the first pilot 90mm gun motor carriage T53E1 in travel order at Aberdeen in December 1942. Note the outriggers attached to the suspension bogies.

To utilize available production facilities at Chrysler, the hulls of the T53E1s were assembled by riveting, unlike the welded construction of the original T53. The R975 C1 engine was located at the rear of the chassis as in the standard tank, with the 90mm gun mount in the center. The suspension units were spaced as on the medium tank M4A4 requiring 83 track shoes per side. Outriggers attached to the front and rear bogie assemblies could be extended to stabilize the mount. They were stowed by clamping to the center bogie. Hinged side armor plates 1/2 inches thick swung down at each side of the gun mount forming a firing platform.

The first pilot T53E1 carried its weapon on the modified 90mm gun mount M1A1 with the elevation ranging from +80 degrees to -0 degrees 11 minutes. Pilot number 2 was fitted with the M1A1E1 mount which had the trunnions raised by 4 inches. This extended the elevation range from +79 degrees 47 minutes to -4 degrees 38 minutes. The first pilot was equipped with a bolted shield of 1/2 inch thick homogeneous armor protecting the top, front, and sides of the mount. Road tests at Aberdeen revealed a tendency for the bolts to loosen during cross-country operation. The shield on pilot number 2 consisted of two semicircular sections of 1/2 inch armor open at the top and rear with a somewhat lower silhouette. Both pilots secured the 90mm gun in a traveling lock hinged to the rear hull plate. The T53E1s carried a crew of five and stowed about 40 rounds of 90mm ammunition. Accompanying vehicles were required for additional ammunition, personnel, and antiaircraft fire control equipment.

The first pilot T53E1 was at Aberdeen before the end of 1942 and it was followed shortly by number 2. Tests showed considerable difficulty in leveling the vehicle and in the use of the outriggers, particularly on uneven terrain. Although the Tank Destroyer Board had lost all interest in the dual purpose weapon, it was hoped that it might be useful as a self-propelled antiaircraft gun. The second pilot was shipped to the Antiaircraft Artillery Board at Camp Davis for evaluation. The Board reported that the T53E1 was unsatisfactory because of problems in servicing the weapon and inadequate room for ammunition and personnel. They also objected to the high distinctive silhouette and recommended cancellation of the project. The Ordnance Committee agreed and approved the termination of the T53 and T53E1 projects on 25 May 1944.

The second pilot T53E1 is shown below in January 1943. The new shield is smaller and completely open at the top.

The Canadian self-propelled 3.7 inch antiaircraft gun is in firing position at maximum elevation at the left. Above, the gun is lowered into the travel position and the firing platform is folded up to provide side armor protection.

A Canadian effort to produce a dual purpose self-propelled gun mounted the British 3.7 inch antiaircraft gun on the Ram chassis. With its high silhouette, it was somewhat similar in appearance to the T53 and T53E1. The powerful 3.7 inch gun was pedestal mounted in the center of the vehicle with a shield fitted for direct fire against ground targets. Tests produced similar results to those for the U.S. dual purpose experiments and it was considered unsatisfactory for either the antitank or antiaircraft role. Only the pilot vehicle was completed.

The most successful self-propelled antiaircraft weapon to use the Sherman chassis also was a Canadian development. The requirement for an antiaircraft tank was issued during 1943 and a pilot was constructed at the Waterloo Manufacturing Company. Designated as the 20mm quad AA tank, Skink, it mounted four 20mm guns in a special turret on the hull of the Canadian Grizzly (M4A1). The original design specified the use of four 20mm Hispano Suiza cannon and a wooden mock-up and a steel pilot turret were constructed for these guns. Later specifications changed the armament to four 20mm Polsten cannon requiring a redesign of the mount. A welded turret was considered because of manufacturing problems with the cast design. It had proven difficult to obtain an

Below, the mock-up of the welded turret for the Hispano Suiza guns is installed on the Grizzly chassis (left). The welded steel pilot turret armed with these weapons is below at the right.

The Skink appears above in the form that entered production with the cast turret and armed with the 20mm Polsten cannon. The photographs below were taken during trials and the gunner's hatch is open in all views. The Skink is fitted with the short pitch Canadian dry pin track and the 17 tooth sprockets.

accurately balanced casting with the required ballistic properties. However, these problems were solved and the cast turret was selected for production.

Except for stowage changes, the hull of the Skink was identical to the Canadian manufactured M4A1. The new turret carried three of the five man crew and was installed on the standard 69 inch turret ring. The cast turret armor was 2-1/4 inches thick in front and 2 inches on the sides and rear. Four 20mm Polsten guns were mounted in pairs on each side of the gunner who was located in the front center of the turret. A hatch above the gunner carried an unshielded nonrotating Vickers periscope which could be used for sighting tracer aimed fire when the tank was closed up. For air targets, the hatch was opened to permit the use of the U.S. Navy Mk IX reflector sight. Sixtyfour 30 round magazines were carried in the sponson racks for the 20mm guns. Loading required about 20 seconds and the guns could be fired all together, singly, or in pairs. Oilgear hydraulic drives traversed the turret and elevated the guns. The mount rotated 360 degrees at elevations from +80 to -5 degrees. To achieve a traverse rate of 10 rpm, the engine driven generator was modified and a newly developed high output auxiliary generator was installed.

The loader and the tank commander were located at the rear of the turret on the left and right respectively. Each had his own hatch equipped with a rotating Vickers type periscope fitted with an armored shield and a rear vision device. A British Number 19 radio set was installed in the turret bustle also providing a five station communication system for the crew.

After testing, the Skink entered production at the Montreal Locomotive Works in January 1944. However, by this time, Allied air superiority had all but eliminated the need for an antiaircraft tank and work was suspended after the production of three complete tanks and eight additional turrets for conversion kits.

Shipped to Europe, the Skink was tested further in Britain and one was evaluated in operations with the First Canadian Army in northwest Europe during February and March of 1945. Although deprived of its designated role by a lack of enemy aircraft, the Skink proved quite effective against ground targets. It was considered far superior to the earlier Crusader AA tanks in both roles and was successfully used to clean up enemy infantry positions bypassed by the first wave of armor. The 20mm high explosive incendiary ammunition often set fire to buildings forcing the enemy into the open.

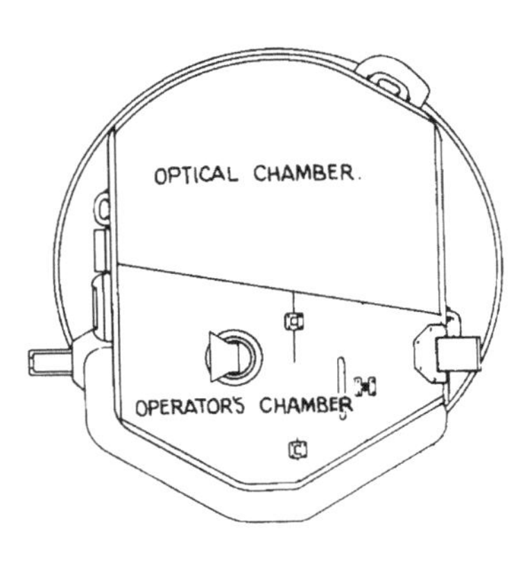

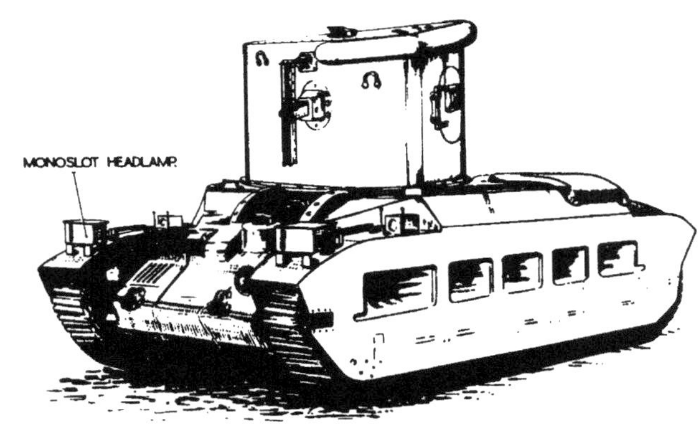

An early experimental lamp unit (above left) is installed on a carrier for trials about 1932. The top drawing at the right is a plan view of the CDL turret showing the operator's compartment and the lamp chamber. The lower sketch shows the CDL turret fitted on the Matilda tank.

SEARCHLIGHT TANKS

An organization known as the de Thoren Syndicate was formed in 1933 to develop a high intensity searchlight for night use on the battlefield. Managed by Mr. Marcel Mitzakis, the syndicate's tactical advisor was Major General J.F.C. Fuller, a pioneer in the employment of armor during and after World War I. The first trials of the new light were in France and in February 1937, a demonstration was held in Britain on the Salisbury Plain at the request of the War Office. Three sets of equipment were ordered for additional tests, but the final trials were delayed until June 1940. That same month, the War Office took over the project and authorized the construction of 300 turret mounted lights for tank installation. For security reasons, they were referred to as the Canal Defense Light or CDL for short.

Intended for the infantry tanks, the searchlight turret was first installed on the Matilda and later the Churchill was considered for such use. However, the U.S. medium tank M3 proved to be the best chassis for the new equipment. With its sponson mounted 75, the main armament was retained when the special searchlight installation replaced the standard 37mm gun turret. Available in quantity, the M3 became the standard CDL tank.

The CDL equipment was demonstrated to a group of U.S. officers in early October 1942 at Lowther Castle in Cumberland. Among those present were General Dwight D. Eisenhower, General Mark W. Clark, and Major General Barnes of the Ordnance Department. Obtaining the technical details of the special equipment, General Barnes returned from

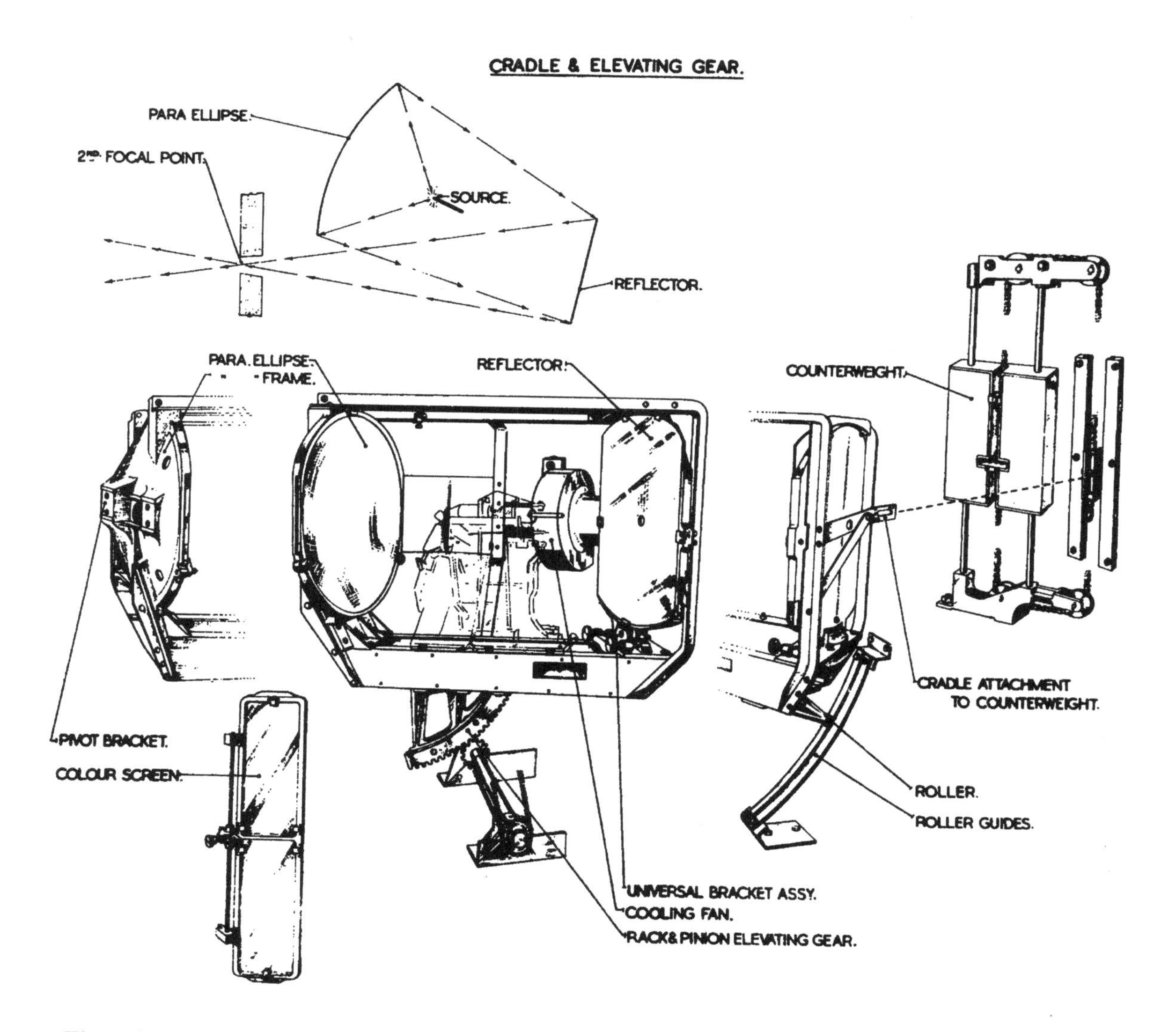

The optics of the CDL are sketched above. The heart of the system was the mirror which was parabolic in the vertical plane and elliptical in the horizontal plane. With this arrangement, a carbon arc at the focal point produced a normal searchlight beam when viewed from the side, but in the horizontal plane the light passed through a second focal point 60 to 70 inches from the mirror. A flat aluminum reflector directed the beam from the parabolic-elliptical mirror toward the front of the turret where it passed through a vertical slot located at the second focal point. Thus the high intensity beam was brought out through a narrow slot with practically no loss of light.

Britain and presented this information to a Board headed by General Devers in Detroit on 19 February 1943. The Board recommended that the CDL tanks be produced in the United States and that special units be trained to operate them. To maintain the secrecy about the project, the tanks were designated as Leaflets and the training program was referred to by the code name Cassock.

The special CDL turret was designed with a high intensity carbon arc lamp installed in a separate compartment on the right side. The left side was occupied by a single operator who also manned the machine gun mounted in the front wall. The turret had cast steel sides 2.55 inches thick with a rolled plate top bolted in place. An armored bulkhead separated the operator from the lamp. The light was exposed through a vertical slot 24 inches high by 2-3/8 inches wide and produced a beam about 340 yards wide and 35 yards high at 1000 yards range. The slot was opened and closed by an internally mounted armor plate shutter. This shutter was operated either manually or automatically at two rates of speed by an electric motor producing a dazzling flicker. Colored filters also could be inserted into the 13,000,000 candlepower beam.

Above is a British CDL tank of the 79th Armoured Division. There is a dummy gun on the turret front and the door in the left rear turret wall has been welded up.

When combined with the blinding effect of the flickering light they were intended to confuse the enemy during a night assault.

The British and U.S. manufactured turrets were essentially the same differing only in minor details. Both models used only a manual traverse system. The British turrets were armed with the 7.92mm Besa machine gun while the U.S. version was fitted with a ball mount carrying a .30 caliber Browning. A small circular pistol port was installed in the upper front of the early British turrets and a similar rectangular opening was provided on the U.S. model. Later British designs eliminated the pistol port completely and it was welded up on the earlier turrets. The rectangular opening on the early U.S. design was replaced by a small circular plug type vision port. The early British and American turrets were fitted with a circular door in the left rear wall in addition to the folding roof hatch. These doors were solid in the U.S. design, but they carried a round pistol port on the British model. Later British turrets eliminated both door and pistol port and a solid plate was welded into the opening on the early production castings. In service, a dummy gun was attached to the front of many British turrets simulating the appearance of the M3s 37mm cannon.

The M3 CDL tank carried a crew of five. The driver remained in his usual position in the front center of the hull with the seat for the gunner at his right. A seat for the tank commander was provided to the left of the driver and each had a periscope installed in the hull roof. These were the Vickers type on the British vehicles and the standard M6 periscopes on the U.S. tanks. The loader's station was behind the gunner and the CDL operator rode in the turret. Either the M6 or

The sketches below show the early (left) and late (right) design British CDL turrets. Note the vision port above the machine gun mount and the circular door in the left rear wall of the early turret. Both features were eliminated from the later design.

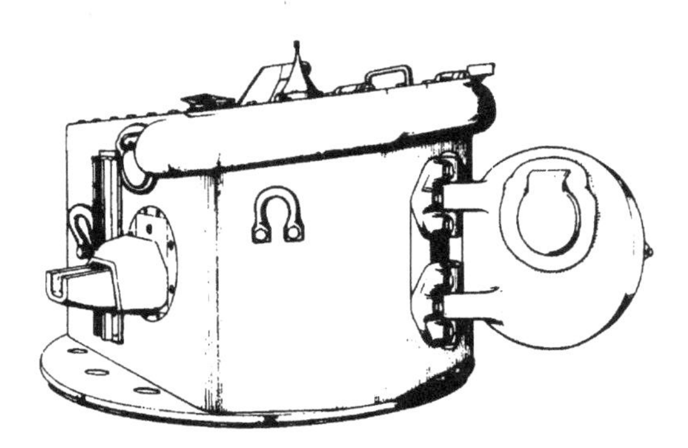

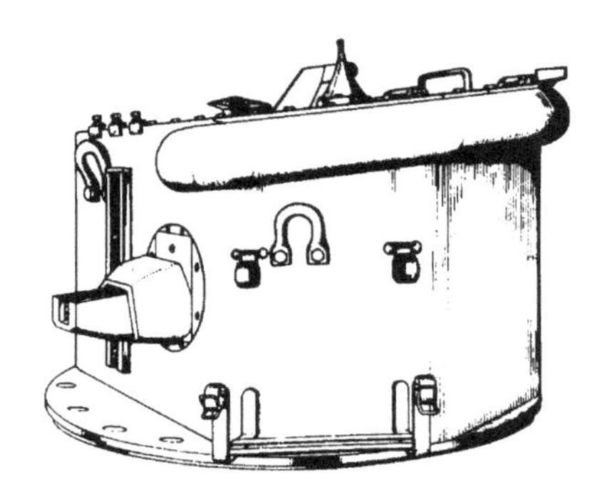

A U.S. CDL (left) is compared with its British equivalent (right) above. The U.S. vehicle is based on the medium tank M3A1. Below at the left are some postwar photographs of U.S. CDLs. An armor shield has been added to the 75mm gun mount on all of the U.S.vehicles.

the Vickers type periscope was installed in the turret roof. The power supply for the arc lamp consisted of a 10 kilowatt DC generator and regulator located at the left rear of the hull compartment and driven by a power takeoff from the engine.

According to General Fuller, 1850 M3s were converted to CDL tanks in Britain. Six complete British turrets were shipped to Aberdeen in late 1942 where they were used to convert six M3s. Five of these were then sent to the Special Training Group at Fort Knox and the sixth was broken down into subassemblies to serve as pilot models for the various component manufacturers.

The American Locomotive Company received the contract to remanufacture the M3 chassis to the CDL configuration. For security reasons they were designated as the Shop Tractor T10. The turrets were built by the Pressed Steel Car Company as the coast defense or "S" turret. The actual arc lamps were procured by the Corps of Engineers from the Mole-Richardson Company. Differing from the original British model, these lamps were modified from a standard design which could be placed immediately in production. Tests subsequently proved that they were also more rugged and less susceptible to dust effects. Final assembly was carried out at Rock Island Arsenal where tight security could be maintained. American Locomotive delivered the first T10 in June 1943 and had converted 355 by the end of the year. An additional 142 were completed in 1944 for a total production of 497 U.S. CDL tanks. Both M3s and M3A1s were used for the U.S. vehicles. The 75mm gun mount on these tanks was fitted with the auxiliary rotor shield to improve the armor protection.

A camouflaged British M3 CDL appears above and below. In the top photograph, the light is operating.

In Britain and the Middle East, the 1st and 35th Tank Brigades, consisting of five armored regiments, were trained in the use of the CDL. The 9th and 10th Armored Groups were organized in the United States and trained in secret at Fort Knox and at a remote section of the California-Arizona maneuver area. This force included six tank battalions (special), one armored infantry battalion, and two ordnance heavy maintenance companies. Both groups were assembled in Wales adjacent to the British CDL units prior to D-day.

None of the CDL tanks were moved to the continent until well after the invasion. The British 1st Tank Brigade, consisting of the 11th, 42nd, and 49th Royal Tank Regiments, arrived in France on 11 August as part of the 79th Armoured Division. The U.S. 10th Armored Group followed on 24 August and was bivouacked in the Avranches area. It included the 701st, 736th, and 748th Medium Tank Battalions (Special), the 526th Armored Infantry Battalion, the 554th Ordnance Heavy Maintenance Company, and the 333rd Ordnance Depot Company. The British 35th Tank Brigade and the U.S. 9th Armored Group remained in Britain.

The Top Secret security classification which had protected the project since its inception now proved to be its downfall. Most combat commanders were not aware of the CDL project or its capabilities and they

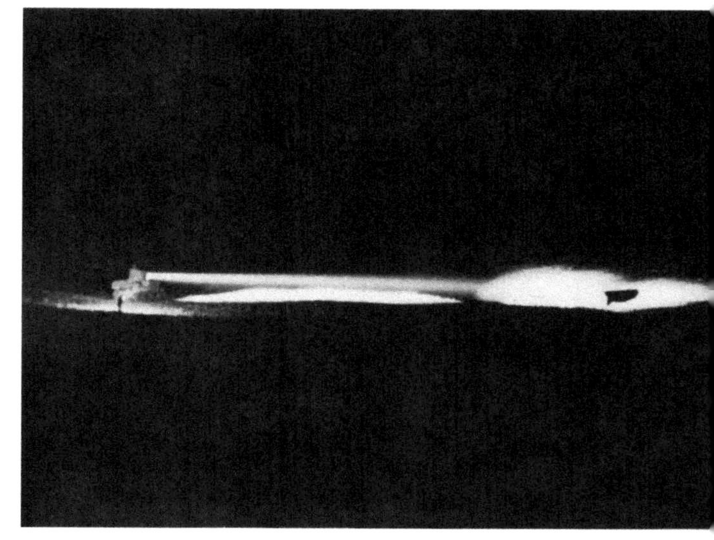

Above, the CDLs are operating at night. At the left, the wedge shaped beams of four CDLs can be seen in the background. At the right, note the appearance of a normal parallel beam searchlight when viewed from the side.

were not about to try an unknown weapon without a chance to become familiar with it. Unfortunately, the rapidly moving operations in the late Summer and Fall of 1944 did not permit the opportunity for such familiarization and the CDL units remained unemployed.

Losses during the fighting in France greatly reduced the strength of the standard tank units. By November, conditions reached a point where such a highly trained group of armored troops could not be permitted to remain idle. Except for B Squadron of the 49th RTR, the British force was converted to other tasks. The three battalions in the U.S. 10th Armored Group were reorganized as standard tank battalions and the CDL equipment was placed in storage. Still in Britain, the 9th Armored Group also was converted. From its three battalions, the 738th and 739th became mine exploder units and the 740th reorganized as a standard tank battalion. Thus the CDLs were never employed as originally intended. Some of them were used during the defense of the Rhine river crossings. The British squadron operated in the north and 64 of the U.S. CDL tanks were brought forward and 21 were assigned to First Army, 28 to Third Army, and 15 to Ninth Army. Crews were obtained from the former CDL battalions. The searchlight tanks proved extremely effective in protecting the bridges, particularly in the Remagen area. In March 1945, a cadre of trained CDL armored and ordnance personnel returned to the United States with 60 of the special tanks for possible employment in other theaters of operation. The Tenth Army requested 18 to 20 CDLs for operations on Okinawa, but they did not arrive until after the fighting was over in late June. Some of the British CDLs were shipped to India with the 43rd RTR during the Summer of 1945.

Below, the CDL tanks of the 43rd RTR are shown in India shortly after the war. A very short dummy gun is attached to the turret front of the tank on the right.

The "E" vehicle with the double light unit in a cast turret installed on an M4A1 hull is shown above at the left. Note that the total turret armament is the single .30 caliber machine gun in the center ball mount. At the right is the British equivalent using a combination welded and cast turret.

Experiments at Fort Knox investigated the use of infrared filters on the CDL tanks. The Armored Board concluded that the effectiveness of such equipment was limited by the viewing apparatus available at that time. They recommended further development if a viewing device could be produced which would permit observation of enemy vehicles at ranges up to 400 yards.

Since the M3 tank was becoming obsolete, studies began to develop a CDL turret for installation on the Sherman chassis. The first design, started in June 1943, mounted two arc lamps in a large cast turret. The operator sat in the center with a lamp compartment on either side. Both lamps were stabilized in elevation, but only a manual turret traverse was provided. A single .30 caliber machine gun was fitted in a ball mount near the center of the turret face with a plug type view port on the upper right. A circular escape door was installed in the rear wall of the operator's compartment. The two lamps required a 20 kilowatt generator which was driven by a heavier power takeoff arrangement from the main engine. One of these turrets was installed on an M4A1 chassis and tested at Fort Knox from May through June 1944. Designated as the "E" vehicle, it also was referred to as the M4 Leaflet, double unit. Two similar vehicles were designed and built in Britain based on the M4 chassis. The British turrets were assembled by welding, but were similar in design with a single machine gun in front. The second British turret had a bustle which provided a seat for the tank commander above and behind the CDL operator.

The tests in Britain and at Fort Knox showed the new CDL to be much more mobile than the M3 version. Its armor protection was better, but the lack of a heavy gun was the deciding factor. An essentially unarmed armored searchlight was considered a waste of good tank chassis and no further vehicles were built.

To correct the shortcomings of the "E" vehicle, a new CDL design based on the Sherman was started in May 1944. Designated as the"E" vehicle with special stowage, it mounted a single light unit coaxially with an M6 lightweight 75mm gun. The latter used a concentric recoil mechanism saving considerable space in the turret. The coaxial machine gun was eliminated, but both gun and light were stabilized in elevation. The normal three man turret crew was retained, but the gunner and tank commander were moved to the left side and the loader worked behind the gun mount. The tank could be readily identified by the commander's cupola on the left and the vertical light slot to the right of the cannon. The turret was provided with a power traverse mechanism and simplified controls for the light shutter. Stowage was arranged for 83 rounds of 75mm ammunition.

A pilot vehicle was converted from an M4A1, registration number W-3070679. This was originally a 76mm gun wet stowage tank. The turret was rebuilt by cutting away the front section and replacing it with a new casting. Completed in January 1945, the new CDL was tested at Fort Knox. The Armored Board concluded in June that the "E" vehicle with special stowage was superior to all of the earlier CDL tanks. They recommended its use to meet all future requirements and suggested that a coaxial machine gun be added. By this time the war was ending and further

The postwar view above in the storage yard at Aberdeen is the only photograph the author has been able to locate showing the "E" vehicle with special stowage. Unfortunately, the turret is reversed, but note the commander's hatch on the left and the short barreled cannon in the 76 turret.

work was stopped. However, the design was to be revived five years later after the outbreak of a new war.

In 1950, a request from the Eighth Army in Korea for a means of direct visible battlefield illumination gave new life to the old project. Based on the chassis of the M4A3 with the horizontal volute spring suspension it was renamed the searchlight tank T52. However, a cost analysis showed that four medium tank battalions could be equipped with standard 18 inch searchlights for the cost of one T52. For that kind of saving, the loss of a few unprotected searchlights was perfectly acceptable and the searchlight tank project was dropped.

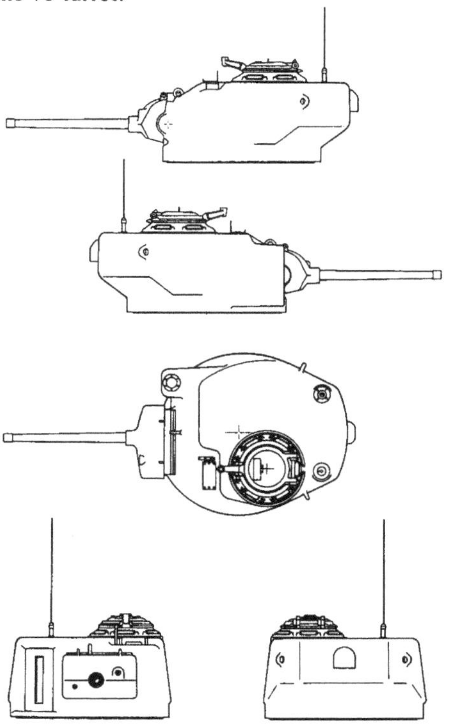

The drawings at the right show the turret design for the searchlight tank T52.

Scale 1:96

The E2 flame thrower is installed (above) in the turret of medium tank M2 number 8. Below, the E2 is seen firing using unthickened gasoline fuel.

FLAME THROWER TANKS

Prior to the entry of the United States into World War II, the Chemical Warfare Service (CWS) studied the installation of flame throwers in medium tanks. During this period, the E2 experimental flame equipment was mounted in the turret of a medium tank M2 replacing the 37mm gun. In August 1942, a shortened version of this flame gun, designated the E3, was tested at Edgewood Arsenal in the medium tank M3. As on the M2, it replaced the 37mm gun in the turret. The 75mm gun also was removed from the M3 and the sponson opening was blocked off with a steel plate. The E3 flame thrower was pump pressurized compared to nitrogen gas pressurization on the E2. Unfortunately, the E3 was unsatisfactory since the pump action caused the deterioration of the early type thickened fuel. The tests of these flame thrower tanks failed to arouse any interest from the using arms mainly because of their limited range. In the case of the E2, this was only about 35 yards using unthickened gasoline. At the time, the interest of the Armored Force was centered on the long range fighting in North Africa and those operations did not show many opportunities for the employment of such a short range weapon.

The E3 flame thrower replaced the 37mm gun in the turret of the medium tank M3. This vehicle was used in the test program during the Summer of 1942.

The action on Guadalcanal in the Fall of 1942 was quite another story. Against a well dug in enemy concealed in the jungle, the flame thrower was an essential weapon. However, the short range and small fuel capacity of the portable models limited their usefulness and the operators were dangerously exposed when approaching the enemy positions. An ideal solution was a tank mounted weapon protected by armor with a large fuel capacity. Early field experiments attempted to mount the M1A1 portable flame thrower on the light tank. Although some limited success was achieved, they were extremely unreliable and often failed to ignite or broke down just when needed most. A better solution was the installation of the Canadian Ronson flame thrower in the light tank M3A1. Replacing the tank's 37mm gun, it proved reliable and was used effectively on Saipan during June 1944 and in later operations.

Although the light tanks were useful, the vulnerability of their thin armor was recognized very early. Similar objections applied to the use of the landing vehicle, tracked (LVT) as a mechanized flame thrower. In December 1943, the Commanding General of the Central Pacific Area requested information on the status of tank mounted flame thrower development. Later that same month, requisitions were submitted for 40 of the new E4-5 models which were expected to be available at an early date. It was hoped that these auxiliary flame throwers could be used for the Marianas operation scheduled for the Summer of 1944.

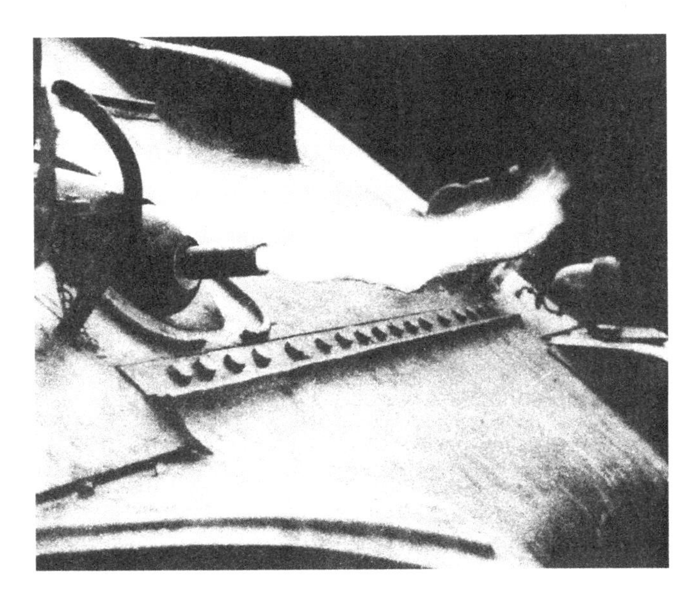

The M3-4-3 bow mount flame thrower is shown above. Fuel ignition can be seen at the left. At the right, the flame gun is installed in the bow ball mount and the .30 caliber machine gun is stowed in the rack on the transmission fuel unit. The sponson fuel tank can be seen at the right edge of the photograph.

Unfortunately, none arrived in time for use in Army tanks, but the Marine Corps managed to obtain a few. Six were installed in M4A2s of the 3rd Tank Battalion, 3rd Marine Division and were committed to action on 22 July at Asan Point on Guam.

The E5 flame gun replaced the bow machine gun and had an effective range of about 60 yards at 10 degrees elevation using 4.2 per cent Napalm. The latter fuel was gasoline thickened with a gelling agent derived from napthenic and palmitic acids from which it got its name. The fuel was propelled by compressed air at an operating pressure of 350 to 375 psi. A single E4 24 gallon fuel tank was mounted in the right sponson and it was possible to fit an additional tank over the transmission between the driver and the flame gun operator. The combination of the E4 sponson fuel tank and the E5 gun became the E4-5 flame thrower. Although it operated satisfactorily, the E4-5 was limited along with later auxiliary flame throwers by its short range and low fuel capacity. It was standardized as the M3-4-3 in 1945. This terminology indicated the combination of the M3 sponson fuel tank, the M4 transmission fuel tank, and the M3 bow mount flame gun.

Below, the M3-4-3 flame thrower is firing using thickened gasoline fuel in a demonstration during training exercises.

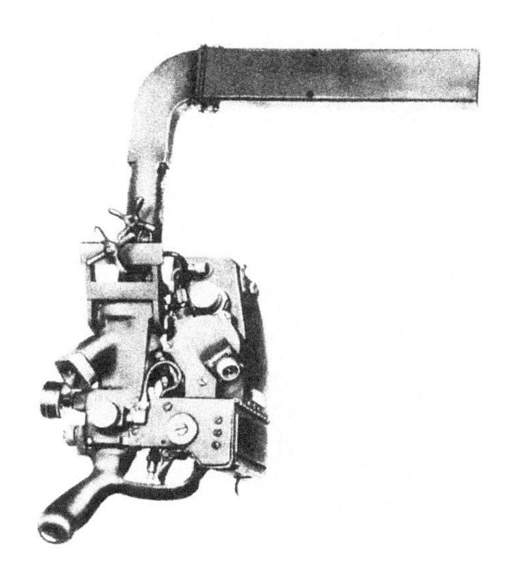

Above at the left is the E6R3 periscope type flame gun. At the top right is the POA-CWS·H4R2-H5 bow mount flame thrower which was fitted coaxially with the .30 caliber machine gun thus retaining the tank's full armament.

Later auxiliary flame gun developments included the E6R3 and the E12R3. These were designed to fit alongside the periscope in the assistant driver's hatch or in the turret roof. Since they did not displace any of the tank's armament, this arrangement was preferred by the Armored Force. However, they also were subject to the same limitations of range and fuel capacity as the other auxiliary units. Some of the periscope flame guns were fed by the standard fuel units used with the bow mount flame thrower. An example of such an arrangement was the M3-4-E6R3.

Because of the shortage of main armament flame throwers, periscope mounted equipment was manufactured in Hawaii prior to the invasion of Okinawa. Both development and production were carried out by a composite team of Army, Navy, and Marine Corps personnel under the leadership of Colonel George F. Unmacht, CWS. The flame gun was similar in design to one tested by the Armored Board consisting of a section of tube inserted through a hole in the assistant driver's periscope mount. When available, the tankage for the bow mount flame gun was used, otherwise, similar containers were manufactured at Pearl Harbor. One hundred and seventysix of these auxiliary flame throwers were completed in time for the fighting on Iwo and Okinawa. However, they were not fully utilized because of the preference for the main armament flame thrower with its larger capacity and longer range. Issued on a basis of 18 per tank battalion, these weapons were the only periscope mounted flame throwers to see action before the war ended.

Even though they were unpopular with the tank crews, the auxiliary flame throwers were used in the Pacific until the fighting ceased. In Europe, a few of the E4-5s were employed, but they were considered unsatisfactory in comparison with the British equipment.

At the right, Colonel George F. Unmacht (third officer from the right) is at a demonstration for Lieutenant General Steyer at Schofield Barracks, Hawaii on 23 March 1945. In the background is a school model of a flame thrower fitted into an M34A1 gun mount.

At the left is the POA-CWS-H1 main armament flame thrower installed in the Sherman.

The demand from the Pacific theater became more insistent for a main armament flame thrower mounted on a medium tank. In September 1944, the Tenth Army was forming in Hawaii for the invasion of Okinawa. At that time, they requested 54 flame thrower tanks to equip a complete battalion. A pilot model was demonstrated in October using a modified Ronson flame gun replacing the cannon in the turret of a medium tank M4. The range of elevation was the same as for the 75mm gun, but the traverse was limited to 260 degrees. The test results were excellent, but Tenth Army objected to the howitzer like appearance of the flame gun shroud since it did not have the same silhouette as the 75mm gun. The equipment was redesigned to fit inside a salvaged 75mm gun tube. The new version was accepted on 2 November and designated as the POA-CWS-H1. This referred to its origin in the Pacific Ocean Area with the H indicating Hawaii. Fourteen salvaged gun tubes were available for use on the project and permission was received to cut up new guns to obtain the balance.

The POA-CWS-H1 carried 290 gallons of fuel in four hull tanks below the turret. The turret basket was shortened and a new floor was installed to provide adequate space. The fuel tanks were pressurized by carbon dioxide to an operating pressure of 300 to 350 psi. The carbon dioxide was stored as a liquid in the right sponson and heated to pressurize the fuel system. A range of 60 to 80 yards was obtained at 10 degrees elevation with 6 per cent Napalm.

Early in November, a directive was received to provide eight main armament flame thrower tanks to the Marine Corps for use at Iwo Jima. Eight M4A3s were made available for conversion. Since the development work had been on an M4, some modifications were necessary. The rush to complete the tanks resulted in a few bugs that had to be worked out during the training program. The first four tanks were issued to the 4th Tank Battalion, 4th Marine Division. The major problems were corrected and a few modifications were added by the troops.

One tank mounted an extra .50 caliber machine gun on the turret to the left of the flame gun and had 4 inches of reinforced concrete poured along the outside of each sponson as protection against magnetic mines.

One of the POA-CWS-H1 flame throwers mounted in the M4A3 in action with the 4th Marine Division on Iwo Jima. In this view, the fuel is being sprayed, but it has not been ignited. Note the protective wooden planking on the sponsons.

An M4 flame thrower tank of the 713th Tank Battalion supporting troops of the 7th Infantry Division on Okinawa. The tank is firing at Japanese cave positions on top of Hill 95 on 22 June 1945.

The remaining four tanks went to the 5th Tank Battalion, 5th Marine Division where operators were trained during December and January.

All eight flame thrower tanks landed on Iwo during the first day of the invasion, 19 February 1945. They were not employed for the first two days, but subsequently they were in action for the remainder of the campaign. Unlike the vehicles armed with the auxiliary flame gun, they were well liked by the crews. On several occasions the tanks were knocked out, but no explosion or fire occurred. At the end of the fighting, the 5th Marine Tank Battalion recommended that a section of nine flame thrower tanks be made an organic part of the battalion.

In Hawaii, work continued to convert the 54 M4s for the Tenth Army. By this time, requests were being received for additional main armament flame thrower tanks which far exceeded the limited production capacity and Tenth Army directed that the battalion equipped with the 54 vehicles would be used to support all of the divisions in the Okinawa campaign. The 713th Tank Battalion was designated on 1 November 1944 as the unit to receive the new tanks and some of its personnel were assigned to assist in the conversion work. Thus training began as the equipment was built and tested.

The battalion sailed from Pearl Harbor on 4 March 1945 arriving off Okinawa on 2 April, the day after the invasion. They went ashore on the 7th and were committed to action on the 19th. During the campaign, the battalion was in action almost continuously for 70 days. Fortyone of the tanks were knocked out and 26 of those were repaired and returned to duty. The main armament flame thrower tanks maintained their good reputation and no personnel were killed inside one as a result of enemy action.

U.S. main armament flame thrower tanks in action against Japanese cave positions on Okinawa during June 1945. The flame thrower tanks shown here were based on the late model M4 with the combination rolled and cast upper hull.

The POA-CWS-H5 flame thrower mounting the flame gun coaxially with the 105mm howitzer during tests in Hawaii in July 1945. Note that this flame thrower tank is fitted with the wide-track horizontal volute spring suspension.

One of the few objections to the main armament flame thrower tank was the lack of a cannon for self protection. To correct this, the POA-CWS team under Colonel Unmacht prepared a new design mounting the flame gun alongside the cannon instead of replacing it. Starting in late 1944, this arrangement was applied to vehicles armed with the 75mm gun and the 105mm howitzer. The design retained the full capacity of flame thrower fuel, but the cannon ammunition was reduced to 40 rounds for the 75mm gun or 20 rounds for the 105mm howitzer.

Seventytwo of the cannon armed flame thrower tanks were requested by the U.S. Marine Corps in preparation for the invasion of Japan. With the limited resources available in Hawaii, conversion proceeded slowly. During the fighting on Okinawa, Tenth Army requested 18 of the new flame thrower tanks and they were enroute to the island when the battle ended. A total of 70 tanks had been converted when Japan surrendered ending the war.

Another experiment by the POA-CWS group ended in failure. This was an attempt to mount a Navy Mk I flame thrower on the M3A5 medium tank. Since this equipment had previously proved to be too heavy for use on a landing craft, it was, not surprisingly, too much for the tank chassis and the project was dropped.

Four POA-CWS-H5 flame thrower tanks during firing tests in Hawaii using Napalm thickened fuel, 26 April 1945. These tanks mount the flame gun coaxially with the 75.

Although too late for use in World War II, the POA-CWS-H5 was employed in Korea. Below, a U.S. Marine Corps flame thrower tank rolls through Yong Dung Po during the advance on Seoul. This tank has its flame thrower mounted alongside a 105mm howitzer.

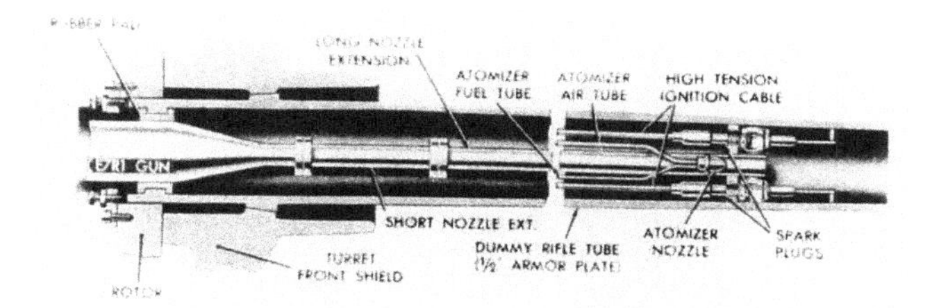

Above is a sectional view of the E7R1 flame gun installed in the mechanized flame thrower E12-7R1. The complete vehicle, at the right, was finally designated as the flame thrower tank M42B1.

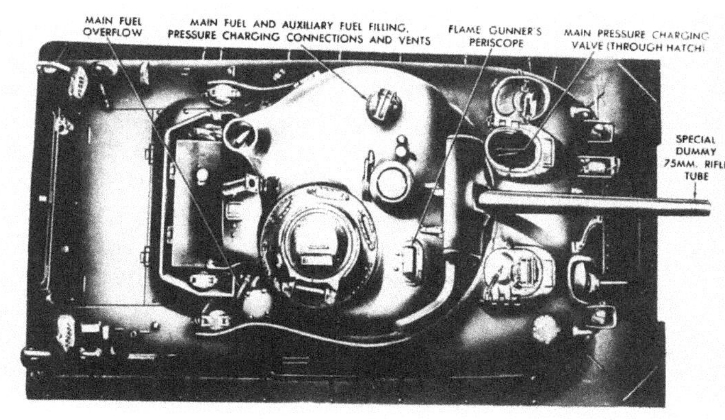

In response to the early requests from the Pacific theater, a program was started by the National Defense Research Committee (NDRC) to develop a main armament mechanized flame thrower. By the Summer of 1943, sufficient progress had been made to mount several units in M5A1 light tanks for tests. Designated as the "Q" model ("Q" for Quickie), they were tested by the Armored Force during the Winter of 1943-44. After modification, the tanks were shipped to the Pacific for combat testing during the latter stages of the Luzon campaign in April-June 1945. At that time, the flame throwers were officially designated as the E7-7.

Conferences between the Army Ground Forces, the Army Service Forces, and the NDRC in the early Summer of 1944 authorized the procurement of 20 main armament flame throwers for installation in the medium tank M4A1. Although several new designs were under development, only the E7 gun had been service tested and it was decided to use this proven design as a basis for the production equipment.

Designated as the E12-7R1, the new flame thrower was designed for mounting in the medium tank M4A1 or M4A3. The batteries and generator regulator were moved from the hull floor to the left sponson and the hull was rewired. The turret basket was rebuilt and shortened by 7 inches to provide space for two fuel tanks in the lower hull. A third tank was vertically mounted in the basket and all three were connected in series. Pressurized to 325-350 psi by air or nitrogen, the net fuel capacity was 275 gallons. The flame gun replaced the 75mm cannon in the turret, but the .30 caliber coaxial machine gun and the other normal tank armament were retained. The flame gun shroud was designed to simulate the appearance of the 75mm gun, but the top was removable for easy service. Elevation ranged from +25 to -12 degrees with a 360 degree traverse. Using 8 per cent Napalm, the E12-7R1 attained an effective range of 125 yards at 10 degrees elevation. Without the cannon there was no need for the loader and the crew was reduced to four. The tank commander and gunner occupied their normal positions in the turret.

Construction started at the M.W. Kellogg Company in November 1944 and the 20 tanks on the initial order were completed by April 1945. In January, another 300 had been ordered plus 50 additional units for installation in the LVT A1. Standardized as the mechanized flame thrower M5-4, 642 units were eventually authorized for procurement. With the end of the war, production was limited to 151 mounted in M4A1 tanks plus ten for the amphibious vehicles. The latter were designated as the E14-7R2.

The first 22 flame throwers installed in the M4A1s differed in some details from the later production. For example, the net fuel capacity was slightly greater at 285 gallons and the dummy gun shroud was 1/2 inch thick homogeneous steel armor. The shrouds on the later models were formed from 1/2 inch face-hardened plate. Seventeen of these tanks were shipped to the Pacific, but none were in combat prior to the end of the war. To simplify the storage and issue of vehicles and parts, it was recommended that the tanks with the M5-4 be assigned an Ordnance designation. OCM 29167 specified that the vehicles based on the M4A1 and M4A3 be designated as the flame thrower tanks M42B1 and M42B3 respectively. This action was approved on 20 December 1945.

The E13-13 mechanized flame thrower on display at the Ordnance Museum, Aberdeen Proving Ground. Note the hinged section in the top of the dummy gun tube to permit access to the flame gun.

A contract with the Morgan Construction Company in February 1944 initiated the development of the E13-13 mechanized flame thrower based on the M4A1 medium tank. The E13-13 stowed the fuel at a low pressure of 50-75 psi in three tanks. Rubber bladders were used in all fuel containers to separate the fuel from the air thus preventing the formation of explosive mixtures. A double pneumatic ram system was installed in the turret and the two cylinders alternately supplied high pressure fuel from the low pressure tanks. The cannon was replaced by the flame gun in the M34A1 mount and it was enclosed by a shroud which simulated the appearance of the 75mm gun. Part of the top section on the shroud was hinged to permit easy access to the flame gun. The standard secondary tank armament was retained including the .30 caliber coaxial machine gun. The firing controls were modified to include those for the flame thrower and the gyrostabilizer was removed, but the standard traverse mechanism remained intact. The weapon had a full 360 degree traverse at elevations from +25 to -12 degrees. With some nozzles, the performance closely matched that of the M5-4. Tests showed that the E13-13 operated satisfactorily, but it was extremely complicated. Since tests indicated that no significant hazard reduction resulted from the low pressure fuel storage, only one pilot tank was built.

Massachusetts Institute of Technology received a contract in July 1944 to develop a mechanized flame thrower designated as the E13R1-13R2. An M4A1 with the 76mm gun and wet stowage was converted for this installation. The larger turret provided more space and the batteries were already located in the left sponson eliminating the rewiring necessary on the earlier vehicles. Three high pressure fuel tanks operating at 300-350psi were installed with two in the hull below the turret and one in the basket. These tanks were fitted with the rubber bladders to separate the fuel from the air and they were connected in parallel.

The 76 was replaced by the flame gun and the mount also was fitted with two .30 caliber coaxial machine guns. A .50 caliber machine gun was carried on the turret top as well as the usual .30 caliber weapon in the bow mount. As on the E13-13, the crew was reduced to four with the gunner and tank commander occupying their normal positions. The flame gun shroud simulated the appearance of the 75mm gun M3 and part of the top half was hinged to permit service. The E13R2 flame gun was simple in construction and easy to maintain, but some important controls were carried in the dummy gun shroud where they might have been vulnerable to enemy fire.

Tests at Edgewood Arsenal showed that the E13R1-13R2 functioned perfectly. The range per-

The E13R1-E13R2 mechanized flame thrower on display at the Ordnance Museum. On this vehicle, the flame thrower is installed in the larger 76mm turret.

formance was almost identical to the M5-4 using 8 per cent Napalm.

Operations in the Pacific proved the effectiveness of the main armament flame thrower tank. Although many combat reports recommended that such tanks be armed with a cannon in addition to the flame equipment, opinion was divided on this point. At Okinawa, the Commanding Generals of the 24th Corps and the 77th Infantry Division favored the use of tanks armed only with a flame thrower. They felt that such vehicles were more effective in their primary mission. Similar opinions were expressed by some Marine units, but most of the tank battalions wanted a cannon, even if the ammunition supply was small because of the limited space. The Armored Board agreed with the latter viewpoint and as early as April 1945, Iowa University received a contract to develop the E19-19 mechanized flame thrower. This unit was to be installed in the wet stowage M4A3 armed with the 76mm gun and the tank was to retain its full armament and crew. It was intended that all of the flame thrower components would be supplied as a kit so that any M4A3 could be modified in the field.

Preliminary studies to determine the best method of mounting the flame gun covered six different locations. Arrangements 1 and 2 placed it on the gun shield coaxial with the 76mm gun and to its left and right respectively. Space was limited near the cannon and the flexible joints in the fuel lines could not be mounted on the axis of rotation thus requiring three such joints.

Plan 3 put the flame gun above the main gun shield to the right of the 76. It was linked to the cannon for movement in elevation. Unfortunately, if adequate armor was provided for the flame equipment in this location, it obscured the gunner's vision.

Plan 4 mounted the flame gun in the center of the front hull plate. This eliminated the use of slip rings for the turret mount, but the traverse was restricted to 180 degrees. There also was the possibility of interference between the flame thrower and the cannon.

Design 5 placed the flame gun in a blister on the front side of the turret to the left of the gun shield. The shield was modified by cutting off the end 19-1/2 inches from the cannon center line and welding on a new extension. The latter served as a partial shield for the flame gun and transmitted motion in elevation from the 76 mount. A pinion and bevel sector gears moved the flame gun at a ratio of 2:1 compared to the cannon. Thus the elevation for the flame equipment ranged from +50 to -20 degrees with a full 360 degree traverse. It was intended to rebuild the gunner's periscopic sight to permit a selection of movement to follow either the cannon or the flame thrower.

Plan number 6 installed the flame gun in a blister over the turret pistol port. This permitted a 360 degree traverse with the turret and an elevation range of +60 to -10 degrees.

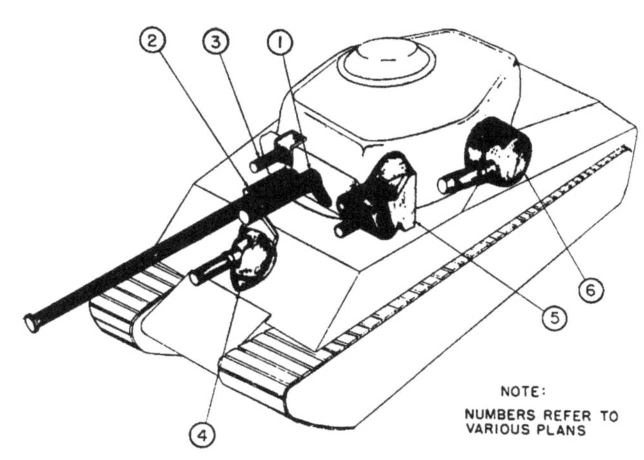

The sketch above shows the various arrangements studied for the location of the flame gun on the E19-19 mechanized flame thrower.

Below is a top sectional view of plan 5 which was adopted for installation.

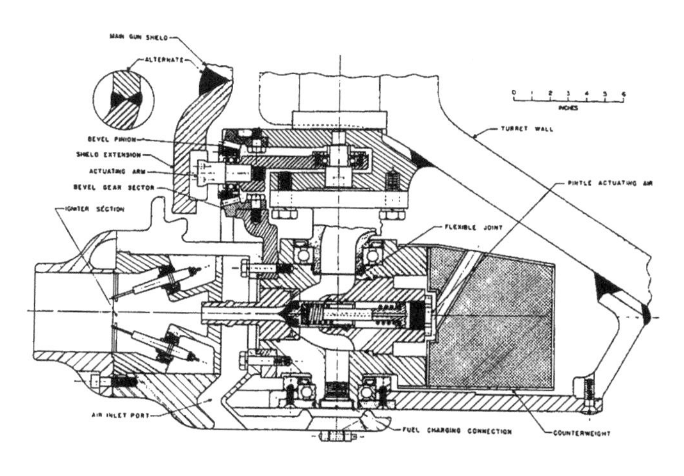

Scale models and layout drawings were prepared for all six locations and numbers 2 and 3 were dropped at an early stage. Plan 5 was finally selected for full development and the detailed design work started. The right side of the hull was used for fuel storage with a 100 gallon tank below the turret and a 30 gallon tank in the sponson. Air pressurized the fuel tanks to 390 psi. Maximum firing times of 25 to 30 seconds were estimated because of the limited fuel capacity. The flame thrower replaced slightly less than half of the 76mm ammunition supply and the tank retained its full secondary armament.

Development work on the E19-19 was halted at the end of the war. At that time a wooden mock-up had been completed of the flame gun assembly and working models of the gun and ignition system were ready for test.

An artist's concept of the flame thrower tank T33.

Experiments with coaxial cannon and flame gun mounts led to a new development contract in May 1945. The new E20-20 flame thrower was installed in a tank converted from the heavily armored M4A3E2. Fitted with a special cast turret and the horizontal volute spring suspension, it was designated by the Ordnance Committee as the flame thrower tank T33.

To save space, the lightweight 75mm gun M6 with its concentric recoil system was provided as main armament alongside the flame thrower and the two mounts were geared together. The flame gun had a separate shield to the right of the combination gun mount M64 which carried the 75 and its coaxial .30 caliber machine gun. An auxiliary E21 flame gun was originally specified for mounting in the periscope holder on the tank commander's vision cupola. It could be traversed approximately 240 degrees to the sides and rear of the turret providing close-in protection. It could not be aimed forward in order to prevent firing into the turret roof at its maximum depression. When the pilot T33 was finally built, the E12R4 periscope flame gun was substituted.

Two fuel tanks in the lower hull and two in the turret provided a net capacity of about 250 gallons for use by both flame guns. Forty rounds of 75mm ammunition were carried for the cannon. The T33 was originally designed for a normal five man crew with the tank commander located at the center rear of the turret. Forward of the commander's vision cupola there were two oval hatches in the turret roof for the gunner and the loader. Later in the development, the crew was reduced to four by dropping the assistant driver. The bow machine gun was then eliminated and its mount welded up.

The E20 flame gun had an elevation range of +45 to -15 degrees, but the 75mm cannon reached only from +13 to -10 degrees. OCM 30383 specified the replacement of the 75mm gun M6 by the newer M17. This was an improved version of the same lightweight cannon fitted with a muzzle brake. However, no M17s were manufactured and the standard M6 was installed without a stabilizer.

Original plans called for the procurement of 20 T33s with the possible production of 600 additional tanks. After the end of the war with Japan, the order was cut to three pilot models all of which were converted from M4A3E2s. These vehicles were identified as follows;

Pilot #1	USA 3082940	Ord S/N 50343
Pilot #2	USA 3083011	Ord S/N 50414
Pilot #3	USA 3083021	Ord S/N 50424

After the end of the war, work proceeded slowly and the first pilot was delivered to Aberdeen in September 1947. The second and third arrived in January 1948. Tests were carried out at Aberdeen, but no additional pilots were produced.

The flame thrower tank T33 (above and below) during the test program at Aberdeen in June 1948. Note that the bow machine gun mount has been eliminated from the M4A3E2 hull converted for this vehicle. The E12R4 periscope type flame gun can be seen on the commander's vision cupola.

The flame thrower tank T33 (above) firing its flame gun at 10 degrees depression. The tank is using 7 per cent Napalm thickened gasoline during these tests at Fort Knox.

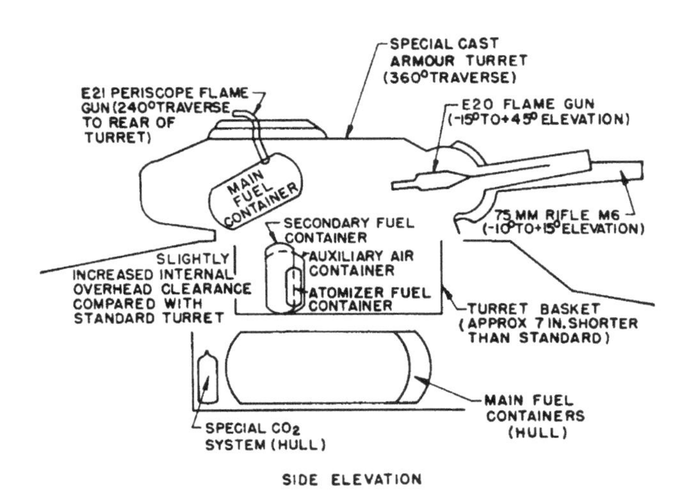

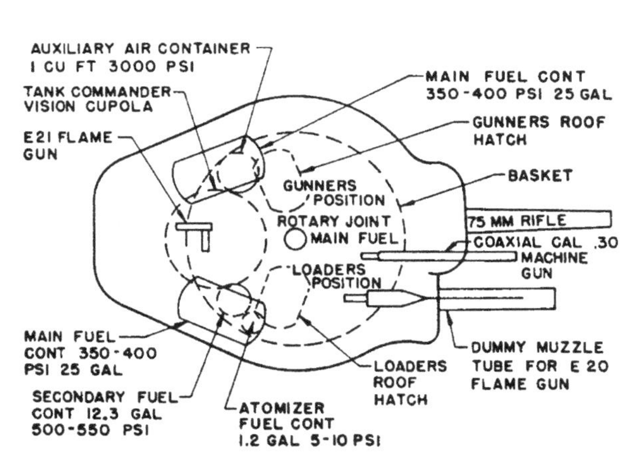

TURRET PLAN VIEW

Influenced by tests of the Canadian Badger, two of the T33s were converted in 1953 to the self-propelled flame thrower T68. Similar in appearance to the Canadian vehicle, their registration numbers were USA 3082940 and USA 3083021. The turrets were removed and replaced with a soft steel cover fitted with a vision cupola and a .50 caliber machine gun mount. A Canadian Iroquois flame gun, designated as the E33, was installed in the bow machine gun position. The vehicle carried a crew of three (commander, driver, flame thrower operator) and 220 gallons of fuel for the flame gun. The T68 was tested at Aberdeen from 18 November to 11 December 1953.

In early 1945, the CWS requested the NDRC to reopen studies of pump pressurized flame throwers. Previous attempts to build such units had been unsuccessful and compressed gas had become the standard method of fuel propulsion. However, studies late in the war showed that some of the difficulties were due to the early type of fuel thickeners. They also indicated some theoretical advantages for pumps over the compressed gas system. With direct pump pressurization, the fuel tanks were maintained at about 5 psi. At such a low pressure, they could be designed to fit the space available in the vehicle and did not require the cylindrical shape necessary to contain a high pressure fuel. Thus the capacity could be increased and the danger of tank explosions resulting from battle damage was reduced.

Eastman Kodak Company received a contract to develop a pump pressurized flame thrower for test purposes. The first unit was installed on a Buick automobile chassis operated by a chain drive from the propeller shaft. The E7 flame gun was used with the experimental equipment. Tests showed that the new unit compared favorably in range performance with the M5-4, but considerable difficulty resulted from holdup in the tanks, particularly with viscous fuels. When using 8 per cent Napalm, this amounted to 20 or 30 per cent of the total tank capacity.

After the initial tests, Kodak was requested to install the equipment in an M4A3 medium tank. Designated as the combat vehicle flame thrower E21-7R1, it was completed in 1947 and successfully tested at Edgewood Arsenal.

The arrangement of the armament and the flame thrower installation in the T33 is shown schematically at the left.

These two photographs show the self-propelled flame thrower T68 at Aberdeen in December 1953. Note the .50 caliber machine gun mount on the late model tank commander's vision cupola.

A Sherman Crocodile towing the trailer containing its fuel and pressurization system. The flame gun can be seen mounted to the right of the bow gunner's hatch.

Although the auxiliary flame throwers were unpopular with the U.S. Army in Europe, the British Crocodile was widely admired. Troops which received support from these tanks wanted all they could get. On the Crocodile, the flame gun replaced the bow machine gun mount in the Churchill tank and its fuel and pressurization system was towed in a separate trailer. The Crocodiles were part of the British 79th Armoured Division and they were detached whenever required to support British and American units.

U.S. interest in the Crocodile began long before D-day. After a demonstration of the prototype in March 1943, a study was conducted on U.S. requirements for such equipment. This resulted in the recommendation that 100 Shermans be fitted with the complete Crocodile apparatus and that an additional 25 trailers be procured as a reserve. Approved by the Theater Commander on 16 July, the request was submitted to the British War Office in August. The Petroleum Warfare Department completed a wooden mock-up on a Sherman by 10 October and work commenced on a prototype. After successful tests in February 1944, the equipment was redesigned for production and a soft steel pilot was available in March. For the 100 units, it was planned to obtain components common to both the Churchill and the Sherman equipment in Britain while the special items for the Sherman would be procured from the United States. However, a preliminary order was placed for six Sherman Crocodiles to be manufactured in Britain.

Unfortunately, the Churchill Crocodiles had the usual problems with a new weapon and their performance did not show up well during the first month of fighting in Normandy. As a result, interest waned and the U.S. Army cancelled its requirement on 13 August.

The E4-5 auxiliary flame thrower had been demonstrated to the troops and was believed to be available in quantity. Although its range and capacity were limited, it did not require a trailer. The latter feature of the Crocodile did not appeal to the U.S. tankers who feared that it would restrict their maneuverability.

Four of the six Crocodiles in the preliminary order were completed and issued to the U.S. Ninth Army in late November. Here they equipped a platoon in the 739th Tank Battalion (Special). This was one of the former CDL outfits that had been converted to a mine exploder battalion. The 739th employed their four flame thrower tanks in action with great effect and the troops wanted more of them. The Ninth Army tried to get additional Sherman Crocodiles, first requesting the remaining two of the original order and later approximately 60 to equip a complete battalion. Both requests were rejected because of interference with British requirements and the belief that U.S. equipment would soon be available.

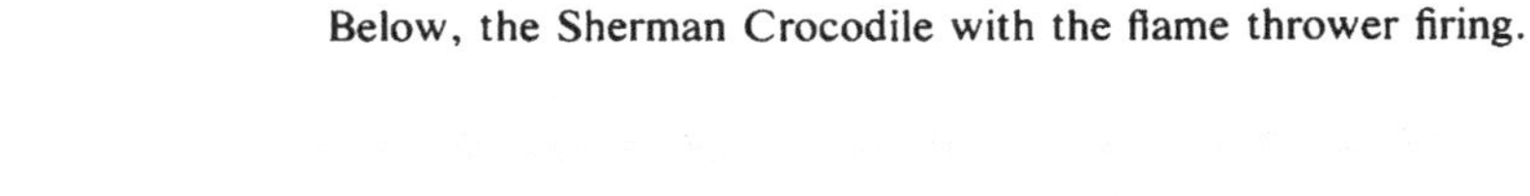

Below, the Sherman Crocodile with the flame thrower firing.

The Sherman Adder based on the Sherman V is shown above. The armored container for the fuel and pressurization system can be seen on the rear hull in the left photograph. Note the armored duct for the fuel and gas pressure lines along the top of the right sponson.

Other British flame thrower tanks based on the Sherman included the Salamander series. Running through eight major models, they were all fitted to the Sherman and the initial version also was installed in the Churchill. The first model used a Wasp IIA flame gun with an armored sheath located in the turret below the 75. Designed by the Petroleum Warfare Department, it had a net fuel capacity of 240 to 275 gallons in three tanks. Two of these were mounted in the sponsons and one was below the turret. The prototype, demonstrated in August 1944, showed a maximum range of 90 to 100 yards.

The Salamander Types II and III, developed by Lagonda, were fitted with a Wasp flame gun inside a 75mm barrel. Type II also carried a flame gun in the loader's periscope mount. Different arrangements of fuel tankage and pressurization were tried out in the II and III. Types IV through VIII tested various flame gun locations as well as methods of pressurization and tank arrangement. These were all designed by the Petroleum Warfare Department. On Types VI and VIII, the flame gun was installed in an armored blister on the side of the turret and in VII it was fitted into the antenna socket on the right front hull. Types II and III carried a four man crew while the others retained the usual five men.

The Sherman Adder mounted a flame gun on the assistant driver's periscope. It was fed from a fuel tank externally mounted in an armored container on the rear hull plate. The fuel and gas pressure lines ran through an armored duct along the top right side of the hull to the forward ventilator. The latter was replaced by a special casting which provided an inlet. Inside the hull, the lines connected to the flame gun in the periscope mount. Interference required the modification of the right front sponson ammunition rack reducing the number of 75mm rounds from 17 to 13. With an 80 gallon capacity, the Adder had a range of 80 to 90 yards. Another version of the Adder mounted one or two 30 gallon fuel tanks in the right sponson completely eliminating the 17 round ammunition rack.

The Sherman Adder at the right is fitted with a vision cupola and armor skirts to protect the suspension.

Above is the Wasp flame thrower mounted on top of a turretless Ram tank during firing tests.

Although the Wasp flame thrower was an operational success mounted on the Universal carrier, the vehicle's light armor left it vulnerable to enemy fire. To obtain greater protection, the flame equipment was mounted experimentally on a turretless Ram tank. A further modification relocated the flame gun to the bow mount replacing the machine gun. This arrangement proved satisfactory and it was designated as the Badger. Appearing in early 1945, it was used operationally by the 4th Canadian Armoured Brigade.

The success of the Ram Badger led to the postwar Canadian development of a similar vehicle based on the Sherman. The latter fitted a flame gun in the bow machine gun port of a turretless M4A2 equipped with the horizontal volute spring suspension. The turret was replaced by a low silhouette steel cover fitted with a vision cupola.

Work started to convert three M4A2s in October 1947, but difficulties in obtaining suitable high pressure gasoline suction hoses delayed the delivery of the first pilot tank until May 1948. Other high priority work held up the completion of the second and third vehicles until March 1949. The flame thrower was a Wasp IIC with an effective range of 125 yards. Elevation ranged from +30 to -10 degrees and the maximum traverse was 30 degrees right and 23 degrees left. The two fuel tanks had a total capacity of 150 gallons and were pressurized to about 250 psi. The Sherman Badger created the interest which resulted in the experiments with the U.S. self-propelled flame thrower T68.

At the left is the pilot Ram Badger. The Wasp flame gun has replaced the bow machine gun in the ball mount on this later model Ram chassis.

The Sherman Badger (above) had the Wasp IIC flame gun installed in the bow mount of a turretless Sherman III equipped with the wide-track horizontal volute spring suspension.

Below, the Sherman Badger is test firing at 15 degrees elevation using 6 per cent Napalm thickened gasoline.

A Sherman DD tank disembarks from a landing craft during training exercises.

FLOTATION DEVICES AND FORDING EQUIPMENT

Armored support during the initial assault was considered an essential feature of the Normandy invasion plans. The disaster at Dieppe had shown that landing craft were extremely vulnerable when unloading their tanks on the beach. If the tanks could be provided with flotation equipment and some kind of propulsion they could be launched out of range of the enemy guns. Swimming in under their own power, they would be dispersed and present a more difficult target.

A flotation device invented by Mr. Nicholas Straussler had proven successful when applied to the Valentine and this tank was originally considered for the assault role. However, in April 1943, development of the specialized armor necessary for the invasion was centralized in the British 79th Armoured Division under Major General P.C.S. Hobart. General Hobart noted that the Valentine was obsolescent and hence inadequate as a fighting tank for such an important task. He insisted that the flotation equipment be applied to the Sherman, then the first line tank in both the British and U.S. armored units. This application was successful and the new secret weapon was referred to as the Duplex Drive or DD tank.

The increased displacement necessary for flotation was obtained by the use of a collapsible rubberized canvas folding screen mounted on a 3/16 inch thick mild steel platform welded around the waterproofed tank hull at the fender line. The canvas screen was erected by inflating 36 tubular rubber pillars with compressed air. It was then locked in place by 13 steel struts to prevent collapse if the air pillars were damaged. Erecting the screen raised the height of the DD tank based on the Sherman V to about 13 feet. Three tubular steel frames running around the screen provided support against the outside water pressure. The canvas was sewn to metal strips which were then attached to these frames. The screen thickness was doubled below the middle frame and tripled below the bottom frame. It was attached to the hull by steel beading bolted to the platform flange and sealed with sponge rubber. To collapse the screen, the steel struts were unlocked by a hydraulic system and the air was released from the inflated pillars. The canvas assembly was then folded into place by elastic bands attached by metal rings to the inside surface.

Compressed air to inflate the pillars was supplied by two bottles mounted on the front hull. When the screen was collapsed, the tank's turret armament had a clear field of fire. If the screen was intact, it masked the bow machine gun even in the collapsed position.

The early Sherman DD with the screen fully extended is shown above. The propellers can be seen lowered into the driving position in the left photograph.

In the water, the DD tanks were driven by two propellers connected to the tank's tracks. Standard sprocket plates attached to the outside of both special idlers engaged the tracks and transmitted power through a bevel gear and pinion to the propellers. When not in use, the two 26 inch diameter propellers were disengaged and swung upward to obtain adequate ground clearance. In the operating position, they were held in gear by their own weight and forward thrust. The propellers rotated in opposite directions and could be swiveled either hydraulically or manually for steering. The maximum speed in the water was 5 to 6 miles/hour.

When afloat, the DD based on the Sherman V had a freeboard of 4 feet in front and 3 feet in the rear. With less displacement, the freeboard on the shorter Sherman III was 3 feet in front and 2 feet 6 inches in the rear. A small electrically driven bilge pump controlled by the driver was used to remove water from inside or on top of the hull. Periscope extensions could be installed for the driver and tank commander to provide vision over the top of the screen. Steering was aided by sighting rods fitted in sockets on the upper edge of the screen in front of each periscope. A small platform welded to the right rear of the turret allowed the tank commander to stand outside and steer manually with a detachable tiller. This outside helmsman also had a compass which provided corrections for the directional gyroscope used by the driver during the final approach.

At the left below, the early Sherman DD is afloat controlled from the auxiliary steering position at the top rear of the turret. The periscopes are not fitted. Below at the right, the screen is lowered and the propellers are raised into the position for land operation.

Details can be seen above of the DD steering system and the propellers raised for land travel. At the right is the auxiliary steering position showing the pilot platform and steering lever. These two views are of a U.S. DD based on the M4A1.

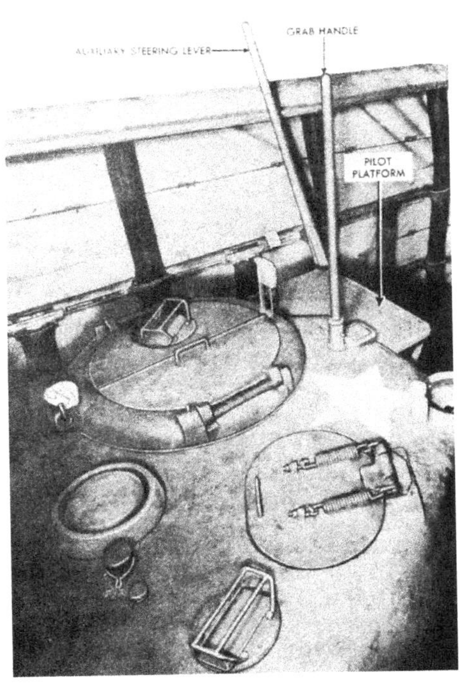

Prior to the availability of the Sherman DD, the Valentine was used to develop the methods for using the new weapon. Delivery of the Valentine DDs started in late July 1943 and under the driving leadership of General Hobart, experiments started at once. By the end of the year, the basic techniques of DD operation had been worked out. Thus began the program that was to train five British and two Canadian armored regiments in addition to three U.S. tank battalions.

A demonstration on 27 January 1944 drew enthusiastic approval of the DD from General Eisenhower. He directed that they also be used to support the U.S. assault divisions during the coming invasion. General Hobart pointed out that the limited facilities available could not possibly produce sufficient DDs in time for use by both the British and U.S. forces. This resulted in quick action. The following day a British DD expert was flown to the United States with a complete set of drawings and the first 100 American built DD tanks were delivered at Liverpool within six weeks. These appear to have been based on the M4 and M4A1 while the British conversions used primarily the M4A2 and M4A4.

The U.S. 70th, 741st, and 743rd Tank Battalions were trained in time for D-day. They joined the British 4/7 Royal Dragoon Guards, 13/18 Hussars, and the Nottinghamshire Yeomanry. The Canadian DDs were manned by the 1st Hussars and the Fort Garry Horse. On 6 June, the rough seas resulted in heavy losses when the DDs were launched at long distances from the beach. The 741st lost 27 out of 29 tanks before they reached the shore. In the case of the 743rd, the Navy, noting the dangerous conditions, took the DDs all the way into the beach. The same was done for the tanks of

In the photograph below, the DD is operating in waves approximately 2½ feet high during the test program.

Above, a British DD tank is in action near Ranville in Normandy on 10-11 June 1944. Note that the screen has been cut away to expose the bow machine gun mount.

the Nottinghamshire Yeomanry and the 4/7 Royal Dragoon Guards. In the other units, the DDs swam in and made it to shore, although they were launched at closer range than originally intended. In the confusion resulting from the change of plans, most of the DDs arrived late, landing after the infantry was ashore. However, they immediately went into action providing vital support for the assault troops.

After Normandy, the DDs were employed in river crossing operations during the remainder of the campaign in northwest Europe. The most important of these was the assault across the Rhine in March 1945. In addition to the units mentioned earlier, C Company of the 736th Tank Battalion was trained on the DD for this operation. The final use of the DD in northwest Europe occurred on 29 April 1945 with the assault crossing of the Elbe river by a squadron from the Staffordshire Yeomanry.

Below, U.S. DD tanks can be seen unloading from an LST during landing operations in southern France.

The 753rd Tank Battalion (above) supporting the 36th Infantry Division with DD tanks during the invasion of southern France, 15 August 1944.

Below, the 781st Tank Battalion during training exercises with DDs in the Neckar River sector, Germany, 13 April 1945. This is a DD I with the extended rear screen.

The Sherman IIIAY DD III is shown at the left above before installation of the screen. At the right, the same tank appears with the screen fully extended.

Either DD or DD I was added to the standard British designation for those tanks fitted with the duplex drive equipment. DD I referred to those modified or produced to the late standard with turret struts, self-locking struts, and the extended rear screen. Thus one based on the M4A2 became the Sherman III DD I and the M4A4 was the Sherman V DD I. A later version fitted with power steering and an air compressor became the DD II. A DD tank manufactured in the U.S. based on the 76mm gun M4A2 with the horizontal volute spring suspension was the Sherman IIIAY DD III.

Below, the Sherman IIIAY DD III with the screen folded and the propellers in the raised position. Note the side skirts on this tank.

The sketch at the left shows the Belch apparatus installed around the top of the DD screen. At the right, the device is in operation as the DD moves through some burning oil.

Fears of damage from burning oil on the water surface resulted in the development of protective spray equipment sometimes referred to as the Belch apparatus. It consisted of a small gasoline engine driven pump which piped sea water to jets placed around the top frame of the screen. With these in operation, the DD could safely pass through a flame barrage without damage.

Although the DD tanks swam easily enough, climbing ashore was sometimes difficult, particularly if the bank was steep or soft. Efforts to solve this problem included experiments with rockets installed to give the tank a boost as it made its exit.

Another device was the Ginandit designed by Straussler to permit the DDs to negotiate mud banks during river crossing operations. It consisted of a folded mat mounted on a rack above the front of the tank. This mat was projected in front of the vehicle to provide good traction over soft ground. Preliminary tests showed that a gap often remained between the tank and the near end of the mat after it was in place. To correct this problem, the design was modified to include and additional mud mat mounted vertically at the front of the vehicle. As the tank approached the bank, a spade was released which swung down between the tracks. When this spade dug into the ground, the

Firing the solid rockets to help the tank climb ashore produced a spectacular sight (at left). At the right, the rockets can be seen attached to the sides of the tank below the sponsons.

At the left is the Ginandit with the DD screen fully extended. The folded mat is installed on the rack at the top front and the vertical mud mat is in position.

vertical mud mat was automatically dropped directly in front of the tracks. The tank climbed onto the edge of this mat and the Ginandit was then projected in front of the vehicle using compressed air. The DD tank could then pass over the mats and the same pathway was available for following vehicles.

Development of the Ginandit was originally authorized on 22 January 1945 and experiments continued until early 1946.

The Sherman DD Topee is shown at the right. It consisted of a light armor plate container to protect the folded DD screen against damage from small arms fire, brush, or trees. The upper photograph shows the screen stowed with the armored covers closed. In the bottom photograph, the screen is fully extended with the armored covers hanging down around the container.

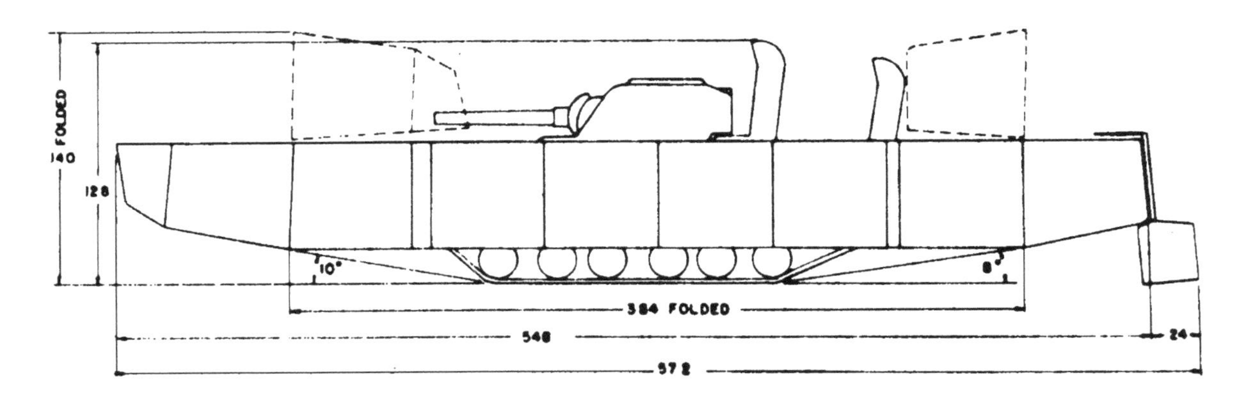

The general arrangement of the T6 device for use with the medium tank M4 series is sketched above. Note how the end floats could be folded on top of the assembly to reduce the overall length.

Although used by U.S. troops in Europe, the DD tank was not favored by either the Armored Board or the Ordnance Department. They were particularly critical of its lack of seaworthiness and the fact that its guns could not be fired while afloat.

Ordnance tested several types of flotation equipment at Aberdeen in early 1944. They considered the most promising of these to be the one designed by Major Q. Berg and Captain H.F. Blankenship. For obvious reasons it was originally referred to as the BB device. This was later changed to the T6 device for swimming the medium tank M4 series.

The T6 consisted of compartmented steel floats which were attached to the front, rear, and both sides of the tank. To decrease their vulnerability to damage, the float compartments were filled with plastic foam covered with waterproof cellophane. Propulsion was by the reaction from the track movement in the water giving a maximum speed of about 4 miles/hour. The tank was steered by twin rudders on the rear float connected by control ropes to the turret hatch.

Fully assembled, the width of the T6 was 132 inches with an overall length of 572 inches. The latter could be reduced to 384 inches by folding the front and rear floats on top of the assembly. Size was one disadvantage of this equipment. Even with the floats folded, the number of tanks that could be carried by a landing craft was greatly reduced. However, the T6 proved quite seaworthy and all of the turret weapons could be fired during the landing approach. Six prototypes were tested and 500 conversion kits were manufactured which could be fitted to all tanks of the M4 series.

Some of the T6s were employed during the invasion of Okinawa on 1 April 1945. Many landed successfully, but the reefs which surrounded the landing beaches sometimes proved their undoing. If the long extension of the front float struck the reef before the tracks could reach the bottom, the tank was prevented from climbing out. Standard tanks, waterproofed for deep water fording, were more successful. Unloaded from landing craft directly onto the reef, they were usually able to wade into the beach. The DD, without the excessive overhang, probably would have operated satisfactorily. The T6 was standardized later as the device, M19.

A medium tank M4A1 (below) is fitted with the T6 device on the island of Bougainville, 27 October 1944.

Above, a medium tank M4 is swimming with the T12 device. An outboard motor is attached to the rear of each 15 ton engineer pontoon for propulsion.

Other flotation equipment such as the Yagow device, the Blankenship device, the wet ferry, and the T12 device also were tested. The Yagow was similar, but somewhat inferior to the DD and the Blankenship design had a structural failure during the test. Two DUKWs formed the wet ferry which was considered suitable as a field expedient for river crossings. The T12 device attached two 15 ton engineer pontoons to the Sherman. The Armored Board considered that if modified, it also would be acceptable as a field expedient.

Despite the experiments with swimming tanks, most of the amphibious operations put the armored vehicles directly ashore from landing craft. Frequently, this required the vehicle to ford water of considerable depth in their approach to the beach. As a result, kits were developed to adapt the tanks and other vehicles for deep water fording. Properly waterproofed and fitted with the fording kit, a Sherman could operate in surf up to about 6 feet deep. Similar kits were developed for the self-propelled artillery and other vehicles based on the tank chassis.

The deep water fording equipment is being installed in the lower photograph at the right. The upper view shows the tank wading through deep water. The general arrangement of the fording apparatus can be seen in the sketch below.

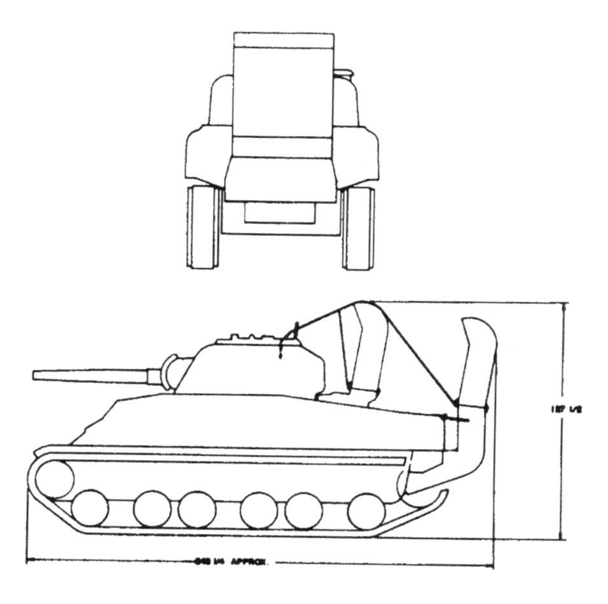

The tank mounting bulldozer M1 is installed above. The armored cover behind the front center protected the hydraulic jack that moved the blade. Note the blade jettisoning cable passing through the bow machine gun mount.

ENGINEER ARMORED VEHICLES

Operations throughout the world revealed the need for an armored vehicle capable of performing engineering tasks such as clearing roadways or filling craters. Heavy losses among bulldozer operators resulted in the application of armor to the construction machines as a field expedient. This provided limited protection, but was inadequate if the dozer was required to clear obstacles under heavy fire. In January 1942, it was proposed that a bulldozer blade be installed on a tank. Such an arrangement had the advantage of heavy armor protection as well as retaining the tank's normal firepower. Early experiments at the Desert Warfare Center had mounted V-shaped blades on tanks for use in mine clearance and road construction. This program had ended in failure, but the Engineer Board continued to experiment. Working with the Ordnance Department and two manufacturers of tractor blades, two models were produced in early 1943. Both were essentially mine excavators with V-shaped toothed blades and were relatively inefficient for normal bulldozer operations.

Although their funds were cut off in June 1943, the Engineer Board convinced the two manufacturers to construct pilot models of an improved tankdozer at no cost to the government. Using a straight toothless blade, the first was completed by Le Tourneau and tested in June at Fort Belvoir, Virginia. A similar model constructed by La Plante-Choate also was tested and both were successful with earth moving capacities comparable to a Caterpillar D-8 tractor. Procurement of a tankdozer combining the best features of both types was immediately authorized and it was subsequently standardized as the bulldozer, tank mounting, M1. A total of 1957 tankdozer conversion kits were produced by the end of the war.

As a tankdozer, the standard Sherman had considerable obstacle clearing ability, thus allowing combat engineers to operate under heavy fire. This capability was extremely important to plans for the rapidly approaching Normandy invasion. In the absence of a specialized engineer armored vehicle, the assault troops were issued tankdozers with 16 of them being assigned to the landing on Omaha beach. Unfortunately, ten of the tanks were lost before reaching the shore and one of the remaining six arrived without its blade. Their loss no doubt contributed to the heavy casualties suffered by the combat engineers on D-day.

The tank mounting bulldozer M1A1 is installed above (left) on the M4A3 with the horizontal volute spring suspension. At the top right is the T7 tank mounting bulldozer which was independent of the tank's suspension system. At the right is the standardized tank mounting bulldozer M2.

The tankdozers served in all theaters of war and proved particularly valuable in the mountainous Italian terrain and in the jungles of the Pacific.

The M1 tank mounting bulldozer was designed for installation on the Sherman equipped with the narrow tracks and the vertical volute spring suspension. The blade was 124 inches wide and it was mounted on side arms pivoted from the center bogie assemblies. A later version designated as the M1A1 had a 138 inch blade width and could be fitted on Shermans with either the original running gear or the newer wide tracked horizontal volute spring suspension. It could also be installed on the M4E9 type spaced out suspension.

In early 1945, the linkage mounted dozer developed for the high speed tractors was adapted to the medium tank. Attached to the front hull, this design was independent of the running gear and could be mounted on almost any tank. Designated as the T7, this bulldozer was fitted with blades varying in width from 124 to 146 inches. After modification, it was standardized as the bulldozer, tank mounting, M2.

In Italy, the tankdozer found an additional use. The limited space on the Anzio beachhead made proper dispersion of the ammunition dumps impossible and if a fire started in one area, it had to be rapidly extinguished to prevent spreading. The Anzio ammunition officer suggested mounting a bulldozer blade on the front of a tank. Protected by the armor, dirt could be pushed over the burning ammunition smothering the fire. Tankdozers were improvised by attaching standard bulldozer blades to M4 tanks and T2 tank recovery vehicles. Four of these shipped to Anzio in April 1944 were an immediate success. They were able to extinguish fires that could not have been controlled in any other way. In May, some of the standard conversion kits became available from the United States and further vehicles were converted to tankdozers.

One of the tankdozers improvised to fight ammunition dump fires at Anzio can be seen at the left.

Above is another tankdozer improvised in Italy using components available in the field.

The problem of fighting ammunition fires led to a development program at Fort Belvoir. In early 1944, the Engineer Board began studies of an ammunition dump fire fighter based on the Sherman tank. Although equipped with a dozer blade, this vehicle was much more than a tankdozer. The turret and armament were removed and replaced by a superstructure mounting two water nozzles, each capable of 180 degrees rotation and plus or minus 30 degrees elevation. All mounts were powered by electric motors and controlled from inside the tank. The nozzles were fed from a 1500 gallon internally mounted reservoir by a centrifugal pump at a rate of 500 gallons per minute. A separate 8-cylinder 85 horsepower engine was used to drive the pump. A 150 gallon foam reservoir was carried on the rear deck. The foam solution could be injected into the suction side of the water pump when required. The hull floor was reinforced by an additional 5/8 inch thick steel plate and the vehicle was sealed for blast protection. It was operated by a crew consisting of the driver, assistant driver, and the fire fighter. All three crew members were provided with oxygen masks. The dozer blade could be jettisoned in emergencies and a tow cable was attached to the rear as a means of retrieving the vehicle from a fire if it should become disabled. Fully loaded, the fire fighting tank weighed about 80,000 pounds. Tests were still in progress early in the postwar period.

The ammunition dump fire fighter developed at Fort Belvoir is shown at the left. Below, it is in operation fighting a gasoline fire.

The first pilot engineer armored vehicle as originally constructed with the 7.2 inch T2 rocket launcher installed on the turret. Note the double doors in the turret front.

A consequence of the Dieppe raid in August 1942 was a reexamination of methods for clearing beach obstacles. In Britain, this resulted in the development of the Armoured Vehicle, Royal Engineers (AVRE) based on the Churchill tank. In February 1943, the Army Ground Forces approved a Corps of Engineers recommendation that similar studies be conducted in the United States. To insure coordination with the Navy, a test site was selected near the Amphibious Training Base at Fort Pierce, Florida. Beach and underwater obstacles were erected and used to test various techniques for their destruction. The test group recommended the development of an engineer armored vehicle to attack these obstacles and in August, approval was received to build such a vehicle based on the Sherman tank.

The first pilot was converted from an M4A3 at Fort Belvoir and preliminary tests were carried out in the Engineer Board demolition area. The 75mm gun mount was removed and replaced in the turret front by a double door of 1 inch steel armor plate. The 75mm ammunition racks and other equipment were removed to increase the interior space and a side door was installed in the right sponson between the middle and rear suspension bogies. Hand rails and a rear step were welded to the outside of the hull and attachments were provided for a dozer blade. The sole example of the experimental T2 rocket launcher was permanently mounted on top of the turret. This launcher fired the same 7.2 inch rockets as the T40, but was of much sturdier construction with 48 inch rails compared to the 90 inch rails of the T40. After limited tests at Belvoir, the first pilot was shipped to Fort Pierce arriving about 20 March 1944.

A second pilot was converted at Fort Pierce from an M4A1 to check the adaptability of the conversion kit to both cast and welded hull tanks. Examination of the first pilot showed that the flat 1 inch thick turret doors were the most vulnerable spot on the tank. They also were inconvenient and dangerous to use when under fire. On the second pilot, the cannon was replaced by a steel plug, but the gun mount and shield remained in place protecting the turret front. The turret door was replaced by a second sponson door located on the left side just forward of the middle bogie center line. As on the first pilot, the dozer blade was installed and the hand rails and rear step were welded to the hull.

Tests on the T2 launcher showed that it was less accurate than the T40 which was then in production. Although it was more rugged, the T2 could not be jettisoned and it did not allow the periscopic sight to be used for aiming. Hence, it was decided to arm the second pilot with a modified T40 (T64) and a trunnion arm was welded to the gun shield to move the launcher in elevation. A special switch was installed for selective firing when both explosive and smoke rounds were loaded in the launcher.

The first pilot engineer armored vehicle after modification. The T2 launcher has been removed and a second side door is located in the left sponson.

Above is the second pilot engineer armored vehicle fitted with the T40 rocket launcher and the tank mounting bulldozer M1. The view through the sponson door (top right) shows the explosive charges stowed in the turret basket and the wooden platform used to bridge the gap between the basket floor and the door.

Manned by a crew of six, the vehicle carried 1000 pounds of Composition C2 or tetrytol on the turret basket floor. Additional explosives could be stowed in the right sponson and below the turret floor. With the driver and assistant driver in the front hull, a four man demolition team rode in the turret. When hand placing charges, three men worked outside with the fourth in the turret tossing out explosives. Wooden platforms were made to fit between the side doors and the turret basket for easier access.

A number of accessories were tested with the engineer armored vehicle. These included the M8 armored trailer which could carry up to 2200 pounds of explosive charges. Toboggan type pallets also were used to tow loads of explosive. Both wood and steel charge placers were tested for use against different types of walls. Referred to as the Doozit, they were carried on the dozer blade. A mine plow was tested, but it was too lightly constructed for satisfactory use. The demolition snake could be used, but required the removal of the dozer hydraulic jack assembly to allow installation of the snake pushing cable. In addition to the .30 caliber bow machine gun, an 81mm mortar could be fitted in the turret firing out of the hatch. Tested by firing white phosphorus shells with no powder increment, a range table was obtained for short distances.

Perhaps the greatest obstacle to the adoption of the engineer armored vehicle was that it did not fit into any standard organization. The Engineer Board and School joined in the recommendation that special engineer units be organized to use the new vehicle. The War Plans Division rejected this approach considering it impractical to establish a new organization for one implement of war.

Although 100 conversion kits were authorized for procurement, only two engineer armored vehicles with crews and instructors were at a port of embarkation on VJ-day. Thus the U.S. made no use of this type of vehicle in the fighting and the troops continued to attack obstacles with satchel charges and other hand placed explosives. The wisdom of the British method of centralizing the development and use of such specialized equipment in one unit is clearly apparent.

At the right, the 81mm mortar is mounted in the turret hatch of the engineer armored vehicle. Firing white phosphorus shells, it could provide smoke cover for engineer operations.

At the right is the 7.2 inch rocket launcher T76 (top photograph) fitted into the turret of an M4A1. Below the T76 is the T76E1 installed in a Sherman with the horizontal volute spring suspension. This tank also has the 7.2 inch rocket launcher T73 on the turret and it is modified as an engineer armored vehicle with side doors and a dozer blade.

Tests revealed many problems with the turret mounted rocket launchers. They were vulnerable to heavy caliber machine gun fire and frequently unreliable. As a result, a program began to develop a tank mounted launcher with the rockets completely enclosed by the heavy armor. On two of these vehicles, a 7.2 inch rocket launcher replaced the cannon in the tank turret. The first carried the T76 launcher with an open space between the tube and the loading port in the turret face. The rocket was loaded from inside the turret and the port was closed before firing. The rocket blast then escaped through the opening at the base of the tube. Modification later changed the designation to the T76E1. Twenty 7.2 inch rockets were stowed inside the tank. With a 360 degree traverse, the launcher had an elevation range of +30 to 0 degrees.

A later development mounted the 7.2 inch rocket launcher T105 in the tank turret. This was a single rail breech loading launcher with armor plate on the top, sides, and bottom to protect the loaded round. The T105 was to be furnished as a kit to replace the 75mm gun or 105mm howitzer mount. The baseplate of the rocket launcher was welded over the opening in the turret face. Like the T76, the demolition rockets were stowed inside and placed in the launcher one at a time. After the rocket was loaded, the breech was closed forcing the exhaust gases to escape in the forward direction. Neither of these launchers reached the combat troops before the end of hostilities.

Below, the 7.2 inch rocket launcher T105 is mounted in the turret of a medium tank M4A1.

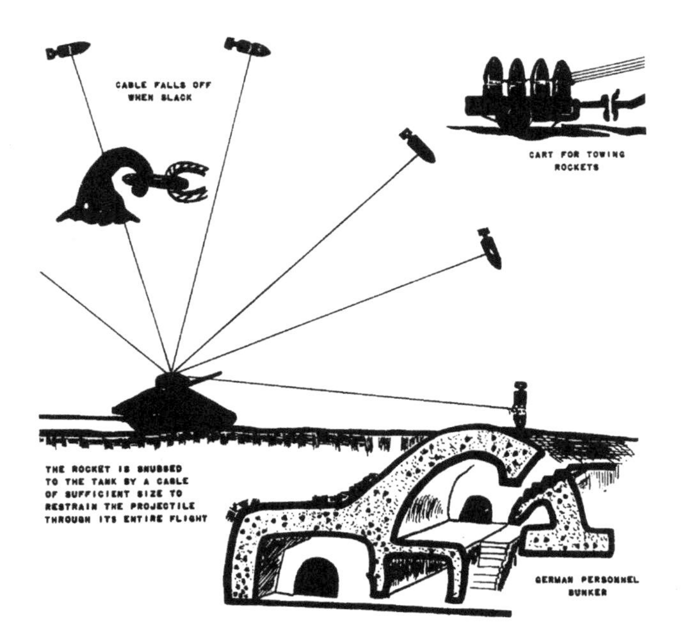

The sketch at the left from the test report indicates the proposed use of the cable bomb against heavy fortified positions.

At the right is a preliminary design sketch of the cable bomb with two large vertical fins. There were no horizontal fins.

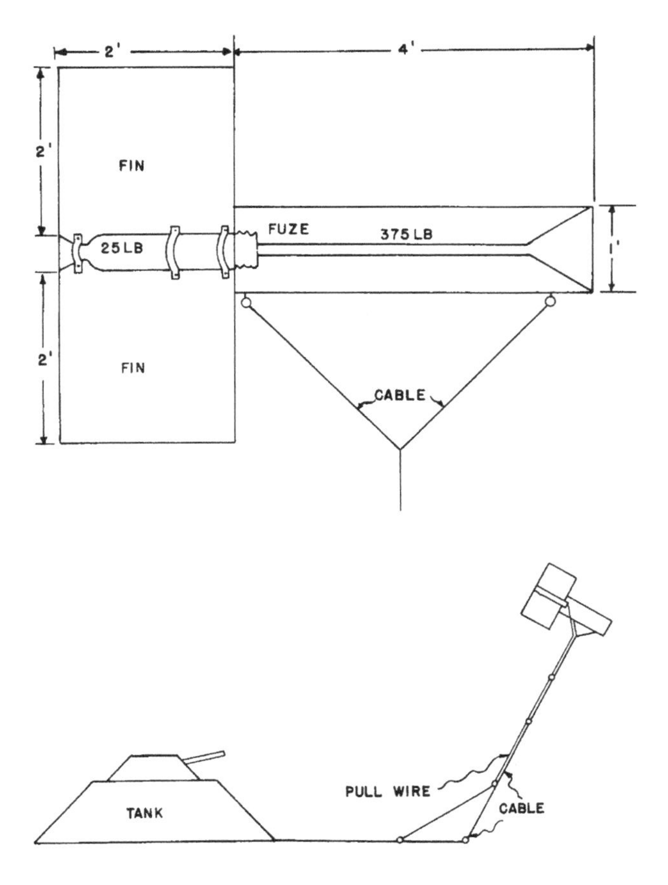

Another assault weapon proposed for use with the Sherman was the cable bomb. At the request of the Corps of Engineers during the Summer of 1944, the NDRC studied the feasibility of a tethered rocket propelled bomb for the destruction of heavily fortified bunkers. Several of these bombs were to be towed behind the tank in an armored trailer to within 50 feet of the target. Each bomb was attached to the tank by a 50 foot cable and when the rocket was fired, it traveled in an arc from the trailer over the tank to impact on the target. It was proposed that the trailer carry up to six bombs with three having hollow charges to penetrate the heavy concrete roof of the bunkers. The other bombs were to carry incendiary or fragmentation warheads. Tests at Allegany Ballistics Laboratory showed that the concept was practical and that it was very accurate. These tests used a 250 pound general purpose aircraft bomb propelled by a 4.5 inch T22 rocket motor. However, the project was dropped because of higher priority work on minefield clearance.

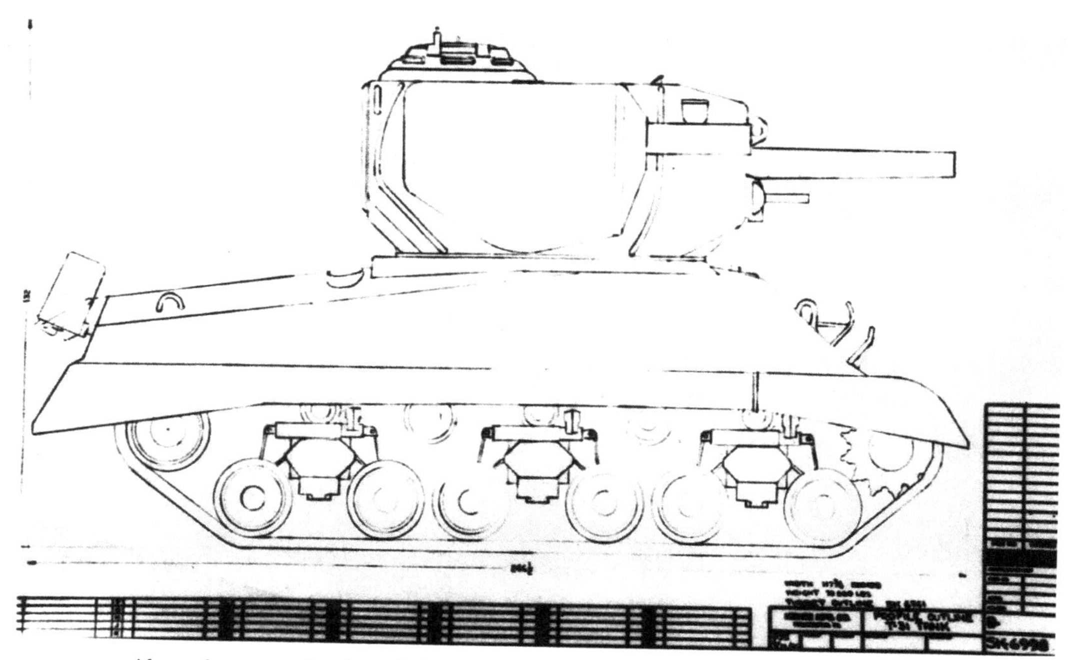

Above is a reproduction of the original profile drawing for the demolition tank T31.

Although considered suitable as an interim solution, many features of the converted engineer armored vehicle were unsatisfactory. The interior was crowded, access was restricted, and the stowage was poorly arranged. In particular, the turret mounted rocket launcher was inadequate as the main demolition weapon. To resolve these problems, a meeting was held at Fort Pierce in early November 1944 between representatives of the Engineer Board and the Joint Army-Navy Experimental and Testing Board (JANET). On 11 November, the senior member of the latter wrote to the Army Service Forces requesting the development of the engineer armored vehicle T2. The letter also outlined its desired characteristics. The M4A3 tank with the wide-track horizontal volute spring suspension was specified as the basic vehicle, but the belly armor was to be increased for protection against land mines. Other features included an improved dozer blade and mine excavator as well as a periscope type flame thrower in the assistant driver's hatch. A new special turret was required armed with a 7.2 inch automatic single rail rocket launcher on each side and two .30 caliber machine guns in front. Three pilot vehicles were requested as soon as possible.

The Ordnance Subcommittee on Automotive Equipment spelled out the characteristics in greater detail and recommended the procurement of four pilots. This action, reported in OCM 26173, also designated the vehicle as the demolition tank T31. Design layouts were started in January 1945 and the following month, a contract was negotiated with the Heinz Manufacturing Company to build four pilots. Heinz immediately started construction of a mock-up to study the equipment arrangement and stowage.

The T31's main armament was specified as two T94 7.2 inch rocket launchers with one mounted on each side of a narrow turret. Each revolver type launcher carried five rockets and was enclosed in an armored blister. The launcher cylinder could be reloaded from inside the turret and a minimum of 30 rockets were carried. The front and sides of the special turret were 2-1/2 inches thick. The double rear access doors were 1-1/2 inches thick. Two .30 caliber machine guns were fitted in ball mounts in the turret front with one on each side of a dummy 105mm howitzer. A .50 caliber machine gun was located on a pedestal at the rear of the roof alongside the tank commander's vision cupola. The latter was raised about 3 inches to improve the downward vision over the flat turret roof. Periscopes also were provided in the turret roof and a vision block was installed in the left rear door. The latter also contained a ball type pistol port.

The hull was based on the M4A3 with the horizontal volute spring suspension except that the floor was increased to maximum thickness of 1-1/2 inches. Fittings were provided for attaching an M1A1 bulldozer and a 50 gallon flame thrower unit was installed in the right sponson. An E12R3 periscope

The photographs above and at the left show the demolition tank T31 as it was delivered to Aberdeen in October 1945.

flame gun was fitted in either the assistant driver's hatch or the commander's vision cupola. The standard .30 caliber bow machine gun was retained.

Although the OCM called for four pilots, initial work began on a single soft plate turret. This was considered necessary to work out the installation of the experimental T94 rocket launchers. Work on this first pilot started in April 1945 and was completed in August. It was then shipped to Aberdeen for proof tests and demonstrations for the Corps of Engineers and the Armored Command. The launchers failed to operate satisfactorily during the tests. The left one froze completely and the right one could be rotated only by hand when loaded. By this time, the war was over and only limited funds were available. It was considered that further development of an engineer vehicle should be based on a more modern tank since the M4 series was no longer in production. Cancellation of the project was approved by OCM 30058 on 17 January 1946 and no further pilots were constructed.

Above an experimental folding bridge is installed on one of the T32 motor carriage pilots.

The Sherman served as a basis for numerous specialized engineer vehicles. The British converted many of their older tanks to carriers for cribs and fascines used to fill antitank ditches and other holes blocking the progress of the armored units. Many of the chassis were fitted with portable bridges. Some of these, referred to as Arks, could then be driven into the ditch or other gap forming a bridge over which other vehicles could pass.

The U.S. 1st Armored Division experimented with similar field modifications in early 1945. Tested in the Prato area of Italy, they included fascine carriers based on turretless Shermans as well as portable bridges carried on both tanks and tank recovery vehicles. Similar experiments were applied to the Sherman long after the war. In 1955, an Ark type vehicle was under test. Named the self-propelled assault bridge (SPAB), it was capable of spanning a gap of about 60 feet. The prototype SPAB was built and tested by the 2nd Armored Division in Europe.

Above a turretless British Sherman II has been modified as a fascine carrier.

Below, a steel treadway bridge is placed in position by a tank recovery vehicle T2. These are 1st Armored Division troops in the Mignano area of Italy on 22 February 1944.

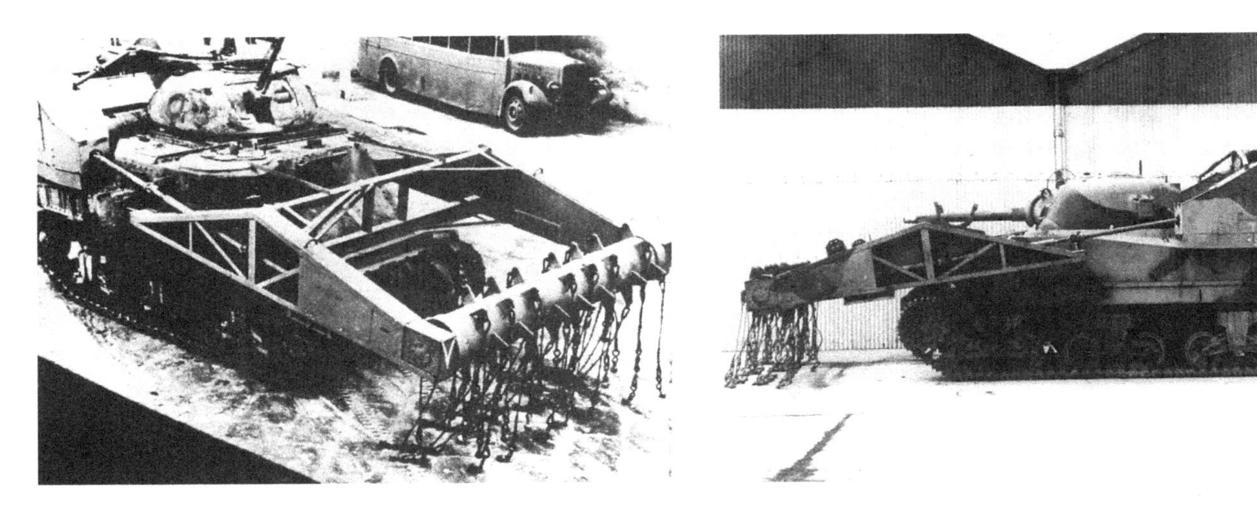

The British Scorpion mine exploder equipment is shown above adapted to the Grant (left) and the Sherman (right). Note the excessive width of this installation resulting from the overhang of the outboard engines.

MINE CLEARANCE EQUIPMENT

During the planning for D-day, a rapid means of clearing the extensive minefields expected in Normandy was considered essential for the success of the invasion. As for the other types of specialized armor, the development of such equipment and its associated tactical doctrine was assigned by the British to their 79th Armoured Division. Previous efforts to build mechanized mine clearing apparatus had met with only limited success in the desert.

One early mine clearing device was the rotary flail consisting of a cylindrical rotor with chains attached. When rotated, the chains beat the ground ahead of the vehicle in the hope of detonating any mines at a safe distance. The early flails fitted to the Matilda and Valentine tanks were unreliable, but they were improved with further development. The Scorpion was one of these which was installed on both the Grant and the Sherman. The Scorpions used one or two auxiliary engines to drive the chain flail. These auxiliary engines increased the width of the tank making it difficult to cross bridges or maneuver in other tight places. A later development was the Pram Scorpion based on the Sherman which was powered by the tank's main engine through attachments to the front drive sprockets. The chain rotor was carried on two side arms pivoted on the front suspension bogies and supported by rollers in front of each track. Another flail device installed on the Sherman was designated as the Marquis. Like the Scorpion, it was driven by auxiliary engines. However, they were enclosed in an armored housing which

The Pram Scorpion is at the left below. At the right is the Marquis with the turret replaced by an armored housing for the auxiliary engines necessary to drive the flail.

The most successful of the flail type mine exploders was the Crab (above). This photograph shows the Crab I with hydraulic rams installed on each side of the tank to lift the flail assembly. The wire cutter is the toothed disc at each end of the rotor.

replaced the tank's turret. None of these experimental vehicles were adopted by the 79th Armoured Division. Under General Hobart's direction, a simpler, more rugged flail type exploder was developed for operational use. This was the Crab which again used the main tank engine to drive the flail.

Unlike the earlier Marquis, the Crab retained the full turret armament of the Sherman. Only the bow machine gun was eliminated by interference with the rotor assembly. However, the position of the flail rotor restricted the 75mm gun from firing between 10 and 2 o'clock.

To obtain power for the Crab's flail required some modification of the tank's power train. The standard front propeller shaft was replaced by a shorter one and a power takeoff which operated a chain drive extending through the right side of the tank. The power was then transmitted through a carden shaft and universal joint to a bevel gear box at the right end of the flail rotor. This assembly transmitted approximately 285 horsepower when flailing. Fortythree chains were attached to the surface of the rotor and a cutter for wire entanglements was installed at each end.

On the Crab I, an hydraulic ram on each side of the tank was used to raise and lower the rotor assembly. For normal travel, the rotor was elevated and locked to provide clearance in front of the vehicle. In the flailing position, it was lowered until the side arms were horizontal. When operating over rough terrain, the fixed position of the rotor prevented uniform coverage ahead of the tank and the device was modified to follow the contour of the ground. On this new version, known as the Crab II, the rotor was balanced by an adjustable weight installed at the rear of the left side arm and the hydraulic ram was eliminated on that side. This arrangement allowed a constant height of 4 feet 3 inches to be maintained regardless of the terrain. The rotor was locked in a fixed position for wire cutting.

This is the Crab II with the weight at the rear of the left side arm to balance the rotor permitting it to follow the ground contour. There is only one hydraulic ram to lift the flail assembly.

To ease the load on the engine when flailing in heavy ground, an auxiliary gear box was installed on late model Crabs. With a gear ratio of 1.84:1, it permitted an efficient engine speed to be maintained during operation. When flailing, the Crab traveled at a maximum speed of 1.25 miles/hour. This corresponded to a rotor speed of 142 rpm.

The heavy dust cloud thrown up by the chains made direction keeping difficult and the Crabs were equipped with a directional gyro and a magnetic compass. The gyro was used by the driver for steering and required frequent corrections from the compass. The latter was installed in a binnacle which could be raised well above the turret to escape the effect of the steel armor. It was viewed by an optical system from within the tank. The Crabs also were fitted with equipment for marking the paths as they were cleared of mines.

Tests showed that the Crabs were not completely effective in exploding the mines. However, they did have a high percentage of success thus reducing losses to an acceptable level. At that time, they were also the most efficient device available with enough mobility for operations under combat conditions.

Approved by General Hobart, the Crabs were adopted by the 79th Armoured Division. The 30th Tank Brigade was converted to use the Crab and it employed them operationally until the end of the war.

The Lobster was an experimental flail device attached to the Sherman similar to the Crab. The rotor body was of open construction permitting better vision ahead of the tank. The flail chains were attached to extensions to increase the effective rotor diameter. However, with the successful development and operational use of the Crab II, further experiments with the Lobster were terminated.

The Crab II below is equipped with direction keeping lights and lane marking equipment. Note the cover around the gun mount to seal out dust and flying dirt.

At the left is the Lobster flail tank. The discs mounted on the smaller diameter roller were less vulnerable to damage and did not restrict the driver's vision as much as the Crab type rotor. A somewhat similar small diameter rotor was tested experimentally after the war for the Crab II.

At the right, a Crab I flail tank moves toward the Orne River during the Normandy fighting in July 1944. Below, a Crab I is in operation. With its fixed flail height, this Crab I would probably miss any mines in the ditch. These flail tanks are based on the Sherman V.

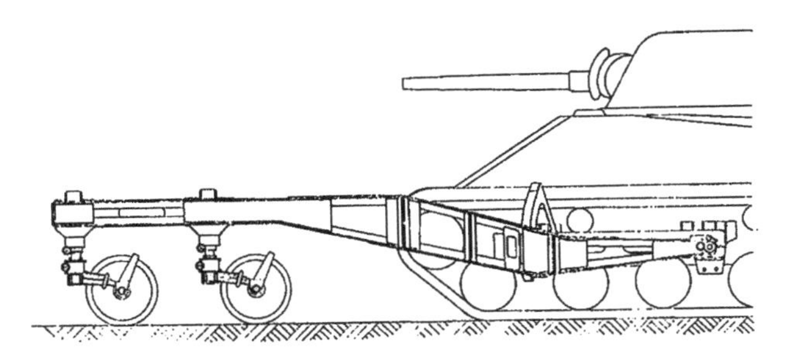

The sketch at the left is a side view of the AMRCR device attached to the Sherman V.

Experiments with roller type mine exploders also continued in Britain and some of them were tested on the Sherman. One of these was designated as the Attachment, Anti-Mine Reconnaissance Castor Roller (AMRCR). Type No. 1A, Mk I of this device was intended for use with the Sherman V. The equipment consisted of four spring mounted castoring rollers attached to a framework which positioned two rollers in front of each track. Each roller was assembled from 18 steel plates. Fourteen of these were 1 inch thick and 19-1/2 inches in diameter. The remaining four were 1/2 inch thick and 26 inches in diameter. Four of the smaller diameter plates were assembled between each of the larger ones and the two remaining small plates were placed on the outside with one on each side of the assembly. Each roller weighed something over 1800 pounds. The framework carrying the four rollers was bolted to brackets on each side of the tank and the whole apparatus could be jettisoned by using an explosive device without exposing the crew. The mounting frame was quite flexible in torsion and each roller had independent leaf and coil springing. This permitted ground contact over rough terrain with a maximum height difference of 3 feet between the front roller on one side and the rear roller on the other. Unfortunately, like many similar devices, it was cumbersome to maneuver and did not reach operational use.

Another roller type mine exploder was known as the Canadian Indestructible Roller Device (CIRD). Two versions were fitted to the Sherman. Differing in detail design, they were designated by their roller width as the 15-1/2 inch CIRD/Sherman and the 18 inch CIRD/Sherman. The narrow rollers were 25 inches in diameter compared to 28 inches for the later version and they weighed 1075 and 1680 pounds respectively. The rollers were forged from solid armor steel. Two of these were pivoted from a crossbar attached to side arms extending in front of the tank. Each roller covered a path in front of one tank track. When its weight detonated a mine, the roller was blasted upward and forward over the crossbar. As the tank continued to advance, a spade on the roller arm dug into the ground lifting the side arms until they passed over the roller returning it to the normal trailing position. When detonating mines, the speed of the CIRD/Sherman was 5 to 7 miles/hour, but for normal travel on roads it could operate up to 15 miles/hour.

Some explosive mine clearance devices also were tested on the Sherman equipped with the CIRD. One of these was known as the Flying Bangalore. Two rocket propelled bangalore torpedoes which could be fired ahead of the tank were mounted on each side arm of the CIRD. Intended mainly for the clearance of barbed wire, they also would detonate any mines in the immediate vicinity. The bangalores were fitted with hooks or small grapnels to engage the wire entanglement.

The 18 inch CIRD Sherman can be seen in the two views at the right. These rollers would cover the full track width only when the tank was moving straight ahead. On turns, the sliding tracks would move out of the safe path.

The 3 inch British Snake (at the right) is being pushed by a Sherman of the 79th Armoured Division. The chain between the towing lugs on the tank engages the rear of the Snake to push it forward.

The Tapeworm was a 2-3/4 inch diameter explosive filled canvas hose 500 yards long. Stowed in a trailer, it was towed by a Sherman fitted with the CIRD to the edge of the minefield. The trailer was dropped at that point and the explosive loaded hose was pulled out by the tank as it crossed the minefield. When fully extended, the Tapeworm was detonated setting off any mines not exploded by the CIRD thus providing a safe path for following vehicles. The first 50 feet of the hose next to the tank was loaded with sand for the protection of the towing vehicle. Intended for use during the assault, a disadvantage of the Tapeworm was that the tank had to cross the minefield before the charge was in place. Thus, it was vulnerable to damage from the mines or covering gun fire before its mission was complete.

A much more successful type of explosive mine clearance equipment was the Snake. This device was assembled from 20 foot lengths of 3 inch pipe. After joining, the pipe was towed by a tank to the edge of the enemy minefield. The tank was then moved to the rear of the assembly and pushed it the remaining distance. When detonated, the Snake cleared a path about 20 feet wide through shallow buried German mines. A Sherman could push a 400 foot length and additional Snakes were used to breach minefields of greater depth. The Snake was pushed using a loop of chain attached to the tank's front towing lugs. When in place, it was disconnected by the assistant driver working through the floor escape hatch.

A more sophisticated explosive device for use during the assault was the 2 inch Conger Mk I. Tested in early 1944, it was installed in a trailer converted from a universal carrier from which the engine had been removed. A box containing 330 yards of 2 inch hose was fitted in the rear of the carrier. The remaining space was filled with a tank of liquid explosive, compressed air bottles, and a 5 inch Number 3, Mk I rocket in its launcher. Towed to the minefield by a Sherman or Churchill tank, the carrier was dropped and one end of the hose was attached to the rocket with the other remaining connected to the carrier. The rocket was fired carrying the hose across the minefield and it was then filled with liquid explosive using compressed air. The carrier was removed and a delay fuze fired the charge blasting a path through the minefield. The Conger was introduced into operations in northwest Europe, but the liquid nitroglycerine type explosive was extremely dangerous to handle and its use was limited.

At the left below is the Conger trailer containing the hose, liquid explosive, and rocket launcher. At the right below, the Conger hose is in flight.

The Bullshorn plow can be seen above at the left during tests prior to D-day. The 79th Armoured Division insignia appears on the tank's differential housing. At the right above is the MDI plow folded in its travel position.

The photographs below at the left show the Lulu mine detecting apparatus installed on a Sherman III. In the upper view the equipment is in the operating position while in the lower, it is stowed for travel.

Several types of plows were tested as mine clearance equipment by both the Obstacle Assault Centre and the 79th Armoured Division. The former evaluated some modified agricultural equipment in this role and designed several specialized devices. These included the Farmer Front, the Farmer Track, and the Farmer Deck. None was considered adequate for service and further work was dropped. Experiments in the 79th Armoured Division tested the Bullshorn plow as well as the Jeffries and MDI plows on both the Sherman and Churchill. The Bullshorn placed one plowshare ahead of each track attached to a framework fitted on the front of the tank. As it moved forward, the plowshares were intended to scoop up any mines and deposit them unexploded to the side out of the tank's path. The Bullshorn plow saw limited use by the 79th Armoured Division on the Normandy beaches. The Jeffries and MDI plows were somewhat similar except that the plow arms could be folded back when not in use. They did not see operational service.

The roller type mine detector known as Lulu was tried out with the Sherman. The electrical detector coils were fitted in three lightweight wooden rollers installed in a tricycle arrangement with two in front of the tracks and one behind the tank in the center. Light and sound signals inside the tank indicated when a roller passed over a mine. It could then be removed by accompanying troops. Obviously a mine detected in front of the tracks had to be removed before the tank could proceed. Such an arrangement was both awkward and slow and tests showed the equipment was easily damaged. It did not pass beyond the experimental stage.

The arrangement for pushing (upper view) and towing (lower view) the demolition snake M3 can be seen at the left. The large round nose assembly attached to the front of the snake guided it over and around obstacles.

Mine clearance experiments in the United States were carried on parallel with those in Britain. However, the effort was split between the Ordnance Department and the Corps of Engineers. Ordnance was concerned primarily with mechanical equipment while the Engineers experimented with explosive devices. The first of the latter to be tested was the bangalore torpedo. This was an explosive loaded pipe assembled in sections to the desired length and originally developed for cutting barbed wire and destroying other obstacles. The bangalore torpedo would detonate the German antitank mines, but the path cleared was too narrow for satisfactory use. Further experiments were conducted with a Canadian Snake. Since this was a 3 inch diameter pipe, it carried more explosive than the 2-1/8 inch diameter bangalore torpedo. Also, the Snake was pushed forward by a tank giving the mine clearance team greater protection from defensive small arms fire.

At the request of the Engineer Board, the Armco International Corporation designed an improved explosive device from longitudinally corrugated steel plates. A double row of explosive cartridges were packed between the plates when it was assembled in the field. After testing, an improved version was standardized as the demolition snake M2. (The M1 snake was a rocket propelled device for clearing antipersonnel minefields.) Fully assembled, the M2 was 400 feet long, weighed 12,500 pounds, and carried 3200 pounds of explosive. An improved design replaced the circular explosive cartridges with a heavier type having an elliptical cross section. The total weight increased to 15,000 pounds with a 4500 pound explosive charge and it was designated as the demolition snake M2A1. An even later version replaced the corrugated steel with aluminum plates reducing the overall weight to 9000 pounds, but retaining the same explosive charge as the M2A1. This model was designated as the demolition snake M3.

The demolition snakes were usually towed by a tank to the minefield and then pushed into place. They were detonated by firing the tank's machine gun at an impact sensitive fuze. In most soils, the M3 produced a shallow crater 320 feet long by 16 to 20 feet wide providing an obvious path for the tanks through the minefield. A disadvantage of these explosive devices was that mines on the edge of the blast might not be detonated, but they were often damaged and became very sensitive and dangerous to remove by hand.

Personnel of the lst Armored Division assemble an M2 snake before the breakout from Anzio.

At the left is the Dragon M1 mine clearing vehicle. The hose was stowed in the rectangular container mounted above the rocket launcher tube on the front armor plate.

Liquid explosives also were the subject of numerous experiments. Under the direction of the NDRC, several formulations were developed based on desensitized nitroglycerine. For minefield clearance, handling equipment similar to the British Conger was installed in a prototype vehicle by the M.W. Kellogg Company. Named the Dragon M1, it used an M10A1 tank destroyer chassis with tanks installed to hold 2250 pounds of liquid explosive. A 500 foot length of 3 inch diameter Neoprene-impregnated Fiberglas hose was propelled across the minefield by a rocket. The 2250 pounds of liquid explosive could then be forced into the hose in 1-1/2 minutes using 70 psi air pressure.

A second prototype, referred to as the Dragon M2, was designed to use three tanks with a total liquid explosive capacity of 4500 pounds. These were to be installed in a Sherman with the crew reduced to a driver, an assistant driver, and an explosive operator. Three 150 foot 3 inch diameter hoses were part of this equipment. They were launched using a rocket and yoke mechanism designed to insure that the three hoses fell in a lane no wider than 15 feet. This was necessary since tests had shown that detonation of a single hose did not clear an adequate path for tanks through the relatively insensitive Japanese land mines. These same tests indicated that three hoses lying symmetrically in a 15 foot lane would clear a path of sufficient width. The development program was still in progress at the end of the war. However, it is doubtful that the troops would have appreciated a device that required them to ride with over two tons of nitroglycerine, desensitized or not.

The design concept for the Dragon M2 is reproduced below. The rocket launcher replaces the gun in an M4A3 and the hose and liquid explosive are stowed inside the hull.

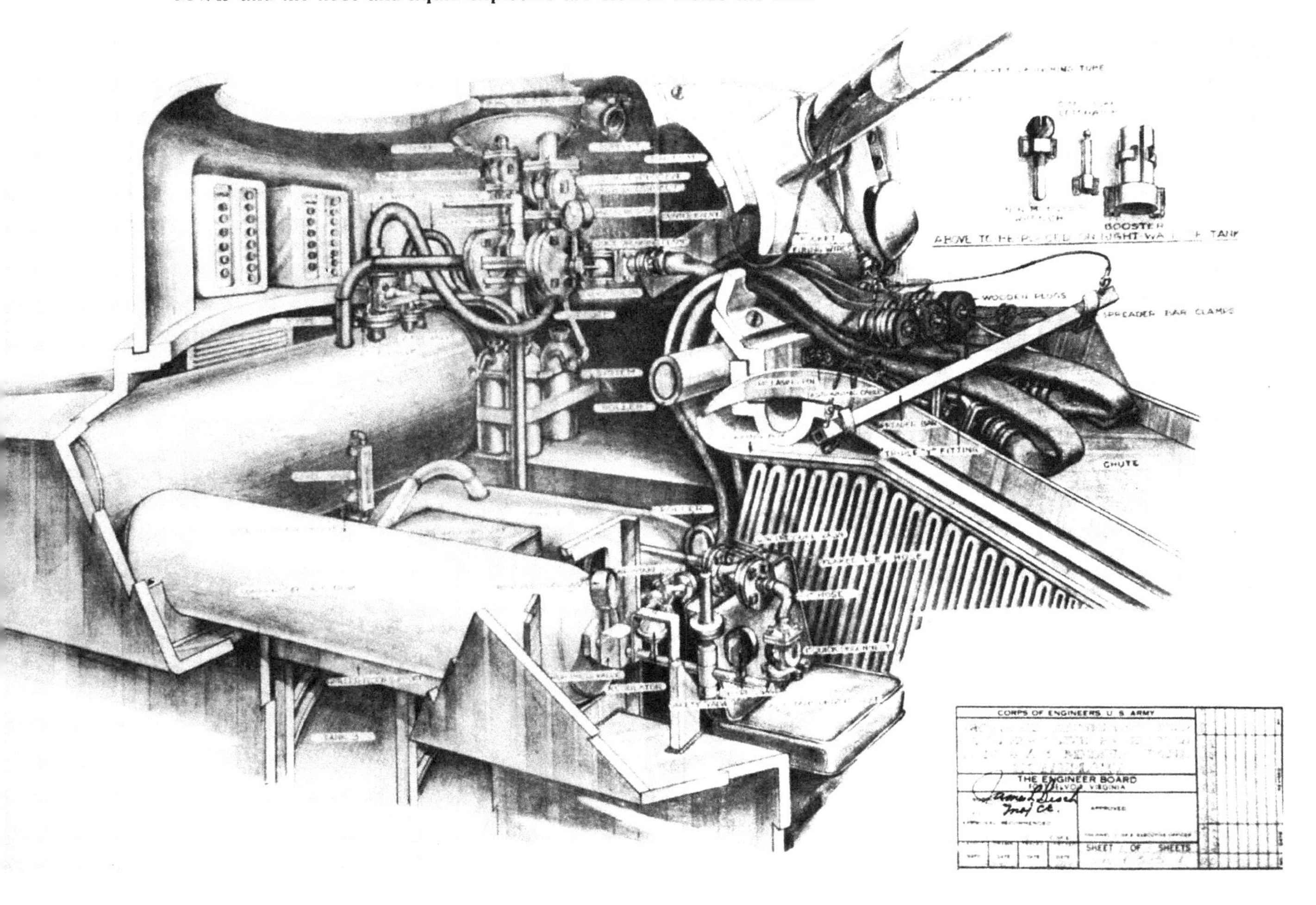

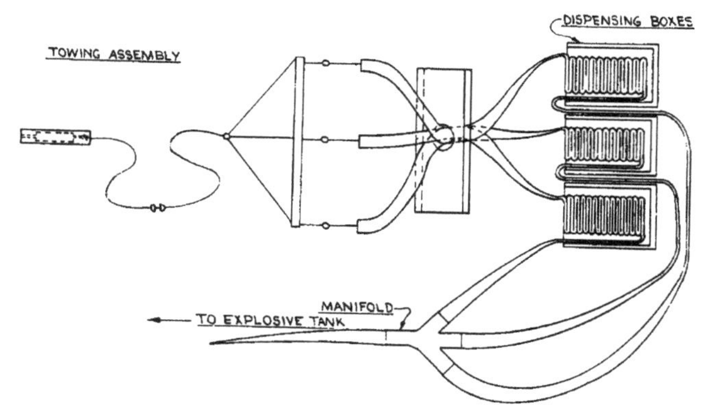

The arrangement of the three hoses and the towing rocket on the Dragon M2 is shown schematically at the left.

Another explosive device was the projected line charge M1. The charge was approximately 3-1/2 inches in diameter and 300 feet long. It consisted of about 4 pounds per foot of plastic explosive Composition C2 molded around a 3/4 inch nylon center rope. The explosive was covered with a knitted nylon sleeve tied to the center rope every 6 inches giving the appearance of a giant link sausage.

The charge was attached to a rocket propulsion unit and stowed in a plywood pallet. The tail of the charge was anchored to the pallet by a 150 foot length of the nylon rope. Up to four of these pallets could be towed behind a Sherman to the edge of the minefield. A wooden rocket launcher installed in the pallet was then pivoted up to an angle of 55 degrees. Firing the rocket carried the charge across the minefield where it was detonated clearing a path through the mines. The projected line charge was considered ready for operational use at the end of the war.

Above at the right, the projected line charge is extended over the ground after firing during tests at Fort Belvoir. Below is the empty pallet with the rocket launcher still raised in the firing position.

Above is the mine clearance machine based on the M3 medium tank developed by the FAETC in North Africa. At the left below, Captain Hubert G. Reuther poses with his crew in front of their invention.

In mid 1943, the Fifth Army Engineer Training Center (FAETC) in North Africa investigated the use of shaped charges for minefield clearance. These charges were exploded in the air above the field depending on the blast wave to detonate the mines. Promising results from the early tests led to the development of a mine clearance machine based on the M3 medium tank. The turret was replaced by a special fixed superstructure and a 25 foot long rotating boom was pivoted at the center above the left front of the tank. Each end of the boom was fitted with a magnetically operated carrier for picking up an explosive charge as it revolved through the special superstructure. As the boom continued to rotate, the charge was carried forward to about 12 feet in front of the tank and 10 feet in the air. At this point, the explosive was dropped until the attached electrical wires pulled a trigger firing it 6 feet above the ground. Fed continuously, the charges were exploded in front of the tank alternately on each side at 12 foot intervals. The two lines of explosions were about 10 feet apart. Since the charges were effective in detonating the U.S. M1A1 mine over a 7 foot radius, the overlapping blast pattern cleared a safe path approximately 18 feet wide through such mines. An even wider path was obtained with the more blast sensitive German Tellermines.

The 15 pound explosive charges were 10 inches in diameter by 5 inches high with a convex top and a slightly concave bottom. With a stowage capacity for 170 such charges, a 1000 foot lane could be cleared before reloading. The recommended forward speed of the tank was 3 to 5 miles/hour, although the initial tests were run at 1-1/4 miles/hour.

The mine clearance machine was demonstrated before a group of officers at the FAETC on 6-7 November 1943. Unfortunately, the power takeoff which operated the boom failed before the demonstration was complete. With the limited facilities available in North Africa, satisfactory repairs could not be made. However, the results were promising enough to initiate a development program on this method of mine clearance at Fort Belvoir. Captain Hubert G. Reuther, who had been in charge of the work in North Africa, was transferred to Fort Belvoir to continue the development.

The Pancake mine clearance device based on the medium tank M4 is shown above with a close-up of a charge suspended from the launching head at the right.

The new project specified that the mine clearance machine be based on the medium tank M4 and that a new launching system be installed using standard conveyor components. With this arrangement, the charges were carried up to the launch position by two armored conveyors, one installed on each side of the tank. Each conveyor was served by an operator who placed the charges on the loading deck in the sponsons and pushed them onto the conveyor. They were then automatically carried forward and launched. The original design specified that the launcher conveyors be adjustable in height so that they could be lowered to a more convenient travel position. However, this feature was dropped from the pilot model and the launchers were fixed. Each armored conveyor was 22 feet long with 11-1/2 feet projecting in front of the tank. They were fixed on spring mounted brackets at an angle so that the discharge head at the forward end was 11 feet above the ground.

The conveyor mechanism consisted of endless roller chains driven by a power takeoff from the tank transmission. A special discharge head at the end of each launcher was fitted with two spring loaded buffer doors to prevent the passage of blast pressure or flash back down the conveyor. Within the discharge head, two toggle hooks engaged the firing wire on the charge. When the charge dropped through the head, the firing wire uncoiled to its full length actuating the toggle hooks and closing the firing circuit. Operation was automatic with the speed limited only by how fast the operators could feed the charges to the conveyors. Stowage space was provided for 160 shaped charges which were estimated to be sufficient to clear a path 800 feet long. All armament was removed from the pilot vehicle, although the bow machine gun and the .50 caliber antiaircraft gun could have been retained.

The project at Fort Belvoir studied a variety of charge designs in an effort to determine the optimium shape. The type chosen for test with the launcher weighed 15 pounds and consisted of cast TNT or 50/50 pentolite. The top and bottom were convex and it was square with rounded corners. For ease of handling, the charge was enclosed in a molded fiber casing.

Referred to as the Pancake device, the mine clearance vehicle was demonstrated at the A.P. Hill Military Reservation on 16 February 1945. The Engineer Board concluded that its performance was inferior to that of the demolition snake and the multiple rocket launcher T59. Further development was discontinued.

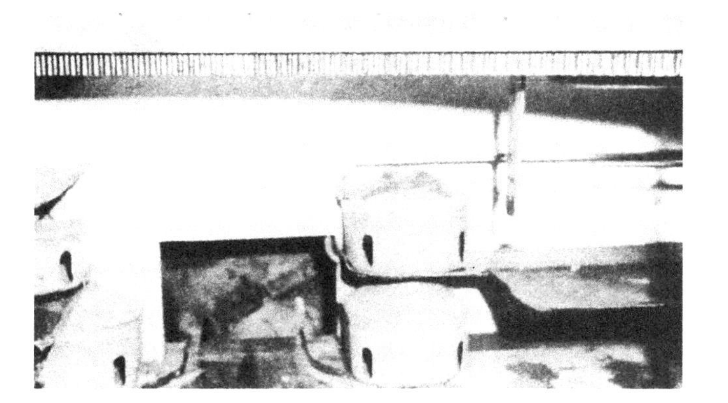

The interior of the Pancake device can be seen at the left. The charges are on the loading deck in the left sponson from which they were pushed through the hole onto the conveyor.

The mine exploder T1 (above and below) installed on medium tank M3, serial number 1821. These photographs were taken at Aberdeen Proving Ground on 22 February 1943.

The early work of the Ordnance Department on mechanical exploders concentrated on roller type equipment. The first of these was the mine exploder T1 fitted to the M3 medium tank. It consisted of two large rollers pushed in front of the tank with one ahead of each track. Each roller was assembled from four heavy steel discs 40 inches in diameter spaced apart on a central shaft. A third roller of five such discs was towed at the center rear of the tank to give complete path coverage.

An improved model designated as the mine exploder T1E1 was built by Gar Wood Industries and demonstrated at Aberdeen on 10 December 1943. It was mounted on the M32 tank recovery vehicle. All three rollers were now located in front with the vehicle's crane being used to lift them out of the craters resulting from the mine explosions. Each roller consisted of six loosely mounted discs 48 inches in diameter and 2 inches thick. Spacers were welded to the 1290 pound discs and the entire assembly weighed about 36,000 pounds. Nicknamed Earthworm, 75 T1E1s were produced by Gar Wood during April 1944.

With an operating speed of about 3 miles/hour, the T1E1 was extremely effective in detonating mines and it was almost indestructible. Unfortunately, it was also very difficult to maneuver and on rough terrain it became impossible. In an effort to improve the mobility, the center roller was eliminated and the two outer rollers were expanded to seven discs. These discs were reduced in thickness to 1-1/2 inches and the diameter was increased to 72 inches. To hold the weight to 1500 pounds, eight large circular holes were cut in each disc. Including its installation bracket, the complete assembly weighed about 28,000 pounds. Designated as the mine exploder T1E2, it also was installed on the M32 recovery vehicle. With just two rollers,

Above is the mine exploder T1E1 based on the M32 tank recovery vehicle. The crane was essential in handling the unwieldy rollers.

only partial coverage was obtained. This was 40-1/2 inches wide per roller compared to the complete 119 inch wide path cleared by the T1E1.

The sketch at the lower left depicts the mine exploder T1E2 installed on the tank recovery vehicle M32. The photograph (lower right) is a top view of this equipment.

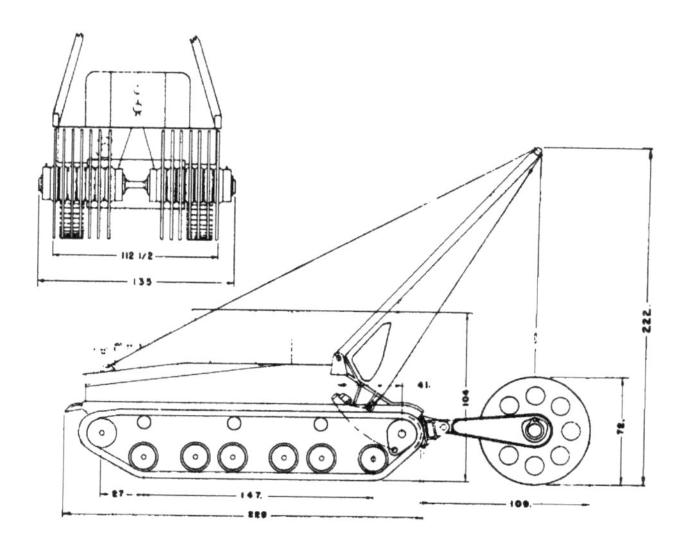

The production pilot mine exploder T1E3 is shown here (above and below) fitted to the medium tank M4A1. Note the drive chains from the sprockets on each side.

The T1E2 was still very difficult to maneuver and the tank recovery vehicle did not carry a cannon. To correct both points, the mine exploder T1E3 was designed for installation on the Sherman which retained its full turret armament. Although the T1E3's two rollers were originally designed with four discs each, five were used in the final version. The 2-3/4 inch thick discs were 96 inches in diameter and four large oval holes reduced the weight of each to 4600 pounds. The complete assembly weighed about 59,000 pounds. Partial coverage was obtained with a 33-3/4 inch wide path for each track. The loosely mounted discs were driven by roller chains from the tank sprockets and the spacers were keyed and grooved to permit articulation. Whiting Corporation produced 200 of the T1E3s between March and December 1944.

Four pilot T1E3s were constructed and in May 1944, two were shipped to Britain and two to Italy. Named Aunt Jemima, the first two were demonstrated to U.S. and British officers on 28 and 31 May. As a result, Major General Grow requested that three T1E3s be assigned to his 6th Armored Division.

Further shipments arrived and by mid July, 16 T1E1s, 27 T1E3s, and 9 British Crabs had been issued to the First Army. The 6th Armored Division used two of the T1E3s in their attack south of Lessay, France on the morning of 29 July. The exploders led for the first 10 miles until one of them developed a transmission oil leak. Since no mines had been encountered, the column continued alone and rapidly left the exploders behind. They later found limited use near Brest and in the area between Nancy and Metz, but their poor mobility continued to be a major drawback.

In September 1944, orders were received to convert the 738th and 739th Tank Battalions (Special) to mine exploder units. These were two of the CDL battalions and they began training for their new role on 20 September. An organization chart dated October

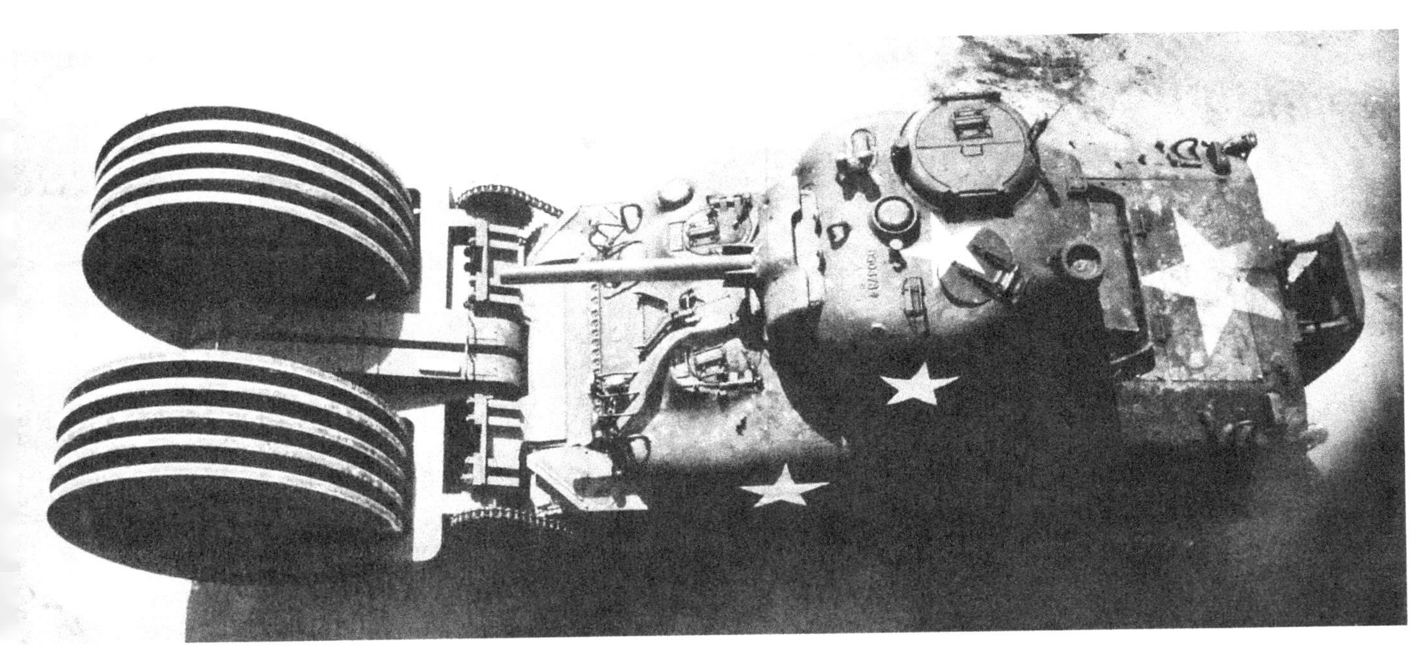

Above, Aunt Jemima 1 and 2 at the May 1944 demonstration in Britain. The curved plate on the rear was to permit pushing by a second helper tank if the exploder was stuck. The major problem with these heavy exploders is best illustrated by the bogged T1E3 belonging to the 739th Tank Battalion at the right.

1944 showed a strength of 18 T1E1s, 24 T1E3s, 12 tankdozers, and 18 76mm gun M4A3s in each battalion. These units also received some of the British Crabs and part of them used the DD tank in the Rhine crossing.

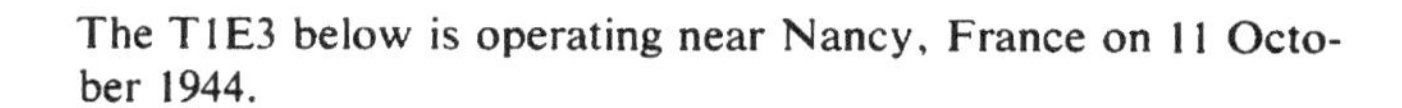

The T1E3 below is operating near Nancy, France on 11 October 1944.

A mine exploder T1E1 (above) attached to the 2nd Armored Division moves along the road toward Houffalize, Belgium on 16 January 1945. Below, a British Crab I operated by U.S. troops passes through Vicht, Germany on 21 February 1945 during preparations for the assault across the Roer River.

At the right is a T1E3 fitted with discs having serrated edges to improve the traction. In some sources, this equipment has been incorrectly identified as the T1E6. Note the use of the second tank to help push the heavy exploder.

The mine exploder T1E5 was a further development of the T1E3. The number of discs per roller was increased from five to six thus permitting complete coverage when using two exploders in echelon. Each roller covered 40 inches leaving a 36 inch gap in the center. The discs were 2-1/2 inches thick by 72 inches in diameter and their serrated edges improved the traction on rough ground. Four holes reduced the disc weight to 2150 pounds with the total assembly weighing about 41,000 pounds. The chain drive was used as on the T1E3, but the articulation of the discs was increased to 4 inches. The T1E5's maneuverability was still less than that of the T1E4, but its overall mobility was considered better with its lighter weight.

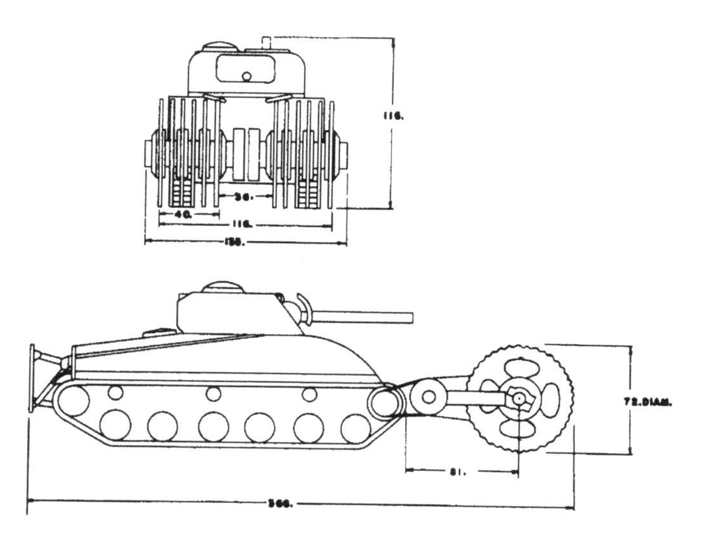

The drawing at the left shows the general arrangement of the mine exploder T1E5. Two views of the roller assembly at the Whiting Corporation factory appear at the bottom of the page.

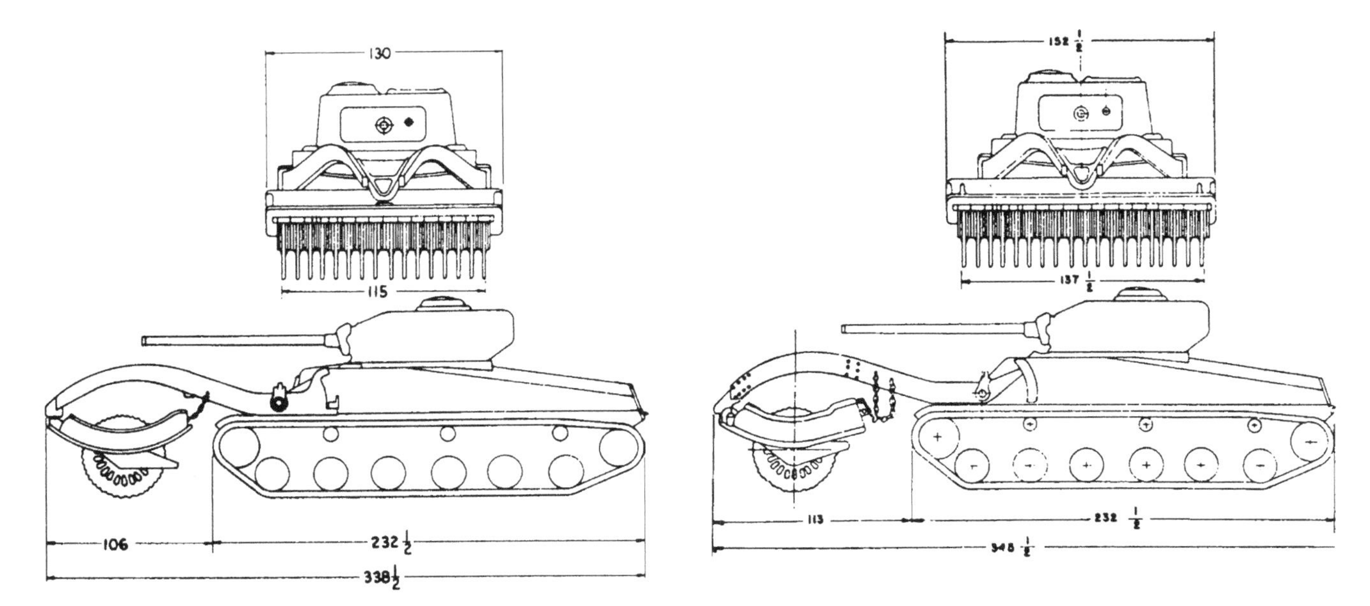

The sketches above compare the mine exploders T1E4 (left) and T1E6 (right). On the latter, the number of discs has been increased from 16 to 19. Further details of the frame and disc assembly can be seen in the drawing below.

Further work attempted to improve the mobility of the roller type mine exploders. A new design proposed by Chrysler used 16 serrated steel discs 48 inches in diameter on a single roller. Each disc weighed 2600 pounds with a total weight of around 48,000 pounds. Designated as the mine exploder T1E4, it gave complete coverage over a path 115 inches wide. Two booms attached to the tank extended over the roller and towed the exploder assembly from a ball and socket on its front frame. The T1E4 showed some improvement in maneuverability with a minimum turning radius of 35 feet compared to 82 feet for the T1E3. Its average operating speed was 5 miles/hour. The T1E4 was placed in limited procurement in 1945.

The T1E6 was identical with the T1E4, except that the frame was widened and the number of discs was increased from 16 to 19. The greater width permitted the use of the exploder on wide-track tanks with the horizontal volute spring suspension. Also placed in limited procurement, five of the T1E6s were built by Whiting Corporation during the last half of 1945.

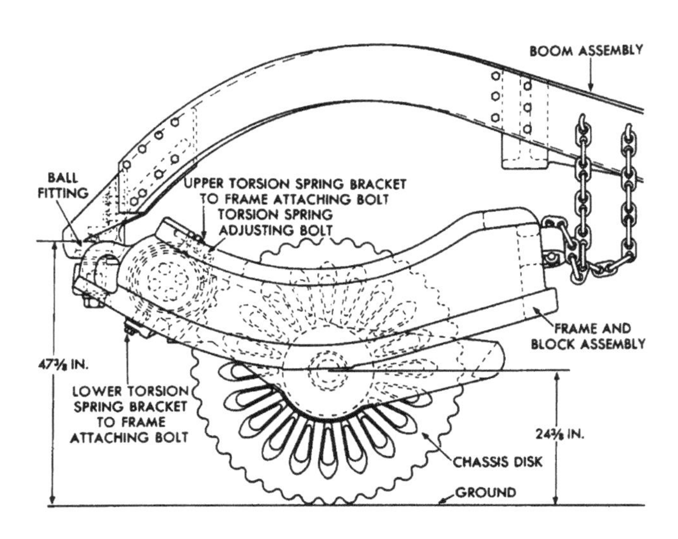

The photographs below show the pilot mine exploder T1E4 installed on a 76mm gun tank. However, it was recommended that tanks with short barreled cannon be used for this application.

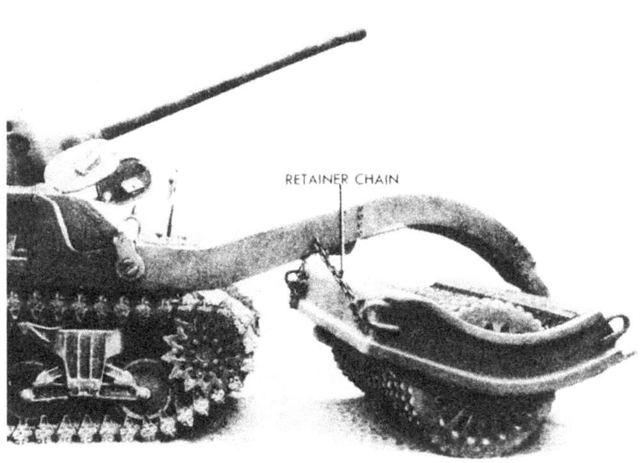

The drag type mine exploder T2E1 is at the right. In practice, this device proved unsatisfactory because it tended to pile up earth ahead of the exploder and bridge over mines leaving them intact.

The mine exploder T2 was a drag type device assembled on the light tank M3 and was not used on the Sherman. Another version, designated as the T2E1, was developed for the Marine Corps. It also was a drag type using heavy armor plate slabs mounted on a horizontal shaft attached to the boom of an M32 tank recovery vehicle. Test results on this equipment were unsatisfactory and the project was dropped.

The T3 designation was applied to the U.S. version of the early Scorpion flail tank. Tested at Aberdeen, the pilot was assembled on an M4A4 and the flail was powered by an auxiliary engine mounted outboard on the right side of the hull.

Thirty T3s were converted at Pressed Steel Car Company in April 1943 and rushed overseas. These production Scorpions differed from the pilot by substituting a mechanically operated height adjustment for the pilot's hydraulic device and the auxiliary engine was more powerful. The chains were arranged in a spiral pattern around the drum on the production model and a shield was added to prevent dirt and debris from being thrown against the front of the tank. Pressed Steel Car converted an additional 11 T3s in July bringing the total production to 41.

Twelve of the Scorpions were used by the 6617th Mine Clearing Company. This unit was formed from the 16th Armored Engineers in the 1st Armored Division. They were in action during the breakout from Anzio and the drive toward Rome. However, the extra weight and width of the T3 limited its maneuverability and it was frequently disabled by the mine explosions. After an initial trial, it was considered unsatisfactory and removed from service.

At the right is the pilot mine exploder T3 without chains. The boom is locked in the elevated position. Below, one of the production T3s is flailing during a demonstration in North Africa in July 1943.

The mine exploder T3E1 is shown above without its flail chains at the Chrysler Engineering Division after installation of the hydraulic boom control. The general arrangement of the T3E1 can be seen in the sketch below.

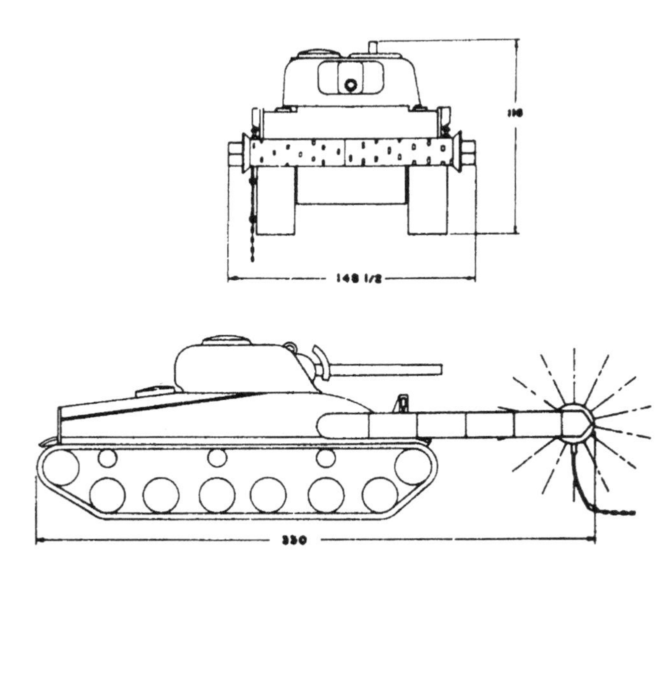

An improved flail tank was designated as the mine exploder T3E1 by OCM 20966 on 17 June 1943. Driven by a power takeoff from the tank engine, the rotor speed was 178 rpm compared to a maximum of 75 rpm for the T3. The flail equipment weighed 5600 pounds, about half that of the Scorpion, and it gave complete coverage over a path 116 inches wide. With an operating speed of 1.8 miles/hour, the minimum turning radius was 31 feet. Without the outboard auxiliary engine, the width was reduced to 143-1/2 inches. Tests showed that the T3E1 was relatively ineffective in detonating mines partially because of its inability to follow the ground contour. Like the T3, it was disliked because of the rocks and dust thrown up obscuring the vision of the tank crew.

The NDRC studied the problem of flail type mine exploders and completed a series of model tests in December 1943. This program indicated that the flailing action would be more effective using a larger diameter drum. To check these results, a partial full scale exploder was converted from a T3 and tested at Aberdeen in August 1944. Dubbed the Rotoflail, it proved to be the most efficient U.S. flail tested up to that time, although the larger drum obscured the driver's vision. OCM 27570, dated 12 April 1945, recommended the construction of two full scale Rotoflails designating them as the mine exploder T3E2. Work on these was in progress at the end of the war.

At the left is the T3 used as a partial full scale test rig for the Rotoflail.

In addition to the T3 series, several flail type mine exploders were improvised in the field and applied to the Sherman. One of these, constructed by the Seabees for the U.S. Marines, attached the flail chains to relatively stiff lengths of wire rope which were in turn fixed to the drum. A similar construction was recommended by the NDRC for the T3E2.

After the war, little work was done on flail type mine exploders until fighting broke out in Korea during the Summer of 1950. At that time, several flails were constructed based on the M4A3 with the horizontal volute spring suspension. They carried wire cutters at the end of the drum similar to those on the British Crab and were fitted with 72 chains with end hammers. Other flails were improvised in the field for use in Korea.

Above is the improvised flail tank constructed for the U.S. Marine Corps by the Seabees in November 1944.

Below is one of the six flail tanks converted in Japan from late model M4A3s for use in Korea. As can be seen here, an auxiliary engine was used to drive the flail. This vehicle was operated by the 245th Heavy Tank Battalion of the 45th Infantry Division in June 1952.

A model of the mine excavator T5 appears above at the left. At the right is its later development, the mine excavator T5E2.

In addition to the exploders, a number of excavators were developed to scoop up mines and deposit them to one side. The first experiments resulted in the mine excavator T4. Its straight moldboard was mounted diagonally across the front of the vehicle and it was fitted with slanting forks. After modification to the T4E1, tests showed that the design was unsatisfactory and work shifted to two new models using a V-type moldboard. These were designated as the mine excavators T5 and T6. Teeth were spaced 6 inches apart along the bottom of the T5's V-shaped moldboard and it was curved to prevent mines from being pushed over the top during operation. After some modification, it was redesignated as the T5E1. The T6 also had problems, particularly in controlling the depth of cut and changes resulted in the T6E1 and T6E2. After tests, the Armored Board recommended that the best features of the T5E1 and the T6E2 be combined in a new design. This appeared as the T5E2 and was modified still further resulting in the T5E3. The latter was approved as a limited procurement item in June 1944 and the other projects were ended. La Plante-Choate produced 100 T5E3s starting in March 1945 and ending in May.

Compared to its predecessors, the T5E3 had improved control, reduced width for transport, and it could be carried at a higher position for landing operations. The effective spilling of the windrows was improved and its lighter weight permitted more armor protection for the jack and hydraulic lines. Weighing about 9000 pounds, its width was 130 inches with the wings folded or 168 inches when they were extended. The T5E3 could be jettisoned by using a single lever inside the tank. Because of the Japanese practice of dispersing very heavy charges in their minefields, the T5E3 excavator was the only type of the new mine clearance equipment to be shipped to the Pacific.

The production mine excavator T5E3 is shown at the left below with the wings extended and the blade lowered. The general arrangement of this device is sketched below.

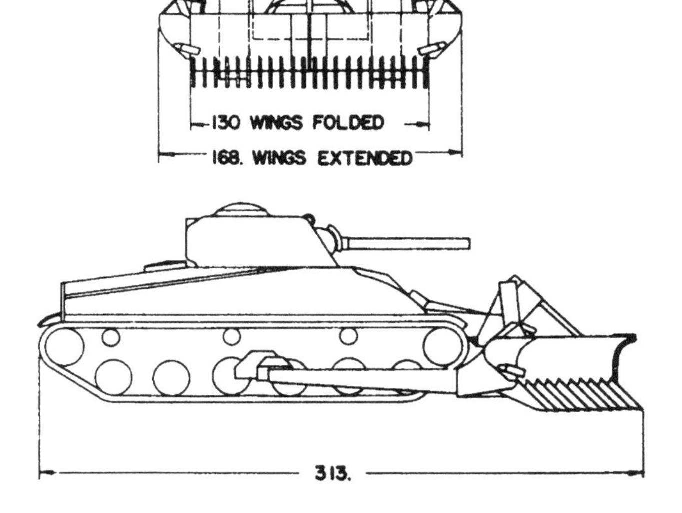

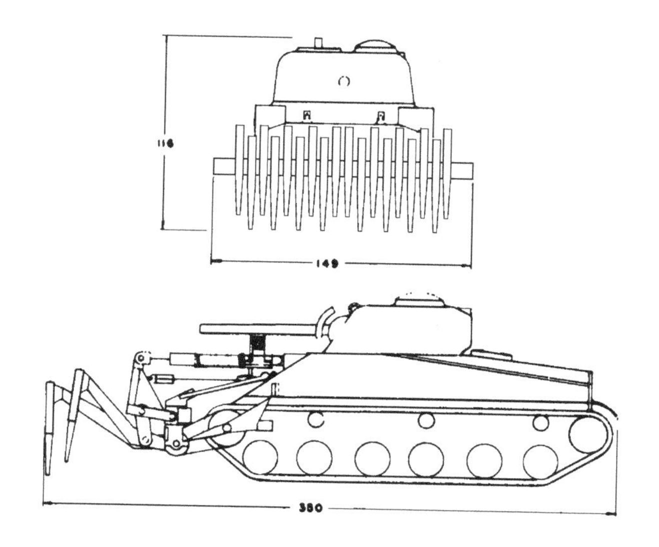

The mine exploder T8 with a full set of exploders is illustrated in the artist's concept above and in the drawing at the left.

Unlike the T1 series which were intended to be indestructible, the mine exploder T7 submitted by the John Deere Company used a number of expendable hollow rollers. These were filled with dirt or gravel and pushed in front of the tank. However, tests by the Armored Board showed unsatisfactory results and the project was cancelled.

A unique exploder design resulted from the suggestion of Lieutenant Colonel A.R. Williams. Eighteen plunger type shock absorber exploder units were to be mounted in front of the tank and powered by a gear drive from each sprocket. The exploders were actuated by eccentrics on a cross shaft connected to the gear drive. Rods mounted in the sliding cylinders were moved in the vertical direction striking the ground like a jackhammer. The impact had an effective pressure of over 900 psi when the tank was moving at 3 miles/hour. At this normal operating speed, the rods struck about 7 inches apart which was the same as their lateral spacing. Complete coverage was obtained over a path 120 inches wide. Each exploder weighed about 400 pounds and the entire assembly with drives totaled approximately 10,000 pounds. When the exploder tip detonated a mine, the force of the blast was absorbed by the spring inside the unit and by throttling oil through an orifice.

Colonel Williams's device was officially designated as the mine exploder T8, but its appearance soon earned the nickname Johnie Walker. Three exploders and one drive unit were installed on an M4A4 for preliminary tests at Aberdeen. Unsatisfactory results required changes in both the exploder and drive. A set of six exploders using the revised design were constructed and subjected to further tests. The T8 proved reasonably effective in detonating mines, but it was difficult to maneuver over rough ground. Some of the exploder tips were damaged during the test and no further pilots were constructed.

The T8 during the early tests with three exploder units can be seen below at the left. The view at the right shows six redesigned exploders installed for the final test program.

Above is the mine exploder T9 with its tank bogged down in the mud during tests. In the artist's concept below, the whole apparatus operates perfectly. Unfortunately, this seldom occurred in practice.

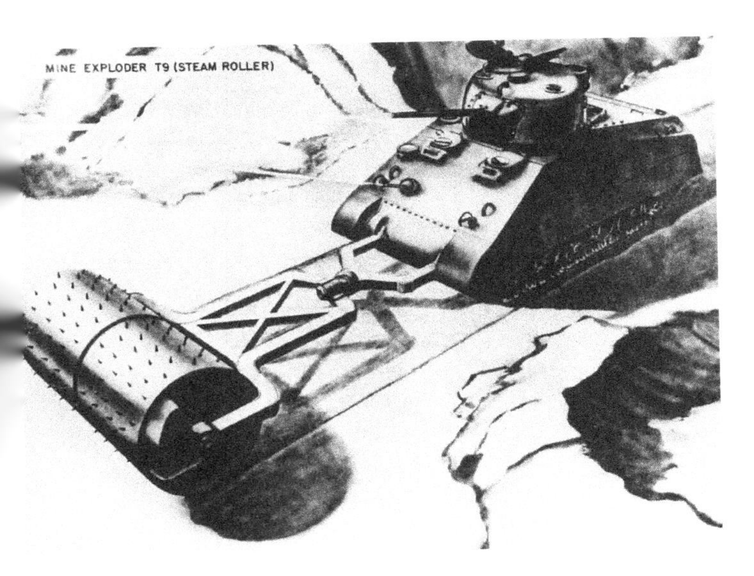

The sheepsfoot roller used for compacting soil on construction projects provided the inspiration for the mine exploder T9. The device consisted of a large cylindrical roller covered with 6 inch spuds which was pushed ahead of the tank. Preliminary tests using a half section of the roller showed that it effectively detonated mines and was relatively indestructible. The second half of the roller drum, the axle, and pushing frame were subsequently completed and shipped to Aberdeen. It was apparent that once again, the critical problem was mobility. The T9 covered a full 120 inch wide path, but with its axle and pushing frame, it weighed about 84,000 pounds.

To lighten the device, a second pilot was designed with the roller diameter reduced to 66 inches. The walls were thinner and it was covered with smaller spuds. It still cleared a 120 inch wide path, but the overall weight was reduced to approximately 64,000 pounds. Like the first version, the pushing frame was adjustable in length. The assembly could be extended from 236 to 314 inches in front of the tank. Designated as the mine exploder T9E1, it was completed at the Blaw Knox Company in early 1944. Tested at Aberdeen, the mobility was still the limiting factor. Despite the weight reduction effort, the T9E1 still weighed about the same as the tank that pushed it. Experience had shown that such heavy equipment was impractical for use under combat conditions.

Below, the T9E1 mine exploder is being tested at Aberdeen in April 1944. Note the lighter construction of the roller compared with the T9 above.

At the right is an artist's sketch of the NDRC self-propelled mine exploder dubbed the Tricycle.

The NDRC designed a self-propelled mine exploder using two large power driven wheels 96 inches in diameter mounted on a common shaft. Heavy steel discs were loosely mounted on the shaft allowing articulation when moving over rough ground. Thus they would explode any mines between the two wheels. A long trail extended behind the exploder assembly to a third wheel in the rear. Referred to as the Tricycle, plans called for the installation of an engine in each large wheel. Tests were run at Aberdeen in late 1943 using just the wheel and trail assembly without the engines or the loose center discs. The exploder proved effective, but the cast steel shoes on the driving wheels required some redesign and work was stopped in favor of later projects.

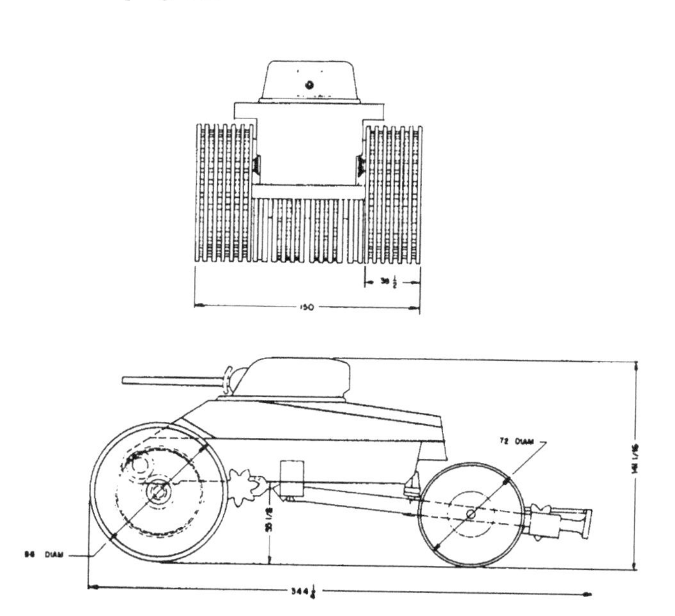

The NDRC device provided the inspiration for an improved self-propelled exploder using the medium tank chassis. Fisher was awarded a contract to design and build a pilot of the mine exploder T10. This vehicle was converted from an M4A2 by removing the tracks and suspension units. The armor was cut back at the front of the sponsons and the rear floor thickness was increased to 1 inch. Two 96 inch diameter rollers were mounted at the front of the tank driven by additional gearing from the final drive. Each of the front rollers was 36-1/2 inches wide and the gap between them was covered by a 72 inch diameter double roller trailing at the rear of the tank. This arrangement moved the bottom of the hull up to 55-1/2 inches above the ground. A path 153 inches wide was covered and the overall weight was 116,400 pounds. The T10 moved at 2 miles/hour when exploding mines and could reach a maximum of 7 miles/hour on roads.

Tested at Aberdeen in June 1944, the T10 was considered unsatisfactory. Even if the usual development problems had been solved, its great weight and slow speed would have limited its value in combat.

The drawing at the left and the photographs below show the mine exploder T10. Note the areas cut back at the front of each sponson to allow clearance for the large exploder wheels.

At the left, the 115 pound shell is loaded on the 60mm spigot mortar installed in the M7 motor carriage. At the right, five of the spigots are mounted on the front of an M4A4. This tank was used for experiments with swimming devices and the spigot mortars were considered for use in destroying obstacles during assault landings.

Experiments with 60mm spigot mortars mounted on an M7 howitzer motor carriage led to the proposal for the mine exploder T12. Approved for development by OCM 23277 on 23 March 1944, the T12 was designed to carry 25 spigot mortars on a leveling table replacing the tank turret and race ring. They were to be protected by armor in the final design which would raise the height of the vehicle to about 146 inches. This could have been reduced to 114 inches when the armor was removed for shipment. The spigots were mounted at angles increasing from about +45 to +80 degrees resulting in a long narrow impact pattern. The mortar table could be leveled within plus or minus 10 degrees from front to rear or side to side. Firing the 115 pound T13 high explosive shells, a path 20 feet wide and 250 feet deep could be cleared through a minefield starting about 150 feet in front of the vehicle. Five additional spigots were fitted on the front plate with the elevation adjustable from +45 to 0 degrees. These were intended for the destruction of walls or other vertical obstacles.

Three pilot T12s were authorized with only the third to be fitted with armor protection. The first pilot was manufactured by the York Safe and Lock Company and tested at Aberdeen during June 1944. Only 23 spigots were installed on the leveling table on this pilot. The tests were satisfactory, but superior results were being obtained using rocket propelled charges for minefield clearance and further work on the T12 was cancelled.

One type of rocket propelled charge was the 10.75 inch rocket T91. Using a 4.5 inch rocket motor, it was fitted with both point and base detonating fuzes. Early

The mine exploder T12, pilot number 2, is shown below with a full load of shells on the turret table spigots. Like pilot number 1, it did not have the armor installed to protect the shells. Note the fuze extensions which insured that the rounds would explode above ground level.

Above is the experimental prototype used in the development of the rocket launcher T59. The 10.75 inch rocket T91 can be seen at the left.

experiments mounted 18 of the rockets in a tracked trailer towed behind a tank. The track wheels of the trailer were connected to a firing mechanism so that a single rocket was fired automatically for every 20 feet of forward travel. With a range of about 75 feet, the rockets passed over the tank and exploded on impact about 60 feet in front.

Based on these experiments, the rocket was modified and four pilot models were ordered of the newly designed rocket launcher T59. The latter carried 30 rockets and weighed about 30,000 pounds with 1 inch of armor for the full height of the rockets. Fitted with three tracks, it was designed to fire a round for every 15 feet of travel.

The T91 rocket carried 240 pounds of high explosive and was detonated above ground level by an 18 inch fuze extension in the nose. This arrangement prevented excessive cratering and cleared a path about 20 feet wide. The project was cancelled in August 1945 before the T59 pilots were delivered.

The Centipede was a British exploder designed to clear antipersonnel minefields. Several variations were proposed for test at Aberdeen. One used 18 inch diameter steel bound concrete discs. A steel frame carried 23 of these in two rows and the entire assembly was towed behind a tank. The discs were 4-1/4 inches thick and weighed about 100 pounds. The complete assembly including hooks to engage trip wires totaled around 3000 pounds and the overlapping discs had an overall width of 84-1/8 inches. This more than covered the gap between the tank tracks so that the antipersonnel mines were cleared for the full vehicle width.

A smaller version of the Centipede was designated as the mine exploder T13. Using only nine discs, it was pushed through the minefield by a lightly armored modification of the cargo carrier M29. This vehicle's low ground pressure would not detonate a normal antitank mine. However, the Japanese practice of mixing heavy explosive charges with their antipersonnel mines doomed this approach and the project was ended.

The Centipede antipersonnel mine exploder is shown here being towed by an M10A1 gun motor carriage.

The mine resistant vehicle T15 appears above and below after completion at Chrysler in January 1945. Heavy suspension components were installed and rubber covered brackets were fitted to stop the bogie wheels when they were blasted upward by a mine explosion.

The mine exploder T14 was intended to be an essentially indestructible tank based on the Sherman. The design increased the belly armor and beefed up the suspension and tracks in the hope that the vehicle could cross a minefield without damage. Unfortunately, the concept proved impractical and efforts were turned toward building a mine resistant vehicle instead of a mine proof one. Such a vehicle was needed for use with the various mine exploders since the enemy frequently planted coupled mines. This arrangement used a pair of mines placed a sufficient distance apart so that one would explode under the tank when the exploder detonated the other. The exploder would pass over the first mine without any effect, but it would also fire when the second mine exploded.

Chrysler had reworked an early M4 by welding on extra belly armor and modifying the running gear. Tests at Aberdeen showed the need for further changes and a late model M4 was rebuilt as the mine resistant vehicle T15. Sections of heavy cast armor were attached to the hull bottom. The front section was welded to the differential and final drive housing and bolted to the adjacent belly armor to permit removal of the housing. The suspension was fitted with disc type armor plate bogie wheels and each bogie frame was reinforced by an outside plate extending down from the edge of the sponson. A medium weight cast armor track was installed with a pitch of 8-5/8 inches and the normal 16-9/16 inch width. The longer pitch required only 56 shoes per side and a 9 tooth sprocket. Shock mounting was provided for the battery and bracing was added to the transmission. The turret was replaced

The mine resistant vehicle T15E1 (above and below) is shown here in June 1945. Note the solid bogie wheels and the extremely heavy pedestal type track shoes.

by a 1 inch thick flat armor plate cover fitted with a vision cupola and a small oval hatch. The 3.36:1 final drive gear ratio from the M4A3E2 limited the maximum speed to 17.5 miles/hour. Assembled, the vehicle weighed 72,700 pounds.

The mine resistant vehicle T15E1 was similar to the T15, but it was equipped with heavy weight cast prong type tracks, heavier suspension components, and solid cast armor bogie wheels. In each bogie, the front wheel was smooth and the rear wheel was grooved. For test purposes, roller bearings were installed in the front three wheels on each side and bronze bearings were used in the remaining three. An early M4 with the small drivers' hatches was converted for the T15E1 and the 1 inch armor plate replacing the turret was fitted with a vision cupola and a split circular hatch with a .50 caliber machine gun mount.

Designs were prepared for a mine resistant vehicle T15E2 using extra heavy individually sprung suspension units. A 2 inch thick rolled armor belly protecting plate was to be resiliently mounted on belleville springs. A specially designed cast armor cover for the turret opening was to contain six vision blocks and mount the cupola from an M3 medium tank. The project was ended before this version was constructed.

A mine resistant vehicle T15E3 was proposed based on the medium tank M26, but it was cancelled before design started.

Tests of the T15 and T15E1 at Aberdeen showed that the transmission was damaged by the blast of a single heavy T6E1 antitank mine. Some of the suspension components also were damaged on the T15, but its pedestal type tracks survived the blast of a single heavy mine. The tracks and suspension on the T15E1 withstood the repeated blasts from several mines without serious damage. However, with the end of the war and the reduction of the number of development contracts, no further work was done on the T15 series vehicles.

Above is the tank recovery vehicle T2 (M31) with full stowage. This vehicle is based on the medium tank M3 with the air-cooled radial engine.

TANK RECOVERY VEHICLES

The development of the heavy tractor T16 began early in 1942 to provide a prime mover for heavy artillery. Based on the chassis of the medium tank M3A5, it was considered unsatisfactory because of inadequate stowage space. The tests did indicate that a similar design would be suitable for use as a tank recovery vehicle. With the Sherman in full production, large numbers of the earlier vehicle were available. On 24 September 1942, OCM 18928 directed the conversion of 750 M3s to the tank recovery vehicle T2.

The rear of the diesel powered tank recovery vehicle T2 based on the medium tank M3A5 can be seen below.

All armament was removed from the M3 except for one .30 caliber machine gun fixed in the bow mount to the left of the driver. A similar .30 caliber weapon was carried for use on the British type traversing ring in the turret. A door fitted with a dummy gun replaced the 75mm mount. A Gar Wood Model 10-Y 5500 crane was mounted on a special plate that replaced the 37mm gun mount in the turret. A dummy gun was fixed to the rear of the turret so that when it was reversed, the appearance of an armed tank was maintained. The crane had a capacity of 10,000 pounds without the boom jacks. If the latter were placed on the ground, it could carry 30,000 pounds. A jaw clutch type winch was located in the crew compartment. The winch cable could be threaded over rollers in the vehicle floor and taken out under the hull to the front or rear. Alternately, it could be threaded over a fleeting sheave and taken up through the turret and over the boom. The winch capacity was 60,000 pounds.

Shortages of M3s resulted in other tanks of the series being converted. They were identical except that the power takeoff on the vehicles with the air-cooled radial engine was driven by the transmission and located to its left rear. On the ones converted from the diesel powered M3A3 and M3A5, the power takeoff was driven by the engine itself and was located to its front. This change in location resulted in some differences in the winch operator's platform and controls. The T2 was manned by a crew of six.

Conversion of the M3s began at the Baldwin Locomotive Works in October 1942 and continued

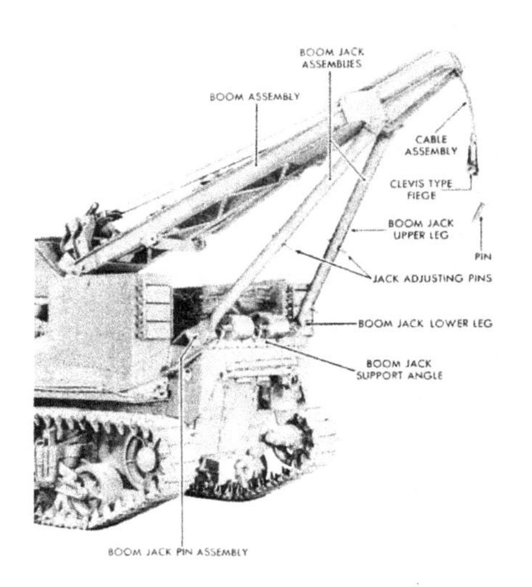

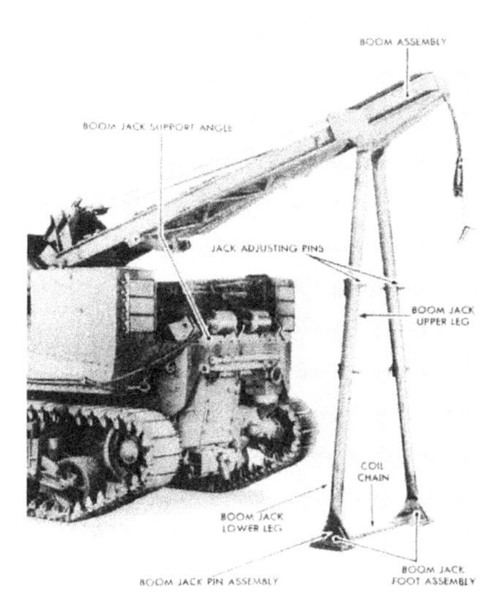

In the views above, the boom jacks are secured to the vehicle at the left and placed on the ground at the right for maximum lifting capacity.

through December 1943 reaching a total of 509. In October 1942, Baldwin also converted two new M3A3s. This began a run which produced 150 additional T2s by the end of 1943. In August of 1943, a quantity of used M3A3s became available for remanufacture and conversion. One hundred and fortysix were rebuilt by the end of the war bringing the total of diesel powered T2s to 296. OCM 21554 recommended classification of the T2 as Limited Standard on 25 August 1943. It assigned the designations tank recovery vehicle M31, M31B1, and M31B2 for those based on the M3, M3A3, and M3A5 respectively.

An M31B1 of Company B, 1st Ordnance Battalion (above right), tows an M10 past a burning Panzer IV near Cisterna, Italy on 25 May 1944. Below an M31B1 of the 7th Armored Division assembles with other vehicles in a field near Chartres, France on 18 August 1944.

The pilot T5 and T5E1 tank recovery vehicles appear above at the left and right respectively.

OCM 19995 on 17 March 1943 recorded that the number of M3 series tanks available was limited and that the manufacture of a recovery vehicle based on each production model of the Sherman had been directed. On 19 April, the Ordnance Committee approved the development of the tank recovery vehicles T5, T5E1, T5E2, T5E3, and T5E4 converted from the medium tanks M4, M4A1, M4A2, M4A3, and M4A4 respectively. The vehicles were to be fitted with a fixed turret using a simplified "A" frame crane design. The Committee also approved the construction of the tank recovery vehicle T7 based on the M4, but using the turret mounted boom arrangement from the T2.

Work on the basic design for the T5 series had started long before on 11 January 1943 at Lima Locomotive. The T5E1 and the T5E3 were the first pilots completed and they were shipped to the Armored Board for test along with the T7. Reporting in early June, the Armored Board recommended that, with minor modifications, the T5 series be placed in immediate production for use by all armored units. They found that the T5s were superior to both the T2 and the T7. The remaining three pilots were completed in August with the T5 going to Aberdeen, the T5E2 to the Tank Destroyer Board at Camp Hood, and the T5E4 to Camp Seeley, California. OCM 21554 recommended standardization of the T5, T5E1, T5E2, T5E3, and T5E4 as the tank recovery vehicles M32, M32B1, M32B2, M32B3, and M32B4 respectively. The same item terminated the T7 project.

The M32 series vehicles were equipped with a 60,000 pound Gar Wood winch driven by a power takeoff from the propeller shaft. This winch was mounted behind the driver's seat on beams extending across the hull with the cable drum on the vehicle centerline. A moveable crane type boom was hinged at the front of the hull and for traveling, it was supported

At the left is the pilot tank recovery vehicle T7 using the same type of turret mounted boom as on the earlier T2.

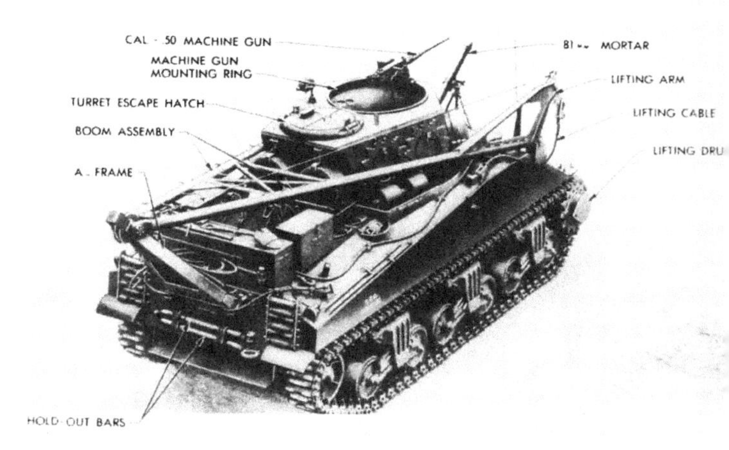

The equipment and stowage on the tank recovery vehicle M32B2 can be seen above. This is an early production vehicle with the turret assembled from flat plates.

At the right below is a later production M32B1. Formed plates were used for the turret resulting in the curved shape.

over the rear deck by an "A" frame seated in sockets welded to the rear hull plate. This position was used for partially lifting and towing a disabled vehicle. The boom also could be swung to a forward position for lifting. The boom struts were 4-1/2 inches in diameter on the early vehicles, but later they were increased to 5-9/16 inches. For lifting loads over 10,000 pounds, stabilizer plates were installed on the front and rear bogies to lock out the spring action. Although 30,000 pounds could be lifted safely, the load was limited to 20,000 pounds if movement was required. The later production vehicles had a new design lifting arm on the right boom strut with three connections instead of two. Used for shifting the boom position, the center connection was for level ground while the top and bottom ones were for upward and downward slopes respectively.

The fixed turret on the early vehicles was fabricated by welding flat steel plates. Later models followed the same outline, but they were assembled from formed plates with rounded fronts and sides. This resulted in circular brackets and shelving inside the turret. An 81mm mortar was mounted on the front hull and the stowage included 30 rounds of smoke ammunition. A .50 caliber machine gun was carried on the open turret ring just in front of the split circular hatch. The tank's .30 caliber bow machine gun was retained in the ball mount.

Lima Locomotive was first into production on the new tank recovery vehicle converting five M32B2s in June 1943. Others were completed intermittently until the following May for a total of 26 diesel powered vehicles. In June through August 1944, Lima also pro-

The M32B1 tank recovery vehicle above has several late production features. The tow hook has been added at the rear below the "A" frame and it is fitted with the spaced out suspension and extended end connectors on both sides of the tracks.

Below at the left, a recovery vehicle crew from the 4th Armored Division prepares a meal in a small French town in the Nancy sector on 11 November 1944.

duced 20 M32B3s. Pressed Steel Car began production of the M32B1 in December 1943 and continued through December 1944 for a total of 475 vehicles. Beginning in May of 1944, they also converted 298 M32B3s by the end of the year. In addition, 163 M32s were built at this location during March through December 1944. Baldwin Locomotive Works and Federal Machine and Welder entered the program in November 1944. The latter produced 400 M32s and M32B1s by the end of May 1945 and Baldwin completed 195 M32B1s by June of that year. The M32B4 did not reach production.

On 28 August 1944, the Ordnance Committee was informed that in 1945, the Marine Corps would require 50 M32B3s equipped with the horizontal volute spring suspension for interchangeability with their fighting tanks. Chrysler was directed to construct a pilot vehicle and on 22 January 1945, OCM 26511 designated the wide-tracked M32B3 as the tank recovery vehicle T14. The new suspension required changes in some of the stowage brackets and a new

The tank recovery vehicle M32A1B3 is shown here (above and below) with the boom in the raised position. In the bottom photograph, the towing hook can be seen lowered to the ground.

boom lifting device. The lifting arm was eliminated from the right strut and replaced by a boom raising sheave mounted on the hull front. Although retained on the pilot, the 81mm mortar was eliminated from the later production vehicles. Adjustable rod type stabilizers were used to lock out the springs on the front and rear bogies during lifting operations. After some changes, 80 of these vehicles were produced by the end of 1945 at Baldwin and International Harvester as T14E1s.

With the widespread adoption of the wide-tracked horizontal volute spring suspension, new designations were assigned. Thus the M32, M32B1, M32B2, and M32B3 became the M32A1, M32A1B1, M32A1B2, and M32A1B3 when fitted with the new running gear. Baldwin converted 37 M32A1B1s during the last half of 1945 and they continued to serve long into the postwar period.

Above is the medium tank recovery vehicle M74. Note the front spade which also could be used as a dozer blade.

After the outbreak of war in Korea, there was an urgent need for an improved recovery vehicle capable of handling the new heavier tanks such as the Patton. Large numbers of World War II M4A3s were available and if successfully converted, they offered an economical solution to the problem. Bowen McLaughlin-York, Inc., then engaged in rebuilding large numbers of the old vehicles, was given an order in May 1952 to produce a pilot model. Delivered to Fort Knox in July, its tests resulted in several changes. These were incorporated in a second pilot which was shipped to Aberdeen in December. Designated as the T74, it was standardized by OCM 34893 on 16 July 1953 as the medium recovery vehicle M74.

Equipped with a 90,000 pound capacity winch, the M74's boom was raised into position by hydraulic cylinders which permitted its use as a live boom. A front spade, provided to stabilize the vehicle for heavy lifting, also could be used as a dozer blade to assist in recovery operations. Manned by a crew of five, the M74 was armed with a .50 caliber machine gun on the commander's vision cupola and a .30 caliber weapon in the hull bow mount. The M74s were converted from the M4A3 tanks at Bowen McLaughlin-York from February 1954 through October 1955. Rock Island Arsenal also scheduled 60 M32B3s for conversion to M74s as late as 1958.

After the Grant and Ram were superseded by the Sherman in the combat units, the British and Canadians converted some of the earlier tanks to recovery vehicles. Designated as Armoured Recovery Vehicles (ARV), they were equipped to remove disabled tanks from the battlefield. On the Grant ARV I, the turret was removed and twin Bren machine guns were mounted in the opening. A jib crane with a chain block hoist could be installed on the front of the vehicle for

Below is a sectional view of the medium tank recovery vehicle M74.

The Grant ARV I is shown above and at the right below. This vehicle is equipped with full stowage including the twin Bren machine guns mounted in the roof hatch.

handling heavy components. The Grant ARV II designation was assigned to the U.S. M31 tank recovery vehicle in British service.

The Australians also modified some of their M3s by removing the armament and fitting a winch inside the hull. These vehicles could be indentified by the large spade and the roller guides for the winch installed at the rear.

The Ram ARV I was converted from the tank by adding towing equipment and a jib crane which could be installed at the front. A large tool bin was located on each side of the rear deck with a reel for wire rope in the center.

The Ram ARV II was a more drastic modification. It included a fixed turret with a dummy gun and a 25 ton winch installed in the fighting compartment.

Below is the Australian ARV converted from the M3 medium tank. Note the large spade in the view at the left.

The Sherman ARV I is shown in the two photographs above. At the left, the boom is installed at the front of the vehicle. At the right, it has been stowed along the side of the sponsons.

Recovery vehicles based on the Sherman also were developed in Britain. The first of these was originally designated as the Sherman ARV, but this later became the Sherman ARV I when subsequent versions appeared. It was converted from the standard tank by removing the turret and rearranging the internal stowage. A circular section of armor plate with a large rectangular double door hatch replaced the turret in the hull roof. For protection, two Bren guns could be mounted in the hatch opening and the tank's .30 caliber bow machine gun was retained. A jib crane with a maximum lifting capacity of 6720 pounds could be mounted at the front of the vehicle. Equipped with a chain block and cable, this crane was used in the field to remove major assemblies such as engines or power trains from the tanks. When not in use, one jib crane boom was stowed on each side of the hull. A swiveling type connector at the rear of the ARV was designed to take two types of Hollebone drawbars. The short drawbar was used for towing vehicles based on

Below, a Sherman ARV I on the Rhine River approaches during the crossing operations on 24 March 1945. Note the extended end connectors installed to reduce the ground pressure.

the Sherman type chassis and the longer version was adapted to the front towing eyes of British built vehicles.

A later British conversion was the Sherman ARV II. The tank turret was replaced by a welded fixed structure mounting a dummy cannon aimed forward slightly to the left of center. A jib crane also was provided on this model in addition to an "A" frame and spade assembly on the rear hull. A winch was installed inside the hull driven by a power takeoff from the main engine.

The Sherman ARV III designation was assigned to the U.S. built recovery vehicles of the M32 series. A number of these were furnished to Britain.

In preparation for the Normandy invasion, some ARV Is were converted to Beach Armoured Recovery Vehicles (BARV) by the installation of a tall superstructure. The vehicles were waterproofed and used to rescue tanks and other equipment from the surf. Since they were used primarily for towing, the jib crane was not fitted. With other modifications, many of the BARVs remained in service long after the war.

The Sherman ARV II with full stowage can be seen in the photographs above and below.

The Sherman BARV appears in the two views below. Waterproofed for deep wading, it could tow swamped vehicles out of the surf.

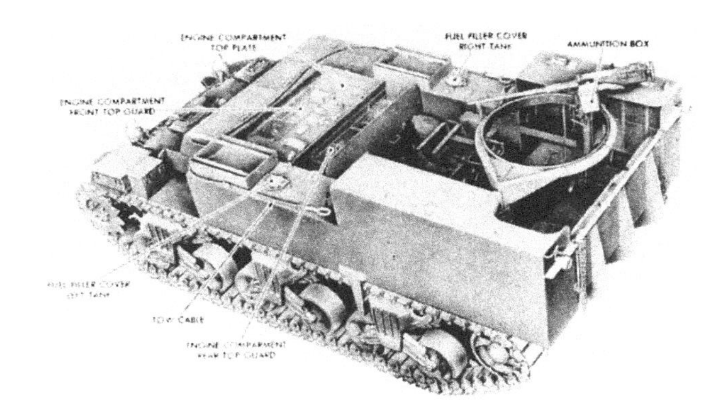

The remanufactured and modernized cargo carrier M30 is shown above. The tailgate is up and locked in the travel position.

CARGO CARRIERS, PRIME MOVERS, AND PERSONNEL CARRIERS

As mentioned earlier, the cargo carrier T14 was developed as a companion vehicle for the 155mm gun motor carriage T6. The T14 had the same general arrangement as the self-propelled gun with the engine shifted forward to just behind the driving compartment. The rear of the vehicle was left clear for the stowage of 40 rounds of 155mm ammunition. A crew of six was carried with two in the driving compartment and four in the rear hull. Armament consisted of a .50 caliber machine gun on a ring mount over the open rear compartment.

Pressed Steel Car Company started production of the T14 in October 1942 and completed their order of 100 vehicles by the end of March 1943. When 74 of the gun motor carriages were remanufactured by Baldwin in early 1944, a similar number of the cargo carriers were rebuilt. Standardized as the cargo carrier M30, they were shipped to Britain and served alongside the M12s during the European campaign.

With the development of the 155mm gun motor carriage T83 as a replacement for the M12, a new companion vehicle was required corresponding to the earlier M30. Designated as the cargo carrier T30, five pilot vehicles were ordered from the Pressed Steel Car Company. The design followed that of the T83 with the gun mount replaced by stowage racks for 100 rounds of 155mm ammunition. Vision cupolas were provided for the driver and assistant driver in the front hull with a .50 caliber machine gun mounted on a ring above the assistant driver's hatch. Folding seats for the remaining two crew members were installed on the rear wall of the ammunition stowage compartment.

After the installation of the 8 inch howitzer on the motor carriage, the T30 was redesigned with universal ammunition racks. This permitted the stowage of three sizes of ammunition without any modification. Either 102 155mm, 66 8 inch, or 32 240mm projectiles could be carried. The modified vehicle was designated as the cargo carrier T30E1. Other changes included the addition of a small ammunition handling crane and relocation of the towing pintle for the M23 ammunition trailer. An air compressor and air brake controls also were provided for the trailer.

Production plans for the cargo carrier were cancelled after the decision to use high speed tractors, if companion vehicles were required for the T83 or T89 motor carriages.

Note the forward tilt to the differential and final drive assembly necessary to align the propeller shaft with the forward mounted engine. This same arrangement was required on the 155mm gun motor carriage M12.

The pilot cargo carrier T30 can be seen in these photographs. The ring mount for the .50 caliber machine gun is located above the assistant driver's cupola, but the weapon has not been installed. As on its companion vehicles, the 155mm gun motor carriage and the 8 inch howitzer motor carriage, the differential and final drive had to be tilted to permit alignment with the forward mounted radial engine.

In outward appearance, the cargo carrier T30E1 was identical to the T30 except for the addition of a small ammunition handling crane at the left rear and the installation of folding steps on the rear of the hull.

The heavy tractor T2. Note the early experimental horizontal volute spring suspension. This vehicle had the same 14-¼ inch track width as the medium tank M2A1.

Development of a full-track prime mover capable of towing the 155mm gun or the 8 inch howitzer began in early 1941. Designated as the heavy tractor T2, it was based on many components from the tank development program. The pilot, constructed by General Motors, used the experimental horizontal volute spring suspension intended for the medium tank M2A1 and the engine was the 6-cylinder diesel which was half of the twin power plant in the medium tank M3A3 and M3A5. With a Hydramatic transmission, the T2 had a maximum speed of 26 miles/hour. Armor protection ranging from 1/4 to 1/2 inches thick was provided for the ten man crew.

The test program showed that the T2's performance was unsatisfactory for its intended use. The project was cancelled in 1942 and the vehicle was used at Aberdeen to test transmissions. A similar design, also authorized in 1941, was designated as the heavy tractor T12. In view of the T2's poor performance, it was cancelled during the same period.

The M3A5 medium tank was used as the basis for the heavy tractor T16. Development of the latter started in early 1942. However, tests showed that the stowage space was inadequate and the project was ended during 1943 in favor of the much superior heavy tractors T22 and T23. The T23 was subsequently standardized as the high speed tractor M6 and the T16 served as the basis for the development of the tank recovery vehicle T2.

At the left and below is the heavy tractor T16. The 40,000 pound Gar Wood winch can be seen in the rear view.

Although the M6 high speed tractor was intended as the prime mover for the 8 inch gun and the 240mm howitzer, production delays required the use of an interim vehicle. Beginning in December 1943, the Chester Tank Depot converted 133 M31 and M32B1 tank recovery vehicles into prime movers completing the job in March 1944. The turret was removed from the M31s as well as the booms, winches, and armament from both vehicles and they were designated as the prime movers M33 and M34 respectively. Starting in January 1944, the Lima Tank Depot performed a similar conversion on 209 M10A1 tank destroyers. The turret and much internal stowage was removed and they were redesignated as the prime mover M35. The job was complete in June. All three expedient prime movers were fitted with compressors to provide high pressure air for the gun and howitzer carriage braking systems.

From top to bottom are the prime movers M33, M34, and M35. The M35 is towing the 8 inch gun M1. Note the driver's bad weather hood.

Kangaroos converted from the British Priests move troops forward in Normandy during August 1944.

The effective use of tanks with infantry required a suitable means of transportation to enable the latter to keep up with the armored vehicles. In many cases, the infantry rode on the tanks themselves, but they were, of course, vulnerable to shell fragments and small arms fire. Field experiments even used tanks to tow the infantry in sledges across fire swept areas. None of these techniques provided an adequate solution to the problem.

In the armored divisions, both the U.S. and German armies transported their infantry in lightly armored half-track vehicles. This was a step in the right direction, but the cross-country mobility and armor protection were inferior to the tank's frequently making close support difficult.

The first really effective armored infantry vehicle appeared in August 1944 during the operations of the 2nd Canadian Corps in Normandy. These troops had been reequipped with the Sexton and the M7 howitzer motor carriages were available for other duties. With the cannon and much internal stowage removed, these Priests were modified for use as armored personnel carriers. They proved extremely successful in keeping up with the tanks and safely delivering the infantry to their objectives.

Although the numbers of Priests available for conversion were limited, large quantities of Ram tanks were on hand after being replaced by Shermans in the armored units. Converted by removing the turret and rearranging the interior, they were adopted as armored personnel carriers for used by the Twentyfirst Army Group. Designated as Kangaroos, each vehicle could carry 11 men in the open topped compartment below the turret ring. This was in addition to the two man crew in the front hull. The Ram's bow machine gun was retained and an additional machine gun frequently was mounted on the turret ring.

Two armored regiments, one British and one Canadian, were converted to Kangaroos and both were assigned to the 79th Armoured Division. The regiments were organized with two squadrons each equipped with 53 Kangaroos. After their introduction, they were in great demand and served until the end of the war in Europe. With armor plate fitted over the turret ring opening, some of the Ram Kangaroos were used as ammunition carriers to replenish the tanks in the forward areas. The British produced additional Kangaroos in Italy by converting both Priests and older model Shermans.

In addition to their use as personnel carriers, deturreted tanks were employed as prime movers for artillery. Modified for this role, they were designated by the British as the Ram Gun Tower or the Sherman Gun Tower. They were often used to tow the 17 pounder guns in the antitank regiments of the armored divisions.

A Kangaroo converted from a late model Ram tank (above) transports the Gordon Highlanders in Tilburg, Holland on 29 October 1944. The Kangaroo at the right is crossing a minefield at Blerick on the west bank of the Maas on 3 December 1944. This vehicle and the one depicted in the sketch below were converted from the earlier Ram with the auxiliary machine gun turret.

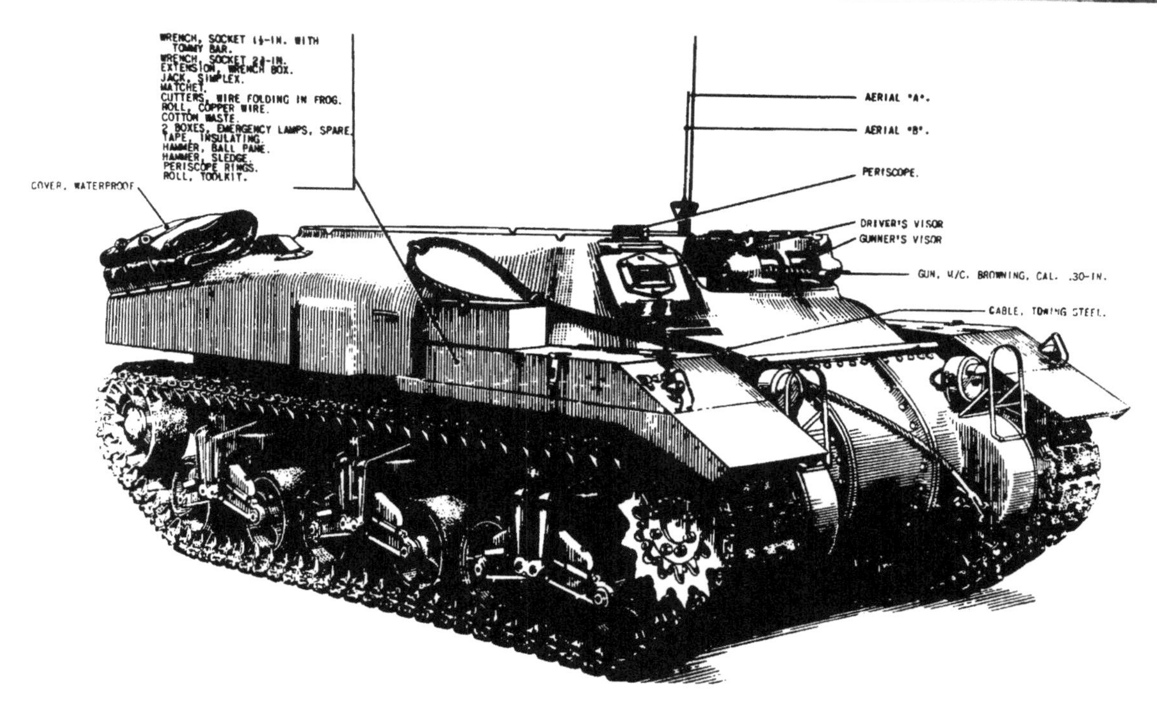

Two conversions of war weary Shermans are illustrated on this page. At the top is a Sherman Kangaroo personnel carrier and below a converted M4A2, Sherman III, serves as the prime mover for a 17 pounder antitank gun.

PART V

POSTWAR SERVICE

Above, a late production M4A3 of the 2nd Armored Division passes a horse drawn Russian vehicle enroute to Berlin in July 1945.

OCCUPATION AND FOREIGN AID

With the end of the European war in May 1945, the composition of the U.S. armored units rapidly changed. Veterans with 30 months of overseas service were relieved and during the next few weeks many thousands of them started the journey home. Outfits such as the 20th Armored Division, which had arrived just as the fighting was ending, also were heading homeward. However, in their case, it was only intended to be a stopover on the way to war still raging in the Pacific. The remaining troops took up their occupation duties in Germany.

The veteran 2nd Armored Division was selected to participate in the victory parade in Berlin and on 3 July began its march to the city where it became the major U.S. occupation force. Other armored units kept the peace between rival factions in such troubled spots as Trieste.

Their turrets shrouded, the tanks of the 4th Armored Division are assembled for occupation duty.

As insurance against a later emergency, complete tanks were "mothballed" in sealed containers at Detroit Arsenal for storage at strategic points around the world.

In the Pacific, fighting continued in the Philippines and the buildup was intensified for the Fall invasion of the Japanese homeland. The atomic bomb and the subsequent Japanese surrender in August brought these preparations to a halt. The new objective was occupation rather than attack.

The early years following the war saw the Sherman still on active duty as a standard medium tank in the U.S. Army. Many of the tanks shipped to Europe as well as those supplied to Britain were used to rebuild the armies of friendly countries liberated by the war. France had received large numbers of Shermans before the end of the fighting and they continued to serve as the primary tank in the French army. With the reorganization of the Italian Armed Forces, the Sherman was supplied again in large quantities. Many of these came from Britain including the Firefly armed with the 17 pounder.

The war in the Pacific had left tons of ordnance equipment scattered over the widely separated former island battlefields. A plan was originated in 1948 by Brigadier General Urban Niblo, Ordnance Officer of the Far East Command, to reclaim much of this materiel. Dubbed "Operation Roll-up", it called for the collection of salvageable items and their shipment to Japan for repair or reconstruction. This program was to be of crucial importance when war broke out in Korea in the Summer of 1950.

Below, a Sherman of the U.S. 15th Tank Company maneuvers near Duino, Free Territory of Trieste on 15 January 1948.

Above, Shermans operate in peacetime training exercises at Fort Knox on 1 May 1950.

Below, the reorganized Italian Armed Forces receive Shermans as the major part of their armored equipment. At the left are a number of 105mm howitzer tanks and at the right quite a few Fireflies are mixed in with the 75mm gun tanks.

The late model M4A3 (above) armed with the 76 and fitted with the horizontal volute spring suspension has just been refurbished at the Tokyo Ordnance Depot. The same treatment was applied to the M4 tankdozer below. Both tanks were photographed in Korea on 2 August 1950.

KOREA TO OBSOLESCENCE

When the North Korean Army struck southward on the morning of 25 June, 1950, the surprise attack rapidly penetrated deep into South Korea. Despite desperate efforts, the defending army was thrown back losing the capital of Seoul. U.S. troops ordered into action under the United Nations were rushed to Korea in early July. Drawn from the occupation forces in Japan, these units were ill equipped for full scale warfare and an intensive effort was made to bring them up to strength in men and materiel.

The first armored units to arrive in Korea were equipped with the light tank M24 which had been used for occupation duty in Japan. It was an excellent reconnaissance vehicle, but it was completely inadequate to face the heavily armed and armored T34/85s now streaming south with the North Korean Army. These Soviet built tanks spearheaded the drive to Seoul and on toward the south.

Thanks to "Operation Roll-up", a considerable number of armored vehicles had been collected in Japan. Rebuilt at the Tokyo Ordnance Depot, they included several models of the Sherman as well as self-propelled artillery. After the fighting started in Korea, activity at the Ordnance Depot shifted into high gear

This M4A3 has had its 75mm gun replaced by the 76 at the Tokyo Ordnance Depot. The higher powered weapon was fitted into the M34A1 mount, but no counterweights were installed to balance the turret. The bottom photograph shows the 76 in the M34A1 combination gun mount.

with about 8000 automotive vehicles being processed through the shops during July and August. In addition to repairs, some of the older M4A3s with the 75 were rearmed with the 76mm gun. Fitted into the smaller turret, it had the appearance of the expedient mount first tried in 1942. Although crowded, it again showed that firepower was the crucial factor. A number of 105mm howitzer motor carriages also were modified to increase the maximum elevation to 67 degrees thus permitting the high angle fire so necessary in the Korean mountains. This was essentially the same modification later standardized as the 105mm howitzer motor carriage M7B2.

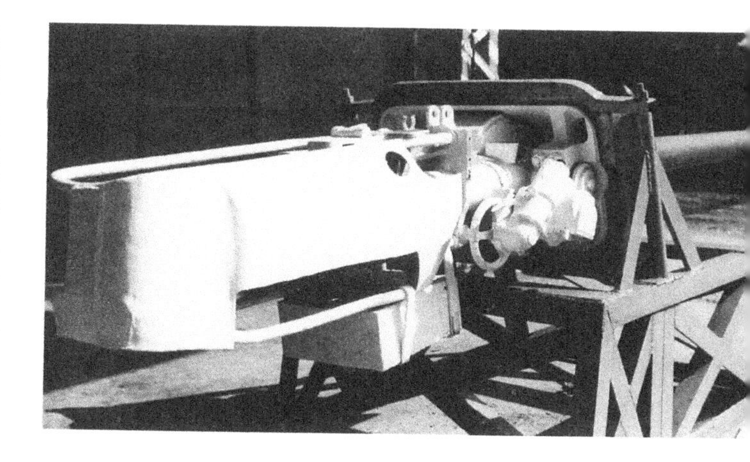

Above, the crews of the 8072nd Tank Battalion prepare their tanks for action at Pusan, Korea on 6 August 1950.

In the middle of July, the 8072nd Medium Tank Battalion was activated in Japan receiving 54 of the rebuilt tanks. These were mainly late production M4A3s with the horizontal volute spring suspension and the 76mm gun. The first to leave for Korea was A Company commanded by Captain James H. Harvey. Arriving at Pusan on the last day of July, they were moved by railroad flatcars to Masan. On the evening of 1 August, the First Platoon under Lieutenant Donald E. Bernard reached the 19th Infantry's position near Chungam-ni. The Second Platoon led by First Lieutenant Herman D. Norrell reached the 27th Infantry at Chindong-ni that same night. Both platoons were in battle the following day. Except for three M26 General Pershings, which had been lost at Chinju on 31 July, these were the first U.S. medium tanks to see action in Korea.

On 4 August, the remainder of the 8072nd arrived at Pusan and three days later the unit was redesignated by Eighth Army as the 89th Tank Battalion. Other armored units were arriving now from the United States and by the latter part of August, over 500 U.S. medium tanks were in the Pusan area. These included one battalion of the new M46 General Pattons and the remainder consisted of about equal numbers of Shermans and Pershings.

Below, a Sherman supporting the 5th Infantry Regiment fires toward Taejong-ni on the road to Chinju, Korea on 9 August 1950.

Note the stowage items such as the spare sprockets and bogie wheels characteristic of the tanks reworked in Tokyo and used in the early days of the Korean fighting. This photograph was dated 12 August 1950.

Thus began the Sherman's second war for the U.S. Army and it was to form a higher percentage of the tank strength as time went on. When the U.N. forces broke out from the Pusan perimeter in late September, the Shermans of the 89th led the attack north commanded by Lieutenant Colonel Welborn G. Dolvin. The 76mm gun tanks accompanied the U.N. forces in the drive across the 38th parallel all the way to the Manchurian border.

In the early battles, the Sherman often fought the T34, frequently with success. The armament of either tank could destroy the other and the heavy 85mm gun of the T34 was offset by the faster shooting stabilized 76 in the Sherman. After the Chinese entered the war near the end of 1950, tank versus tank battles became rare. The opposition was mainly from enemy artillery and infantry antitank weapons.

A Sherman of the 23rd Infantry Regimental Tank Company moves up to attack a North Korean roadblock on 13 August 1950.

Above an M4A3 of A Company, 89th Tank Battalion is ready to provide covering fire for a patrol from the 29th Infantry on 24 August 1950.

An M4A3 attached to the 5th Infantry Regiment prepares to open fire on enemy mortars near Haktong-ni on 28 August 1950.

Shermans of the 89th Tank Battalion (above) support the advance of the 25th Infantry Division near Chinju on 27 September 1950.

An M4A3 with the 5th Infantry Regiment (below) passes a knocked out Soviet built T34/85 near Kumchun on 6 October 1950.

Above, a Sherman is in action with troops of the 1st Cavalry Division during fighting in the railroad yards of Pyongyang, the North Korean capital, on 19 October 1950.

A U.S. Marine Corps howitzer tank (below) has slipped off the icy mountain road during the fighting around Hagaru-ri in late November 1950. Note that these vehicles have been fitted as tankdozers.

Above, U.S. Marine Corps tanks warm up their engines in the falling snow at Koto-ri on 8 December 1950 during the breakout from the Chosin reservoir.

At the right below, Shermans with tiger markings carry troops of the 1st Cavalry Division north of Chipyong on 27 February 1951.

When the Chinese offensive was halted in early 1951, the U.N. forces had been driven back into South Korea and the capital of Seoul was once again in enemy hands. Under the leadership of Lieutenant General Matthew B. Ridgway, the Eighth Army stopped the enemy advance and began a counterattack toward the north.

The lunar year of the Tiger ended on 5 February 1951 and as the tanks rolled north, many were decorated as ferocious cats. Although the paint jobs may have had little effect on Chinese morale, the tank's firepower was another story and by the middle of March they had crossed the Han River and retaken Seoul. The Chinese and North Korean offensives during the Spring were stopped with heavy losses and in some areas, the U.N. forces crossed the old demarcation line at the 38th parallel.

Above, a 76mm high explosive round is loaded into a tank of C Company, 89th Tank Battalion. Below, another tank from the same company pauses on the south bank of the Han River on 7 March 1951 during the drive north.

From the commander's hatch of this 89th Tank Battalion Sherman, the 38th parallel can be seen 1000 yards ahead on 2 April 1951. The barrel of the .50 caliber antiaircraft machine gun protrudes into the left side of the photograph.

With the opening of peace talks in the Summer of 1951, operations were limited to destroying enemy personnel and equipment without attempting to gain additional territory. The campaign took on the aspect of positional warfare with the tanks being used as artillery and in the close support role. The latter involved the defense of U.N. positions and the attack of enemy bunkers during offensive operations. Bunker busting became a regular activity for the Sherman. Although its 76 was less effective than the 90 on the newer tanks, the higher power to weight ratio allowed the Sherman much greater freedom in climbing over the rough terrain. Frequently the tanks were brought up along the skyline providing a nasty shock to the entrenched enemy.

The Sherman continued to serve throughout the campaign and was the most numerous tank in service when the armistice was signed in 1953. Training then replaced battle as new troops relieved the homeward bound combat veterans. Until declared obsolete by the U.S. Army in 1956, the Sherman soldiered on in its peacekeeping role.

Below, the tanks wait for mines to be cleared during operations against the Chinese forces near the 38th parallel, 10 June 1951.

Shermans of the 23rd Infantry Regiment (above) firing as artillery against the Chinese north of Pia-ri on 18 September 1951. Note the use of ramps to increase the maximum elevation of the tank guns.

A 72nd Tank Battalion Sherman (below) engaging in bunker busting against the enemy on Napalm Ridge in support of the 8th Republic of Korea Division, 11 May 1952. The tank has just fired and the gun is in full recoil.

A tank from the 35th Infantry Regiment (above) firing its .50 caliber machine gun against enemy positions in the early evening of 21 August 1952. Note the rugged terrain over which the Sherman successfully operated in Korea.

At the right is a wire cutter adapted in Korea from an M2 tankdozer. It was used to rip up the wires to the electrically controlled land mines which appeared during the period of relatively fixed position warfare.

Above, a U.S. Marine Corps command and communication tank is on standby south of the truce conference site at Panmunjom on 27 June 1952. This vehicle is fitted with several radios and a dummy cannon. Note the howitzer appearance of the dummy gun tube in the M34A1 mount.

After the truce, training continued with the Sherman still in first line service. Here the 2nd Infantry Division conducts training exercises on 15 February 1954.

Above, the Israelis operate standard M4A1s armed with the 76mm gun in the desert. Both the original vertical volute spring suspension (left) and the later wide-track design (right) saw service here.

ISRAELI SERVICE

Although the Sherman appeared in many foreign armies during the postwar years, the outstanding example was in Israel. Beginning with the War of Independence in 1948, Shermans in one form or another served the Israeli Army for over a quarter century with some still in use during the Yom Kippur War of October 1973. This long career began with three Shermans acquired under dubious circumstances from the British Army prior to their departure in June 1948. These were supplemented by others purchased mainly from scrap dealers and put back into operating condition. Most of these had been demilitarized by the removal of the guns and tracks. While the latter also could be obtained from surplus sources, the weapons proved to be a more difficult problem. Some of the early tanks were rearmed with German 1911 Krupp 75mm field guns. These vehicles equipped a battalion in the first Israeli armored brigade in the early 1950s. A few surplus 3 inch guns from M10 tank destroyers also were fitted to some of the vehicles.

By the time the 1956 war erupted in the Sinai, the early hodgepoge of Shermans had been replaced by two far more effective models. The first was the standard 76mm gun tank. Both M4A1s and M4A3s were in service fitted with either the vertical volute spring suspension or the late model wide-track running gear. The second type was an Israeli modification mounting the high velocity 75mm gun from the French AMX 13. This weapon was 62 calibers in length with a muzzle velocity of 3200 ft/sec greatly increasing the tank's firepower. A suitable turret for the new cannon was provided by reworking the original model designed for the 75mm gun. An extension was welded to the front to carry the new mount and it was balanced by a large bustle added at the rear. Most of these vehicles were equipped with the wide-track horizontal volute spring suspension, but some still were fitted with the earlier running gear. Dubbed the Super Sherman, its high powered gun certainly made it a dangerous opponent.

Designated as the M50 by Israel, the Super Sherman appears at the left with the rebuilt turret and the high velocity French 75mm gun. Note the smoke dischargers installed on the side of the turret.

The M50 Super Shermans above are based on both the cast and welded hull tanks. The vehicles at the left retain the original suspension and the split circular hatch for the tank commander. The M50s at the right have been fitted with wide-track suspensions and the vision cupola.

Some details of the M50 turret fitted with the vision cupola can be seen at the right. Note that the small oval hatch has been retained in the turret roof for the loader.

At the left is a Sherman variant captured from Egypt by Israel. On this modification, the complete French turret has been installed replacing the standard turret on a Sherman V. Note the extra applique armor on the left sponson.

At the right above is the French installation of the 105mm gun in the M4A1 turret originally designed for the 76. At the left above is the Israeli Sherman designated as the M51. Note the large double baffle muzzle brake on the latter tank.

In the period between 1956 and 1967, another Israeli Sherman appeared which was undoubtedly the ultimate development of the vehicle as a main battle tank. Experiments in France had successfully installed a 105mm gun in the 76 turret on the M4A1. This gun had a muzzle velocity of 2969 ft/sec (905 m/sec) with a hollow charge projectile that could penetrate 14 inches (360mm) of steel at normal impact. To balance the long barreled weapon, an extension was added to the bustle at the rear of the turret. This approach was adopted in Israel with a 51 caliber 105mm gun being installed in a stabilized mount. The tanks also were rebuilt with the horizontal volute spring suspension and the old power plants were replaced with Cummins VT8-460 diesel engines. This liquid-cooled V8 displaced 950 cubic inches and developed 460 horsepower at 2600 rpm. The maximum speed was about 27 miles/hour and the low fuel consumption increased the range to approximately 150 miles. Sometimes referred to as the Isherman (Israeli Sherman), they were easily identified by the long gun with a large muzzle brake in the modified 76 turret. The powerful cannon allowed it to engage and destroy much later model main battle tanks such as the Soviet built T54 and T55. It proved extremely effective during operations in the Six Day War of 1967. Some of these tanks were still in service when fighting broke out again in 1973. At that time they reportedly engaged the Soviet built T62. It was a fitting conclusion for a tank that opened its battle career at El Alamein 31 years before.

The two views of the Isherman below show tanks converted from the 76mm gun medium tank M4A1. A coaxial searchlight is installed on top of the gun mount of the tank at the right.

The French 155mm M50 gun howitzer is mounted on the two vehicles above. The view at the left shows the weapon on a chassis fitted with the horizontal volute spring suspension while the one at the right retains the earlier suspension.

The Sherman chassis also provided the basis for numerous other Israeli armored vehicles. The M10 tank destroyer armed with the British 17 pounder and the M7 105mm howitzer motor carriage both appeared in Israel. A modified open top chassis was used to mount the French 155mm M50 gun howitzer. These vehicles used both the early and late type suspensions and a .50 caliber machine gun was fitted on a pedestal at the right front of the fighting compartment. A later model longer range 155mm howitzer on a modified Sherman chassis was designated as the L33. It used the horizontal volute spring suspension and the weapon, fitted with a large single baffle muzzle brake, was installed in an enclosed armored fighting compartment. A sliding breechblock and pneumatic ramming helped to maintain a rapid sustained firing rate.

The self-propelled artillery based on the Sherman was rounded out by an open top chassis armed with a 160mm mortar. The front armor folded down to form a firing platform and the vehicle was equipped with the horizontal volute spring suspension.

The M32 tank recovery vehicles also were employed by the Israelis and the Sherman chassis was the basis for an artillery observation post vehicle. Equipped with a platform on the end of a "Cherry Picker" type arm, an observer could be lifted to a good viewpoint high above the ground. With luck, the whole arrangement also could move quickly if it drew enemy attention.

A unique Israeli application of the Sherman was as an armored ambulance. Named the Ambutank, the engine was moved forward leaving the rear of the chassis clear for the installation of an enclosed armored compartment. Doors opened to the rear permitting litters carrying wounded men to be loaded inside. The Ambutank was used during the 1973 war to evacuate wounded under fire.

The L33 155mm howitzer on the wide-tracked Sherman chassis can be seen at the left. This vehicle is provided with all round and overhead armor protection for the howitzer crew.

Additional details of the L33 self-propelled howitzer are shown above. The weapon is firing at the top right.

At the right is the Israeli installation of the 160mm mortar on the late model Sherman chassis. In this view, the side armor is folded up in the travel position providing all round protection for the crew.

Below are two photographs of the Ambutank armored ambulance. Note the similarity to the late version of the vehicle mounting the French 155mm gun howitzer at the top left of the previous page.

As an offensive weapon, the task of the Sherman was to carry the war to the enemy. This is well illustrated by the photograph above taken late in its career. Here the tiger marked tanks of C Company, 89th Tank Battalion cross the Han River in the drive back northward in Korea on 7 March 1951.

CONCLUSION

A basic principle of warfare was expressed accurately, if not grammatically, by the famous Confederate cavalryman, General Nathan Bedford Forrest. His maxim of "get thar fustest with the mostest" aptly described the doctrine taught in the Armored Force and applied by leaders like Patton. Such operations required a mobile, extremely reliable, armored vehicle capable of running for long periods with a minimum of maintenance and repair. Despite its other defects, the Sherman tank precisely filled these requirements. Its relatively simple design, derived from the prewar component development program, resulted in a robust reliable tank ideal for executing such a doctrine. The Sherman's medium weight and relatively narrow width also allowed it to operate over most of the roads and bridges found in Europe.

The weakest point in the design was the main armament and this remained so throughout its career in the U.S. Army. Even the 75mm gun which armed the original Sherman had required that the prewar concept of a medium tank be revised. Early battle reports from Europe showed that the 37mm gun of the then standard medium tank M2A1 would be obsolete long before it came off the assembly line. Yet, the critical war situation demanded maximum tank production as quickly as possible. The solution was to add a 75mm gun in a sponson mount for which a preliminary design already existed. With other modifications, the new tank entered production as the M3.

Considerable criticism has been leveled at the decision to produce the M3 pending the design of a suitable 75mm gun turret. As far as the Ordnance Department was concerned, it was never considered anything but an interim vehicle, a compromise to permit the most rapid production of a new medium tank. It is well to consider the implications of this decision. By opting for immediate production, the first M3s were coming off the assembly lines by June 1941, three months before the first pilot of the M4 with its turret mounted 75 was complete. The early availability of the M3 allowed the testing and evaluation of the chassis which resulted in many modifications applying directly to the M4. With the M3s being issued to the troops, many problems were uncovered and solved before M4 production started thus greatly reducing the time necessary to make it a battleworthy tank. As a result, less than eight months elapsed between the start of production in February 1942 and the Sherman's introduction into battle at Alamein in October.

If the decision had been made to limit the quantity of M3s and to wait for the M4 for all out production, the gestation period of the latter would not have been significantly reduced. In fact, without the experience gained from the M3 production and testing, it probably would have been increased. In addition, no 75mm gun tanks would have been available in time for the fighting at Gazala. Without the heavy losses inflicted by the M3s, the enemy might well have broken through to Suez. Rommel himself, describes the shock at the first encounter with the M3 and its 75mm gun. On balance, it seems that the compromise was a good one.

Effective as it was when introduced in the Sherman at El Alamein, the 75mm gun M3 was already inferior to the 7.5cm KwK 40 in the late model Panzer IV and a few months later it was to be completely outclassed with the appearance of the 8.8cm KwK 36 in the Tiger I. The problem had been recognized early in 1942 and development began on the 76mm gun, but as long as the opposition consisted of Panzer IIIs and IVs the situation was not serious since the 75 could easily destroy either enemy tank. However, with the appearance of heavy German armor, the lack of firepower became critical. The demand for a more powerful gun swept aside the objections to the 76 and it was quickly accepted. Unfortunately, by this time, the Germans had moved on to even more powerful weapons such as the 7.5cm KwK 42 and the 8.8cm KwK 43 and the catch-up game continued. The proposal to install the 90mm gun in the Sherman would have helped the situation, but it would not have equaled the most powerful German guns already in service. The basic problem was, of course, that the need for a powerful high velocity tank gun was not realized until it was too late to provide one.

An ideal solution to the armament problem would have been the adoption of the British 17 pounder as the standard Allied tank gun. Such a decision, taken in 1942, would have insured quantity production of 17 pounder Shermans well before D-day. Installed in a properly designed turret such as that used with the 76, the 17 pounder would have provided the Sherman with firepower equivalent to the German Panther's 7.5cm KwK 42 and it would have been available in quantity for the campaign in northwest Europe. Fitted in a larger turret, its operation would have been far more efficient than the improvised installation on the British Firefly.

Hindsight can easily show what should have been done. Unfortunately, things were not at all that clear at the time. The suggestion to adopt the British weapon was made by Colonel G.B. Jarrett and others, but their recommendation was rejected. At that time, the 76 appeared to be more than adequate as far as power was concerned and it was a much lighter weapon. Its smaller cartridge case was easier to handle allowing a higher firing rate and a larger ammunition supply. As a result, the 76 was selected as the new tank weapon and, as we have seen, even it had to overcome serious objections.

Despite its shortcomings, the Sherman was a decisive weapon of war. Produced in greater numbers than any other U.S. tank before or since, it was a factor essential to victory all around the world. A total of 49,234 Shermans of all types were built in the United States during the war. The Canadian Grizzly and Ram production raised these numbers to 51,371 and if the M3 series is included, the total reaches 57,629 new fighting tanks. In addition, 5880 early Shermans of all types were remanufactured and modernized. In all the world, only the Soviet T34 was produced in comparable numbers. This parallel was not lost on the Germans who referred to the Sherman as the T34 of the west.

Perhaps the outstanding feature of the Sherman was the great flexibility of its design which permitted continuous modification and improvement throughout its life. An example of this was the large 69 inch diameter turret ring which allowed the installation of increasingly larger weapons. In fact, this was the same ring diameter used on the 90mm gun Pershing which came into service near the end of the war.

The wide-track 76mm gun M4A3 was a new tank compared to the early M4A1 introduced in 1942. Yet it was developed directly from the early design with which it had many components in common. This capacity for growth continued after the war and was exemplified by the Israeli Shermans which were challenging modern main battle tanks thirty years after El Alamein.

The changes in the Sherman during its service in the U.S. Army are strikingly apparent when comparing the two photographs below. At the left is an M4A1 with the 75mm gun and the original suspension operated by the 1st Armored Division at Anzio. At the right, a 70th Tank Battalion wide-tracked M4A3 armed with the 76 bypasses a bridge in Korea.

PART IV

REFERENCE DATA

This late production M4A3(76) HVSS is shown with the tiger markings used by C Company, 89th Tank Battalion during the early 1951 drive north in Korea. However, the tanks of the 89th were not fitted with sandshields.

A crew from the 5th Armored Division loads high explosive and armor piercing ammunition into their Sherman during training exercises. The "Super" on the cartridge cases of the HE rounds indicates a propellant supercharge.

Shermans of C Company, 10th Tank Battalion, 5th Armored Division move along a road during maneuvers in the United States.

This Sherman photographed during training exercises mounts a .30 caliber antiaircraft machine gun. Note the early tanker helmet.

Many of the tankers who trained in California (above) for the desert war saw action under far different conditions such as those below. These Shermans of the 40th Tank Battalion, 7th Armored Division are near St. Vith, Belgium on 24 January 1945 during the battle in the Ardennes.

Above an M4A1 of D Company, 11th Tank Battalion, 10th Armored Division is shown training in the United States.

Below, a 105mm howitzer motor carriage M7 is silhouetted against the sky while firing during a demonstration. Note the smoke and muzzle flash from the 105.

Details of the early production M7 can be seen in these photographs taken during the 1943 maneuvers. As the markings indicate, this vehicle belongs to the Armored School Demonstration Regiment.

Above, an M3-4-3 bow mount flame thrower is firing using unthickened fuel. Note the large flame and fairly short range. Below, a T1E3 mine exploder is operating northeast of Nancy, France prior to the crossing of the Moselle River. This exploder is attached to the 25th Armored Engineer Battalion of the 6th Armored Division.

ACCEPTANCES OF SHERMANS AND RELATED VEHICLES FROM U.S. PRODUCTION DURING THE PERIOD 1940-1945*

Vehicle	Total Acceptances	First Acceptances	Final Acceptances
Medium Tank M2A1	94	December 1940	August 1941
Medium Tank M3	4,924	June 1941	August 1942
Medium Tank M3A1	300	January 1942	July 1942
Medium Tank M3A2	12	January 1942	March 1942
Medium Tank M3A3	322	March 1942	December 1942
Medium Tank M3A4	109	June 1942	August 1942
Medium Tank M3A5	591	January 1942	December 1942
Medium Tank M4	6,748	July 1942	January 1944
Medium Tank M4A1	6,281	February 1942	December 1943
Medium Tank M4A2	8,053	April 1942	May 1944
Medium Tank M4A3	1,690	June 1942	September 1943
Medium Tank M4A4	7,499	July 1942	September 1943
Medium Tank M4A6	75	October 1943	February 1944
Medium Tank M4(105)	1,641	February 1944	March 1945
Medium Tank M4A1(76)W	3,426	January 1944	July 1945
Medium Tank M4A2(76)W	2,915	May 1944	May 1945
Medium Tank M4A3(75)W	3,071	February 1944	March 1945
Medium Tank M4A3(76)W	4,542	March 1944	April 1945
Medium Tank M4A3(105)	3,039	May 1944	June 1945
Assault Tank M4A3E2	254	June 1944	July 1944
3 inch GMC M10	4,993	September 1942	December 1943
3 inch GMC M10A1	1,713	October 1942	December 1943
90mm GMC M36	1,413	April 1944	July 1945
90mm GMC M36B1	187	October 1944	December 1944
90mm GMC M36B2	724	May 1945	September 1945
105mm HMC M7	3,490	April 1942	July 1945
105mm HMC M7B1	826	March 1944	February 1945
155mm GMC M12	100	September 1942	March 1943
155mm GMC M40	418	February 1945	September 1945
8 inch HMC M43	48	June 1945	September 1945
TRV M31	509	December 1942	December 1943
TRV M31B1	296	October 1942	December 1943
TRV M32	163	March 1944	December 1944
TRV M32B1	1,055	December 1943	May 1945
TRV M32A1B1	37	May 1945	August 1945
TRV M32B2	26	June 1943	May 1944
TRV M32B3	318	May 1944	December 1944
TRV T14E1	80	March 1945	July 1945
Prime Mover M33	109	December 1943	February 1944
Prime Mover M34	24	March 1944	March 1944
Prime Mover M35	209	January 1944	June 1944
Shop Tractor T10 (CDL tanks)	497	June 1943	February 1944

*Includes conversions such as CDL tanks, 90mm GMC M36 series, TRVs, and Prime Movers

DISTRIBUTION OF SHERMANS AND RELATED VEHICLES TO INTERNATIONAL AID UNDER THE LEND-LEASE PROGRAM AS OF 1 SEPTEMBER 1945*

Vehicle	Vehicles Assigned To: United Kingdom	Soviet Union	Other	Total International Aid
Medium Tank M3	2,653	1,386		4,039
Medium Tank M3A3	49		77	126
Medium Tank M3A5	185		23	208
Medium Tank M4	2,096		53	2,149
Medium Tank M4A1	942		4	946
Medium Tank M4A2	5,041	1,990	382	7,413
Medium Tank M4A3	7			7
Medium Tank M4A4	7,167	2	274	7,443
Medium Tank M4(105)	593			593
Medium Tank M4A1(76)W	1,330			1,330
Medium Tank M4A2(76)W	5	2,073		2,078
3 inch GMC M10	1,648	52	155	1,855
105mm HMC M7	828		179	1,007
TRV M32 Series	134			134

*Transfers in theaters of operation and minor shipments made after 1 September 1945 are not included

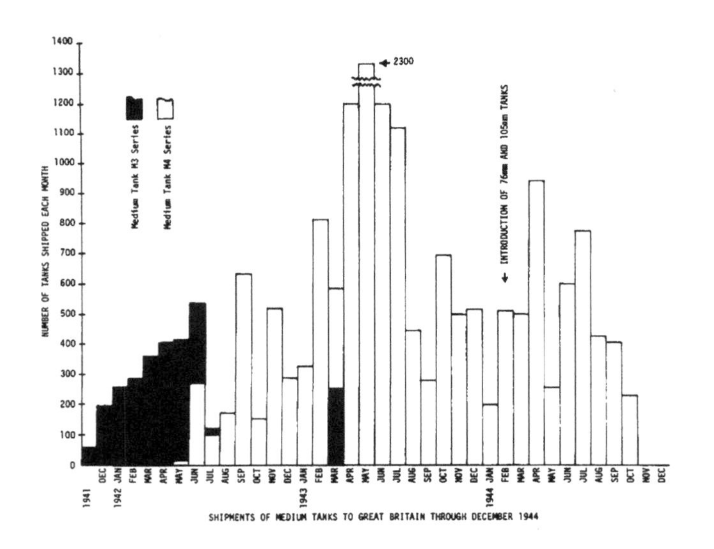

SHIPMENTS OF MEDIUM TANKS TO GREAT BRITAIN THROUGH DECEMBER 1944

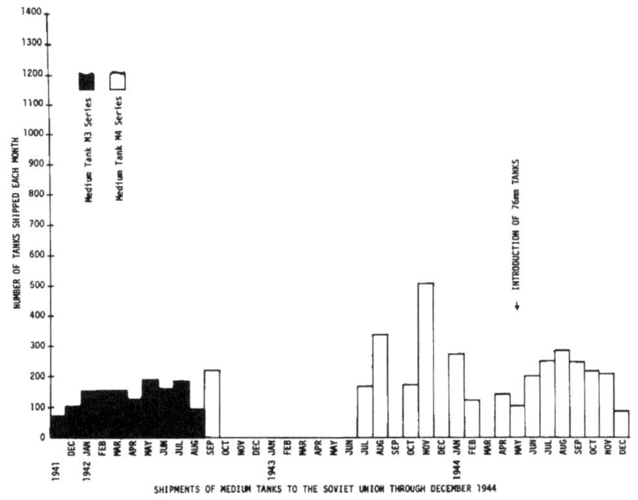

SHIPMENTS OF MEDIUM TANKS TO THE SOVIET UNION THROUGH DECEMBER 1944

VEHICLE DATA SHEETS

The data sheets in this section cover all of the major production models of the Sherman and its immediate predecessor the medium tank M3. Sheets are also included for the more important artillery motor carriages as well as the most significant British modifications.

Depending upon the source, dimensional and weight data may vary widely for any particular vehicle as a result of modifications, differences in stowage, or methods of measurement. An effort has been made to obtain values under similar conditions in order to permit a valid comparison between vehicles. When possible, actual weights and measurements taken from a specific vehicle were used and checked against the arsenal drawings. If the data represent a single experimental item, the actual numbers were reported. However, if the vehicle was intended to be representative of a production run, the weight values were rounded off to the nearest 100 pounds. For production vehicles where actual measurements of a single item were not available, average weights were used and these were usually quoted to the nearest 1000 pounds.

The terminology in the data sheets is generally self-explanatory, but a few items may benefit from further clarification. For example, the tread is defined as the distance between the centerline of each track. The fire height is the distance from the ground to the centerline of the main weapon bore when it is at zero elevation. The ground contact length at zero penetration is defined as the distance between the centers of the front and rear road wheels. This value was used to calculate the ground contact area in order to compute the ground pressure. Engine power and torque are reported as gross and net values. The former refers to the shaft output including only those accessories essential to the engine operation. The effect of such items as air cleaners, generators, and fans were excluded. The net horsepower and torque reflect the values actually obtained with the engine installed in the vehicle including all of its normal accessories. Weights are quoted for each vehicle unstowed and combat loaded. The combat weight includes the crew and a full load of fuel and ammunition. All power to weight ratios and ground pressures were calculated using the combat weight.

Stowage items varied widely during the production period. Also, changing requirements from the front and improvements from the development program produced drastic changes throughout the war. Since space does not permit the inclusion of separate data sheets for each modification, a vehicle may represent the standard of the early, middle, or late period of its production run. Where applicable, the approximate production period is indicated at the top.

MEDIUM TANK M3

GENERAL DATA

Crew:	6 or 7 men
Length: w/75mm Gun M2, w/o sandshields	222 inches
Length: w/75mm Gun M3, w/o sandshields	241 inches
Length: w/o gun, w/o sandshields	222 inches
Gun Overhang: 75mm Gun M3	19 inches
Width: Over side doors	107 inches
Height: Over cupola	123 inches
Tread:	83 inches
Ground Clearance:	17 inches
Fire Height: 75mm gun	69 inches
Turret Ring Diameter: (inside)	54.5 inches
Weight, Combat Loaded:	61,500 pounds*
Weight, Unstowed:	57,400 pounds*
Power to Weight Ratio: Net	11.1 hp/ton
Gross	13.0 hp/ton
Ground Pressure: Zero penetration	12.6 psi

*All weights based on T48 or T51 tracks

ARMOR

Type: Turret, cast homogeneous steel; Hull, rolled homogeneous steel; riveted assembly

Hull Thickness:	Actual	Angle w/Vertical
Front, Upper	2.0 inches	30 degrees
Middle	1.5 inches	53 degrees
Lower	2.0 inches	0 to 45 degrees
Sides	1.5 inches	0 degrees
Rear	1.5 inches	0 to 10 degrees
Top	0.5 inches	83 to 90 degrees
Floor, Front	1.0 inches	90 degrees
Rear	0.5 inches	90 degrees
Turret Thickness:		
Front	2.0 inches	47 degrees
Sides	2.0 inches	5 degrees
Rear	2.0 inches	5 degrees
Top	0.875 inches	90 degrees

ARMAMENT

Primary: 75mm Gun M2 or M3 in Mount M1 in right front of hull

Traverse: Manual	30 degrees (15 degrees L or R)
Elevation: Manual	+20 to −9 degrees
Firing Rate: (max)	20 rounds/minute
Loading System:	Manual
Stabilizer System:	Elevation only

37mm Gun M5 or M6 in Mount M24 in turret

Traverse: Hydraulic and manual	360 degrees
Traverse Rate: (max)	20 seconds/360 degrees
Elevation: Manual	+60 to −7 degrees
Firing Rate: (max)	30 rounds/minute
Loading System:	Manual
Stabilizer System:	Elevation only

Secondary:
- (1) .30 caliber MG M1919A4 in turret cupola
- (1) .30 caliber MG M1919A4 coaxial w/37mm gun in turret
- (1) .30 caliber MG M1919A4 fixed in front plate*
- Provision for (1) .45 caliber SMG M1928A1*

* (2) in early production vehicles

AMMUNITION

- 50 rounds 75mm
- 178 rounds 37mm
- 1200 rounds .45 caliber
- 9200 rounds .30 caliber
- 12 hand grenades

FIRE CONTROL AND VISION EQUIPMENT

Primary Weapon:	Direct	Indirect
75mm Gun	Periscope M1 with Telescope M21A1	Gunner's Quadrant M1
37mm Gun	Periscope M2 with Telescope M19A1	

Vision Devices:	Direct	Indirect
Driver	Hatch	Protectoscope (1)
Gunner (75)	None	Periscope M1 (1)
Loader (75)	Hatch and pistol port	Protectoscope (1)
Commander	Hatch and vision slots (2)	Protectoscope (1)
Gunner (37)	None	Periscope M2 (1)
Loader (37)	Pistol port	Protectoscope (1)

Total Periscopes: M1 (1), M2 (1)
Total Protectoscopes: (7)*
Total Pistol Ports: Hull (4)#, Turret (1)
*Very late production (6), #Very late production (3)

ENGINE

Make and Model: Wright (Continental) R975 EC2
Type: 9 cylinder, 4 cycle, radial
Cooling System: Air Ignition: Magneto

Displacement:	973 cubic inches
Bore and Stroke:	5 x 5.5 inches
Compression Ratio:	6.3:1
Net Horsepower (max):	340 hp at 2400 rpm
Gross Horsepower (max):	400 hp at 2400 rpm
Net Torque (max):	800 ft-lb at 1800 rpm
Gross Torque (max):	890 ft-lb at 1800 rpm
Weight:	1137 lb, dry
Fuel: 92 octane gasoline	175 gallons
Engine Oil:	36 quarts

POWER TRAIN

Clutch: Dry disc, 2 or 3 plate
Transmission: Synchromesh, 5 speeds forward, 1 reverse

Gear Ratios:				
	1st	7.56:1	4th	1.11:1
	2nd	3.11:1	5th	0.73:1
	3rd	1.78:1	reverse	5.65:1

Steering: Controlled differential
Bevel Gear Ratio: 3.53:1 Steering Ratio: 1.515:1
Brakes: Mechanical, external contracting
Final Drive: Herringbone gear Gear Ratio: 2.84:1
Drive Sprocket: At front of vehicle with 13 teeth
Pitch Diameter: 25.038 inches

RUNNING GEAR

Suspension: Vertical volute spring
12 wheels in 6 bogies (3 bogies/track)
Tire Size: 20 x 9 inches
6 track return rollers (1 on top of each bogie)*
Adjustable idler at rear of each track
Idler Size: 22 x 9 inches
Tracks: Outside guide; T41, T48, T49, and T51
Type: (T41) Double pin, 16.0 inch width, smooth, rubber
(T48) Double pin, 16.56 inch width, chevron, rubber
(T49) Double pin, 16.56 inch width, parallel bar, steel
(T51) Double pin, 16.56 inch width, smooth, rubber
Pitch: 6 inches
Shoes per Vehicle: 158 (79/track)
Ground Contact Length: 147 inches
*At rear of bogie on late production tanks

ELECTRICAL SYSTEM

Nominal Voltage: 24 volts DC
Main Generator: (1) 24 volts, 50 amperes, driven by power take-off from main engine
Auxiliary Generator: (1) 30 volts, 50 amperes, driven by the auxiliary engine
Battery: (2) 12 volts in series

COMMUNICATIONS

Radio: SCR 508 in left front sponson; SCR 506* (command tanks only) in right rear sponson
Interphone: (part of radio) 5 stations plus earphones for all crew members
*Early vehicles may be equipped with SCR 245

FIRE PROTECTION

(2) 10 pound carbon dioxide, fixed
(2) 4 pound carbon dioxide, portable

PERFORMANCE

Maximum Speed: Sustained, level road	21 miles/hour
Short periods, level	24 miles/hour
Maximum Grade:	60 per cent
Maximum Trench:	7.5 feet
Maximum Vertical Wall:	24 inches
Maximum Fording Depth:	40 inches
Minimum Turning Circle: (diameter)	62 feet
Cruising Range: Roads	approx. 120 miles

CRUISER TANK GRANT I

GENERAL DATA

Crew:	6 or 7 men
Length: w/75mm Gun M2, w/o sandshields	222 inches
Length: w/o gun, w/o sandshields	222 inches
Gun Overhang:	0 inches
Width: Over side doors	107 inches
Height: Over turret periscope	119 inches
Tread:	83 inches
Ground Clearance:	17 inches
Fire Height: 75mm gun	69 inches
Turret Ring Diameter: (inside)	54.5 inches
Weight, Combat Loaded:	62,000 pounds*
Weight, Unstowed:	58,000 pounds*
Power to Weight Ratio: Net	11.0 hp/ton
Gross	12.9 hp/ton
Ground Pressure: Zero penetration	12.7 psi

*All weights based on T51 tracks

ARMOR

Type: Turret, cast homogeneous steel; Hull, rolled homogeneous steel; riveted assembly

Hull Thickness:	Actual	Angle w/Vertical
Front, Upper	2.0 inches	30 degrees
Middle	1.5 inches	53 degrees
Lower	2.0 inches	0 to 45 degrees
Sides	1.5 inches	0 degrees
Rear	1.5 inches	0 to 10 degrees
Top	0.5 inches	83 to 90 degrees
Floor, Front	1.0 inches	90 degrees
Rear	0.5 inches	90 degrees
Turret Thickness:		
Front	3.0 inches	47 degrees
Sides	2.0 inches	0 to 30 degrees
Rear	2.0 inches	0 degrees
Top	1.25 inches	80 to 90 degrees

ARMAMENT

Primary: 75mm Gun M2 in Mount M1 in right front of hull

Traverse: Manual	30 degrees (15 degrees L or R)
Elevation: Manual	+20 to −9 degrees
Firing Rate: (max)	20 rounds/minute
Loading System:	Manual
Stabilizer System:	Elevation only

37mm Gun M5 or M6 in Mount M24 in turret

Traverse: Hydraulic and manual	360 degrees
Traverse Rate: (max)	20 seconds/360 degrees
Elevation: Manual	+60 to −7 degrees
Firing Rate: (max)	30 rounds/minute
Loading System:	Manual
Stabilizer System:	Elevation only

Secondary:
(1) .30 caliber MG M1919A4 coaxial w/37mm gun in turret
(2) .30 caliber MG M1919A4 fixed in front plate*
Optional (1) .30 caliber MG M1919A4 flexible AA on turret hatch
(1) 2 inch Mortar Mk I (smoke) fixed in turret
Provision for (2) .45 caliber SMG M1928A1
* (1) in late production vehicles

AMMUNITION

65 rounds 75mm	14 rounds 2 inch (smoke)
128 rounds 37mm	6 hand grenades
640 rounds .45 caliber	
4084 rounds .30 caliber	

FIRE CONTROL AND VISION EQUIPMENT

Primary Weapon:	Direct	Indirect
75mm Gun	Periscope M1 with Telescope M45	
37mm Gun	Periscope M2 with Telescope M40	

Vision Devices:	Direct	Indirect
Driver	Hatch	Protectoscope (1)
Gunner (75)	None	Periscope M1 (1)
Loader (75)	Hatch and pistol port	Protectoscope (1)
Commander	Hatch	Periscope, Vickers (1)
Gunner (37)	Pistol port	Periscope M2 (1) and Protectoscope (1)
Loader (37)	Pistol port	Protectoscope (1)

Total Periscopes: (3)
Total Protectoscopes: (7)
Total Pistol Ports: Hull (4), Turret (2)

ENGINE

Make and Model: Wright (Continental) R975 EC2
Type: 9 cylinder, 4 cycle, radial
Cooling System: Air Ignition: Magneto

Displacement:	973 cubic inches
Bore and Stroke:	5 x 5.5 inches
Compression Ratio:	6.3:1
Net Horsepower (max):	340 hp at 2400 rpm
Gross Horsepower (max):	400 hp at 2400 rpm
Net Torque (max):	800 ft-lb at 1800 rpm
Gross Torque (max):	890 ft-lb at 1800 rpm
Weight:	1137 lb, dry
Fuel: 92 octane gasoline	175 gallons
Engine Oil:	36 quarts

POWER TRAIN

Clutch: Dry disc, 2 or 3 plate
Transmission: Synchromesh, 5 speeds forward, 1 reverse

Gear Ratios:				
	1st	7.56:1	4th	1.11:1
	2nd	3.11:1	5th	0.73:1
	3rd	1.78:1	reverse	5.65:1

Steering: Controlled differential
Bevel Gear Ratio: 3.53:1 Steering Ratio: 1.515:1
Brakes: Mechanical, external contracting
Final Drive: Herringbone gear Gear Ratio: 2.84:1
Drive Sprocket: At front of vehicle with 13 teeth
Pitch Diameter: 25.038 inches

RUNNING GEAR

Suspension: Vertical volute spring
12 wheels in 6 bogies (3 bogies/track)
Tire Size: 20 x 9 inches
6 track return rollers (1 on top of each bogie)
Adjustable idler at rear of each track
Idler Size: 22 x 9 inches
Tracks: Outside guide; WE 210, T41, T48, and T51
Type: (WE 210) Double pin, 16.0 inch width, double I, rubber
(T41) Double pin, 16.0 inch width, smooth rubber
(T48) Double pin, 16.56 inch width, chevron, rubber
(T51) Double pin, 16.56 inch width, smooth, rubber
Pitch: 6 inches
Shoes per Vehicle: 158 (79/track)
Ground Contact Length: 147 inches

ELECTRICAL SYSTEM

Nominal Voltage: 24 volts DC
Main Generator: (1) 24 volts, 50 amperes, driven by power take-off from main engine
Auxiliary Generator: (1) 30 volts, 50 amperes, driven by the auxiliary engine
Battery: (2) 12 volts in series

COMMUNICATIONS

Radio: British Wireless Set No. 19 in rear of turret
Interphone: (part of radio) 5 stations plus earphones for all crew members

FIRE PROTECTION

(2) 10 pound carbon dioxide, fixed
(2) 4 pound carbon dioxide, portable
(2) Pyrene, portable

PERFORMANCE

Maximum Speed: Sustained, level road	21 miles/hour
Short periods, level	24 miles/hour
Maximum Grade:	60 per cent
Maximum Trench:	7.5 feet
Maximum Vertical Wall:	24 inches
Maximum Fording Depth:	40 inches
Minimum Turning Circle: (diameter)	62 feet
Cruising Range: Roads	approx. 120 miles

MEDIUM TANK M3A1

GENERAL DATA

Crew:	6 or 7 men
Length: w/75mm Gun M2, w/o sandshields	222 inches
Length: w/75mm Gun M3, w/o sandshields	241 inches
Length: w/o gun, w/o sandshields	222 inches
Gun Overhang: 75mm Gun M3	19 inches
Width: Over side doors	107 inches
Height: Over cupola	123 inches
Tread:	83 inches
Ground Clearance:	17 inches
Fire Height: 75mm gun	69 inches
Turret Ring Diameter: (inside)	54.5 inches
Weight, Combat Loaded:	63,000 pounds*
Weight, Unstowed:	58,900 pounds*
Power to Weight Ratio: Net	10.8 hp/ton
Gross	12.7 hp/ton
Ground Pressure: Zero penetration	12.9 psi

*All weights based on T48 or T51 tracks

ARMOR

Type: Turret, cast homogeneous steel; Upper hull cast, lower hull rolled, homogeneous steel; riveted assembly

Hull Thickness:	Actual	Angle w/Vertical
Front, Upper	2.0 inches	30 degrees
Middle	1.5 inches	53 degrees
Lower	2.0 inches	0 to 45 degrees
Sides	1.5 inches	0 degrees
Rear	1.5 inches	0 to 10 degrees
Top	0.5 inches	83 to 90 degrees
Floor, Front	1.0 inches	90 degrees
Rear	0.5 inches	90 degrees
Turret Thickness:		
Front	2.0 inches	47 degrees
Sides	2.0 inches	5 degrees
Rear	2.0 inches	5 degrees
Top	0.875 inches	90 degrees

ARMAMENT

Primary: 75mm Gun M2 or M3 in Mount M1 in right front of hull

Traverse: Manual	30 degrees (15 degrees L or R)
Elevation: Manual	+20 to −9 degrees
Firing Rate: (max)	20 rounds/minute
Loading System:	Manual
Stabilizer System:	Elevation only

37mm Gun M5 or M6 in Mount M24 in turret

Traverse: Hydraulic and manual	360 degrees
Traverse Rate: (max)	20 seconds/360 degrees
Elevation: Manual	+60 to −7 degrees
Firing Rate: (max)	30 rounds/minute
Loading System:	Manual
Stabilizer System:	Elevation only

Secondary:
- (1) .30 caliber MG M1919A4 in turret cupola
- (1) .30 caliber MG M1919A4 coaxial w/37mm gun in turret
- (1) .30 caliber MG M1919A4 fixed in front plate*
- Provision for (1) .45 caliber SMG M1928A1*

*(2) in early production vehicles

AMMUNITION

50 rounds 75mm	12 hand grenades
178 rounds 37mm	
1200 rounds .45 caliber	
9200 rounds .30 caliber	

FIRE CONTROL AND VISION EQUIPMENT

Primary Weapon:	Direct	Indirect
75mm Gun	Periscope M1 with Telescope M21A1	Gunner's Quadrant M1
37mm Gun	Periscope M2 with Telescope M19A1	

Vision Devices:	Direct	Indirect
Driver	Hatch	Protectoscope (1)
Gunner (75)	None	Periscope M1 (1)
Loader (75)	Hatch and pistol port	Protectoscope (1)
Commander	Hatch and vision slots (2)	Protectoscope (1)
Gunner (37)	None	Periscope M2 (1)
Loader (37)	Pistol port	Protectoscope (1)

Total Periscopes: M1 (1), M2 (1)
Total Protectoscopes: (6)*
Total Pistol Ports: Hull (3)#, Turret (1)

*Very late production (5), #Very late production (2)

ENGINE

Make and Model: Wright (Continental) R975 EC2
Type: 9 cylinder, 4 cycle, radial
Cooling System: Air Ignition: Magneto

Displacement:	973 cubic inches
Bore and Stroke:	5 x 5.5 inches
Compression Ratio:	6.3:1
Net Horsepower (max):	340 hp at 2400 rpm
Gross Horsepower (max):	400 hp at 2400 rpm
Net Torque (max):	800 ft-lb at 1800 rpm
Gross Torque (max):	890 ft-lb at 1800 rpm
Weight:	1137 lb, dry
Fuel: 92 octane gasoline	175 gallons
Engine Oil:	36 quarts

POWER TRAIN

Clutch: Dry disc, 2 or 3 plate
Transmission: Synchromesh, 5 speeds forward, 1 reverse

Gear Ratios:				
1st	7.56:1	4th	1.11:1
2nd	3.11:1	5th	0.73:1
3rd	1.78:1	reverse	5.65:1

Steering: Controlled differential
Bevel Gear Ratio: 3.53:1 Steering Ratio: 1.515:1
Brakes: Mechanical, external contracting
Final Drive: Herringbone gear Gear Ratio: 2.84:1
Drive Sprocket: At front of vehicle with 13 teeth
Pitch Diameter: 25.038 inches

RUNNING GEAR

Suspension: Vertical volute spring
- 12 wheels in 6 bogies (3 bogies/track)
- Tire Size: 20 x 9 inches
- 6 track return rollers (1 on top of each bogie)*
- Adjustable idler at rear of each track
- Idler Size: 22 x 9 inches

Tracks: Outside guide; T41, T48, T49, and T51
- Type: (T41) Double pin, 16.0 inch width, smooth, rubber
- (T48) Double pin, 16.56 inch width, chevron, rubber
- (T49) Double pin, 16.56 inch width, parallel bar, steel
- (T51) Double pin, 16.56 inch width, smooth, rubber

Pitch: 6 inches
Shoes per Vehicle: 158 (79/track)
Ground Contact Length: 147 inches

*At rear of bogie on late production tanks

ELECTRICAL SYSTEM

Nominal Voltage: 24 volts DC
Main Generator: (1) 24 volts, 50 amperes, driven by power take-off from main engine
Auxiliary Generator: (1) 30 volts, 50 amperes, driven by the auxiliary engine
Battery: (2) 12 volts in series

COMMUNICATIONS

Radio: SCR 508 in left front sponson; SCR 506*(command tanks only) in right rear sponson
Interphone: (part of radio) 5 stations plus earphones for all crew members

*Early vehicles may be equipped with SCR 245

FIRE PROTECTION

- (2) 10 pound carbon dioxide, fixed
- (2) 4 pound carbon dioxide, portable

PERFORMANCE

Maximum Speed: Sustained, level road	21 miles/hour
Short periods, level	24 miles/hour
Maximum Grade:	60 per cent
Maximum Trench:	7.5 feet
Maximum Vertical Wall:	24 inches
Maximum Fording Depth:	40 inches
Minimum Turning Circle: (diameter)	62 feet
Cruising Range: Roads	approx. 120 miles

MEDIUM TANK M3A2

GENERAL DATA

Crew:	6 or 7 men
Length: w/75mm Gun M2, w/o sandshields	222 inches
Length: w/75mm Gun M3, w/o sandshields	241 inches
Length: w/o gun, w/o sandshields	222 inches
Gun Overhang: 75mm Gun M3	19 inches
Width: Over side doors	107 inches
Height: Over cupola	123 inches
Tread:	83 inches
Ground Clearance:	17 inches
Fire Height: 75mm gun	69 inches
Turret Ring Diameter: (inside)	54.5 inches
Weight, Combat Loaded:	60,400 pounds*
Weight, Unstowed:	56,300 pounds*
Power to Weight Ratio: Net	11.3 hp/ton
Gross	13.2 hp/ton
Ground Pressure: Zero penetration	12.4 psi

*All weights based on T48 or T51 tracks

ARMOR

Type: Turret, cast homogeneous steel; Hull, rolled homogeneous steel; welded assembly

	Actual	Angle w/Vertical
Hull Thickness:		
Front, Upper	2.0 inches	30 degrees
Middle	1.5 inches	53 degrees
Lower	2.0 inches	0 to 45 degrees
Sides	1.5 inches	0 degrees
Rear	1.5 inches	0 to 10 degrees
Top	0.5 inches	83 to 90 degrees
Floor, Front	1.0 inches	90 degrees
Rear	0.5 inches	90 degrees
Turret Thickness:		
Front	2.0 inches	47 degrees
Sides	2.0 inches	5 degrees
Rear	2.0 inches	5 degrees
Top	0.875 inches	90 degrees

ARMAMENT

Primary: 75mm Gun M2 or M3 in Mount M1 in right front of hull

Traverse: Manual	30 degrees (15 degrees L or R)
Elevation: Manual	+20 to −9 degrees
Firing Rate: (max)	20 rounds/minute
Loading System:	Manual
Stabilizer System:	Elevation only

37mm Gun M5 or M6 in Mount M24 in turret

Traverse: Hydraulic and manual	360 degrees
Traverse Rate: (max)	20 seconds/360 degrees
Elevation: Manual	+60 to −7 degrees
Firing Rate: (max)	30 rounds/minute
Loading System:	Manual
Stabilizer System:	Elevation only

Secondary:
(1) .30 caliber MG M1919A4 in turret cupola
(1) .30 caliber MG M1919A4 coaxial w/37mm gun in turret
(1) .30 caliber MG M1919A4 fixed in front plate*
Provision for (1) .45 caliber SMG M1928A1*
* (2) in early production vehicles

AMMUNITION

50 rounds 75mm
178 rounds 37mm
1200 rounds .45 caliber
9200 rounds .30 caliber
12 hand grenades

FIRE CONTROL AND VISION EQUIPMENT

Primary Weapon:	Direct	Indirect
75mm Gun	Periscope M1 with Telescope M21A1	Gunner's Quadrant M1
37mm Gun	Periscope M2 with Telescope M19A1	

Vision Devices:	Direct	Indirect
Driver	Hatch	Protectoscope (1)
Gunner (75)	None	Periscope M1 (1)
Loader (75)	Hatch and pistol port	Protectoscope (1)
Commander	Hatch and vision slots (2)	Protectoscope (1)
Gunner (37)	None	Periscope M2 (1)
Loader (37)	Pistol port	Protectoscope (1)

Total Periscopes: M1 (1), M2 (1)
Total Protectoscopes: (7)*
Total Pistol Ports: Hull (4)#, Turret (1)
*Very late production (6), #Very late production (3)

ENGINE

Make and Model: Wright (Continental) R975 EC2
Type: 9 cylinder, 4 cycle, radial
Cooling System: Air   Ignition: Magneto

Displacement:	973 cubic inches
Bore and Stroke:	5 x 5.5 inches
Compression Ratio:	6.3:1
Net Horsepower (max):	340 hp at 2400 rpm
Gross Horsepower (max):	400 hp at 2400 rpm
Net Torque (max):	800 ft-lb at 1800 rpm
Gross Torque (max):	890 ft-lb at 1800 rpm
Weight:	1137 lb, dry
Fuel: 92 octane gasoline	175 gallons
Engine Oil:	36 quarts

POWER TRAIN

Clutch: Dry disc, 2 or 3 plate
Transmission: Synchromesh, 5 speeds forward, 1 reverse

Gear Ratios:				
1st	7.56:1	4th	1.11:1
2nd	3.11:1	5th	0.73:1
3rd	1.78:1	reverse	5.65:1

Steering: Controlled differential
Bevel Gear Ratio: 3.53:1   Steering Ratio: 1.515:1
Brakes: Mechanical, external contracting
Final Drive: Herringbone gear   Gear Ratio: 2.84:1
Drive Sprocket: At front of vehicle with 13 teeth
Pitch Diameter: 25.038 inches

RUNNING GEAR

Suspension: Vertical volute spring
12 wheels in 6 bogies (3 bogies/track)
Tire Size: 20 x 9 inches
6 track return rollers (1 on top of each bogie)*
Adjustable idler at rear of each track
Idler Size: 22 x 9 inches
Tracks: Outside guide; T41, T48, T49, and T51
Type: (T41) Double pin, 16.0 inch width, smooth, rubber
(T48) Double pin, 16.56 inch width, chevron, rubber
(T49) Double pin, 16.56 inch width, parallel bar, steel
(T51) Double pin, 16.56 inch width, smooth, rubber
Pitch: 6 inches
Shoes per Vehicle: 158 (79/track)
Ground Contact Length: 147 inches
*At rear of bogie on late production tanks

ELECTRICAL SYSTEM

Nominal Voltage: 24 volts DC
Main Generator: (1) 24 volts, 50 amperes, driven by power take-off from main engine
Auxiliary Generator: (1) 30 volts, 50 amperes, driven by the auxiliary engine
Battery: (2) 12 volts in series

COMMUNICATIONS

Radio: SCR 508 in left front sponson; SCR 506* (command tanks only) in right rear sponson
Interphone: (part of radio) 5 stations plus earphones for all crew members
*Early vehicles may be equipped with SCR 245

FIRE PROTECTION

(2) 10 pound carbon dioxide, fixed
(2) 4 pound carbon dioxide, portable

PERFORMANCE

Maximum Speed: Sustained, level road	21 miles/hour
Short periods, level	24 miles/hour
Maximum Grade:	60 per cent
Maximum Trench:	7.5 feet
Maximum Vertical Wall:	24 inches
Maximum Fording Depth:	40 inches
Minimum Turning Circle: (diameter)	62 feet
Cruising Range: Roads	approx. 120 miles

MEDIUM TANK M3A3

GENERAL DATA

Crew:	6 or 7 men
Length: w/75mm Gun M2, w/o sandshields	222 inches
Length: w/75mm Gun M3, w/o sandshields	241 inches
Length: w/o gun, w/o sandshields	222 inches
Gun Overhang: 75mm Gun M3	19 inches
Width: Over side doors	107 inches
Height: Over cupola	123 inches
Tread:	83 inches
Ground Clearance:	17 inches
Fire Height: 75mm gun	69 inches
Turret Ring Diameter: (inside)	54.5 inches
Weight, Combat Loaded:	63,000 pounds*
Weight, Unstowed:	59,000 pounds*
Power to Weight Ratio: Net	11.9 hp/ton
Gross	13.0 hp/ton
Ground Pressure: Zero penetration	12.9 psi

*All weights based on T48 or T51 tracks

ARMOR

Type: Turret, cast homogeneous steel; Hull, rolled homogeneous steel; welded assembly

Hull Thickness:	Actual	Angle w/Vertical
Front, Upper	2.0 inches	30 degrees
Middle	1.5 inches	53 degrees
Lower	2.0 inches	0 to 45 degrees
Sides	1.5 inches	0 degrees
Rear	1.5 inches	0 to 10 degrees
Top	0.5 inches	83 to 90 degrees
Floor, Front	1.0 inches	90 degrees
Rear	0.5 inches	90 degrees
Turret Thickness:		
Front	2.0 inches	47 degrees
Sides	2.0 inches	5 degrees
Rear	2.0 inches	5 degrees
Top	0.875 inches	90 degrees

ARMAMENT

Primary: 75mm Gun M2 or M3 in Mount M1 in right front of hull

Traverse: Manual	30 degrees (15 degrees L or R)
Elevation: Manual	+20 to −9 degrees
Firing Rate: (max)	20 rounds/minute
Loading System:	Manual
Stabilizer System:	Elevation only

37mm Gun M5 or M6 in Mount M24 in turret

Traverse: Hydraulic and manual	360 degrees
Traverse Rate: (max)	20 seconds/360 degrees
Elevation: Manual	+60 to −7 degrees
Firing Rate: (max)	30 rounds/minute
Loading System:	Manual
Stabilizer System:	Elevation only

Secondary:
- (1) .30 caliber MG M1919A4 in turret cupola
- (1) .30 caliber MG M1919A4 coaxial w/37mm gun in turret
- (1) .30 caliber MG M1919A4 fixed in front plate*
- Provision for (1) .45 caliber SMG M1928A1*

* (2) in early production vehicles

AMMUNITION

50 rounds 75mm	12 hand grenades
178 rounds 37mm	
1200 rounds .45 caliber	
9200 rounds .30 caliber	

FIRE CONTROL AND VISION EQUIPMENT

Primary Weapon:	Direct	Indirect
75mm Gun	Periscope M1 with Telescope M21A1	Gunner's Quadrant M1
37mm Gun	Periscope M2 with Telescope M19A1	

Vision Devices:	Direct	Indirect
Driver	Hatch	Protectoscope (1)
Gunner (75)	None	Periscope M1 (1)
Loader (75)	Hatch and pistol port	Protectoscope (1)
Commander	Hatch and vision slots (2)	Protectoscope (1)
Gunner (37)	None	Periscope M2 (1)
Loader (37)	Pistol port	Protectoscope (1)

Total Periscopes: M1 (1), M2 (1)
Total Protectoscopes: (7)*
Total Pistol Ports: Hull (4)#, Turret (1)

*Very late production (6), #Very late production (3)

ENGINE

Make and Model: General Motors 6046
Type: 12 cylinder, 2 cycle, twin in-line
Cooling System: Liquid Ignition: Compression

Displacement:	850 cubic inches
Bore and Stroke:	4.25 x 5 inches
Compression Ratio:	16:1
Net Horsepower (max):	375 hp at 2100 rpm*
Gross Horsepower (max):	410 hp at 2900 rpm#
Net Torque (max):	1000 ft-lb at 1400 rpm*
Gross Torque (max):	885 ft-lb at 1900 rpm#
Weight:	5110 lb, dry
Fuel: 40 cetane diesel oil	148 gallons
Engine Oil:	28 quarts

*Crankshaft rpm #Propeller shaft rpm

POWER TRAIN

Clutch: Dry disc, 2 plate (2)
Transfer Case Gear Ratio: 0.73:1
Transmission: Synchromesh, 5 speeds forward, 1 reverse

Gear Ratios:				
1st	7.56:1	4th	1.11:1
2nd	3.11:1	5th	0.73:1
3rd	1.78:1	reverse	5.65:1

Steering: Controlled differential
Bevel Gear Ratio: 3.53:1 Steering Ratio: 1.515:1
Brakes: Mechanical, external contracting
Final Drive: Herringbone gear Gear Ratio: 2.84:1
Drive Sprocket: At front of vehicle with 13 teeth
Pitch Diameter: 25.038 inches

RUNNING GEAR

Suspension: Vertical volute spring
12 wheels in 6 bogies (3 bogies/track)
Tire Size: 20 x 9 inches
6 track return rollers (1 on top of each bogie)
Adjustable idler at rear of each track
Idler Size: 22 x 9 inches
Tracks: Outside guide; T41, T48, T49, and T51
Type: (T41) Double pin, 16.0 inch width, smooth, rubber
(T48) Double pin, 16.56 inch width, chevron, rubber
(T49) Double pin, 16.56 inch width, parallel bar, steel
(T51) Double pin, 16.56 inch width, smooth, rubber
Pitch: 6 inches
Shoes per Vehicle: 158 (79/track)
Ground Contact Length: 147 inches

ELECTRICAL SYSTEM

Nominal Voltage: 24 volts DC
Main Generator: (1) 24 volts, 50 amperes, driven by power take-off from main engine
Auxiliary Generator: (1) 30 volts, 50 amperes, driven by the auxiliary engine
Battery: (2) 12 volts in series

COMMUNICATIONS

Radio: SCR 508 in left front sponson; SCR 506* (command tanks only) in right rear sponson
Interphone: (part of radio) 5 stations plus earphones for all crew members

*Early vehicles may be equipped with SCR 245

FIRE PROTECTION

(2) 10 pound carbon dioxide, fixed
(2) 4 pound carbon dioxide, portable

PERFORMANCE

Maximum Speed: Sustained, level road	25 miles/hour
Short periods, level	30 miles/hour
Maximum Grade:	60 per cent
Maximum Trench:	7.5 feet
Maximum Vertical Wall:	24 inches
Maximum Fording Depth:	36 inches
Minimum Turning Circle: (diameter)	62 feet
Cruising Range: Roads	approx. 150 miles

MEDIUM TANK M3A4

GENERAL DATA

Crew:	6 or 7 men
Length: w/75mm Gun M2, w/o sandshields	242 inches
Length: w/75mm Gun M3, w/o sandshields	261 inches
Length: w/o gun, w/o sandshields	242 inches
Gun Overhang: 75mm Gun M3	19 inches
Width: w/o side doors	104 inches
Height: Over cupola	123 inches
Tread:	83 inches
Ground Clearance:	16 inches
Fire Height: 75mm gun	69 inches
Turret Ring Diameter: (inside)	54.5 inches
Weight, Combat Loaded:	64,000 pounds*
Weight, Unstowed:	60,000 pounds*
Power to Weight Ratio: Net	11.6 hp/ton
Gross	13.3 hp/ton
Ground Pressure: Zero penetration	12.1 psi

*All weights based on T48 or T51 tracks

ARMOR

Type: Turret, cast homogeneous steel; Hull, rolled homogeneous steel; riveted assembly

Hull Thickness:	Actual	Angle w/Vertical
Front, Upper	2.0 inches	30 degrees
Middle	1.5 inches	53 degrees
Lower	2.0 inches	0 to 45 degrees
Sides	1.5 inches	0 degrees
Rear	1.5 inches	0 to 20 degrees
Top	0.5 inches	83 to 90 degrees
Floor, Front	1.0 inches	90 degrees
Rear	0.5 inches	90 degrees
Turret Thickness:		
Front	2.0 inches	47 degrees
Sides	2.0 inches	5 degrees
Rear	2.0 inches	5 degrees
Top	0.875 inches	90 degrees

ARMAMENT

Primary: 75mm Gun M2 or M3 in Mount M1 in right front of hull

Traverse: Manual	30 degrees (15 degrees L or R)
Elevation: Manual	+20 to −9 degrees
Firing Rate: (max)	20 rounds/minute
Loading System:	Manual
Stabilizer System:	Elevation only

37mm Gun M5 or M6 in Mount M24 in turret

Traverse: Hydraulic and manual	360 degrees
Traverse Rate: (max)	20 seconds/360 degrees
Elevation: Manual	+60 to −7 degrees
Firing Rate: (max)	30 rounds/minute
Loading System:	Manual
Stabilizer System:	Elevation only

Secondary:
(1) .30 caliber MG M1919A4 in turret cupola
(1) .30 caliber MG M1919A4 coaxial w/37mm gun in turret
(1) .30 caliber MG M1919A4 fixed in front plate*
Provision for (1) .45 caliber SMG M1928A1*
* (2) in early production vehicles

AMMUNITION

50 rounds 75mm	12 hand grenades
178 rounds 37mm	
1200 rounds .45 caliber	
9200 rounds .30 caliber	

FIRE CONTROL AND VISION EQUIPMENT

Primary Weapon:	Direct	Indirect
75mm Gun	Periscope M1 with Telescope M21A1	Gunner's Quadrant M1
37mm Gun	Periscope M2 with Telescope M19A1	

Vision Devices:	Direct	Indirect
Driver	Hatch	Protectoscope (1)
Gunner (75)	None	Periscope M1 (1)
Loader (75)	Hatch and pistol port	Protectoscope (1)
Commander	Hatch and vision slots (2)	Protectoscope (1)
Gunner (37)	None	Periscope M2 (1)
Loader (37)	Pistol port	Protectoscope (1)

Total Periscopes: M1 (1), M2 (1)
Total Protectoscopes: (7)*
Total Pistol Ports: Hull (4)#, Turret (1)
*Very late production (6), #Very late production (3)

ENGINE

Make and Model: Chrysler A57
Type: 30 cylinder, 4 cycle, multibank
Cooling System: Liquid   Ignition: Battery

Displacement:	1253 cubic inches
Bore and Stroke:	4.37 x 4.5 inches
Compression Ratio:	6.2:1
Net Horsepower (max):	370 hp at 2400 rpm#
Gross Horsepower (max):	425 hp at 2850 rpm*
Net Torque (max):	1020 ft-lb at 1200 rpm#
Gross Torque (max):	1060 ft-lb at 1400 rpm*
Weight:	5400 lb, dry
Fuel: 80 octane gasoline	160 gallons
Engine Oil:	32 quarts

#Propeller shaft rpm   *Crankshaft rpm

POWER TRAIN

Transfer Gear Ratio: 1.19:1
Clutch: Dry disc, 2 plate
Transmission: Synchromesh, 5 speeds forward, 1 reverse

Gear Ratios:			
1st	7.56:1	4th	1.11:1
2nd	3.11:1	5th	0.73:1
3rd	1.78:1	reverse	5.65:1

Steering: Controlled differential
Bevel Gear Ratio: 3.53:1   Steering Ratio: 1.515:1
Brakes: Mechanical, external contracting
Final Drive: Herringbone gear   Gear Ratio: 2.84:1
Drive Sprocket: At front of vehicle with 13 teeth
Pitch Diameter: 25.038 inches

RUNNING GEAR

Suspension: Vertical volute spring
12 wheels in 6 bogies (3 bogies/track)
Tire Size: 20 x 9 inches
6 track return rollers (1 at rear of each bogie)*
Adjustable idler at rear of each track
Idler Size: 22 x 9 inches
Tracks: Outside guide; T41, T48, T49, and T51
Type: (T41) Double pin, 16.0 inch width, smooth, rubber
(T48) Double pin, 16.56 inch width, chevron, rubber
(T49) Double pin, 16.56 inch width, parallel bar, steel
(T51) Double pin, 16.56 inch width, smooth, rubber
Pitch: 6 inches
Shoes per Vehicle: 166 (83/track)
Ground Contact Length: 160 inches
*On top of bogie on early tanks

ELECTRICAL SYSTEM

Nominal Voltage: 24 volts DC
Main Generator: (1) 24 volts, 50 amperes, driven by power take-off from main engine
Auxiliary Generator: (1) 30 volts, 50 amperes, driven by the auxiliary engine
Battery: (2) 12 volts in series

COMMUNICATIONS

Radio: SCR 508 in left front sponson; SCR 506* (command tanks only) in right rear sponson
Interphone: (part of radio) 5 stations plus earphones for all crew members
*Early vehicles may be equipped with SCR 245

FIRE PROTECTION

(2) 10 pound carbon dioxide, fixed
(2) 4 pound carbon dioxide, portable

PERFORMANCE

Maximum Speed: Sustained, level road	20 miles/hour
Short periods, level	25 miles/hour
Maximum Grade:	60 per cent
Maximum Trench:	8 feet
Maximum Vertical Wall:	24 inches
Maximum Fording Depth:	40 inches
Minimum Turning Circle: (diameter)	70 feet
Cruising Range: Roads	approx. 100 miles

MEDIUM TANK M3A5

GENERAL DATA

Crew:	6 or 7 men
Length: w/75mm Gun M2, w/o sandshields	222 inches
Length: w/75mm Gun M3, w/o sandshields	241 inches
Length: w/o gun, w/o sandshields	222 inches
Gun Overhang: 75mm Gun M3	19 inches
Width: Over side doors	107 inches
Height: Over cupola	123 inches
Tread:	83 inches
Ground Clearance:	17 inches
Fire Height: 75mm gun	69 inches
Turret Ring Diameter: (inside)	54.5 inches
Weight, Combat Loaded:	64,000 pounds*
Weight, Unstowed:	60,000 pounds*
Power to Weight Ratio: Net	11.7 hp/ton
Gross	12.8 hp/ton
Ground Pressure: Zero penetration	13.1 psi

*All weights based on T48 or T51 tracks

ARMOR

Type: Turret, cast homogeneous steel; Hull, rolled homogeneous steel; riveted assembly

Hull Thickness:	Actual	Angle w/Vertical
Front, Upper	2.0 inches	30 degrees
Middle	1.5 inches	53 degrees
Lower	2.0 inches	0 to 45 degrees
Sides	1.5 inches	0 degrees
Rear	1.5 inches	0 to 10 degrees
Top	0.5 inches	83 to 90 degrees
Floor, Front	1.0 inches	90 degrees
Rear	0.5 inches	90 degrees
Turret Thickness:		
Front	2.0 inches	47 degrees
Sides	2.0 inches	5 degrees
Rear	2.0 inches	5 degrees
Top	0.875 inches	90 degrees

ARMAMENT

Primary: 75mm Gun M2 or M3 in Mount M1 in right front of hull

Traverse: Manual	30 degrees (15 degrees L or R)
Elevation: Manual	+20 to −9 degrees
Firing Rate: (max)	20 rounds/minute
Loading System:	Manual
Stabilizer System:	Elevation only

37mm Gun M5 or M6 in Mount M24 in turret

Traverse: Hydraulic and manual	360 degrees
Traverse Rate: (max)	20 seconds/360 degrees
Elevation: Manual	+60 to −7 degrees
Firing Rate: (max)	30 rounds/minute
Loading System:	Manual
Stabilizer System:	Elevation only

Secondary:
- (1) .30 caliber MG M1919A4 in turret cupola
- (1) .30 caliber MG M1919A4 coaxial w/37mm gun in turret
- (1) .30 caliber MG M1919A4 fixed in front plate*
- Provision for (1) .45 caliber SMG M1928A1*

*(2) in early production vehicles

AMMUNITION

50 rounds 75mm	12 hand grenades
178 rounds 37mm	
1200 rounds .45 caliber	
9200 rounds .30 caliber	

FIRE CONTROL AND VISION EQUIPMENT

Primary Weapon:	Direct	Indirect
75mm Gun	Periscope M1 with Telescope M21A1	Gunner's Quadrant M1
37mm Gun	Periscope M2 with Telescope M19A1	

Vision Devices:	Direct	Indirect
Driver	Hatch	Protectoscope (1)
Gunner (75)	None	Periscope M1 (1)
Loader (75)	Hatch and pistol port	Protectoscope (1)
Commander	Hatch and vision slots (2)	Protectoscope (1)
Gunner (37)	None	Periscope M2 (1)
Loader (37)	Pistol port	Protectoscope (1)

Total Periscopes: M1 (1), M2 (1)
Total Protectoscopes: (7)*
Total Pistol Ports: Hull (4)#, Turret (1)
*Very late production (6), #Very late production (3)

ENGINE

Make and Model: General Motors 6046
Type: 12 cylinder, 2 cycle, twin in-line
Cooling System: Liquid   Ignition: Compression

Displacement:	850 cubic inches
Bore and Stroke:	4.25 x 5 inches
Compression Ratio:	16:1
Net Horsepower (max):	375 hp at 2100 rpm*
Gross Horsepower (max):	410 hp at 2900 rpm#
Net Torque (max):	1000 ft-lb at 1400 rpm*
Gross Torque (max):	885 ft-lb at 1900 rpm#
Weight:	5110 lb, dry
Fuel: 40 cetane diesel oil	148 gallons
Engine Oil:	28 quarts

*Crankshaft rpm   #Propeller shaft rpm

POWER TRAIN

Clutch: Dry disc, 2 plate (2)
Transfer Case Gear Ratio: 0.73:1
Transmission: Synchromesh, 5 speeds forward, 1 reverse

Gear Ratios:				
	1st	7.56:1	4th	1.11:1
	2nd	3.11:1	5th	0.73:1
	3rd	1.78:1	reverse	5.65:1

Steering: Controlled differential
Bevel Gear Ratio: 3.53:1   Steering Ratio: 1.515:1
Brakes: Mechanical, external contracting
Final Drive: Herringbone gear   Gear Ratio: 2.84:1
Drive Sprocket: At front of vehicle with 13 teeth
Pitch Diameter: 25.038 inches

RUNNING GEAR

Suspension: Vertical volute spring
12 wheels in 6 bogies (3 bogies/track)
Tire Size: 20 x 9 inches
6 track return rollers (1 on top of each bogie)
Adjustable idler at rear of each track
Idler Size: 22 x 9 inches
Tracks: Outside guide; T41, T48, T49, and T51
Type: (T41) Double pin, 16.0 inch width, smooth, rubber
(T48) Double pin, 16.56 inch width, chevron, rubber
(T49) Double pin, 16.56 inch width, parallel bar, steel
(T51) Double pin, 16.56 inch width, smooth, rubber
Pitch: 6 inches
Shoes per Vehicle: 158 (79/track)
Ground Contact Length: 147 inches

ELECTRICAL SYSTEM

Nominal Voltage: 24 volts DC
Main Generator: (1) 24 volts, 50 amperes, driven by power take-off from main engine
Auxiliary Generator: (1) 30 volts, 50 amperes, driven by the auxiliary engine
Battery: (2) 12 volts in series

COMMUNICATIONS

Radio: SCR 508 in left front sponson; SCR 506* (command tanks only) in right rear sponson
Interphone: (part of radio) 5 stations plus earphones for all crew members
*Early vehicles may be equipped with SCR 245

FIRE PROTECTION

(2) 10 pound carbon dioxide, fixed
(2) 4 pound carbon dioxide, portable

PERFORMANCE

Maximum Speed: Sustained, level road	25 miles/hour
Short periods, level	30 miles/hour
Maximum Grade:	60 per cent
Maximum Trench:	7.5 feet
Maximum Vertical Wall:	24 inches
Maximum Fording Depth:	40 inches
Minimum Turning Circle: (diameter)	62 feet
Cruising Range: Roads	approx. 150 miles

CRUISER TANK RAM I

GENERAL DATA

Crew:	5 men
Length: Gun forward, w/front fender	228 inches
Length: Gun to rear, w/front fender	228 inches
Length: w/o gun, w/front fender	228 inches
Gun Overhang: Gun forward	0 inches
Width: Over side doors	113 inches
Height: Over turret periscope	105 inches
Tread:	83 inches
Ground Clearance:	17 inches
Fire Height:	87 inches
Turret Ring Diameter: (inside)	60 inches
Weight, Combat Loaded:	64,000 pounds
Weight, Unstowed:	60,000 pounds
Power to Weight Ratio: Net	10.6 hp/ton
Gross	12.5 hp/ton
Ground Pressure: Zero penetration	13.1 psi

ARMOR

Type: Turret, cast homogeneous steel; Upper hull cast, lower hull rolled, homogeneous steel; riveted assembly

Hull Thickness:	Actual	Angle w/Vertical
Front, Upper	3.0 to 1.75 inches	0 to 53 degrees
Lower	2.0 inches	0 to 45 degrees
Sides	2.5 to 1.5 inches	0 degrees
Rear	1.5 inches	0 degrees
Top	1.5 to 1.0 inches	83 to 90 degrees
Floor, Front	1.0 inches	90 degrees
Rear	0.5 inches	90 degrees
Turret Thickness:		
Front	3.0 inches	0 to 25 degrees
Sides	3.0 to 2.5 inches	0 to 10 degrees
Rear	2.5 inches	0 degrees
Top	1.0 inches	90 degrees

ARMAMENT

Primary: 2pdr Gun Mk IX or X in combination mount in turret

Traverse: Hydraulic and manual	360 degrees
Traverse Rate: (max)	20 seconds/360 degrees
Elevation: Manual	+20 to −10 degrees
Firing Rate: (max)	30 rounds/minute
Loading System:	Manual
Stabilizer System:	None

Secondary:
- (1) .30 caliber MG M1919A4 flexible for AA mount in turret hatch
- (1) .30 caliber MG M1919A4 coaxial w/2pdr gun in turret
- (1) .30 caliber MG M1919A4 in bow cupola mount
- (1) 2 inch Mortar Mk I (smoke) fixed in turret
- Provision for (2) .45 caliber SMG M1928A1

AMMUNITION

171 rounds 2pdr	44 rounds 2 inch (smoke)
440 rounds .45 caliber	6 hand grenades No. 36, Mk I
4715 rounds .30 caliber	

FIRE CONTROL AND VISION EQUIPMENT

Primary Weapon:	Direct	Indirect
	Telescope No. 33 Mk I	

Vision Devices:	Direct	Indirect
Driver	Hatch	Periscope (1) and Protectoscope (1)
Asst. Driver	Hatch	Protectoscope (1)
Commander	Hatch	Periscope (1)
Gunner	Pistol port	Periscope (1) and Protectoscope (1)
Loader	Pistol port	Protectoscope (1)

Total Periscopes: (3)
Total Protectoscopes: (6)
Total Pistol Ports: Hull (2), Turret (2)

ENGINE

Make and Model: Wright (Continental) R975 EC2
Type: 9 cylinder, 4 cycle, radial
Cooling System: Air   Ignition: Magneto

Displacement:	973 cubic inches
Bore and Stroke:	5 x 5.5 inches
Compression Ratio:	6.3:1
Net Horsepower (max):	340 hp at 2400 rpm
Gross Horsepower (max):	400 hp at 2400 rpm
Net Torque (max):	800 ft-lb at 1800 rpm
Gross Torque (max):	890 ft-lb at 1800 rpm
Weight:	1137 lb, dry
Fuel: 92 octane gasoline	175 gallons
Engine Oil:	36 quarts

POWER TRAIN

Clutch: Dry disc, 3 plate
Transmission: Synchromesh, 5 speeds forward, 1 reverse

Gear Ratios:			
1st	7.56:1	4th	1.11:1
2nd	3.11:1	5th	0.73:1
3rd	1.78:1	reverse	5.65:1

Steering: Controlled differential
Bevel Gear Ratio: 3.53:1   Steering Ratio: 1.515:1
Brakes: Mechanical, external contracting
Final Drive: Herringbone gear   Gear Ratio: 2.84:1
Drive Sprocket: At front of vehicle with 13 teeth
Pitch Diameter: 25.038 inches

RUNNING GEAR

Suspension: Vertical volute spring
12 wheels in 6 bogies (3 bogies/track)
Tire Size: 20 x 9 inches
6 track return rollers (1 on top of each bogie)
Adjustable idler at rear of each track
Idler Size: 22 x 9 inches
Tracks: Outside guide; T41
Type: (T41) Double pin, 16.0 inch width, smooth, rubber
Pitch: 6 inches
Shoes per Vehicle: 158 (79/track)
Ground Contact Length: 147 inches

ELECTRICAL SYSTEM

Nominal Voltage: 24 volts DC
Main Generator: (1) 24 volts, 50 amperes, driven by power take-off from main engine
Auxiliary Generator: (1) 30 volts, 50 amperes, driven by the auxiliary engine
Battery: (2) 12 volts in series

COMMUNICATIONS

Radio: British Wireless Set No. 19 in rear of turret
Interphone: (part of radio) 5 stations

FIRE PROTECTION

(2) 10 pound carbon dioxide, fixed
(4) Pyrene, portable

PERFORMANCE

Maximum Speed: Sustained, level road	21 miles/hour
Short periods, level	24 miles/hour
Maximum Grade:	60 per cent
Maximum Trench:	7.5 feet
Maximum Vertical Wall:	24 inches
Maximum Fording Depth:	40 inches
Minimum Turning Circle: (diameter)	62 feet
Cruising Range: Roads	approx. 120 miles

CRUISER TANK RAM II

GENERAL DATA

Crew:	5 men
Length: Gun forward, w/front fender	228 inches
Length: Gun to rear, w/front fender	228 inches
Length: w/o gun, w/front fender	228 inches
Gun Overhang: Gun forward	0 inches
Width: w/o side doors or vent	109 inches
Height: Over turret periscope	105 inches
Tread:	83 inches
Ground Clearance:	17 inches
Fire Height:	87 inches
Turret Ring Diameter: (inside)	60 inches
Weight, Combat Loaded:	65,000 pounds
Weight, Unstowed:	61,000 pounds
Power to Weight Ratio: Net	10.8 hp/ton
Gross	12.3 hp/ton
Ground Pressure: Zero penetration	13.4 psi

ARMOR

Type: Turret, cast homogeneous steel; Upper hull cast, lower hull rolled, homogeneous steel: riveted assembly

Hull Thickness:	Actual	Angle w/Vertical
Front, Upper	3.0 to 2.0 inches	0 to 53 degrees
Lower	2.0 inches	0 to 45 degrees
Sides	2.5 to 1.25 inches	0 degrees
Rear	1.5 inches	0 degrees
Top	1.5 to 1.0 inches	83 to 90 degrees
Floor, Front	1.0 inches	90 degrees
Rear	0.5 inches	90 degrees
Turret Thickness:		
Front	3.0 inches	0 to 25 degrees
Sides	3.0 to 2.5 inches	0 to 10 degrees
Rear	2.5 inches	0 degrees
Top	1.0 inches	90 degrees

ARMAMENT

Primary: 6pdr Gun Mk III or V in combination mount in turret

Traverse: Hydraulic and manual	360 degrees
Traverse Rate: (max)	20 seconds/360 degrees
Elevation: Manual	+20 to −7.5 degrees
Firing Rate: (max)	25 rounds/minute
Loading System:	Manual
Stabilizer System:	Elevation only

Secondary:
- (1) .30 caliber MG M1919A4 flexible for AA mount in turret hatch
- (1) .30 caliber MG M1919A4 coaxial w/6pdr gun in turret
- (1) .30 caliber MG M1919A4 in bow ball mount (or cupola)
- (1) 2 inch Mortar Mk I (smoke) fixed in turret
- Provision for (2) .45 caliber SMG M1928A1

AMMUNITION

- 92 rounds 6pdr
- 440 rounds .45 caliber
- 4440 rounds .30 caliber
- 43 rounds 2 inch (smoke)
- 6 hand grenades No. 36, Mk I

FIRE CONTROL AND VISION EQUIPMENT

Primary Weapon:	Direct	Indirect
	Telescope No. 39 Mk IS	

Vision Devices:	Direct	Indirect
Driver	Hatch	Periscope (1) and Protectoscope (1)
Asst. Driver	Hatch	Periscope (1)
Commander	Hatch	Periscope (1)
Gunner	Pistol port	None
Loader	Pistol port	None

Total Periscopes: (3)
Total Protectoscopes: (1)
Total Pistol Ports: Hull (0), Turret (2)

ENGINE

Make and Model: Continental R975 C1
Type: 9 cylinder, 4 cycle, radial
Cooling System: Air Ignition: Magneto

Displacement:	973 cubic inches
Bore and Stroke:	5 x 5.5 inches
Compression Ratio:	5.7:1
Net Horsepower (max):	350 hp at 2400 rpm
Gross Horsepower (max):	400 hp at 2400 rpm
Net Torque (max):	800 ft-lb at 1800 rpm
Gross Torque (max):	890 ft-lb at 1800 rpm
Weight:	1137 lb, dry
Fuel: 80 octane gasoline	175 gallons
Engine Oil:	36 quarts

POWER TRAIN

Clutch: Dry disc, 2 or 3 plate
Transmission: Synchromesh, 5 speeds forward, 1 reverse

Gear Ratios:	1st	7.56:1	4th	1.11:1
	2nd	3.11:1	5th	0.73:1
	3rd	1.78:1	reverse	5.65:1

Steering: Controlled differential
Bevel Gear Ratio: 3.53:1 Steering Ratio: 1.515:1
Brakes: Mechanical, external contracting
Final Drive: Herringbone gear Gear Ratio: 2.84:1
Drive Sprocket: At front of vehicle with 13 teeth
Pitch Diameter: 25.038 inches

RUNNING GEAR

Suspension: Vertical volute spring
- 12 wheels in 6 bogies (3 bogies/track)
- Tire Size: 20 x 9 inches
- 6 track return rollers (1 at rear of each bogie)
- Adjustable idler at rear of each track
- Idler Size: 22 x 9 inches

Tracks: Outside guide; WE 210, T49, and T51
Type: (WE 210) Double pin, 16.0 inch width, double I, rubber
(T49) Double pin, 16.56 inch width, parallel bar, steel
(T51) Double pin, 16.56 inch width, smooth, rubber
Pitch: 6 inches
Shoes per Vehicle: 158 (79/track)
Ground Contact Length: 147 inches

ELECTRICAL SYSTEM

Nominal Voltage: 24 volts DC
Main Generator: (1) 24 volts, 50 amperes, driven by power take-off from main engine
Auxiliary Generator: (1) 30 volts, 50 amperes, driven by the auxiliary engine
Battery: (2) 12 volts in series

COMMUNICATIONS

Radio: British Wireless Set No. 19 in rear of turret
Interphone: (part of radio) 5 stations

FIRE PROTECTION

- (2) 10 pound carbon dioxide, fixed
- (2) Pyrene, portable
- (2) methyl bromide

PERFORMANCE

Maximum Speed: Sustained, level road	21 miles/hour
Short periods, level	24 miles/hour
Maximum Grade:	60 per cent
Maximum Trench:	7.5 feet
Maximum Vertical Wall:	24 inches
Maximum Fording Depth:	40 inches
Minimum Turning Circle: (diameter)	62 feet
Cruising Range: Roads	approx. 120 miles

MEDIUM TANK T6

GENERAL DATA

Crew:	5 men
Length: Gun forward, w/o sandshields	222 inches
Length: Gun to rear, w/o sandshields	222 inches
Length: w/o gun, w/o sandshields	222 inches
Gun Overhang: Gun forward	0 inches
Width: Over side doors	107 inches
Height: w/cupola	115 inches
Tread:	83 inches
Ground Clearance:	17 inches
Fire Height:	88 inches
Turret Ring Diameter: (inside)	69 inches
Weight, Combat Loaded:	60,058 pounds
Weight, Unstowed:	56,265 pounds
Power to Weight Ratio: Net	11.3 hp/ton
Gross	13.3 hp/ton
Ground Pressure: Zero penetration	12.3 psi

ARMOR

Type: Turret, cast homogeneous steel; Upper hull cast, lower hull rolled, homogeneous steel; riveted assembly

Hull Thickness:	Actual	Angle w/Vertical
Front, Upper	2.0 inches	37 to 55 degrees
Lower	2.0 inches	0 to 45 degrees
Sides	1.5 inches	0 degrees
Rear	1.5 inches	0 to 10 degrees
Top	1.0 inches	83 to 90 degrees
Floor, Front	1.0 inches	90 degrees
Rear	0.5 inches	90 degrees
Turret Thickness:		
Gun Shield	3.0 inches	0 degrees
Front	3.0 inches	30 degrees
Sides	2.0 inches	5 degrees
Rear	2.0 inches	0 degrees
Top	1.0 inches	90 degrees

ARMAMENT

Primary: 75mm Gun M2 in Mount T48 in turret

Traverse: Hydraulic and manual	360 degrees
Traverse Rate: (max)	15 seconds/360 degrees
Elevation: Manual	+25 to −12 degrees
Firing Rate: (max)	20 rounds/minute
Loading System:	Manual
Stabilizer System:	Elevation only

Secondary:
- (1) .30 caliber MG M1919A4 in turret cupola
- (1) .30 caliber MG M1919A4 coaxial w/75mm gun in turret
- (1) .30 caliber MG M1919A4 in bow mount
- (2) .30 caliber MG M1919A4 fixed in front plate
- Provision for (1) .45 caliber SMG M1928A1

AMMUNITION

75 rounds 75mm
1200 rounds .45 caliber
10,000 rounds .30 caliber
12 hand grenades

FIRE CONTROL AND VISION EQUIPMENT

Primary Weapon:	Direct	Indirect
	Sight rotor with telescope	Gunner's Quadrant M1
Vision Devices:	**Direct**	**Indirect**
Driver	Hatch and vision slot	Periscope (1)
Asst. Driver	Vision slot	Protectoscope (1)
Commander	Hatch and vision slots (2)	Protectoscope (1)
Gunner	Pistol port	Sight rotor w/telescope and Protectoscope (1)
Loader	Pistol port	Protectoscope (1)

Total Periscopes: (1)
Total Protectoscopes: (4)
Total Pistol Ports: Hull (0), Turret (2)

ENGINE

Make and Model: Wright (Continental) R975 EC2
Type: 9 cylinder, 4 cycle, radial
Cooling System: Air Ignition: Magneto

Displacement:	973 cubic inches
Bore and Stroke:	5 x 5.5 inches
Compression Ratio:	6.3:1
Net Horsepower (max):	340 hp at 2400 rpm
Gross Horsepower (max):	400 hp at 2400 rpm
Net Torque (max):	800 ft-lb at 1800 rpm
Gross Torque (max):	890 ft-lb at 1800 rpm
Weight:	1137 lb, dry
Fuel: 92 octane gasoline	175 gallons
Engine Oil:	36 quarts

POWER TRAIN

Clutch: Dry disc, 3 plate
Transmission: Synchromesh, 5 speeds forward, 1 reverse

Gear Ratios:				
	1st	7.56:1	4th	1.11:1
	2nd	3.11:1	5th	0.73:1
	3rd	1.78:1	reverse	5.65:1

Steering: Controlled differential
Bevel Gear Ratio: 3.53:1 Steering Rato: 1.515:1
Brakes: Mechanical, external contracting
Final Drive: Herringbone gear Gear Ratio: 2.84:1
Drive Sprocket: At front of vehicle with 13 teeth
Pitch Diameter: 25.038 inches

RUNNING GEAR

Suspension: Vertical volute spring
12 wheels in 6 bogies (3 bogies/track)
Tire Size: 20 x 9 inches
6 track return rollers (1 on top of each bogie)
Adjustable idler at rear of each track
Idler Size: 22 x 9 inches
Tracks: Outside guide; T48 and T51
Type: (T48) Double pin, 16.56 inch width, chevron, rubber
(T51) Double pin, 16.56 inch width, smooth, rubber
Pitch: 6 inches
Shoes per Vehicle: 158 (79/track)
Ground Contact Length: 147 inches

ELECTRICAL SYSTEM

Nominal Voltage: 24 volts DC
Main Generator: (1) 24 volts, 50 amperes, driven by power take-off from main engine
Auxiliary Generator: (1) 30 volts, 50 amperes, driven by the auxiliary engine
Battery: (2) 12 volts in series

COMMUNICATIONS

Radio: SCR 508, 528, or 538 in rear of turret; SCR 506 (command tanks only) in right front sponson
Interphone: (part of radio) 5 stations

FIRE PROTECTION

(2) 10 pound carbon dioxide, fixed
(2) 4 pound carbon dioxide, portable

PERFORMANCE

Maximum Speed: Sustained, level road	21 miles/hour
Short periods, level	24 miles/hour
Maximum Grade:	60 per cent
Maximum Trench:	7.5 feet
Maximum Vertical Wall:	24 inches
Maximum Fording Depth:	40 inches
Minimum Turning Circle: (diameter)	62 feet
Cruising Range: Roads	approx. 120 miles

MEDIUM TANK M4 (mid-production)

GENERAL DATA

Crew:	5 men
Length: Gun forward, w/o sandshields	232 inches
Length: Gun to rear, w/o sandshields	232 inches
Length: w/o gun, w/o sandshields	232 inches
Gun Overhang: w/o sandshields	0 inches
Width: w/o sandshields	103 inches
Height: Over turret hatch	108 inches
Tread:	83 inches
Ground Clearance:	17 inches
Fire Height:	88 inches
Turret Ring Diameter: (inside)	69 inches
Weight, Combat Loaded:	66,900 pounds*
Weight, Unstowed:	62,800 pounds*
Power to Weight Ratio: Net	10.5 hp/ton
Gross	12.0 hp/ton
Ground Pressure: Zero penetration	13.7 psi

*All weights based on T48 or T51 tracks

ARMOR

Type: Turret, cast homogeneous steel; Hull, rolled and cast homogeneous steel; Welded assembly

Hull Thickness:	Actual	Angle w/Vertical
Front, Upper	2.0 inches	56 degrees
Lower	2.0 inches	0 to 56 degrees
Sides	1.5 inches	0 degrees
Rear	1.5 inches	0 to 10 degrees
Top	0.75 inches	83 to 90 degrees
Floor, Front	1.0 inches	90 degrees
Rear	0.5 inches	90 degrees
Turret Thickness:		
Gun Shield	3.5 inches	0 degrees
Rotor Shield	2.0 inches	0 degrees
Front	3.0 inches	30 degrees
Sides	2.0 inches	5 degrees
Rear	2.0 inches	0 degrees
Top	1.0 inches	90 degrees

ARMAMENT

Primary: 75mm Gun M3 in Mount M34A1 in turret*

Traverse: Hydraulic and manual	360 degrees
Traverse Rate: (max)	15 second/360 degrees
Elevation: Manual	+25 to −10 degrees
Firing Rate: (max)	20 rounds/minute
Loading System:	Manual
Stabilizer System:	Elevation only

Secondary:
- (1) .50 caliber MG HB M2 flexible AA mount on turret
- (1) .30 caliber MG M1919A4 coaxial w/75mm gun in turret
- (1) .30 caliber MG M1919A4 in bow mount
- (1) 2 inch Mortar M3 (smoke) fixed in turret
- Provision for (1) .45 caliber SMG M1928A1

*Mount M34 in earlier production tanks

AMMUNITION

97 rounds 75mm	12 rounds 2 inch (smoke)
300 rounds .50 caliber	12 hand grenades
600 rounds .45 caliber	
4750 rounds .30 caliber	

FIRE CONTROL AND VISION EQUIPMENT

Primary Weapon:	Direct	Indirect
	Telescope M55	Azimuth Indicator M19
	Periscope M4 with	Gunner's Quadrant M1
	Telescope M38	Elevation Quadrant M9

Vision Devices:	Direct	Indirect
Driver	Hatch	Periscope M6 (2)
Asst. Driver	Hatch	Periscope M6 (2)
Commander	Hatch	Periscope M6 (1)
Gunner	None	Periscope M4 (1)
Loader	Pistol port	Periscope M6 (1)

Total Periscopes: M4 (1), M6 (6)
Total Pistol Ports: Hull (0), Turret (1)

ENGINE

Make and Model: Continental R975 C1
Type: 9 cylinder, 4 cycle, radial
Cooling System: Air Ignition: Magneto

Displacement:	973 cubic inches
Bore and Stroke:	5 x 5.5 inches
Compression Ratio:	5.7:1
Net Horsepower (max):	350 hp at 2400 rpm
Gross Horsepower (max):	400 hp at 2400 rpm
Net Torque (max):	800 ft-lb at 1800 rpm
Gross Torque (max):	890 ft-lb at 1800 rpm
Weight:	1137 lb, dry
Fuel: 80 octane gasoline	175 gallons
Engine Oil:	36 quarts

POWER TRAIN

Clutch: Dry disc, 2 plate
Transmission: Synchromesh, 5 speeds forward, 1 reverse

Gear Ratios:				
1st	7.56:1		4th	1.11:1
2nd	3.11:1		5th	0.73:1
3rd	1.78:1		reverse	5.65:1

Steering: Controlled differential
  Bevel Gear Ratio: 3.53:1 Steering Ratio: 1.515:1
Brakes: Mechanical, external contracting
Final Drive: Herringbone gear Gear Ratio: 2.84:1
Drive Sprocket: At front of vehicle with 13 teeth
  Pitch Diameter: 25.038 inches

RUNNING GEAR

Suspension: Vertical volute spring
  12 wheels in 6 bogies (3 bogies/track)
  Tire Size: 20 x 9 inches
  6 track return rollers (1 at rear of each bogie)
  Adjustable idler at rear of each track
  Idler Size: 22 x 9 inches
Tracks: Outside guide; T48, T49, T51, and T54E1
  Type: (T48) Double pin, 16.56 inch width, chevron, rubber
    (T49) Double pin, 16.56 inch width, parallel bar, steel
    (T51) Double pin, 16.56 inch width, smooth, rubber
    (T54E1) Double pin, 16.56 inch width, chevron, steel
  Pitch: 6 inches
  Shoes per Vehicle: 158 (79/track)
  Ground Contact Length: 147 inches

ELECTRICAL SYSTEM

Nominal Voltage: 24 volts DC
Main Generator: (1) 24 volts, 50 amperes, driven by power take-off from main engine
Auxiliary Generator: (1) 30 volts, 50 amperes, driven by the auxiliary engine
Battery: (2) 12 volts in series

COMMUNICATONS

Radio: SCR 508, 528, or 538 in rear of turret; SCR 506* (command tanks only) in right front sponson
Interphone: (part of radio) 5 stations
Flag Set M238, Panel Set AP50A, Spotlight, Siren
Flares: 3 each, M17, M18, M19, and M21 (command tanks only)
Ground Signals Projector M4 (command tanks only)
  *Early vehicles may be equipped with SCR 245

FIRE AND GAS PROTECTION

- (2) 10 pound carbon dioxide, fixed
- (2) 4 pound carbon dioxide, portable
- (2) 1½ quart decontaminating apparatus

PERFORMANCE

Maximum Speed: Sustained, level road	21 miles/hour
Short periods, level	24 miles/hour
Maximum Grade:	60 per cent
Maximum Trench:	7.5 feet
Maximum Vertical Wall:	24 inches
Maximum Fording Depth:	40 inches
Minimum Turning Circle: (diameter)	62 feet
Cruising Range: Roads	approx. 120 miles

MEDIUM TANK M4(105)

GENERAL DATA

Crew:	5 men
Length: Howitzer forward, w/sandshields	244 inches
Length: Howitzer to rear, w/sandshields	244 inches
Length: w/sandshields, w/o howitzer	244 inches
Howitzer Overhang: Howitzer forward	0 inches
Width: w/sandshields	105 inches
Height: Over cupola	115.7 inches
Tread:	83 inches
Ground Clearance:	17 inches
Fire Height:	88 inches
Turret Ring Diameter: (inside)	69 inches
Weight, Combat Loaded:	69,400 pounds*
Weight, Unstowed:	62,800 pounds*
Power to Weight Ratio: Net	11.5 hp/ton
Gross	13.3 hp/ton
Ground Pressure: Zero penetration	14.3 psi

*All weights based on T48 or T51 tracks

ARMOR

Type: Turret, cast homogeneous steel; Hull, rolled and cast homogeneous steel; Welded assembly

Hull Thickness:	Actual	Angle w/Vertical
Front, Upper	2.5 inches	47 degrees
Lower	4.25 to 2.0 inches	0 to 56 degrees
Sides	1.5 inches	0 degrees
Rear	1.5 inches	10 degrees
Top	0.75 inches	83 to 90 degrees
Floor, Front	1.0 inches	90 degrees
Rear	0.5 inches	90 degrees
Turret Thickness:		
Gun Shield	3.6 inches	0 degrees
Front	3.0 inches	30 degrees
Sides	2.0 inches	0 to 5 degrees
Rear	2.0 inches	0 degrees
Top	1.0 inches	90 degrees

ARMAMENT

Primary: 105mm Howitzer M4 in Mount M52 in turret

Traverse: Hydraulic* and manual	360 degrees
Traverse Rate: (max)	15 seconds/360 degrees
Elevation: Manual	+35 to −10 degrees
Firing Rate: (max)	8 rounds/minute
Loading System:	Manual
Stabilizer System:	Elevation only*

Secondary:

(1) .50 caliber MG HB M2 flexible AA mount on turret
(1) .30 caliber MG M1919A4 coaxial w/105mm howitzer in turret
(1) .30 caliber MG M1919A4 in bow mount
(1) 2 inch Mortar M3 (smoke) fixed in turret
Provision for (5) .45 caliber SMG M3

*No power traverse or stabilizer on early production tanks

AMMUNITION

66 rounds 105mm	12 rounds 2 inch (smoke)
600 rounds .50 caliber	12 hand grenades
900 rounds .45 caliber	
4000 rounds .30 caliber	

FIRE CONTROL AND VISION EQUIPMENT

Primary Weapon:	Direct	Indirect
	Telescope M72D	Azimuth Indicator M19
	Periscope M4A1 with	Gunner's Quadrant M1
	Telescope M77C	Elevation Quadrant M9

Vision Devices:	Direct	Indirect
Driver	Hatch	Periscope M6 (2)
Asst. Driver	Hatch	Periscope M6 (2)
Commander	Vision cupola and hatch	Periscope M6 (1)
Gunner	None	Periscope M4A1 (1)
Loader	Hatch and pistol port	Periscope M6 (1)

Total Periscopes: M4A1 (1), M6 (6)
Total Pistol Ports: Hull (0), Turret (1)
Vision Cupolas: (1) w/6 vision blocks on turret top

ENGINE

Make and Model: Continental R975 C4
Type: 9 cylinder, 4 cycle, radial
Cooling System: Air Ignition: Magneto

Displacement:	973 cubic inches
Bore and Stroke:	5 x 5.5 inches
Compression Ratio:	5.7:1
Net Horsepower (max):	400 hp at 2400 rpm
Gross Horsepower (max):	460 hp at 2400 rpm
Net Torque (max):	940 ft-lb at 1700 rpm
Gross Torque (max):	1025 ft-lb at 1800 rpm
Weight:	1212 lb, dry
Fuel: 80 octane gasoline	175 gallons
Engine Oil:	36 quarts

POWER TRAIN

Clutch: Dry disc, 2 plate
Transmission: Synchromesh, 5 speeds forward, 1 reverse

Gear Ratios:				
1st	7.56:1	4th	1.11:1
2nd	3.11:1	5th	0.73:1
3rd	1.78:1	reverse	5.65:1

Steering: Controlled differential
Bevel Gear Ratio: 3.53:1 Steering Ratio: 1.515:1
Brakes: Mechanical, external contracting
Final Drive: Herringbone gear Gear Ratio: 2.84:1
Drive Sprocket: At front of vehicle with 13 teeth
Pitch Diameter: 25.038 inches

RUNNING GEAR

Suspension: Vertical volute spring
12 wheels in 6 bogies (3 bogies/track)
Tire Size: 20 x 9 inches
6 track return rollers (1 at rear of each bogie)
Adjustable idler at rear of each track
Idler Size: 22 x 9 inches
Tracks: Outside guide; T48, T49, T51, and T54E1
Type: (T48) Double pin, 16.56 inch width, chevron, rubber
(T49) Double pin, 16.56 inch width, parallel bar, steel
(T51) Double pin, 16.56 inch width, smooth, rubber
(T54E1) Double pin, 16.56 inch width, chevron, steel
Pitch: 6 inches
Shoes per Vehicle: 158 (79/track)
Ground Contact Length: 147 inches

ELECTRICAL SYSTEM

Nominal Voltage: 24 volts DC
Main Generator: (1) 24 volts, 50 amperes, driven by power take-off from main engine
Auxiliary Generator: (1) 30 volts, 50 amperes, driven by the auxiliary engine
Battery: (2) 12 volts in series

COMMUNICATIONS

Radio: SCR 508, 528, or 538 in rear of turret; SCR 506 (command tanks only) in right front sponson
Interphone: (part of radio) 5 stations
Flag Set M238, Panel Set AP50A, Spotlight, Siren
Flares: 3 each, M17, M18, M19, and M21 (command tanks only)
Ground Signals Projector M4 (command tanks only)

FIRE AND GAS PROTECTION

(2) 10 pound carbon dioxide, fixed
(2) 4 pound carbon dioxide, portable
(2) 1½ quart decontaminating apparatus

PERFORMANCE

Maximum Speed: Sustained, level road	21 miles/hour
Short periods, level	24 miles/hour
Maximum Grade:	60 per cent
Maximum Trench:	7.5 feet
Maximum Vertical Wall:	24 inches
Maximum Fording Depth:	40 inches
Minimum Turning Circle: (diameter)	62 feet
Cruising Range: Roads	approx. 100 miles

MEDIUM TANK M4A1 (early production)

GENERAL DATA

Crew:	5 men
Length: Gun forward, w/o sandshields	230 inches
Length: Gun to rear, w/o sandshields	230 inches
Length: w/o gun, w/o sandshields	230 inches
Gun Overhang: w/o sandshields	0 inches
Width: w/o sandshields	103 inches
Height: Over turret hatch	108 inches
Tread:	83 inches
Ground Clearance:	17 inches
Fire Height:	88 inches
Turret Ring Diameter: (inside)	69 inches
Weight, Combat Loaded:	66,800 pounds*
Weight, Unstowed:	62,700 pounds*
Power to Weight Ratio: Net	10.5 hp/ton
Gross	12.0 hp/ton
Ground Pressure: Zero penetration	13.7 psi

*All weights based on T48 or T51 tracks

ARMOR

Type: Turret, cast homogeneous steel; Upper hull cast, lower hull rolled, homogeneous steel; Welded assembly

Hull Thickness:	Actual	Angle w/Vertical
Front, Upper	2.0 inches	37 to 55 degrees
Lower	2.0 inches	0 to 45 degrees
Sides	1.5 inches	0 degrees
Rear	1.5 inches	0 to 10 degrees
Top	0.75 to 0.5 inches	90 to 83 degrees
Floor, Front	1.0 inches	90 degrees
Rear	0.5 inches	90 degrees
Turret Thickness:		
Gun Shield	3.0 inches	0 degrees
Rotor Shield	2.0 inches	0 degrees
Front	3.0 inches	30 degrees
Sides	2.0 inches	5 degrees
Rear	2.0 inches	0 degrees
Top	1.0 inches	90 degrees

ARMAMENT

Primary: 75mm Gun M3 in Mount M34 in turret*

Traverse: Hydraulic and manual	360 degrees
Traverse Rate: (max)	15 seconds/360 degrees
Elevation: Manual	+25 to −12 degrees
Firing Rate: (max)	20 rounds/minute
Loading System:	Manual
Stabilizer System:	Elevation only

Secondary:
- (1) .50 caliber MG HB M2 flexible AA mount on turret
- (1) .30 caliber MG M1919A4 coaxial w/75mm gun in turret
- (1) .30 caliber MG M1919A4 in bow mount
- Provision for (1) .45 caliber SMG M1928A1

*Mount M34A1 in later production tanks

AMMUNITION

90 rounds 75mm	12 hand grenades
300 rounds .50 caliber	
600 rounds .45 caliber	
4750 rounds .30 caliber	

FIRE CONTROL AND VISION EQUIPMENT

Primary Weapon:	Direct	Indirect
	Periscope M4 with Telescope M38	Azimuth Indicator M19
		Gunner's Quadrant M1
		Elevation Quadrant M9

Vision Devices:	Direct	Indirect
Driver	Hatch and vision slot	Periscope M6 (1)*
Asst. Driver	Hatch and vision slot	Periscope M6 (1)*
Commander	Hatch	Periscope M6 (1)
Gunner	None	Periscope M4 (1)
Loader	Pistol port	Periscope M6 (1)

Total Periscopes: M4 (1), M6 (4)
Total Pistol Ports: Hull (0), Turret (1)
*(2) in later tanks replacing vision slots

ENGINE

Make and Model: Continental R975 C1
Type: 9 cylinder, 4 cycle, radial
Cooling System: Air   Ignition: Magneto

Displacement:	973 cubic inches
Bore and Stroke:	5 x 5.5 inches
Compression Ratio:	5.7:1
Net Horsepower (max):	350 hp at 2400 rpm
Gross Horsepower (max):	400 hp at 2400 rpm
Net Torque (max):	800 ft-lb at 1800 rpm
Gross Torque (max):	890 ft-lb at 1800 rpm
Weight:	1137 lb, dry
Fuel: 80 octane gasoline	175 gallons
Engine Oil:	36 quarts

POWER TRAIN

Clutch: Dry disc, 2 plate
Transmission: Synchromesh, 5 speeds forward, 1 reverse

Gear Ratios:				
1st	7.56:1	4th	1.11:1
2nd	3.11:1	5th	0.73:1
3rd	1.78:1	reverse	5.65:1

Steering: Controlled differential
Bevel Gear Ratio: 3.53:1   Steering Ratio: 1.515:1
Brakes: Mechanical, external contracting
Final Drive: Herringbone gear   Gear Ratio: 2.84:1
Drive Sprocket: At front of vehicle with 13 teeth
Pitch Diameter: 25.038 inches

RUNNING GEAR

Suspension: Vertical volute spring
12 wheels in 6 bogies (3 bogies/track)
Tire Size: 20 x 9 inches
6 track return rollers (1 on top of each bogie)*
Adjustable idler at rear of each track
Idler Size: 22 x 9 inches
Tracks: Outside guide; T48, T49, T51, and T54E1
Type: (T48) Double pin, 16.56 inch width, chevron, rubber
(T49) Double pin, 16.56 inch width, parallel bar, steel
(T51) Double pin, 16.56 inch width, smooth, rubber
(T54E1) Double pin, 16.56 inch width, chevron, steel
Pitch: 6 inches
Shoes per Vehicle: 158 (79/track)
Ground Contact Length: 147 inches
*At rear on later production tanks

ELECTRICAL SYSTEM

Nominal Voltage: 24 volts DC
Main Generator: (1) 24 volts, 50 amperes, driven by power take-off from main engine
Auxiliary Generator: (1) 30 volts, 50 amperes, driven by the auxiliary engine
Battery: (2) 12 volts in series

COMMUNICATIONS

Radio: SCR 508, 528, or 538 in rear of turret; SCR 506* (command tanks only) in right front sponson
Interphone: (part of radio) 5 stations
Flag Set M238, Panel Set AP50A, Spotlight, Siren
Flares: 3 each, M17, M18, M19, and M21 (command tanks only)
Ground Signals Projector M4 (command tanks only)
*Early vehicles may be equipped with SCR 245

FIRE AND GAS PROTECTION

(2) 10 pound carbon dioxide, fixed
(2) 4 pound carbon dioxide, portable
(2) 1½ quart decontaminating apparatus

PERFORMANCE

Maximum Speed: Sustained, level road	21 miles/hour
Short periods, level	24 miles/hour
Maximum Grade:	60 per cent
Maximum Trench:	7.5 feet
Maximum Vertical Wall:	24 inches
Maximum Fording Depth:	40 inches
Minimum Turning Circle: (diameter)	62 feet
Cruising Range: Roads	approx. 120 miles

MEDIUM TANK M4A1(76)W

GENERAL DATA

Crew:	5 men
Length: Gun forward, w/sandshields and muzzle brake	294 inches
Length: Gun to rear, w/sandshields and muzzle brake	287 inches
Length: w/sandshields, w/o gun	244 inches
Gun Overhang: Gun forward, w/muzzle brake	50 inches
Width: w/sandshields	105 inches
Height: Over cupola	117 inches
Tread:	83 inches
Ground Clearance:	17 inches
Fire Height:	90 inches
Turret Ring Diameter: (inside)	69 inches
Weight, Combat Loaded:	70,600 pounds*
Weight, Unstowed:	64,600 pounds*
Power to Weight Ratio: Net	11.3 hp/ton
Gross	13.0 hp/ton
Ground Pressure: Zero penetration	14.5 psi

*All weights based on T48 or T51 tracks

ARMOR

Type: Turret, cast homogeneous steel; Upper hull cast, lower hull rolled, homogeneous steel; Welded assembly

	Actual	Angle w/Vertical
Hull Thickness:		
Front, Upper	2.5 inches	37 to 55 degrees
Lower	4.25 to 2.0 inches	0 to 56 degrees
Sides	1.5 inches	0 degrees
Rear	1.5 inches	10 to 20 degrees
Top	0.75 inches	83 to 90 degrees
Floor, Front	1.0 inches	90 degrees
Rear	0.5 inches	90 degrees
Turret Thickness:		
Gun Shield	3.5 inches	0 degrees
Front	2.5 inches	40 to 45 degrees
Sides	2.5 inches	0 to 13 degrees
Rear	2.5 inches	0 degrees
Top	1.0 inches	90 degrees

ARMAMENT

Primary: 76mm Gun M1A1, M1A1C, or M1A2 in Mount M62 in turret

Traverse: Hydraulic and manual	360 degrees
Traverse Rate: (max)	15 seconds/360 degrees
Elevation: Manual	+25 to −10 degrees
Firing Rate: (max)	20 rounds/minute
Loading System:	Manual
Stabilizer System:	Elevation only

Secondary:
- (1) .50 caliber MG HB M2 flexible AA mount on turret
- (1) .30 caliber MG M1919A4 coaxial w/76mm gun in turret
- (1) .30 caliber MG M1919A4 in bow mount
- (1) 2 inch Mortar M3 (smoke) fixed in turret
- Provision for (5) .45 caliber SMG M3

AMMUNITION

71 rounds 76mm	12 rounds 2 inch (smoke)
600 rounds .50 caliber	12 hand grenades
900 rounds .45 caliber	
6250 rounds .30 caliber	

FIRE CONTROL AND VISION EQUIPMENT

Primary Weapon:	Direct	Indirect
	Telescope M71D	Azimuth Indicator M19
	Periscope M4A1 with Telescope M47A2	Gunner's Quadrant M1
		Elevation Quadrant M9

Vision Devices	Direct	Indirect
Driver	Hatch	Periscope M6 (2)
Asst. Driver	Hatch	Periscope M6 (2)
Commander	Vision cupola and hatch	Periscope M6 (1)
Gunner	None	Periscope M4A1 (1)
Loader	Hatch and pistol port	Periscope M6 (1)

Total Periscopes: M4A1 (1), M6 (6)
Total Pistol Ports: Hull (0), Turret (1)
Vision Cupolas: (1) w/6 vision blocks on turret top

ENGINE

Make and Model: Continental R975 C4
Type: 9 cylinder, 4 cycle, radial
Cooling System: Air Ignition: Magneto

Displacement:	973 cubic inches
Bore and Stroke:	5 x 5.5 inches
Compression Ratio:	5.7:1
Net Horsepower (max):	400 hp at 2400 rpm
Gross Horsepower (max):	460 hp at 2400 rpm
Net Torque (max):	940 ft-lb at 1700 rpm
Gross Torque (max):	1025 ft-lb at 1800 rpm
Weight:	1212 lb, dry
Fuel: 80 octane gasoline	175 gallons
Engine Oil:	36 quarts

POWER TRAIN

Clutch: Dry disc, 2 plate
Transmission: Synchromesh, 5 speeds forward, 1 reverse

Gear Ratios:			
1st	7.56:1	4th	1.11:1
2nd	3.11:1	5th	0.73:1
3rd	1.78:1	reverse	5.65:1

Steering: Controlled differential
Bevel Gear Ratio: 3.53:1 Steering Ratio: 1.515:1
Brakes: Mechanical, external contracting
Final Drive: Herringbone gear Gear Ratio: 2.84:1
Drive Sprocket: At front of vehicle with 13 teeth
Pitch Diameter: 25.038 inches

RUNNING GEAR

Suspension: Vertical volute spring
- 12 wheels in 6 bogies (3 bogies/track)
- Tire Size: 20 x 9 inches
- 6 track return rollers (1 at rear of each bogie)
- Adjustable idler at rear of each track
- Idler Size: 22 x 9 inches

Tracks: Outside guide; T48, T49, T51, and T54E1
- Type: (T48) Double pin, 16.56 inch width, chevron, rubber
- (T49) Double pin, 16.56 inch width, parallel bar, steel
- (T51) Double pin, 16.56 inch width, smooth, rubber
- (T54E1) Double pin, 16.56 inch width, chevron, steel
- Pitch: 6 inches
- Shoes per Vehicle: 158 (79/track)
- Ground Contact Length: 147 inches

ELECTRICAL SYSTEM

Nominal Voltage: 24 volts DC
Main Generator: (1) 24 volts, 50 amperes, driven by power take-off from main engine
Auxiliary Generator: (1) 30 volts, 50 amperes, driven by the auxiliary engine
Battery: (2) 12 volts in series

COMMUNICATIONS

Radio: SCR 508, 528, or 538 in rear of turret; SCR 506 (command tanks only) in right front sponson
Interphone: (part of radio) 5 stations
Flag Set M238, Panel Set AP50A, Spotlight, Siren
Flares: 3 each, M17, M18, M19, and M21 (command tanks only)
Ground Signals Projector M4 (command tanks only)

FIRE AND GAS PROTECTION

- (2) 10 pound carbon dioxide, fixed
- (2) 4 pound carbon dioxide, portable
- (2) 1½ quart decontaminating apparatus

PERFORMANCE

Maximum Speed: Sustained, level road	21 miles/hour
Short periods, level	24 miles/hour
Maximum Grade:	60 per cent
Maximum Trench:	7.5 feet
Maximum Vertical Wall:	24 inches
Maximum Fording Depth:	40 inches
Minimum Turning Circle: (diameter)	62 feet
Cruising Range: Road:	approx. 100 miles

MEDIUM TANK M4A2 (late production)

GENERAL DATA

Crew:	5 men
Length: Gun forward, w/o sandshields	233 inches
Length: Gun to rear, w/o sandshields	233 inches
Length: w/o gun, w/o sandshields	233 inches
Gun Overhang: Gun forward	0 inches
Width: w/o sandshields	103 inches
Height: Over turret hatch	108 inches
Tread:	83 inches
Ground Clearance:	17 inches
Fire Height:	88 inches
Turret Ring Diameter: (inside)	69 inches
Weight, Combat Loaded:	70,200 pounds*
Weight, Unstowed:	66,000 pounds*
Power to Weight Ratio: Net	10.7 hp/ton
Gross	11.7 hp/ton
Ground Pressure: Zero penetration	14.4 psi

*All weights based on T48 or T51 tracks

ARMOR

Type: Turret, cast homogeneous steel; Hull, rolled and cast homogeneous steel; Welded assembly

Hull Thickness:	Actual	Angle w/Vertical
Front, Upper	2.5 inches	47 degrees
Lower	4.25 to 2.0 inches	0 to 56 degrees
Sides	1.5 inches	0 degrees
Rear	1.5 inches	10 to 12 degrees
Top	0.75 inches	83 to 90 degrees
Floor, Front	1.0 inches	90 degrees
Rear	0.5 inches	90 degrees
Turret Thickness:		
Gun Shield	3.5 inches	0 degrees
Rotor Shield	2.0 inches	0 degrees
Front	3.0 inches	30 degrees
Sides	2.0 inches	5 degrees
Rear	2.0 inches	0 degrees
Top	1.0 inches	90 degrees

ARMAMENT

Primary: 75mm Gun M3 in Mount M34A1 in turret*

Traverse: Hydraulic and manual	360 degrees
Traverse Rate: (max)	15 seconds/360 degrees
Elevation: Manual	+25 to −10 degrees
Firing Rate: (max)	20 rounds/minute
Loading System:	Manual
Stabilizer System:	Elevation only

Secondary:
- (1) .50 caliber MG HB M2 flexible AA mount on turret
- (1) .30 caliber MG M1919A4 coaxial w/75mm gun in turret
- (1) .30 caliber MG M1919A4 in bow mount
- (1) 2 inch Mortar M3 (smoke) fixed in turret
- Provision for (1) .45 caliber SMG M1928A1

*Mount M34 in earlier production tanks

AMMUNITION

97 rounds 75mm	12 rounds 2 inch (smoke)
300 rounds .50 caliber	12 hand grenades
600 rounds .45 caliber	
4750 rounds .30 caliber	

FIRE CONTROL AND VISION EQUIPMENT

Primary Weapon:	Direct	Indirect
	Telescope M55	Azimuth Indicator M19
	Periscope M4 with	Gunner's Quadrant M1
	Telescope M38	Elevation Quadrant M9

Vision Devices:	Direct	Indirect
Driver	Hatch	Periscope M6 (2)
Asst. Driver	Hatch	Periscope M6 (2)
Commander	Hatch	Periscope M6 (1)
Gunner	None	Periscope M4 (1)
Loader	Pistol port	Periscope M6 (1)

Total Periscopes: M4 (1), M6 (6)

Total Pistol Ports: Hull (0), Turret (1)

ENGINE

Make and Model: General Motors 6046

Type: 12 cylinder, 2 cycle, twin in-line

Cooling System: Liquid   Ignition: Compression

Displacement:	850 cubic inches
Bore and Stroke:	4.25 x 5 inches
Compression Ratio:	16:1
Net Horsepower (max):	375 hp at 2100 rpm*
Gross Horsepower (max):	410 hp at 2900 rpm#
Net Torque (max):	1000 ft-lb at 1400 rpm*
Gross Torque (max):	885 ft-lb at 1900 rpm#
Weight:	5110 lb, dry
Fuel: 40 cetane diesel oil	148 gallons
Engine Oil:	28 quarts

*Crankshaft rpm   #Propeller shaft rpm

POWER TRAIN

Clutch: Dry disc, 2 plate (2)

Transfer Case Gear Ratio: 0.73:1

Transmission: Synchromesh, 5 speeds forward, 1 reverse

Gear Ratios:				
1st	7.56:1	4th	1.11:1
2nd	3.11:1	5th	0.73:1
3rd	1.78:1	reverse	5.65:1

Steering: Controlled differential
Bevel Gear Ratio: 3.53:1   Steering Ratio: 1.515:1

Brakes: Mechanical, external contracting

Final Drive: Herringbone gear   Gear Ratio: 2.84:1

Drive Sprocket: At front of vehicle with 13 teeth
Pitch Diameter: 25.038 inches

RUNNING GEAR

Suspension: Vertical volute spring
- 12 wheels in 6 bogies (3 bogies/track)
- Tire Size: 20 x 9 inches
- 6 track return rollers (1 at rear of each bogie)*
- Adjustable idler at rear of each track
- Idler Size: 22 x 9 inches

Tracks: Outside guide; T48, T49, T51, and T54E1
- Type: (T48) Double pin, 16.56 inch width, chevron, rubber
  - (T49) Double pin, 16.56 inch width, parallel bar, steel
  - (T51) Double pin, 16.56 inch width, smooth, rubber
  - (T54E1) Double pin, 16.56 inch width, chevron, steel
- Pitch: 6 inches
- Shoes per Vehicle: 158 (79/track)
- Ground Contact Length: 147 inches

*On top of bogie on early tanks

ELECTRICAL SYSTEM

Nominal Voltage: 24 volts DC

Main Generator: (2) 24 volts, 50 amperes, driven by power take-off from main engine

Auxiliary Generator: (1) 30 volts, 50 amperes, driven by the auxiliary engine

Battery: (2) 12 volts in series

COMMUNICATIONS

Radio: SCR 508, 528, or 538 in rear of turret; SCR 506* (command tanks only) in right front sponson

Interphone: (part of radio) 5 stations

Flag Set M238, Panel Set AP50A, Spotlight, Siren

Flares: 3 each, M17, M18, M19, and M21 (command tanks only)

Ground Signals Projector M4 (command tanks only)

*Early vehicles may be equipped with SCR 245

FIRE AND GAS PROTECTION
- (2) 10 pound carbon dioxide, fixed
- (2) 4 pound carbon dioxide, portable
- (2) 1½ quart decontaminating apparatus

PERFORMANCE

Maximum Speed: Sustained, level road	25 miles/hour
Short periods, level	30 miles/hour
Maximum Grade:	60 per cent
Maximum Trench:	7.5 feet
Maximum Vertical Wall:	24 inches
Maximum Fording Depth:	40 inches
Minimum Turning Circle: (diameter)	62 feet
Cruising Range: Roads	approx. 150 miles

MEDIUM TANK M4A2(76)W

GENERAL DATA

Crew:	5 men
Length: Gun forward, w/sandshields and muzzle brake	298 inches
Length: Gun to rear, w/sandshields and muzzle brake	287 inches
Length: w/sandshields, w/o gun	248 inches
Gun Overhang: Gun forward, w/muzzle brake	50 inches
Width: w/sandshields	105 inches
Height: Over cupola	117 inches
Tread:	83 inches
Ground Clearance:	17 inches
Fire Height:	90 inches
Turret Ring Diameter: (inside)	69 inches
Weight, Combat Loaded:	73,400 pounds*
Weight, Unstowed:	67,300 pounds*
Power to Weight Ratio: Net	10.2 hp/ton
Gross	11.2 hp/ton
Ground Pressure: Zero penetration	15.1 psi

*All weights based on T48 or T51 tracks

ARMOR

Type: Turret, cast homogeneous steel; Hull, rolled and cast homogeneous steel; Welded assembly

Hull Thickness:	Actual	Angle w/Vertical
Front, Upper	2.5 inches	47 degrees
Lower	4.25 to 2.0 inches	0 to 56 degrees
Sides	1.5 inches	0 degrees
Rear	1.5 inches	10 to 12 degrees
Top	0.75 inches	83 to 90 degrees
Floor, Front	1.0 inches	90 degrees
Rear	0.5 inches	90 degrees
Turret Thickness:		
Gun Shield	3.5 inches	0 degrees
Front	2.5 inches	40 to 45 degrees
Sides	2.5 inches	0 to 13 degrees
Rear	2.5 inches	0 degrees
Top	1.0 inches	90 degrees

ARMAMENT

Primary: 76mm Gun M1A1, M1A1C, or M1A2 in Mount M62 in turret

Traverse: Hydraulic and manual	360 degrees
Traverse Rate: (max)	15 seconds/360 degrees
Elevation: Manual	+25 to −10 degrees
Firing Rate: (max)	20 rounds/minute
Loading System:	Manual
Stabilizer System:	Elevation only

Secondary:
- (1) .50 caliber MG HB M2 flexible AA mount on turret
- (1) .30 caliber MG M1919A4 coaxial w/76mm gun in turret
- (1) .30 caliber MG M1919A4 in bow mount
- (1) 2 inch Mortar M3 (smoke) fixed in turret
- Provision for (5) .45 caliber SMG M3

AMMUNITION

71 rounds 76mm	14 rounds 2 inch (smoke)
600 rounds .50 caliber	12 hand grenades
900 rounds .45 caliber	
6250 rounds .30 caliber	

FIRE CONTROL AND VISION EQUIPMENT

Primary Weapon:	Direct	Indirect
	Telescope M71D	Azimuth Indicator M19
	Periscope M4A1 with	Gunner's Quadrant M1
	Telescope M47A2	Elevation Quadrant M9

Vision Devices	Direct	Indirect
Driver	Hatch	Periscope M6 (2)
Asst. Driver	Hatch	Periscope M6 (2)
Commander	Vision cupola and hatch	Periscope M6 (1)
Gunner	None	Periscope M4A1 (1)
Loader	Hatch and pistol port	Periscope M6 (1)

Total Periscopes: M4A1 (1), M6 (6)
Total Pistol Ports: Hull (0), Turret (1)
Vision Cupolas: (1) w/6 vision blocks on turret top

ENGINE

Make and Model: General Motors 6046
Type: 12 cylinder, 2 cycle, twin in-line
Cooling System: Liquid   Ignition: Compression

Displacement:	850 cubic inches
Bore and Stroke:	4.25 x 5 inches
Compression Ratio:	16:1
Net Horsepower (max):	375 hp at 2100 rpm*
Gross Horsepower (max):	410 hp at 2900 rpm#
Net Torque (max):	1000 ft-lb at 1400 rpm*
Gross Torque (max):	885 ft-lb at 1900 rpm#
Weight:	5110 lb, dry
Fuel: 40 cetane diesel oil	148 gallons
Engine Oil:	28 quarts

*Crankshaft rpm   #Propeller shaft rpm

POWER TRAIN

Clutch: Dry disc, 2 plate (2)
Transfer Case Gear Ratio: 0.73:1
Transmission: Synchromesh, 5 speeds forward, 1 reverse

Gear Ratios:				
	1st	7.56:1	4th	1.11:1
	2nd	3.11:1	5th	0.73:1
	3rd	1.78:1	reverse	5.65:1

Steering: Controlled differential
Bevel Gear Ratio: 3.53:1   Steering Rato: 1.515:1
Brakes: Mechanical, external contracting
Final Drive: Herringbone gear   Gear Ratio: 2.84:1
Drive Sprocket: At front of vehicle with 13 teeth
Pitch Diameter: 25.038 inches

RUNNING GEAR

Suspension: Vertical volute spring
- 12 wheels in 6 bogies (3 bogies/track)
- Tire Size: 20 x 9 inches
- 6 track return rollers (1 at rear of each bogie)
- Adjustable idler at rear of each track
- Idler Size: 22 x 9 inches

Tracks: Outside guide; T48, T49, T51, and T54E1
- Type: (T48) Double pin, 16.56 inch width, chevron, rubber
  - (T49) Double pin, 16.56 inch width, parallel bar, steel
  - (T51) Double pin, 16.56 inch width, smooth, rubber
  - (T54E1) Double pin, 16.56 inch width, chevron, steel
- Pitch: 6 inches
- Shoes per Vehicle: 158 (79/track)
- Ground Contact Length: 147 inches

ELECTRICAL SYSTEM

Nominal Voltage: 24 volts DC
Main Generator: (2) 24 volts, 50 amperes, driven by power take-off from main engine
Auxiliary Generator: (1) 30 volts, 50 amperes, driven by the auxiliary engine
Battery: (2) 12 volts in series

COMMUNICATIONS

Radio: SCR 508, 528, or 538 in rear of turret, SCR 506 (command tanks only) in right front sponson
Interphone: (part of radio) 5 stations
Flag Set M238, Panel Set AP50A, Spotlight, Siren
Flares: 3 each, M17, M18, M19, and M21 (command tanks only)
Ground Signals Projector M4 (command tanks only)

FIRE AND GAS PROTECTION

- (2) 10 pound carbon dioxide, fixed
- (2) 4 pound carbon dioxide, portable
- (2) 1½ quart decontaminating apparatus

PERFORMANCE

Maximum Speed: Sustained, level road	25 miles/hour
Short periods, level	30 miles/hour
Maximum Grade:	60 per cent
Maximum Trench:	7.5 feet
Maximum Vertical Wall:	24 inches
Maximum Fording Depth:	40 inches
Minimum Turning Circle: (diameter)	62 feet
Cruising Range: Roads	approx. 100 miles

MEDIUM TANK M4A3 (mid-production)

GENERAL DATA

Crew:	5 men
Length: Gun forward, w/o sandshields	232.5 inches
Length: Gun to rear, w/o sandshields	232.5 inches
Length: w/o gun, w/o sandshields	232.5 inches
Gun Overhang: Gun forward	0 inches
Width: w/o sandshields	103 inches
Height: Over turret hatch	108 inches
Tread:	83 inches
Ground Clearance:	17 inches
Fire Height:	88 inches
Turret Ring Diameter: (inside)	69 inches
Weight, Combat Loaded:	66,700 pounds*
Weight, Unstowed:	62,500 pounds*
Power to Weight Ratio: Net	13.5 hp/ton
Gross	15.0 hp/ton
Ground Pressure: Zero penetration	13.7 psi

*All weights based on T48 or T51 tracks

ARMOR

Type: Turret, cast homogeneous steel; Hull, rolled and cast homogeneous steel; Welded assembly

Hull Thickness:	Actual	Angle w/Vertical
Front, Upper	2.0 inches	56 degrees
Lower	2.0 inches	0 to 56 degrees
Sides	1.5 inches	0 degrees
Rear	1.5 inches	10 to 22 degrees
Top	0.75 inches	83 to 90 degrees
Floor, Front	1.0 inches	90 degrees
Rear	0.5 inches	90 degrees
Turret Thickness:		
Gun Shield	3.5 inches	0 degrees
Rotor Shield	2.0 inches	0 degrees
Front	3.0 inches	30 degrees
Sides	2.0 inches	5 degrees
Rear	2.0 inches	0 degrees
Top	1.0 inches	90 degrees

ARMAMENT

Primary: 75mm Gun M3 in Mount M34A1 in turret*

Traverse: Hydraulic and manual	360 degrees
Traverse Rate: (max)	15 seconds/360 degrees
Elevation: Manual	+25 to −10 degrees
Firing Rate: (max)	20 rounds/minute
Loading System:	Manual
Stabilizer System:	Elevation only

Secondary:
- (1) .50 caliber MG HB M2 flexible AA mount on turret
- (1) .30 caliber MG M1919A4 coaxial w/75mm gun in turret
- (1) .30 caliber MG M1919A4 in bow mount
- (1) 2 inch Mortar M3 (smoke) fixed in turret
- Provision for (1) .45 caliber SMG M1928A1

*Mount M34 in earlier production tanks

AMMUNITION

97 rounds 75mm	12 rounds 2 inch (smoke)
300 rounds .50 caliber	12 hand grenades
600 rounds .45 caliber	
4750 rounds .30 caliber	

FIRE CONTROL AND VISION EQUIPMENT

Primary Weapon:	Direct	Indirect
	Telescope M55	Azimuth Indicator M19
	Periscope M4 with	Gunner's Quadrant M1
	Telescope M38	Elevation Quadrant M9
Vision Devices:	Direct	Indirect
Driver	Hatch	Periscope M6 (2)
Asst. Driver	Hatch	Periscope M6 (2)
Commander	Hatch	Periscope M6 (1)
Gunner	None	Periscope M4 (1)
Loader	Pistol port	Periscope M6 (1)

Total Periscopes: M4 (1), M6 (6)

Total Pistol Ports: Hull (0), Turret (1)

ENGINE

Make and Model: Ford GAA

Type: 8 cylinder, 4 cycle, 60 degree vee

Cooling System: Liquid   Ignition: Magneto

Displacement:	1100 cubic inches
Bore and Stroke:	5.4 x 6 inches
Compression Ratio:	7.5:1
Net Horsepower (max):	450 hp at 2600 rpm
Gross Horsepower (max):	500 hp at 2600 rpm
Net Torque (max):	950 ft-lb at 2200 rpm
Gross Torque (max):	1040 ft-lb at 2200 rpm
Weight:	1560 lb, dry
Fuel: 80 octane gasoline	168 gallons
Engine Oil:	32 quarts

POWER TRAIN

Clutch: Dry disc, 2 plate

Transmission: Synchromesh, 5 speeds forward, 1 reverse

Gear Ratios:				
1st	7.56:1	4th	1.11:1
2nd	3.11:1	5th	0.73:1
3rd	1.78:1	reverse	5.65:1

Steering: Controlled differential

Bevel Gear Ratio: 3.53:1   Steering Ratio: 1.515:1

Brakes: Mechanical, external contracting

Final Drive: Herringbone gear   Gear Ratio: 2.84:1

Drive Sprocket: At front of vehicle with 13 teeth

Pitch Diameter: 25.038 inches

RUNNING GEAR

Suspension: Vertical volute spring
- 12 wheels in 6 bogies (3 bogies/track)
- Tire Size: 20 x 9 inches
- 6 track return rollers (1 at rear of each bogie)
- Adjustable idler at rear of each track
- Idler Size: 22 x 9 inches

Tracks: Outside guide: T48, T49, T51, and T54E1

Type: (T48) Double pin, 16.56 inch width, chevron, rubber
(T49) Double pin, 16.56 inch width, parallel bar, steel
(T51) Double pin, 16.56 inch width, smooth, rubber
(T54E1) Double pin, 16.56 inch width, chevron, steel

Pitch: 6 inches

Shoes per Vehicle: 158 (79/track)

Ground Contact Length: 147 inches

ELECTRICAL SYSTEM

Nominal Voltage: 24 volts DC

Main Generator: (2) 30 volts, 50 amperes, driven by power take-off from main engine

Auxiliary Generator: (1) 30 volts, 50 amperes, driven by the auxiliary engine

Battery: (2) 12 volts in series

COMMUNICATIONS

Radio: SCR 508, 528, or 538 in rear of turret; SCR 506* (command tanks only) in right front sponson

Interphone: (part of radio) 5 stations

Flag Set M238, Panel Set AP50A, Spotlight, Siren

Flares: 3 each, M17, M18, M19, and M21 (command tanks only)

Ground Signals Projector M4 (command tanks only)

*Early vehicles may be equipped with SCR 245

FIRE AND GAS PROTECTION
- (2) 10 lb carbon dioxide, fixed
- (2) 4 pound carbon dioxide, portable
- (2) 1½ quart decontaminating apparatus

PERFORMANCE

Maximum Speed: Sustained, level road	26 miles/hour
Maximum Grade:	60 per cent
Maximum Trench:	7.5 feet
Maximum Vertical Wall:	24 inches
Maximum Fording Depth:	36 inches
Minimum Turning Circle: (diameter)	62 feet
Cruising Range: Roads	approx. 130 miles

MEDIUM TANK M4A3(75)W

GENERAL DATA

Crew:	5 men
Length: Gun forward, w/sandshields	247 inches
Length: Gun to rear, w/sandshields	247 inches
Length: w/sandshields, w/o gun	247 inches
Gun Overhang: Gun forward	0 inches
Width: w/sandshields	105 inches
Height: Over cupola	115.7 inches
Tread:	83 inches
Ground Clearance:	17 inches
Fire Height:	88 inches
Turret Ring Diameter: (inside)	69 inches
Weight, Combat Loaded:	69,600 pounds*
Weight, Unstowed:	63,100 pounds*
Power to Weight Ratio: Net	12.9 hp/ton
Gross	14.4 hp/ton
Ground Pressure: Zero penetration	14.3 psi

*All weights based on T48 or T51 tracks

ARMOR

Type: Turret, cast homogeneous steel; Hull, rolled and cast homogeneous steel; Welded assembly

Hull Thickness:	Actual	Angle w/Vertical
Front, Upper	2.5 inches	47 degrees
Lower	4.25 to 2.0 inches	0 to 56 degrees
Sides	1.5 inches	0 degrees
Rear	1.5 inches	10 to 22 degrees
Top	0.75 inches	83 to 90 degrees
Floor, Front	1.0 inches	90 degrees
Rear	0.5 inches	90 degrees
Turret Thickness:		
Gun Shield	3.5 inches	0 degrees
Rotor Shield	2.0 inches	0 degrees
Front	3.0 inches	30 degrees
Sides	2.0 inches	5 degrees
Rear	2.0 inches	0 degrees
Top	1.0 inches	90 degrees

ARMAMENT

Primary: 75mm Gun M3 in Mount M34A1 in turret

Traverse: Hydraulic and manual	360 degrees
Traverse Rate: (max)	15 seconds/360 degrees
Elevation: Manual	+25 to −10 degrees
Firing Rate: (max)	20 rounds/minute
Loading System:	Manual
Stabilizer System:	Elevation only

Secondary:
- (1) .50 caliber MG HB M2 flexible AA mount on turret
- (1) .30 caliber MG M1919A4 coaxial w/75mm gun in turret
- (1) .30 caliber MG M1919A4 in bow mount
- (1) 2 inch Mortar M3 (smoke) fixed in turret
- Provision for (5) .45 caliber SMG M3

AMMUNITION

104 rounds 75mm	18 rounds 2 inch (smoke)
600 rounds .50 caliber	12 hand grenades
900 rounds .45 caliber	
6250 rounds .30 caliber	

FIRE CONTROL AND VISION EQUIPMENT

Primary Weapon:	Direct	Indirect
	Telescope M70F	Azimuth Indicator M19
	Periscope M4A1 with Telescope M38A2	Gunner's Quadrant M1
		Elevation Quadrant M9

Vision Devices:	Direct	Indirect
Driver	Hatch	Periscope M6 (2)
Asst. Driver	Hatch	Periscope M6 (2)
Commander	Vision cupola and hatch	Periscope M6 (1)
Gunner	None	Periscope M4A1 (1)
Loader	Hatch and pistol port	Periscope M6 (1)

Total Periscopes: M4A1 (1), M6 (6)
Total Pistol Ports: Hull (0), Turret (1)
Vision Cupolas: (1) w/6 vision blocks on turret top

ENGINE

Make and Model: Ford GAA
Type: 8 cylinder, 4 cycle, 60 degree vee
Cooling System: Liquid Ignition: Magneto

Displacement:	1100 cubic inches
Bore and Stroke:	5.4 x 6 inches
Compression Ratio:	7.5:1
Net Horsepower (max):	450 hp at 2600 rpm
Gross Horsepower (max):	500 hp at 2600 rpm
Net Torque (max):	950 ft-lb at 2200 rpm
Gross Torque (max):	1040 ft-lb at 2200 rpm
Weight:	1560 lb, dry
Fuel: 80 octane gasoline	168 gallons
Engine Oil:	32 quarts

POWER TRAIN

Clutch: Dry disc, 2 plate
Transmission: Synchromesh, 5 speeds forward, 1 reverse

Gear Ratios:				
1st	7.56:1		4th	1.11:1
2nd	3.11:1		5th	0.73:1
3rd	1.78:1		reverse	5.65:1

Steering: Controlled differential
Bevel Gear Ratio: 3.53:1 Steering Ratio: 1.515:1
Brakes: Mechanical, external contracting
Final Drive: Herringbone gear Gear Ratio: 2.84:1
Drive Sprocket: At front of vehicle with 13 teeth
Pitch Diameter: 25.038 inches

RUNNING GEAR

Suspension: Vertical volute spring
12 wheels in 6 bogies (3 bogies/track)
Tire Size: 20 x 9 inches
6 track return rollers (1 at rear of each bogie)
Adjustable idler at rear of each track
Idler Size: 22 x 9 inches
Tracks: Outside guide; T48, T49, T51, and T54E1
Type: (T48) Double pin, 16.56 inch width, chevron, rubber
(T49) Double pin, 16.56 inch width, parallel bar, steel
(T51) Double pin, 16.56 inch width, smooth, rubber
(T54E1) Double pin, 16.56 inch width, chevron, steel
Pitch: 6 inches
Shoes per Vehicle: 158 (79/track)
Ground Contact Length: 147 inches

ELECTRICAL SYSTEM

Nominal Voltage: 24 volts DC
Main Generator: (1) 30 volts, 50 amperes, driven by power take-off from main engine
Auxiliary Generator: (1) 30 volts, 50 amperes, driven by the auxiliary engine
Battery: (2) 12 volts in series

COMMUNICATIONS

Radio: SCR 508, 528, or 538 in rear of turret; SCR 506 (command tanks only) in right front sponson
Interphone: (part of radio) 5 stations
Flag Set M238, Panel Set AP50A, Spotlight, Siren
Flares: 3 each, M17, M18, M19, and M21 (command tanks only)
Ground Signals Projector M4 (command tanks only)

FIRE AND GAS PROTECTION

(2) 10 pound carbon dioxide, fixed
(2) 4 pound carbon dioxide, portable
(2) 1½ quart decontaminating apparatus

PERFORMANCE

Maximum Speed: Sustained, level road	26 miles/hour
Maximum Grade:	60 per cent
Maximum Trench:	7.5 feet
Maximum Vertical Wall:	24 inches
Maximum Fording Depth:	36 inches
Minimum Turning Circle: (diameter)	62 feet
Cruising Range: Roads	approx. 100 miles

MEDIUM TANK M4A3(76)W HVSS

GENERAL DATA

Crew:	5 men
Length: Gun forward, w/sandshields and muzzle brake	297 inches
Length: Gun to rear, w/sandshields and muzzle brake	287 inches
Length: w/sandshields, w/o gun	247 inches
Gun Overhang: Gun forward, w/muzzle brake	50 inches
Width: w/sandshields	118 inches
Height: Over cupola	117 inches
Tread:	89 inches
Ground Clearance:	17 inches
Fire Height:	90 inches
Turret Ring Diameter: (inside)	69 inches
Weight, Combat Loaded:	74,200 pounds*
Weight, Unstowed:	68,100 pounds*
Power to Weight Ratio: Net	12.1 hp/ton
Gross	13.5 hp/ton
Ground Pressure: Zero penetration	11.0 psi

*All weights based on T66 tracks

ARMOR

Type: Turret, cast homogeneous steel; Hull, rolled and cast homogeneous steel; Welded assembly

Hull Thickness:	Actual	Angle w/Vertical
Front, Upper	2.5 inches	47 degrees
Lower	4.25 to 2.0 inches	0 to 56 degrees
Sides	1.5 inches	0 degrees
Rear	1.5 inches	10 to 22 degrees
Top	0.75 inches	83 to 90 degrees
Floor, Front	1.0 inches	90 degrees
Rear	0.5 inches	90 degrees
Turret Thickness:		
Gun Shield	3.5 inches	0 degrees
Front	2.5 inches	40 to 45 degrees
Sides	2.5 inches	0 to 13 degrees
Rear	2.5 inches	0 degrees
Top	1.0 inches	90 degrees

ARMAMENT

Primary: 76mm Gun M1A1, M1A1C, or M1A2 in Mount M62 in turret

Traverse: Hydraulic and manual	360 degrees
Traverse Rate: (max)	15 seconds/360 degrees
Elevation: Manual	+25 to −10 degrees
Firing Rate: (max)	20 rounds/minute
Loading System:	Manual
Stabilizer System:	Elevation only

Secondary:

(1) .50 caliber MG HB M2 flexible AA mount on turret
(1) .30 caliber MG M1919A4 coaxial w/76mm gun in turret
(1) .30 caliber MG M1919A4 in bow mount
(1) 2 inch Mortar M3 (smoke) fixed in turret
Provision for (5) .45 caliber SMG M3

AMMUNITION

71 rounds 76mm	18 rounds 2 inch (smoke)
600 rounds .50 caliber	12 hand grenades
900 rounds .45 caliber	
6250 rounds .30 caliber	

FIRE CONTROL AND VISION EQUIPMENT

Primary Weapon:	Direct	Indirect
	Telescope M71D	Azimuth Indicator M19
	Periscope M4A1 with Telescope M47A2	Gunner's Quadrant M1
		Elevation Quadrant M9

Vision Devices:	Direct	Indirect
Driver	Hatch	Periscope M6 (2)
Asst. Driver	Hatch	Periscope M6 (2)
Commander	Vision cupola and hatch	Periscope M6 (1)
Gunner	None	Periscope M4A1 (1)
Loader	Hatch and pistol port	Periscope M6 (1)

Total Periscopes: M4A1 (1), M6 (6)
Total Pistol Ports: Hull (0), Turret (1)
Vision Cupolas: (1) w/6 vision blocks on turret top

ENGINE

Make and Model: Ford GAA
Type: 8 cylinder, 4 cycle, 60 degree vee
Cooling System: Liquid   Ignition: Magneto

Displacement:	1100 cubic inches
Bore and Stroke:	5.4 x 6 inches
Compression Ratio:	7.5:1
Net Horsepower (max):	450 hp at 2600 rpm
Gross Horsepower (max):	500 hp at 2600 rpm
Net Torque (max):	950 ft-lb at 2200 rpm
Gross Torque (max):	1040 ft-lb at 2200 rpm
Weight:	1560 lb, dry
Fuel: 80 octane gasoline	168 gallons
Engine Oil:	32 quarts

POWER TRAIN

Clutch: Dry disc, 2 plate
Transmission: Synchromesh, 5 speeds forward, 1 reverse

Gear Ratios:				
1st	7.56:1	4th	1.11:1
2nd	3.11:1	5th	0.73:1
3rd	1.78:1	reverse	5.65:1

Steering: Controlled differential
Bevel Gear Ratio: 3.53:1   Steering Ratio: 1.515:1
Brakes: Mechanical, external contracting
Final Drive: Herringbone gear   Gear Ratio: 2.84:1
Drive Sprocket: At front of vehicle with 13 teeth
Pitch Diameter: 25.038 inches

RUNNING GEAR

Suspension: Horizontal volute spring
12 dual wheels in 6 bogies (3 bogies/track)
Tire Size: 20.5 x 6.25 inches
4 dual track return rollers (2/track)
6 single track return rollers (3/track)
Dual adjustable idler at rear of each track
Idler Tire Size: 22 x 6.25 inches
Shock absorbers fitted on each bogie
Tracks: Center guide; T66, T80, and T84
Type: (T66) Single pin, 23 inch width, cast steel
(T80) Double pin, 23 inch width, rubber and steel
(T84) Double pin, 23 inch width, rubber
Pitch: 6 inches
Shoes per Vehicle: 158 (79/track)
Ground Contact Length: 151 inches

ELECTRICAL SYSTEM

Nominal Voltage: 24 volts DC
Main Generator: (1) 30 volts, 50 amperes, driven by power take-off from main engine
Auxiliary Generator: (1) 30 volts, 50 amperes, driven by the auxiliary engine
Battery: (2) 12 volts in series

COMMUNICATIONS

Radio: SCR 508, 528, or 538 in rear of turret; SCR 506 (command tanks only) in right front sponson
Interphone: (part of radio) 5 stations
Flag Set M238, Panel Set AP50A, Spotlight, Siren
Flares: 3 each, M17, M18, M19, and M21 (command tanks only)
Ground Signals Projector M4 (command tanks only)

FIRE AND GAS PROTECTION

(2) 10 pound carbon dioxide, fixed
(2) 4 pound carbon dioxide, portable
(2) 1½ quart decontaminating apparatus

PERFORMANCE

Maximum Speed: Sustained, level road	26 miles/hour
Maximum Grade:	60 per cent
Maximum Trench:	7.5 feet
Maximum Vertical Wall:	24 inches
Maximum Fording Depth:	36 inches
Minimum Turning Circle: (diameter)	62 feet
Cruising Range: Roads	approx. 100 miles

MEDIUM TANK M4A3(105) HVSS

GENERAL DATA

Crew:	5 men
Length: Howitzer forward, w/sandshields	247 inches
Length: Howitzer to rear, w/sandshields	247 inches
Length: w/sandshields, w/o howitzer	247 inches
Howitzer Overhang: Howitzer forward	0 inches
Width: w/sandshields	118 inches
Height: Over cupola	115.7 inches
Tread:	89 inches
Ground Clearance:	17 inches
Fire Height:	88 inches
Turret Ring Diameter: (inside)	69 inches
Weight, Combat Loaded:	72,900 pounds*
Weight, Unstowed:	66,400 pounds*
Power to Weight Ratio: Net	12.3 hp/ton
Gross	13.7 hp/ton
Ground Pressure: Zero penetration	10.8 psi

*All weights based on T66 tracks

ARMOR

Type: Turret, cast homogeneous steel; Hull, rolled and cast homogeneous steel; Welded assembly

Hull Thickness:	Actual	Angle w/Vertical
Front, Upper	2.5 inches	47 degrees
Lower	4.25 to 2.0 inches	0 to 56 degrees
Sides	1.5 inches	0 degrees
Rear	1.5 inches	10 to 22 degrees
Top	0.75 inches	83 to 90 degrees
Floor, Front	1.0 inches	90 degrees
Rear	0.5 inches	90 degrees
Turret Thickness:		
Gun Shield	3.6 inches	0 degrees
Front	3.0 inches	30 degrees
Sides	2.0 inches	0 to 5 degrees
Rear	2.0 inches	0 degrees
Top	1.0 inches	90 degrees

ARMAMENT

Primary: 105mm Howitzer M4 in Mount M52 in turret

Traverse: Hydraulic* and manual	360 degrees
Traverse Rate: (max)	15 seconds/360 degrees
Elevation: Manual	+35 to −10 degrees
Firing Rate: (max)	8 rounds/minute
Loading System:	Manual
Stabilizer System:	Elevation only*

Secondary:
(1) .50 caliber MG HB M2 flexible AA mount on turret
(1) .30 caliber MG M1919A4 coaxial w/105mm howitzer in turret
(1) .30 caliber MG M1919A4 in bow mount
(1) 2 inch Mortar M3 (smoke) fixed in turret
Provision for (5) .45 caliber SMG M3

*No power traverse or stabilizer on early production tanks

AMMUNITION

66 rounds 105mm	15 rounds 2 inch (smoke)
600 rounds .50 caliber	12 hand grenades
900 rounds .45 caliber	
4000 rounds .30 caliber	

FIRE CONTROL AND VISION EQUIPMENT

Primary Weapon:	Direct	Indirect
	Telescope M72D	Azimuth Indicator M19
	Periscope M4A1 with Telescope M77C	Gunner's Quadrant M1
		Elevation quadrant M9

Vision Devices:	Direct	Indirect
Driver	Hatch	Periscope M6 (2)
Asst. Driver	Hatch	Periscope M6 (2)
Commander	Vision cupola and hatch	Periscope M6 (1)
Gunner	None	Periscope M4A1 (1)
Loader	Hatch and pistol port	Periscope M6 (1)

Total Periscopes: M4A1 (1), M6 (6)
Total Pistol Ports: Hull (0), Turret (1)
Vision Cupolas: (1) w/6 vision blocks on turret top

ENGINE

Make and Model: Ford GAA
Type: 8 cylinder, 4 cycle, 60 degree vee
Cooling System: Liquid Ignition: Magneto

Displacement:	1100 cubic inches
Bore and Stroke:	5.4 x 6 inches
Compression Ratio:	7.5:1
Net Horsepower (max):	450 hp at 2600 rpm
Gross Horsepower (max):	500 hp at 2600 rpm
Net Torque (max):	950 ft-lb at 2200 rpm
Gross Torque (max):	1040 ft-lb at 2200 rpm
Weight:	1560 lb, dry
Fuel: 80 octane gasoline	168 gallons
Engine Oil:	32 quarts

POWER TRAIN

Clutch: Dry disc, 2 plate
Transmission: Synchromesh, 5 speeds forward, 1 reverse

Gear Ratios:				
1st	7.56:1	4th	1.11:1
2nd	3.11:1	5th	0.73:1
3rd	1.78:1	reverse	5.65:1

Steering: Controlled differential
Bevel Gear Ratio: 3.53:1 Steering Ratio: 1.515:1
Brakes: Mechanical, external contracting
Final Drive: Herringbone gear Gear Ratio: 2.84:1
Drive Sprocket: At front of vehicle with 13 teeth
Pitch Diameter: 25.038 inches

RUNNING GEAR

Suspension: Horizontal volute spring
12 dual wheels in 6 bogies (3 bogies/track)
Tire Size: 20.5 x 6.25 inches
4 dual track return rollers (2/track)
6 single track return rollers (3/track)
Dual adjustable idler at rear of each track
Idler Tire Size: 22 x 6.25 inches
Shock absorbers fitted on each bogie
Tracks: Center guide; T66, T80, and T84
Type: (T66) Single pin, 23 inch width, cast steel
(T80) Double pin, 23 inch width, rubber and steel
(T84) Double pin, 23 inch width, rubber
Pitch: 6 inches
Shoes per Vehicle: 158 (79/track)
Ground Contact Length: 151 inches

ELECTRICAL SYSTEM

Nominal Voltage: 24 volts DC
Main Generator: (1) 30 volts, 50 amperes, driven by power take-off from main engine
Auxiliary Generator: (1) 30 volts, 50 amperes, driven by the auxiliary engine
Battery: (2) 12 volts in series

COMMUNICATIONS

Radio: SCR 508, 528, or 538 in rear of turret; SCR 506 (command tank only) in right front sponson
Interphone: (part of radio) 5 stations
Flag Set M238, Panel Set AP50A, Spotlight, Siren
Flares: 3 each M17, M18, M19, and M21 (command tanks only)
Ground Signals Projector M4 (command tanks only)

FIRE AND GAS PROTECTION

(2) 10 pound carbon dioxide, fixed
(2) 4 pound carbon dioxide, portable
(2) 1½ quart decontaminating apparatus

PERFORMANCE

Maximum Speed: Sustained, level road	26 miles/hour
Maximum Grade:	60 per cent
Maximum Trench:	7.5 feet
Maximum Vertical Wall:	24 inches
Maximum Fording Depth:	36 inches
Minimum Turning Circle: (diameter)	62 feet
Cruising Range: Roads	approx. 100 miles

ASSAULT TANK M4A3E2

GENERAL DATA

Crew:	5 men
Length: Gun forward, w/sandshields	247 inches
Length: Gun to rear, w/sandshields	247 inches
Length: w/sandshields, w/o gun	247 inches
Gun Overhang: Gun forward	0 inches
Width: w/ sandshields	115.6 inches
Height: Over cupola	116.3 inches
Tread:	83 inches
Ground Clearance:	17 inches
Fire Height:	90 inches
Turret Ring Diameter: (inside)	69 inches
Weight, Combat Loaded:	84,000 pounds*
Weight, Unstowed:	77,500 pounds*
Power to Weight Ratio: Net	10.7 hp/ton
Gross	11.9 hp/ton
Ground Pressure: Zero penetration	14.2 psi*

*Based on T48 tracks with duckbill end connectors

ARMOR

Type: Turret, cast homogeneous steel; Hull, rolled and cast homogeneous steel; Welded assembly

Hull Thickness:	Actual	Angle w/Vertical
Front, Upper	4.0 inches	47 degrees
Lower	5.5 to 4.5 inches	0 to 56 degrees
Sides, Upper	3.0 inches	0 degrees
Lower	1.5 inches	0 degrees
Rear	1.5 inches	10 to 22 degrees
Top	0.75 inches	83 to 90 degrees
Floor, Front	1.0 inches	90 degrees
Rear	0.5 inches	90 degrees
Turret Thickness:		
Gun Shield	7.0 inches	0 degrees
Front	6.0 inches	12 degrees
Sides	6.0 inches	6 degrees
Rear	6.0 inches	2 degrees
Top	1.0 inches	90 degrees

ARMAMENT

Primary: 75mm Gun M3 in Mount T110 in turret

Traverse: Hydraulic and manual	360 degrees
Traverse Rate: (max)	15 seconds/360 degrees
Elevation: Manual	+25 to −10 degrees
Firing Rate: (max)	20 rounds/minute
Loading System:	Manual
Stabilizer System:	Elevation only

Secondary:
- (1) .50 caliber MG HB M2 flexible AA mount on turret
- (1) .30 caliber MG M1919A4 coaxial w/75mm gun in turret
- (1) .30 caliber MG M1919A4 in bow mount
- (1) 2 inch Mortar M3 (smoke) fixed in turret
- Provision for (5) .45 caliber SMG M3

AMMUNITION

104 rounds 75mm	18 rounds 2 inch (smoke)
600 rounds .50 caliber	12 hand grenades
900 rounds .45 caliber	
6250 rounds .30 caliber	

FIRE CONTROL AND VISION EQUIPMENT

Primary Weapon:	Direct	Indirect
	Telescope M71G	Azimuth Indicator M20
	Periscope M4A1 with Telescope M38A2	Gunner's Quadrant M1
		Elevation Quadrant M9

Vision Devices:	Direct	Indirect
Driver	Hatch	Periscope M6 (2)
Asst. Driver	Hatch	Periscope M6 (2)
Commander	Vision cupola and hatch	Periscope M6 (1)
Gunner	None	Periscope M4A1 (1)
Loader	Hatch	Periscope M6 (1)

Total Periscopes: M4A1 (1), M6 (6)

Vision Cupolas: (1) w/6 vision blocks on turret top

ENGINE

Make and Model: Ford GAA

Type: 8 cylinder, 4 cycle, 60 degree vee

Cooling System: Liquid Ignition: Magneto

Displacement:	1100 cubic inches
Bore and Stroke:	5.4 x 6 inches
Compression Ratio:	7.5:1
Net Horsepower (max):	450 hp at 2600 rpm
Gross Horsepower (max):	500 hp at 2600 rpm
Net Torque (max):	950 ft-lb at 2200 rpm
Gross Torque (max):	1040 ft-lb at 2200 rpm
Weight:	1560 lb, dry
Fuel: 80 octane gasoline	168 gallons
Engine Oil:	32 quarts

POWER TRAIN

Clutch: Dry disc, 2 plate

Transmission: Synchromesh, 5 speeds forward, 1 reverse

Gear Ratios:				
1st	7.56:1	4th	1.11:1
2nd	3.11:1	5th	0.73:1
3rd	1.78:1	reverse	5.65:1

Steering: Controlled differential
  Bevel Gear Ratio: 3.53:1 Steering Ratio: 1.515:1

Brakes: Mechanical, external contracting

Final Drive: Herringbone gear Gear Ratio: 3.36:1

Drive Sprocket: At front of vehicle with 13 teeth
  Pitch Diameter: 25.038 inches

RUNNING GEAR

Suspension: Vertical volute spring
  12 wheels in 6 bogies (3 bogies/track)
  Tire Size: 20 x 9 inches
  6 track return rollers (1 at rear of each bogie)
  Adjustable idler at rear of each track
  Idler Size: 22 x 9 inches

Tracks: Outside guide; T48 or T51 w/extended end connectors
  Type: (T48) Double pin, 16.56 inch width, chevron, rubber
    (T51) Double pin, 16.56 inch width, smooth, rubber
  Total Track Width: 20.1 inches with end connectors
  Pitch: 6 inches
  Shoes per Vehicle: 158 (79/track)
  Ground Contact Length: 147 inches

ELECTRICAL SYSTEM

Nominal Voltage: 24 volts DC

Main Generator: (1) 30 volts, 50 amperes, driven by power take-off from main engine

Auxiliary Generator: (1) 30 volts, 50 amperes, driven by the auxiliary engine

Battery: (2) 12 volts in series

COMMUNICATIONS

Radio: SCR 508, 528, or 538 in rear of turret; SCR 506 (command tanks only) in right front sponson

Interphone: (part of radio) 5 stations

Flag Set M238, Panel Set AP50A, Spotlight

Flares: 3 each, M17, M18, M19, and M21 (command tanks only)

Ground Signals Projector M4 (command tanks only)

FIRE AND GAS PROTECTION

- (2) 10 pound carbon dioxide, fixed
- (2) 4 pound carbon dioxide, portable
- (2) 1½ quart decontaminating apparatus

PERFORMANCE

Maximum Speed: Sustained, level road	22 miles/hour
Maximum Grade:	60 per cent
Maximum Trench:	7.5 feet
Maximum Vertical Wall:	24 inches
Maximum Fording Depth:	36 inches
Minimum Turning Circle: (diameter)	74 feet
Cruising Range: Roads	approx. 100 miles

MEDIUM TANK M4A4 (early production)

GENERAL DATA

Crew:	5 men
Length: Gun forward, w/o sandshields	238.5 inches
Length: Gun to rear, w/o sandshields	238.5 inches
Length: w/o gun, w/o sandshields	238.5 inches
Gun Overhang: Gun forward	0 inches
Width: w/o sandshields	103 inches
Height: Over turret hatch	108 inches
Tread:	83 inches
Ground Clearance:	16 inches
Fire Height:	88 inches
Turret Ring Diameter: (inside)	69 inches
Weight, Combat Loaded:	69,700 pounds*
Weight, Unstowed:	65,400 pounds*
Power to Weight Ratio: Net	10.6 hp/ton
Gross	12.2 hp/ton
Ground Pressure: Zero penetration	13.2 psi

*All weights based on T48 or T51 tracks

ARMOR

Type: Turret, cast homogeneous steel; Hull, rolled and cast homogeneous steel; Welded assembly

Hull Thickness:	Actual	Angle w/Vertical
Front, Upper	2.0 inches	56 degrees
Lower	2.0 inches	0 to 45 degrees
Sides	1.5 inches	0 degrees
Rear	1.5 inches	0 to 20 degrees
Top	0.75 inches	83 to 90 degrees
Floor, Front	1.0 inches	90 degrees
Rear	0.5 inches	90 degrees
Turret Thickness:		
Gun Shield	3.0 inches	0 degrees
Rotor Shield	2.0 inches	0 degrees
Front	3.0 inches	30 degrees
Sides	2.0 inches	5 degrees
Rear	2.0 inches	0 degrees
Top	1.0 inches	90 degrees

ARMAMENT

Primary: 75mm Gun M3 in Mount M34 in turret*

Traverse: Hydraulic and manual	360 degrees
Traverse Rate: (max)	15 seconds/360 degrees
Elevation: Manual	+25 to −12 degrees
Firing Rate: (max)	20 rounds/minute
Loading System:	Manual
Stabilizer System:	Elevation only

Secondary:
(1) .50 caliber MG HB M2 flexible AA mount on turret
(1) .30 caliber MG M1919A4 coaxial w/75mm gun in turret
(1) .30 caliber MG M1919A4 in bow mount
Provision for (1) .45 caliber SMG M1928A1
*Mount M34A1 in later production tanks

AMMUNITION

97 rounds 75mm — 12 hand grenades
300 rounds .50 caliber
600 rounds .45 caliber
4750 rounds .30 caliber

FIRE CONTROL AND VISION EQUIPMENT

Primary Weapon:	Direct	Indirect
	Periscope M4 with Telescope M38	Azimuth Indicator M19 Gunner's Quadrant M1 Elevation Quadrant M9

Vision Devices:	Direct	Indirect
Driver	Hatch and vision slot	Periscope M6 (1)*
Asst. Driver	Hatch and vision slot	Periscope M6 (1)*
Commander	Hatch	Periscope M6 (1)
Gunner	None	Periscope M4 (1)
Loader	Pistol port	Periscope M6 (1)

Total Periscopes: M4 (1), M6 (4)
Total Pistol Ports: Hull (0), Turret (1)
*(2) in later tanks replacing vision slots

ENGINE

Make and Model: Chrysler A57
Type: 30 cylinder, 4 cycle, multibank
Cooling System: Liquid — Ignition: Battery

Displacement:	1253 cubic inches
Bore and Stroke:	4.37 x 4.5 inches
Compression Ratio:	6.2:1
Net Horsepower (max):	370 hp at 2400 rpm#
Gross Horsepower (max):	425 hp at 2850 rpm*
Net Torque (max):	1020 ft-lb at 1200 rpm#
Gross Torque (max):	1060 ft-lb at 1400 rpm*
Weight:	5400 lb, dry
Fuel: 80 octane gasoline	160 gallons
Engine Oil:	32 quarts

#Propeller shaft rpm — *Crankshaft rpm

POWER TRAIN

Transfer Gear Ratio: 1.19:1
Clutch: Dry disc, 2 plate
Transmission: Synchromesh, 5 speeds forward, 1 reverse

Gear Ratios:				
1st	7.56:1		4th	1.11:1
2nd	3.11:1		5th	0.73:1
3rd	1.78:1		reverse	5.65:1

Steering: Controlled differential
Bevel Gear Ratio: 3.53:1 — Steering Ratio: 1.515:1
Brakes: Mechanical, external contracting
Final Drive: Herringbone gear — Gear Ratio: 2.84:1
Drive Sprocket: At front of vehicle with 13 teeth
Pitch Diameter: 25.038 inches

RUNNING GEAR

Suspension: Vertical volute spring
12 wheels in 6 bogies (3 bogies/track)
Tire Size: 20 x 9 inches
6 track return rollers (1 at rear of each bogie)
Adjustable idler at rear of each track
Idler Size: 22 x 9 inches
Tracks: Outside guide; T48, T49, T51, and T54E1
Type: (T48) Double pin, 16.56 inch width, chevron, rubber
(T49) Double pin, 16.56 inch width, parallel bar, steel
(T51) Double pin, 16.56 inch width, smooth, rubber
(T54E1) Double pin, 16.56 inch width, chevron, steel
Pitch: 6 inches
Shoes per Vehicle: 166 (83/track)
Ground Contact Length: 160 inches

ELECTRICAL SYSTEM

Nominal Voltage: 24 volts DC
Main Generator: (1) 24 volts, 50 amperes, driven by power take-off from main engine
Auxiliary Generator: (1) 30 volts, 50 amperes, driven by the auxiliary engine
Battery: (2) 12 volts in series

COMMUNICATIONS

Radio: SCR 508, 528, or 538 in rear of turret; SCR 506* (command tanks only) in right front sponson
Interphone: (part of radio) 5 stations
Flag Set M238, Panel Set AP50A, Spotlight, Siren
Flares: 3 each, M17, M18, M19, and M21 (command tanks only)
Ground Signals Projector M4 (command tanks only)
*Early vehicles may be equipped with SCR 245

FIRE AND GAS PROTECTION

(2) 10 pound carbon dioxide, fixed
(2) 4 pound carbon dioxide, portable
(2) 1½ quart decontaminating apparatus

PERFORMANCE

Maximum Speed: Sustained, level road	20 miles/hour
Short periods, level	25 miles/hour
Maximum Grade:	60 per cent
Maximum Trench:	8 feet
Maximum Vertical Wall:	24 inches
Maximum Fording Depth:	42 inches
Minimum Turning Circle: (diameter)	70 feet
Cruising Range: Roads	approx. 100 miles

CRUISER TANK SHERMAN VC

GENERAL DATA

Crew:	4 men
Length: Gun forward, w/sandshields and muzzle brake	309 inches
Length: Gun to rear, w/sandshields and muzzle brake	292 inches
Length: w/sandshields, w/o gun	254 inches
Gun Overhang: Gun forward, w/muzzle brake	55 inches
Width: w/sandshields	105 inches
Height: Over turret hatch	108 inches
Tread:	83 inches
Ground Clearance:	17 inches
Fire Height:	88 inches
Turret Ring Diameter: (inside)	69 inches
Weight, Combat Loaded:	72,100 pounds*
Weight, Unstowed:	67,800 pounds*
Power to Weight Ratio: Net	10.3 hp/ton
Gross	11.8 hp/ton
Ground Pressure: Zero penetration	13.6 psi

*All weights based on T48 or T51 tracks

ARMOR

Type: Turret, cast homogeneous steel; Hull, rolled and cast homogeneous steel; Welded assembly

Hull Thickness:	Actual	Angle w/Vertical
Front, Upper	2.0 inches	56 degrees
Lower	2.0 inches	0 to 45 degrees
Sides	1.5 inches	0 degrees
Rear	1.5 inches	0 to 20 degrees
Top	0.75 inches	83 to 90 degrees
Floor, Front	1.0 inches	90 degrees
Rear	0.5 inches	90 degrees
Turret Thickness		
Gun Shield	3.5 inches	0 degrees
Mantlet	1.5 inches	0 degrees
Front	3.0 inches	30 degrees
Sides	2.0 inches	5 degrees
Rear	2.5 inches	0 degrees
Top	1.0 inches	90 degrees

ARMAMENT

Primary: 17pdr Gun Mk IV or VII in Mount No. 2, Mk I in turret

Traverse: Hydraulic and manual	360 degrees
Traverse Rate: (max)	15 seconds/360 degrees
Elevation: Manual	+20 to −5 degrees
Firing Rate: (max)	10 rounds/minute
Loading System:	Manual
Stabilizer System:	None

Secondary:
(1) .50 caliber MG HB M2 flexible AA mount on turret
(1) .30 caliber MG M1919A4 coaxial w/17pdr gun in turret
(1) 2 inch Bomb Thrower Mk I* or IA* fixed in turret
Provision for (1) .45 caliber SMG M1928A1

AMMUNITION

77 rounds 17 pdr	27 rounds 2 inch (smoke)
1170 rounds .50 caliber	9 hand grenades
440 rounds .45 caliber	
5000 rounds .30 caliber	

FIRE CONTROL AND VISION EQUIPMENT

Primary Weapon:	Direct	Indirect
	Telescope Mk 3/1	Azimuth Indicator M19
	Periscope M4 with Telescope M38	Clinometer
		Rangefinder
Vision Devices:	Direct	Indirect
Driver	Hatch	Periscope M6 (2)
Commander	Hatch	Periscope M6 (1)
Gunner	None	Periscope M4 (1)
Loader	Hatch and pistol port	Periscope M6 (1)

Total Periscopes: M4 (1), M6 (4)
Total Pistol Ports: Hull (0), Turret (1)

ENGINE

Make and Model: Chrysler A57
Type: 30 cylinder, 4 cycle, multibank
Cooling System: Liquid Ignition: Battery

Displacement:	1253 cubic inches
Bore and Stroke:	4.37 x 4.5 inches
Compression Ratio:	6.2:1
Net Horsepower (max):	370 hp at 2400 rpm#
Gross Horsepower (max):	425 hp at 2850 rpm*
Net Torque (max):	1020 ft-lb at 1200 rpm#
Gross Torque (max):	1060 ft-lb at 1400 rpm*
Weight:	5400 lb, dry
Fuel: 80 octane gasoline	160 gallons
Engine Oil:	32 quarts

#Propeller shaft rpm *Crankshaft rpm

POWER TRAIN

Transfer Gear Ratio: 1.19:1
Clutch: Dry disc, 2 plate
Transmission: Synchromesh, 5 speeds forward, 1 reverse

Gear Ratios:				
1st	7.56:1		4th	1.11:1
2nd	3.11:1		5th	0.73:1
3rd	1.78:1		reverse	5.65:1

Steering: Controlled differential
Bevel Gear Ratio: 3.53:1 Steering Ratio: 1.515:1
Brakes: Mechanical, external contracting
Final Drive: Herringbone gear Gear Ratio: 2.84:1
Drive Sprocket: At front of vehicle with 13 teeth
Pitch Diameter: 25.038 inches

RUNNING GEAR

Suspension: Vertical volute spring
12 wheels in 6 bogies (3 bogies/track)
Tire Size: 20 x 9 inches
6 track return rollers (1 at rear of each bogie)
Adjustable idler at rear of each track
Idler Size: 22 x 9 inches
Tracks: Outside guide; T48, T49, T51, and T54E1
Type: (T48) Double pin, 16.56 inch width, chevron, rubber
(T49) Double pin, 16.56 inch width, parallel bar, steel
(T51) Double pin, 16.56 inch width, smooth, rubber
(T54E1) Double pin, 16.56 inch width, chevron, steel
Pitch: 6 inches
Shoes per Vehicle: 166 (83/track)
Ground Contact Length: 160 inches

ELECTRICAL SYSTEM

Nominal Voltage: 24 volts DC
Main Generator: (1) 24 volts, 50 amperes, driven by power take-off from main engine
Auxiliary Generator: (1) 30 volts, 50 amperes, driven by the auxiliary engine
Battery: (2) 12 volts in series

COMMUNICATIONS

Radio: British Wireless Set No. 19 in rear of turret
Interphone: (part of radio) 5 stations
Tank Distinguishing Flag Set
Signal Pistol No. 1, 1 inch
Signal Flares

FIRE PROTECTION

(2) 10 pound carbon dioxide, fixed
(2) 4 pound carbon dioxide, portable
(2) methyl bromide, portable

PERFORMANCE

Maximum Speed: Sustained, level road	20 miles/hour
Short periods, level	25 miles/hour
Maximum Grade:	60 per cent
Maximum Trench:	8 feet
Maximum Vertical Wall:	24 inches
Maximum Fording Depth:	42 inches
Minimum Turning Circle: (diameter)	70 feet
Cruising Range: Roads	approx. 100 miles

MEDIUM TANK M4A6 (late production)

GENERAL DATA

Crew:	5 men
Length: Gun forward, w/o sandshields	238.5 inches
Length: Gun to rear, w/o sandshields	238.5 inches
Length: w/o gun, w/o sandshields	238.5 inches
Gun Overhang: Gun forward	0 inches
Width: w/o sandshields	103 inches
Height: Over turret hatch	108 inches
Tread:	83 inches
Ground Clearance:	16 inches
Fire Height:	88 inches
Turret Ring Diameter: (inside)	69 inches
Weight, Combat Loaded:	70,000 pounds*
Weight, Unstowed:	65,800 pounds*
Power to Weight Ratio: Net	12.9 hp/ton
Gross	14.2 hp/ton
Ground Pressure: Zero penetration	13.2 psi

*All weights based on T48 or T51 tracks

ARMOR

Type: Turret, cast homogeneous steel; Hull, rolled and cast homogeneous steel; Welded assembly

Hull Thickness:	Actual	Angle w/Vertical
Front, Upper	2.0 inches	51 degrees
Lower	4.25 to 2.0 inches	0 to 56 degrees
Sides	1.5 inches	0 degrees
Rear	1.5 inches	0 to 20 degrees
Top	0.75 inches	83 to 90 degrees
Floor, Front	1.0 inches	90 degrees
Rear	0.5 inches	90 degrees
Turret Thickness:		
Gun Shield	3.5 inches	0 degrees
Rotor Shield	2.0 inches	0 degrees
Front	3.0 inches	30 degrees
Sides	2.0 inches	5 degrees
Rear	2.0 inches	0 degrees
Top	1.0 inches	90 degrees

ARMAMENT

Primary: 75mm Gun M3 in Mount M34A1 in turret

Traverse: Hydraulic and manual	360 degrees
Traverse Rate: (max)	15 seconds/360 degrees
Elevation: Manual	+25 to −10 degrees
Firing Rate: (max)	20 rounds/minute
Loading System:	Manual
Stabilizer System:	Elevation only

Secondary:
- (1) .50 caliber MG HB M2 flexible AA mount on turret
- (1) .30 caliber MG M1919A4 coaxial w/75mm gun in turret
- (1) .30 caliber MG M1919A4 in bow mount
- (1) 2 inch Mortar M3 (smoke) fixed in turret
- Provision for (1) .45 caliber SMG M1928A1

AMMUNITION

97 rounds 75mm	12 rounds 2 inch (smoke)
300 rounds .50 caliber	12 hand grenades
600 rounds .45 caliber	
4750 rounds .30 caliber	

FIRE CONTROL AND VISION EQUIPMENT

Primary Weapon:	Direct	Indirect
	Telescope M55	Azimuth Indicator M19
	Periscope M4 with Telescope M38	Gunner's Quadrant M1
		Elevation Quadrant M9

Vision Devices:	Direct	Indirect
Driver	Hatch	Periscope M6 (2)
Asst. Driver	Hatch	Periscope M6 (2)
Commander	Hatch	Periscope M6 (1)
Gunner	None	Periscope M4 (1)
Loader	Pistol port	Periscope M6 (1)

Total Periscopes: M4 (1), M6 (6)
Total Pistol Ports: Hull (0), Turret (1)

ENGINE

Make and Model: Ordnance Engine RD-1820
Type: 9 cylinder, 4 cycle, radial
Cooling System: Air Ignition: Compression

Displacement:	1823 cubic inches
Bore and Stroke:	6.1 x 6.9 inches
Compression Ratio:	15.5:1
Net Horsepower (max):	450 hp at 2000 rpm*
Gross Horsepower (max):	497 hp at 3000 rpm#
Net Torque (max):	1470 ft-lb at 1200 rpm*
Gross Torque (max):	945 ft-lb at 2100 rpm#
Weight:	3536 lb, dry
Fuel: 40 cetane diesel oil	138 gallons
Engine Oil:	62 quarts

*Crankshaft rpm #Propeller shaft rpm

POWER TRAIN

Clutch: Dry disc, 2 plate
Transfer Case Gear Ratio: 0.67:1
Transmission: Synchromesh, 5 speeds forward, 1 reverse

Gear Ratios:			
1st	7.56:1	4th	1.11:1
2nd	3.11:1	5th	0.73:1
3rd	1.78:1	reverse	5.65:1

Steering: Controlled differential
Bevel Gear Ratio: 3.53:1 Steering Ratio: 1.515:1
Brakes: Mechanical, external contracting
Final Drive: Herringbone gear Gear Ratio: 2.84:1
Drive Sprocket: At front of vehicle with 13 teeth
Pitch Diameter: 25.038 inches

RUNNING GEAR

Suspension: Vertical volute spring
12 wheels in 6 bogies (3 bogies/track)
Tire Size: 20 x 9 inches
6 track return rollers (1 at rear of each bogie)
Adjustable idler at rear of each track
Idler Size: 22 x 9 inches
Tracks: Outside guide; T48, T49, T51, and T54E1
Type: (T48) Double pin, 16.56 inch width, chevron, rubber
(T49) Double pin, 16.56 inch width, parallel bar, steel
(T51) Double pin, 16.56 inch width, smooth, rubber
(T54E1) Double pin, 16.56 inch width, chevron, steel
Pitch: 6 inches
Shoes per Vehicle: 166 (83/track)
Ground Contact Length: 160 inches

ELECTRICAL SYSTEM

Nominal Voltage: 24 volts DC
Main Generator: (1) 24 volts, 50 amperes, driven by power take-off from main engine
Auxiliary Generator: (1) 30 volts, 50 amperes, driven by the auxiliary engine
Battery: (2) 12 volts in series

COMMUNICATIONS

Radio: SCR 508, 528, or 538 in rear of turret; SCR 506 (command tanks only) in right front sponson
Interphone: (part of radio) 5 stations
Flag Set M238, Panel Set AP50A, Spotlight, Siren
Flares: 3 each, M 17, M18, M19, and M21 (command tanks only)
Ground Signals Projector M4 (command tanks only)

FIRE AND GAS PROTECTION

(2) 10 pound carbon dioxide, fixed
(2) 4 pound carbon dioxide, portable
(2) 1½ quart decontaminating apparatus

PERFORMANCE

Maximum Speed: Sustained, level road	25 miles/hour
Short periods, level	30 miles/hour
Maximum Grade:	60 per cent
Maximum Trench:	8 feet
Maximum Vertical Wall:	24 inches
Maximum Fording Depth:	42 inches
Minimum Turning Circle: (diameter)	70 feet
Cruising Range: Roads	approx. 120 miles

17pdr SELF-PROPELLED GUN ACHILLES IIC
and
3 inch GUN MOTOR CARRIAGE M10

GENERAL DATA

Crew:	5 men
Length: Gun forward (Achilles IIC)	286.3 inches
(3 inch GMC M10)	268.8 inches
Length: Gun to rear (Achilles IIC)	280.0 inches
(3 inch GMC M10)	262.5 inches
Length: w/o gun	235.1 inches
Gun Overhang: Gun forward (Achilles IIC)	51.2 inches
(3 inch GMC M10)	33.7 inches
Width:	120 inches
Height: Over AA MG	114 inches
Tread:	83 inches
Ground Clearance:	17 inches
Fire Height:	83 inches
Turret Ring Diameter: (inside)	69 inches
Weight, Combat Loaded:	65,200 pounds
Weight, Unstowed:	60,000 pounds
Power to Weight Ratio: Net	11.5 hp/ton
Gross	12.6 hp/ton
Ground Pressure: Zero penetration	13.4 psi

ARMOR

Type: Turret, rolled and cast homogeneous steel; Hull, rolled and cast homogeneous steel; Welded assembly

Hull Thickness:	Actual	Angle w/Vertical
Front, Upper	1.5 inches	55 degrees
Lower	2.0 inches	0 to 56 degrees
Sides, Upper	0.75 inches	38 degrees
Lower	1.0 inches	0 degrees
Rear, Upper	0.75 inches	38 degrees
Lower	1.0 inches	0 degrees
Top, Front	0.75 inches	90 degrees
Rear	0.375 inches	90 degrees
Floor	0.5 inches	90 degrees
Turret Thickness:		
Front (gun shield)	2.25 inches	45 degrees
Sides	1.0 inches	15 degrees
Rear	1.0 inches	0 degrees
Top	0.75 inches	90 degrees

ARMAMENT

Primary: (Achilles IIC) 17 pdr Mk V in Mtg No. 3 Mk I in turret
(3 inch GMC M10) 3 inch Gun M7 in Mount M5 in turret

Traverse: Manual	360 degrees
Elevation: Manual (Achilles IIC)	+20 to −5 degrees
(3 inch GMC M10)	+30 to −10 degrees
Firing Rate: (max) (Achilles IIC)	10 rounds/minute
(3 inch GMC M10)	15 rounds/minute
Loading System:	Manual
Stabilizer System:	None

Secondary:
- (1) .50 caliber MG HB M2 flexible AA mount on turret
- (1) 2 inch muzzle loading mortar (Achilles IIC)
- Provision for (4) 9mm Sten SMG Mk III (Achilles IIC)
- Provision for (5) .30 caliber Carbines M1 (3 inch GMC M10)

AMMUNITION

- 50 rounds 17 pdr (Achilles IIC)
- 54 rounds 3 inch (3 inch GMC M10)
- 450 rounds .50 caliber (Achilles)
- 1000 rounds .50 caliber (M10)
- 1024 rounds 9mm Sten (Achilles)
- 450 rounds .30 caliber carbine (M10)
- 9 hand grenades (Achilles)
- 12 hand grenades (M10)
- 36 rounds 2 inch (smoke) (Achilles)
- 4 smoke pots HC M1 (M10)

FIRE CONTROL AND VISION EQUIPMENT

Primary Weapon:	Direct	Indirect
Achilles IIC	Direct sight telescope	Azimuth Indicator M18 Rangefinder
3 inch GMC M10	Telescope M70G	Azimuth Indicator M18 Gunner's Quadrant M1

Vision Devices:	Direct	Indirect
Driver	Hatch	Periscope M6 (2)
Asst. Driver	Hatch	Periscope M6 (1)
Commander	Open turret	None
Gunner	Open turret	None
Loader	Open turret	None

Total Periscopes: M6 (3)

ENGINE

Make and Model: General Motors 6046
Type: 12 cylinder, 2 cycle, twin in-line
Cooling System: Liquid   Ignition: Compression

Displacement:	850 cubic inches
Bore and Stroke:	4.25 x 5 inches
Compression Ratio:	16:1
Net Horsepower (max):	375 hp at 2100 rpm*
Gross Horsepower (max):	410 hp at 2900 rpm#
Net Torque (max):	1000 ft-lb at 1400 rpm*
Gross Torque (max):	885 ft-lb at 1900 rpm#
Weight:	5110 lb, dry
Fuel: 40 cetane diesel oil	165 gallons
Engine Oil:	28 quarts

*Crankshaft rpm   #Propeller shaft rpm

POWER TRAIN

Clutch: Dry disc, 2 plate (2)
Transfer Case Gear Ratio: 0.73:1
Transmission: Synchromesh, 5 speeds forward, 1 reverse

Gear Ratios:				
1st	7.56:1	4th	1.11:1
2nd	3.11:1	5th	0.73:1
3rd	1.78:1	reverse	5.65:1

Steering: Controlled differential
Bevel Gear Ratio: 3.53:1   Steering Ratio: 1.515:1
Brakes: Mechanical, external contracting
Final Drive: Herringbone gear   Gear Ratio: 2.84:1
Drive Sprocket: At front of vehicle with 13 teeth
Pitch Diameter: 25.038 inches

RUNNING GEAR

Suspension: Vertical volute spring
12 wheels in 6 bogies (3 bogies/track)
Tire Size: 20 x 9 inches
6 track return rollers (1 at rear of each bogie)
Adjustable idler at rear of each track
Idler Size: 22 x 9 inches
Tracks: Outside guide; T48, T49, T51, and T54El
Type: (T48) Double pin, 16.56 inch width, chevron, rubber
(T49) Double pin, 16.56 inch width, parallel bar, steel
(T51) Double pin, 16.56 inch width, smooth, rubber
(T54El) Double pin, 16.56 inch width, chevron, steel
Pitch: 6 inches
Shoes per Vehicle: 158 (79/track)
Ground Contact Length: 147 inches

ELECTRICAL SYSTEM

Nominal Voltage: 24 volts DC
Main Generator: (2) 24 volts, 50 amperes, driven by power take-off from main engine
Auxiliary Generator: None
Battery: (2) 12 volts in series

COMMUNICATIONS

Achilles IIC:
Radio: British Wireless Set No. 19 in right front sponson
Interphone: (part of radio) 5 stations
Tank Distinguishing Flag Set
Signal Flares

3 inch Gun Motor Carriage M10:
Radio: SCR 610 in right front sponson
Interphone: RC99, 5 stations
Flag Set M238
Pyrotechnic Pistol M2 w/18 signals

FIRE AND GAS PROTECTION

Achilles IIC:
- (2) 10 pound carbon dioxide, fixed
- (2) 4 pound carbon dioxide, portable
- (2) methyl bromide, portable

3 inch Gun Motor Carriage M10:
- (2) 10 pound carbon dioxide, fixed
- (2) 4 pound carbon dioxide, portable
- (2) 1½ quart decontaminating apparatus

PERFORMANCE

Maximum Speed: Sustained, level road	25 miles/hour
Short periods, level	30 miles/hour
Maximum Grade:	60 per cent
Maximum Trench:	7.5 feet
Maximum Vertical Wall:	24 inches
Maximum Fording Depth:	36 inches
Minimum Turning Circle: (diameter)	62 feet
Cruising Range: Roads	approx. 200 miles

90mm GUN MOTOR CARRIAGE M36

GENERAL DATA

Crew:	5 men
Length: Gun forward, w/o muzzle brake	293.9 inches
Length: Gun to rear, w/o muzzle brake	287.9 inches
Length: w/o gun	235.1 inches
Gun Overhang: Gun forward, w/o muzzle brake	58.8 inches
Width:	120 inches
Height: Over AA MG	129 inches
Tread:	83 inches
Ground Clearance:	17 inches
Fire Height:	85 inches
Turret Ring Diameter: (inside)	69 inches
Weight, Combat Loaded:	63,000 pounds
Weight, Unstowed:	58,000 pounds
Power to Weight Ratio: Net	14.3 hp/ton
Gross	15.9 hp/ton
Ground Pressure: Zero penetration	12.9 psi

ARMOR

Type: Turret, rolled and cast homogeneous steel; Hull, rolled and cast homogeneous steel; Welded assembly

Hull Thickness:	Actual	Angle w/Vertical
Front, Upper	1.5 inches	55 degrees
Lower	4.25 to 2.0 inches	0 to 56 degrees
Sides, Upper	0.75 inches	38 degrees
Lower	1.0 inches	0 degrees
Rear	0.75 inches	0 to 38 degrees
Top, Front	0.75 inches	90 degrees
Rear	0.375 inches	90 degrees
Floor	0.5 inches	90 degrees
Turret Thickness:		
Front (gun shield)	3.0 inches	0 degrees
Sides	1.25 inches	5 degrees
Rear	1.75 to 5.0 inches	0 degrees
Top	0.375 to 1.0 inches	90 degrees

ARMAMENT

Primary: 90mm Gun M3 in Mount M4 (T8) in turret

Traverse: Hydraulic and manual	360 degrees
Traverse Rate: (max)	15 seconds/360 degrees
Elevation: Manual	+20 to −10 degrees
Firing Rate: (max)	8 rounds/minute
Loading System:	Manual
Stabilizer System:	None

Secondary:
- (1) .50 caliber MG HB M2 flexible AA mount on turret
- Provision for (5) .30 caliber Carbines M1

AMMUNITION

47 rounds 90mm	12 hand grenades
1000 rounds .50 caliber	4 smoke pots HC M1
450 rounds .30 caliber (carbine)	

FIRE CONTROL AND VISION EQUIPMENT

Primary Weapon:	Direct	Indirect
	Telescope M76D	Azimuth Indicator M18
		Elevation Quadrant M9
		Gunner's Quadrant M1

Vision Devices:	Direct	Indirect
Driver	Hatch	Periscope M6 (2)
Asst. Driver	Hatch	Periscope M6 (1)
Commander	Open turret	None
Gunner	Open turret	None
Loader	Open turret	None

Total Periscopes: M6 (3)

ENGINE

Make and Model: Ford GAA
Type: 8 cylinder, 4 cycle, 60 degree vee
Cooling System: Liquid Ignition: Magneto

Displacement:	1100 cubic inches
Bore and Stroke:	5.4 x 6 inches
Compression Ratio:	7.5:1
Net Horsepower (max):	450 hp at 2600 rpm
Gross Horsepower (max):	500 hp at 2600 rpm
Net Torque (max):	950 ft-lb at 2200 rpm
Gross Torque (max):	1040 ft-lb at 2200 rpm
Weight:	1560 lb, dry
Fuel: 80 octane gasoline	192 gallons
Engine Oil:	32 quarts

POWER TRAIN

Clutch: Dry disc, 2 plate
Transmission: Synchromesh, 5 speeds forward, 1 reverse

Gear Ratios:				
	1st	7.56:1	4th	1.11:1
	2nd	3.11:1	5th	0.73:1
	3rd	1.78:1	reverse	5.65:1

Steering: Controlled differential
Bevel Gear Ratio: 3.53:1 Steering Ratio: 1.515:1
Brakes: Mechanical, external contracting
Final Drive: Herringbone gear Gear Ratio: 2.84:1
Drive Sprocket: At front of vehicle with 13 teeth
Pitch Diameter: 25.038 inches

RUNNING GEAR

Suspension: Vertical volute spring
- 12 wheels in 6 bogies (3 bogies/track)
- Tire Size: 20 x 9 inches
- 6 track return rollers (1 at rear of each bogie)
- Adjustable idler at rear of each track
- Idler Size: 22 x 9 inches

Tracks: Outside guide; T48, T49, T51, and T54El
- Type: (T48) Double pin, 16.56 inch width, chevron, rubber
- (T49) Double Pin, 16.56 inch width, parallel bar, steel
- (T51) Double pin, 16.56 inch width, smooth, rubber
- (T54El) Double pin, 16.56 inch width, chevron, steel
- Pitch: 6 inches
- Shoes per Vehicle: 158 (79/track)
- Ground Contact Length: 147 inches

ELECTRICAL SYSTEM

Nominal Voltage: 24 volts DC
Main Generator: (2) 30 volts, 50 amperes, driven by power take-off from main engine
Auxiliary Generator: (1) 30 volts, 50 amperes, driven by the auxiliary engine
Battery: (2) 12 volts in series

COMMUNICATIONS

Radio: SCR 610 in right front sponson
Interphone: RC99, 5 stations
Flag Set M238, Panel Set AP50A
Pyrotechnic Hand Projector M9

FIRE AND GAS PROTECTION

- (2) 10 pound carbon dioxide, fixed
- (2) 4 pound carbon dioxide, portable
- (2) 1½ quart decontaminating apparatus

PERFORMANCE

Maximum Speed: Sustained, level road	26 miles/hour
Maximum Grade:	60 per cent
Maximum Trench:	7.5 feet
Maximum Vertical Wall:	24 inches
Maximum Fording Depth:	36 inches
Minimum Turning Circle: (diameter)	62 feet
Cruising Range: Roads	approx. 150 miles

105mm HOWITZER MOTOR CARRIAGE M7

GENERAL DATA

Crew:	7 men
Length: w/sandshields	237 inches
Length: w/o howitzer, w/sandshields	237 inches
Howitzer Overhang: w/sandshields	0 inches
Width: w/sandshields	113 inches
Height: Over AA MG	116 inches
Tread:	83 inches
Ground Clearance:	17 inches
Fire Height:	76 inches
Weight, Combat Loaded:	50,600 pounds
Weight, Unstowed:	43,700 pounds
Power to Weight Ratio: Net	13.8 hp/ton
Gross	15.8 hp/ton
Ground Pressure: Zero penetration	10.4 psi

ARMOR

Type: Rolled and cast homogeneous steel; Welded assembly

Hull Thickness:		Actual	Angle w/Vertical
Front,	Upper	0.5 inches	30 degrees
	Lower	4.25 to 2.0 inches	0 to 56 degrees
Sides,	Upper	0.5 inches	0 degrees
	Lower	1.5 inches (soft)	0 degrees
Rear		0.5 inches	0 degrees
Floor,	Front	1.0 inches	90 degrees
	Rear	0.5 inches	90 degrees

ARMAMENT

Primary: 105mm Howitzer M2A1 in Mount M4 at right front of hull

Traverse: Manual	45 degrees (15 L to 30 R)
Elevation: Manual	+35 to −5 degrees
Firing Rate: (max)	8 rounds/minute
Loading System:	Manual
Stabilizer System:	None

Secondary:
(1) .50 caliber MG HB M2 in ring mount at right front of hull
Provision for (3) .45 caliber SMG M3

AMMUNITION

69 rounds 105mm
300 rounds .50 caliber
1620 rounds .45 caliber
8 hand grenades

FIRE CONTROL AND VISION EQUIPMENT

Primary Weapon:	Direct	Indirect
	Elbow Telescope M16	Panoramic Telescope M12A2
		Range Quadrant M4
Vision Devices:	Direct	Indirect
Driver	Hatch	Protectoscope (1)
Commander	Open top	None
Cannoneers	Open top	None

Total Protectoscopes: (1)

ENGINE

Make and Model: Continental R975 C1
Type: 9 cylinder, 4 cycle, radial
Cooling System: Air   Ignition: Magneto

Displacement:	973 cubic inches
Bore and Stroke:	5 x 5.5 inches
Compression Ratio:	5.7:1
Net Horsepower (max):	350 hp at 2400 rpm
Gross Horsepower (max):	400 hp at 2400 rpm
Net Torque (max):	800 ft-lb at 1800 rpm
Gross Torque (max):	890 ft-lb at 1800 rpm
Weight:	1137 lb, dry
Fuel: 80 octane gasoline	175 gallons
Engine Oil:	36 quarts

POWER TRAIN

Clutch: Dry disc, 2 plate
Transmission: Synchromesh, 5 speeds forward, 1 reverse

Gear Ratios:				
	1st	7.56:1	4th	1.11:1
	2nd	3.11:1	5th	0.73:1
	3rd	1.78:1	reverse	5.65:1

Steering: Controlled differential
Bevel Gear Ratio: 3.53:1   Steering Ratio: 1.515:1
Brakes: Mechanical, external contracting
Final Drive: Herringbone gear   Gear Ratio: 2.84:1
Drive Sprocket: At front of vehicle with 13 teeth
Pitch Diameter: 25.038 inches

RUNNING GEAR

Suspension: Vertical volute spring
12 wheels in 6 bogies (3 bogies/track)
Tire Size: 20 x 9 inches
6 track return rollers (1 at rear of each bogie)
Adjustable idler at rear of each track
Idler Size: 22 x 9 inches
Tracks: Outside guide; T48, T49, T51, and T54E1
Type: (T48) Double pin, 16.56 inch width, chevron, rubber
(T49) Double pin, 16.56 inch width, parallel bar, steel
(T51) Double pin, 16.56 inch width, smooth, rubber
(T54E1) Double pin, 16.56 inch width, chevron, steel
Pitch: 6 inches
Shoes per Vehicle: 158 (79/track)
Ground Contact Length: 147 inches

ELECTRICAL SYSTEM

Nominal Voltage: 24 volts DC
Main Generator: (1) 24 volts, 50 amperes, driven by power take-off from main engine
Auxiliary Generator: None
Battery: (2) 12 volts in series

COMMUNICATIONS

Flag Set M238, Panel Set AP50A

FIRE AND GAS PROTECTION

(2) 10 pound carbon dioxide, fixed
(2) 4 pound carbon dioxide, portable
(3) 1½ quart decontaminating apparatus

PERFORMANCE

Maximum Speed: Sustained, level road	21 miles/hour
Short periods, level	24 miles/hour
Maximum Grade:	60 per cent
Maximum Trench:	7.5 feet
Maximum Vertical Wall:	24 inches
Maximum Fording Depth:	40 inches
Minimum Turning Circle: (diameter)	62 feet
Cruising Range: Roads	approx. 120 miles

25pdr SELF-PROPELLED GUN SEXTON II

GENERAL DATA

Crew:		6 men
Length:		241 inches
Length: w/o gun		241 inches
Gun Overhang:		0 inches
Width:		107 inches
Height:		96 inches
Tread:		83 inches
Ground Clearance:		17 inches
Fire Height:	estimated	84 inches
Weight, Combat Loaded:		57,000 pounds
Weight, Unstowed:	estimated	50,000 pounds
Power to Weight Ratio: Net		14.0 hp/ton
Gross		16.1 hp/ton
Ground Pressure: Zero penetration, C.D.P. tracks		12.5 psi

ARMOR

Type: Rolled and cast homogeneous steel: Welded assembly (lower hulls on early vehicles were riveted)

Hull Thickness:	Actual	Angle w/Vertical
Front, Upper	0.75 inches	25 degrees
Lower	4.25 to 2.0 inches	0 to 56 degrees
Sides, Upper	0.5 inches	0 degrees
Lower	1.5 inches	0 degrees
Rear, Upper	0.5 inches	0 degrees
Lower	1.5 inches	10 degrees
Top	0.5 inches	83 degrees
Floor, Front	1.0 inches	90 degrees
Rear	0.5 inches	90 degrees

ARMAMENT

Primary: 25 pdr Mk II or III in Mtg C Mk I in left front of hull

Traverse: Manual	40 degrees (25 L to 15 R)
Elevation: Manual	+40 to −9 degrees
Firing Rate: (max)	8 rounds/minute
Loading System:	Manual
Stabilizer System:	None

Secondary:
- (2) .303 caliber Bren MG
- (2) .303 caliber Rifles No. 4
- (2) 9mm Sten SMG Mk III

AMMUNITION

- 112 cartridges 25 pdr
- 105 projectiles 25 pdr
- 1500 rounds .303 caliber (Bren)
- 100 rounds .303 caliber (rifle)
- 448 rounds 9mm (Sten)
- 12 hand grenades

FIRE CONTROL AND VISION EQUIPMENT

Primary Weapon:	Direct	Indirect
	Telescope C No. 41	Dial Sight C No. 9
		Field Clinometer Mk 6

Vision Devices:	Direct	Indirect
Driver	Hatch	Protectoscope (1)
Commander	Open top	None
Cannoneers	Open top	None

Total Protectoscopes: (1)

ENGINE

Make and Model: Continental R975 C4
Type: 9 cylinder, 4 cycle, radial
Cooling System: Air Ignition: Magneto

Displacement:	973 cubic inches
Bore and Stroke:	5 x 5.5 inches
Compression Ratio:	5.7:1
Net Horsepower (max):	400 hp at 2400 rpm
Gross Horsepower (max):	460 hp at 2400 rpm
Net Torque (max):	940 ft-lb at 1700 rpm
Gross Torque (max):	1025 ft-lb at 1800 rpm
Weight:	1212 lb, dry
Fuel: 80 octane gasoline	180 gallons
Engine Oil:	36 quarts

POWER TRAIN

Clutch: Dry disc, 2 plate
Transmission: Synchromesh, 5 speeds forward, 1 reverse

Gear Ratios:			
1st	7.56:1	4th	1.11:1
2nd	3.11:1	5th	0.73:1
3rd	1.78:1	reverse	5.65:1

Steering: Controlled differential
Bevel Gear Ratio: 3.53:1 Steering Ratio: 1.515:1
Brakes: Mechanical, external contracting
Final Drive: Herringbone gear Gear Ratio: 2.84:1
Drive Sprocket: At front of vehicle with 17 teeth
Pitch Diameter: 25.03 inches

RUNNING GEAR

Suspension: Vertical volute spring
12 wheels in 6 bogies (3 bogies/track)
Tire Size: 20 x 9 inches
6 track return rollers (1 at rear of each bogie)
Adjustable idler at rear of each track
Idler Size: 22 x 9 inches
Tracks: Outside guide; Canadian dry pin (C.D.P.)
Type: (C.D.P.) Single pin, 15.5 inch wide, cast steel
Pitch: 4.6 inches
Shoes per Vehicle: 204-206 (102-103/track)
Ground Contact Length: 147 inches

ELECTRICAL SYSTEM

Nominal Voltage: 24 volts DC
Main Generator: (1) 24 volts, 50 amperes, driven by power take-off from main engine
Auxiliary Generator: (1) 30 volts, 50 amperes, driven by the auxiliary engine
Battery: (2) 12 volts in series

COMMUNICATIONS

Radio: British Wireless Set No. 19 in rear of fighting compartment
Tannoy loud speaker
Telephone and cable reel

FIRE PROTECTION

- (2) 10 pound carbon dioxide, fixed
- (2) carbon tetrachloride, portable
- (2) methyl bromide, portable

PERFORMANCE

Maximum Speed: Sustained, level road	21 miles/hour
Short periods, level	24 miles/hour
Maximum Grade:	60 per cent
Maximum Trench:	7.5 feet
Maximum Vertical Wall:	24 inches
Maximum Fording Depth:	40 inches
Minimum Turning Circle: (diameter)	62 feet
Cruising Range: Roads	approx. 125 miles

155mm GUN MOTOR CARRIAGE M12

GENERAL DATA

Crew:	6 men
Length: Spade retracted w/o sandshields	266.5 inches
Length: w/o gun spade retracted w/o sandshields	265.0 inches
Gun Overhang: Spade retracted w/o sandshields	1.5 inches
Width: w/o sandshields	105.3 inches
Height: Over gun shield	113.5 inches
Tread:	83 inches
Ground Clearance:	17 inches
Fire Height:	87 inches
Weight, Combat Loaded:	59,000 pounds
Weight, Unstowed:	55,000 pounds
Power to Weight Ratio: Net	11.9 hp/ton
Gross	13.6 hp/ton
Ground Pressure: Zero penetration	12.1 psi

ARMOR

Type: Rolled and cast homogeneous steel; Welded assembly

Hull Thickness:	Actual	Angle w/Vertical
Front, Upper	1.0 inches	30 degrees
Lower	2.0 inches	0 to 46 degrees
Sides, Upper	0.625 inches	0 degrees
Lower	0.75 inches	0 degrees
Rear	0.75 inches	0 degrees
Top	0.5 inches	90 degrees
Floor	0.5 inches	90 degrees
Gun Shield	0.75 inches	approx. 0 degrees

ARMAMENT

Primary: 155mm Gun M1917, M1917A1, or M1918M1 in Mount M4

Traverse: Manual	28 degrees (14 L to 14 R)
Elevation: Manual	+30 to −5 degrees
Firing Rate: (max)	4 rounds/minute
Loading System:	Manual
Stabilizer System:	None

Secondary:

Provision for (5) .30 caliber Carbines M1

(1) Grenade Launcher M8

AMMUNITION

10 rounds 155mm	10 AT rifle grenades
	12 hand grenades

FIRE CONTROL AND VISION EQUIPMENT

Primary Weapon:	Direct	Indirect
	Telescope M53	Panoramic Telescope M6
		Sight Quadrant M1918A1

Vision Devices:	Direct	Indirect
Driver	Hatch	Protectoscope (1)
Asst. Driver	Hatch	Protectoscope (1)
Commander	Open top	None
Cannoneers	Open top	None

Total Protectoscopes: (2)

ENGINE

Make and Model: Continental R975 C1

Type: 9 cylinder, 4 cycle, radial

Cooling System: Air   Ignition: Magneto

Displacement:	973 cubic inches
Bore and Stroke:	5 x 5.5 inches
Compression Ratio:	5.7:1
Net Horsepower (max):	350 hp at 2400 rpm
Gross Horsepower (max):	400 hp at 2400 rpm
Net Torque (max):	800 ft-lb at 1800 rpm
Gross Torque (max):	890 ft-lb at 1800 rpm
Weight:	1137 lb, dry
Fuel: 80 octane gasoline	200 gallons
Engine Oil:	36 quarts

POWER TRAIN

Clutch: Dry disc, 2 plate

Transmission: Synchromesh, 5 speeds forward, 1 reverse

Gear Ratios:				
	1st	7.56:1	4th	1.11:1
	2nd	3.11:1	5th	0.73:1
	3rd	1.78:1	reverse	5.65:1

Steering: Controlled differential

Bevel Gear Ratio: 3.53:1   Steering Ratio: 1.515:1

Brakes: Mechanical, external contracting

Final Drive: Herringbone gear   Gear Ratio: 2.84:1

Drive Sprocket: At front of vehicle with 13 teeth

Pitch Diameter: 25.038 inches

RUNNING GEAR

Suspension: Vertical volute spring

12 wheels in 6 bogies (3 bogies/track)

Tire Size: 20 x 9 inches

6 track return rollers (1 at rear of each bogie)

Adjustable idler at rear of each track

Idler Size: 22 x 9 inches

Tracks: Outside guide; T48, T49, T51, and T54E1

Type: (T48) Double pin, 16.56 inch width, chevron, rubber

(T49) Double pin, 16.56 inch width, parallel bar, steel

(T51) Double pin, 16.56 inch width, smooth, rubber

(T54E1) Double pin, 16.56 inch width, chevron, steel

Pitch: 6 inches

Shoes per Vehicle: 158 (79/track)

Ground Contact Length: 147 inches

ELECTRICAL SYSTEM

Nominal Voltage: 24 volts DC

Main Generator: (1) 24 volts, 50 amperes, driven by power take-off from main engine

Auxiliary Generator: None

Battery: (2) 12 volts in series

COMMUNICATIONS

Flag Set M113

FIRE AND GAS PROTECTION

(2) 10 pound carbon dioxide, fixed

(2) 4 pound carbon dioxide, portable

(2) 1½ quart decontaminating apparatus

PERFORMANCE

Maximum Speed: Sustained, level road	21 miles/hour
Short periods, level	24 miles/hour
Maximum Grade:	60 per cent
Maximum Trench:	7.5 feet
Maximum Vertical Wall:	24 inches
Maximum Fording Depth:	40 inches
Minimum Turning Circle: (diameter)	62 feet
Cruising Range: Roads	approx. 140 miles

155mm GUN MOTOR CARRIAGE M40
and
8 inch HOWITZER MOTOR CARRIAGE M43

GENERAL DATA

Crew:		8 men
Length: (M40)		348.4 inches
(M43)		280.4 inches
Length: w/o cannon (M40)		280.4 inches
(M43)		280.4 inches
Cannon Overhang: (M40)		68 inches
(M43)		0 inches
Width:		124 inches
Height: Over mount		130 inches
Tread:		101 inches
Ground Clearance:		17 inches
Fire Height:		102 inches
Weight, Combat Loaded: (M40)		81,000 pounds
(M43)		80,000 pounds
Weight, Unstowed: (M40)	estimated	71,000 pounds
(M43)	estimated	70,000 pounds
Power to Weight Ratio: Net (M40)		9.9 hp/ton
(M43)		10.0 hp/ton
Gross (M40)		11.4 hp/ton
(M43)		11.5 hp/ton
Ground Pressure: Zero penetration (M40)		10.7 psi
(M43)		10.6 psi

ARMOR

Type: Rolled and cast homogeneous steel; Welded assembly

Hull Thickness:	Actual	Angle w/Vertical
Front, Upper	0.5 inches	58 degrees
Lower	4.25 to 2.0 inches	0 to 46 degrees
Sides, Upper	0.5 inches	0 degrees
Lower	1.0 inches	0 degrees
Rear	0.5 inches	0 degrees
Top	0.5 inches	85 degrees
Floor, Front	1.0 inches	90 degrees
Rear	0.5 inches	90 degrees
Gun Shield	0.5 inches	approx. 45 degrees

ARMAMENT

Primary: (M40) 155mm Gun M1A1 or M2 in Mount M13
(M43) 8 inch Howitzer M1 or M2 in Mount M17

Traverse: Manual	36 degrees (18 L to 18 R)
Elevation: Manual	+45 to −5 degrees
Firing Rate: (max)	1 round/minute
Loading System:	Manual
Stabilizer System:	None

Secondary:
Provision for (8) .30 caliber Carbines M1
(1) Grenade Launcher M8

AMMUNITION

20 rounds 155mm (M40)	10 AT grenades
16 rounds 8 inch (M43)	12 hand grenades
960 rounds .30 caliber (carbine)	

FIRE CONTROL AND VISION EQUIPMENT

Primary Weapon:	Direct	Indirect
	Telescope M69F (M40)	Panoramic Telescope M12
	Telescope M69G (M43)	Gunner's Quadrant M1
	Elbow Telescope M16A1F(M40)	
	Elbow Telescope M16A1G(M43)	

Vision Devices:	Direct	Indirect
Driver	Vision cupola and hatch	Periscope M6 (1)
Asst. Driver	Vision cupola and hatch	Periscope M6 (1)
Commander	Open top	None
Cannoneers	Open top	None

Total Periscopes: M6 (2)

ENGINE

Make and Model: Continental R975 C4
Type: 9 cylinder, 4 cycle, radial
Cooling System: Air Ignition: Magneto

Displacement:	973 cubic inches
Bore and Stroke:	5 x 5.5 inches
Compression Ratio:	5.7:1
Net Horsepower (max):	400 hp at 2400 rpm
Gross Horsepower (max):	460 hp at 2400 rpm
Net Torque (max):	940 ft-lb at 1700 rpm
Gross Torque (max):	1025 ft-lb at 1800 rpm
Weight:	1212 lb, dry
Fuel: 80 octane gasoline	215 gallons
Engine Oil:	36 quarts

POWER TRAIN

Clutch: Dry disc, 2 plate
Transmission: Synchromesh, 5 speeds forward, 1 reverse

Gear Ratios:				
1st	7.56:1	4th	1.11:1
2nd	3.11:1	5th	0.73:1
3rd	1.78:1	reverse	5.65:1

Steering: Controlled differential
Bevel Gear Ratio: 3.53:1 Steering Ratio: 1.515:1
Brakes: Mechanical, external contracting
Final Drive: Herringbone gear Gear Ratio: 2.84:1
Drive Sprocket: At front of vehicle with 13 teeth
Pitch Diameter: 25.038 inches

RUNNING GEAR

Suspension: Horizontal volute spring
12 dual wheels in 6 bogies (3 bogies/track)
Tire Size: 20.5 x 6.25 inches
4 dual track return rollers (2/track)
6 single track return rollers (3/track)
Dual adjustable idler at rear of each track
Idler Tire Size: 22 x 6.25 inches
Shock absorbers fitted on each bogie
Tracks: Center guide; T66, T80, and T84
Type: (T66) Single pin, 23 inch width, cast steel
(T80) Double pin, 23 inch width, rubber and steel
(T84) Double pin, 23 inch width, rubber
Pitch: 6 inches
Shoes per Vehicle: 172 (86/track)
Ground Contact Length: 164 inches

ELECTRICAL SYSTEM

Nominal Voltage: 24 volts DC
Main Generator: (1) 24 volts, 50 amperes, driven by power take-off from main engine
Auxiliary Generator: None
Battery: (2) 12 volts in series

COMMUNICATIONS

Radio: SCR 610 in right front sponson
Interphone: RC99, 4 stations
or
Radio: SCR 608B in right front sponson
Interphone: (part of radio) 4 stations

FIRE AND GAS PROTECTION

(2) 10 pound carbon dioxide, fixed
(2) 4 pound carbon dioxide, portable
(2) 1½ quart decontaminating apparatus

PERFORMANCE

Maximum Speed: Sustained, level road	21 miles/hour
Short periods, level	24 miles/hour
Maximum Grade:	60 per cent
Maximum Trench:	7.7 feet
Maximum Vertical Wall:	24 inches
Maximum Fording Depth:	40 inches
Minimum Turning Circle: (diameter)	83 feet
Cruising Range: Roads	approx. 100 miles

The performance and general characteristics of the weapons mounted on the M3 and M4 series of medium tanks are tabulated in the following data sheets. The more important self-propelled artillery weapons installed on these tank chassis also are included. To avoid confusion, caliber lengths are quoted according to both the U.S. (bore length only) and German (muzzle to rear face of breech) standards. The sketch below defines the other dimensions tabulated.

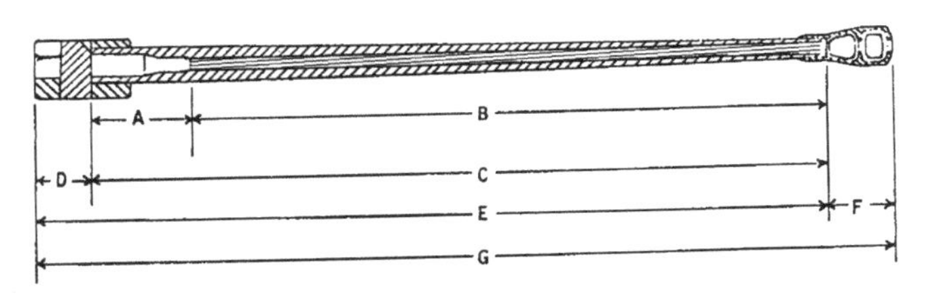

A. Length of Chamber (to rifling)
B. Length of Rifling
C. Length of Bore
D. Depth of Breech Recess
E. Length, Muzzle to Rear Face of Breech
F. Additional Length, Muzzle Brake, Etc.
G. Overall Length

The ammunition is listed by the official nomenclature in use during its period of greatest service. Since this terminology occasionally changed during the service life, a standard nomenclature is added in parentheses to prevent confusion. These standard terms which are used separately and in combination are defined below:

AP	Armor piercing, uncapped
APBC	Armor piercing with ballastic cap, without armor piercing cap
APCBC	Armor piercing with armor piercing cap and ballistic cap
APCR	Armor piercing, composite rigid
APDS	Armor piercing, discarding sabot
CP	Concrete piercing
HE	High explosive
HEAT	High explosive antitank, hollow charge
-T	Tracer

The armor plate angles quoted in the Vehicle Data Sheets were measured between a vertical plane and the plate surface as indicated by the angle α in the simplified sketch at the upper right. The armor penetration performance for the various types of

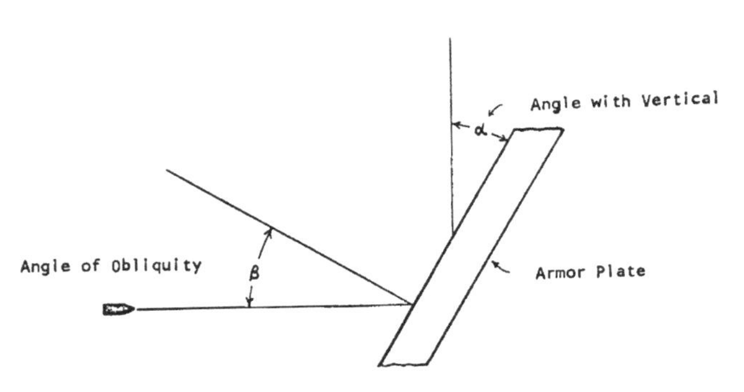

ammunition is usually quoted for a 30 degree angle of obliquity. This angle is defined as the angle between a line perpendicular to the armor plate and the projectile path and it is marked β in the simplified two dimensional sketch. In three dimensions, the calculation of the true angle of obliquity is a bit more complicated as indicated in the drawings below. Here the true angle of obliquity is shown to be the angle whose cosine equals the product of the cosines for the vertical and lateral attack angles.

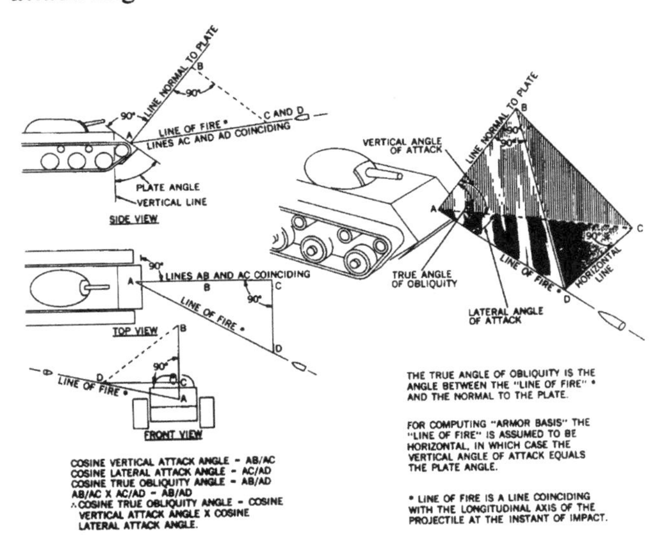

Although armor plate penetration was usually quoted for 30 degree angles of obliquity during the World War II period, the relative performance shown for the various projectiles did not necessarily apply to other angles. For example, at high angles of obliquity, the AP monobloc shot was much more effective than APCBC or APCR against homogeneous armor plate. At low angles, the AP and APCBC were approximately equal and both were surpassed by the APCR at normal combat ranges.

37mm Gun M6*

Carriage and Mount	Medium Tank M3 series	
Length of Chamber (to rifling)	9.55 inches	
Length of Rifling	68.45 inches	
Length of Chamber (to projectile base)	8.1 inches (square base projectiles)	
Travel of Projectile in Bore	69.9 inches (square base projectiles)	
Length of Bore	78.0 inches, 53.5 calibers	
Depth of Breech Recess	4.5 inches	
Length, Muzzle to Rear Face of Breech	82.5 inches, 56.6 calibers	
Additional Length, Muzzle Brake, etc.	None	
Overall Length	82.5 inches	
Diameter of Bore	1.457 inches	
Chamber Capacity	19.35 cubic inches (APC M51), 19.19 cubic inches (HE M63)	
Weight, Tube	138 pounds	
Total Weight	185 pounds	
Type of Breechblock	Semiautomatic, vertical sliding wedge	
Rifling	12 grooves, uniform right-hand twist, one turn in 25 calibers	
Ammunition	Fixed	
Primer	Percussion	
Weight, Complete Round	APC M51 Shot (APCBC-T)	3.48 pounds
	AP M74 Shot (AP-T)	3.34 pounds
	HE M63 Shell (HE)	3.13 pounds
	Canister M2	3.49 pounds
Weight, Projectile	APC M51 Shot (APCBC-T)	1.92 pounds
	AP M74 Shot (AP-T)	1.92 pounds
	HE M63 Shell (HE)	1.61 pounds
	Canister M2 (122 steel balls)	1.94 pounds
Maximum Powder Pressure	50,000 psi	
Maximum Rate of Fire	30 rounds/minute	
Muzzle Velocity	APC M51 Shot (APCBC-T)	2,900 ft/sec
	AP M74 Shot (AP-T)	2,900 ft/sec
	HE M63 Shell (HE)	2,600 ft/sec
	Canister M2	2,500 ft/sec
Muzzle Energy of Projectile, KE=½MV² Rotational energy is neglected and values are based on long tons (2,240 pounds)	APC M51 Shot (APCBC-T)	112 ft-tons
	AP M74 Shot (AP-T)	112 ft-tons
	HE M63 Shell (HE)	75 ft-tons
	Canister M2	84 ft-tons
Maximum Range (independent of mount)	APC M51 Shot (APCBC-T)	12,850 yards
	AP M74 Shot (AP-T)	8,725 yards
	HE M63 Shell (HE)	9,500 yards
	Canister M2	approx. 200 yards

Penetration Performance

	Homogeneous Armor at 30 degrees obliquity			
Range	500 yards	1,000 yards	1,500 yards	2,000 yards
APC M51	2.1 inches (53mm)	1.8 inches (46mm)	1.6 inches (40mm)	1.4 inches (35mm)
	Face-Hardened Armor at 30 degrees obliquity			
Range	500 yards	1,000 yards	1,500 yards	2,000 yards
APC M51	1.8 inches (46mm)	1.6 inches (40mm)	1.5 inches (38mm)	1.3 inches (33mm)

*The 37mm Gun M5 is similar to the M6 except that the bore length is 73 inches and it has a manually operated breech mechanism. When the M5 is fitted with an M6 tube its designation is the 37mm Gun M5A1.

2 pounder Mks IX, IXA, X, and XA*

Carriage and Mount	Cruiser Tank Ram I in combination turret mount			
Length of Chamber (to rifling)	12.91 inches			
Length of Rifling	65.84 inches			
Length of Chamber (to projectile base)	11.068 inches			
Travel of Projectile in Bore	67.682 inches			
Length of Bore	78.75 inches, 50.0 calibers			
Depth of Breech Recess	3.20 inches			
Length, Muzzle to Rear Face of Breech	81.95 inches, 52.0 calibers			
Additional Length, Muzzle Brake, etc.	None			
Overall Length	81.95 inches			
Diameter of Bore	1.575 inches			
Chamber Capacity	24 cubic inches			
Total Weight	287 pounds (Mk IX and Mk X guns), 289 pounds (Mk IXA and Mk XA guns)			
Type of Breechblock	Semiautomatic, vertical sliding wedge			
Rifling	12 grooves, uniform right-hand twist, one turn in 30 calibers			
Ammunition	Fixed			
Primer	Percussion			
Weight, Complete Round	APCBC/T Mk I Shot (APCBC-T)			4.9 pounds
	APHV/T Shot (AP-T)			4.5 pounds
	AP/T Mk I Shot (AP-T)			4.5 pounds
	HE/T Mk II Shell (HE-T)			4.1 pounds
Weight Projectile	APCBC/T Mk I Shot (APCBC-T)			2.7 pounds
	APHV/T Shot (AP-T)			2.4 pounds
	AP/T Mk I Shot (AP-T)			2.4 pounds
	HE/T Mk II Shell (HE-T)			1.9 pounds
Maximum Powder Pressure	44,800 psi			
Maximum Rate of Fire	30 rounds/minute			
Muzzle Velocity	APCBC/T Mk I Shot (APCBC-T)			2,800 ft/sec
	APHV/T Shot (AP-T)			2,800 ft/sec
	AP/T Mk I Shot (AP-T)			2,600 ft/sec
	HE/T Mk II Shell (HE-T)			2,600 ft/sec
Muzzle Energy of Projectile, $KE=\frac{1}{2}MV^2$ Rotational energy is neglected and values are based on long tons (2,240 pounds)	APCBC/T Mk I Shot (APCBC-T)			147 ft-tons
	APHV/T Shot (AP-T)			130 ft-tons
	AP/T Mk I Shot (AP-T)			113 ft-tons
	HE/T Mk II Shell (HE-T)			89 ft-tons
Maximum Range (independent of mount)	APHV/T Shot (AP-T) at 25 degrees elevation			approx. 8,000 yards
Penetration Performance	Homogeneous Armor at 30 degrees obliquity			
Range	250 yards	500 yards	750 yards	1,000 yards
APHV/T	2.5 inches (64mm)	2.2 inches (57mm)	2.0 inches (51mm)	1.8 inches (45mm)
AP/T	2.3 inches (58mm)	2.0 inches (52mm)	1.8 inches (46mm)	1.6 inches (40mm)

*Mk IX is autofrettage construction, Mk X is forged. Mks IXA and XA are modified to expedite production

6 pounder Mks III and V

Carriage and Mount	Cruiser Tank Ram II in combination turret mount
Length of Chamber (to rifling)	18.02 inches
Length of Rifling	78.18 inches (Mk III gun), 94.18 inches (Mk V gun)
Length of Chamber (to projectile base)	16.2 inches
Travel of Projectile in Bore	80.0 inches (Mk III gun), 96.0 inches (Mk V gun)
Length of Bore	96.20 inches, 42.9 calibers (Mk III); 112.20 inches, 50.0 calibers (Mk V)
Depth of Breech Recess	4.75 inches
Length, Muzzle to Rear Face of Breech	100.95 inches, 45.0 calibers (Mk III); 116.95 inches, 52.1 calibers (Mk V)
Additional Length, Muzzle Brake, etc.	None
Overall Length	100.95 inches (Mk III gun), 116.95 inches (Mk V gun)
Diameter of Bore	2.244 inches
Chamber Capacity	100.05 cubic inches (AP-T), 98.87 cubic inches (APCBC-T)
Total Weight	761 pounds (Mk III gun), 727.5 pounds (Mk V gun)
Type of Breechblock	Semiautomatic, vertical sliding wedge
Rifling	24 grooves, uniform right-hand twist, one turn in 30 calibers
Ammunition	Fixed
Primer	Percussion

Weight, Complete Round	APCBC-T	13.88 pounds
	AP-T	12.92 pounds
Weight, Projectile	APCBC-T	7.27 pounds
	AP-T	6.28 pounds
Maximum Powder Pressure	46,000 psi	
Maximum Rate of Fire	30 rounds/minute	

		Mk III gun	Mk V gun
Muzzle Velocity	APCBC-T	2,580 ft/sec	2,700 ft/sec
	AP-T	2,830 ft/sec	2,950 ft/sec
Muzzle Energy of Projectile, $KE = \frac{1}{2}MV^2$ Rotational energy is neglected and values are based on long tons (2,240 pounds)	APCBC-T	335 ft-tons	367 ft-tons
	AP-T	349 ft-tons	379 ft-tons
Maximum Range (independent of mount)	APCBC-T	approx. 13,000 yards	13,500 yards
	AP-T	approx. 8,900 yards	9,300 yards

Penetration Performance, Mk V gun

Homogeneous Armor at 30 degrees obliquity

Range	500 yards	1,000 yards	1,500 yards	2,000 yards
APCBC-T	3.2 inches (81mm)	2.9 inches (74mm)	2.5 inches (63mm)	2.2 inches (56mm)

Face-Hardened Armor at 30 degrees obliquity

Range	500 yards	1,000 yards	1,500 yards	2,000 yards
APCBC-T	3.0 inches (76mm)	2.9 inches (74mm)	2.7 inches (68mm)	2.5 inches (63mm)

75mm Guns M2, M3 and M6

Carriage and Mount	Medium Tank M3 series in Mount M1 (M2 and M3 guns), Medium Tank M4 series in Mounts M34 and M34A1 (M3 gun), Assault Tank T14 in Mount M34A1 (M3 gun), Flame Thrower Tank T33 and Searchlight Tank T52 in Modified Mount M64 (M6 gun)
Length of Chamber (to rifling)	14.4 inches
Length of Rifling	69.6 inches (M2 gun), 96.2 inches (M3 and M6 guns)
Length of Chamber (to projectile base)	12.96 inches (APC M61), 11.5 inches (HE M48)
Travel of Projectile in Bore (M2 gun)	71.0 inches (APC M61), 72.5 inches (HE M48)
(M3 and M6)	97.67 inches (APC M61), 99.1 inches (HE M48)
Length of Bore	84.0 inches, 28.5 calibers (M2); 110.63 inches, 37.5 calibers (M3 and M6)
Depth of Breech Recess	7.75 inches (M2 and M3 guns), 5.75 inches (M6 gun)
Length, Muzzle to Rear Face of Breech	
(M2 gun)	91.75 inches, 31.1 calibers
(M3 gun)	118.38 inches, 40.1 calibers
(M6 gun)	116.38 inches, 39.4 calibers
Additional Length, Muzzle Brake, etc.	None
Overall Length	91.75 inches (M2), 118.38 inches (M3), 116.38 inches (M6)
Diameter of Bore	2.95 inches
Chamber Capacity	88.05 cubic inches (APC M61), 80.57 cubic inches (HE M48)
Total Weight	783 pounds (M2), 893 pounds (M3), 410 pounds (M6)
Type of Breechblock	Semiautomatic sliding wedge, Gun mounted so breechblock slides vertically in Mount M1 and horizontally in Mounts M34, M34A1, and M64
Rifling	24 grooves, uniform right-hand twist, one turn in 25.59 calibers (slope 7 degrees)
Ammunition	Fixed
Primer	Percussion

Weight, Complete Round		
	APC M61 Projectile (APCBC/HE-T)	19.92 pounds
	HVAP T45 Shot (APCR-T)*	13.60 pounds
	AP M72 Shot (AP-T)	18.80 pounds
	HE M48 Shell (HE), Supercharge	19.56 pounds
	HE M48 Shell (HE), Normal	18.80 pounds
	HC BI M89 Shell, Smoke	9.83 pounds
Weight, Projectile		
	APC M61 Projectile (APCBC/HE-T)	14.96 pounds
	HVAP T45 Shot (APCR-T)	8.40 pounds
	AP M72 Shot (AP-T)	13.94 pounds
	HE M48 Shell (HE)	14.70 pounds
	HC BI M89 Shell, Smoke	6.61 pounds

Maximum Powder Pressure	38,000 psi
Maximum Rate of Fire	20 rounds/minute

Muzzle Velocity		M2 gun	M3 & M6 guns
	APC M61 Projectile (APCBC/HE-T)	1,930 ft/sec	2,030 ft/sec
	HVAP T45 Shot (APCR-T)*		2,850 ft/sec
	AP M72 Shot (AP-T)	1,930 ft/sec	2,030 ft/sec
	HE M48 Shell (HE), Supercharge	1,885 ft/sec	1,980 ft/sec
	HE M48 Shell (HE), Normal	1,470 ft/sec	1,520 ft/sec
	HC BI M89 Shell, Smoke	820 ft/sec	850 ft/sec

Muzzle Energy of Projectile, $KE=\frac{1}{2}MV^2$ Rotational energy is neglected and values are based on long tons (2,240 pounds)		M2 gun	M3 & M6 guns
	APC M61 Projectile (APCBC/HE-T)	387 ft-tons	427 ft-tons
	HVAP T45 Shot (APCR-T)*		473 ft-tons
	AP M72 Shot (AP-T)	360 ft-tons	398 ft-tons
	HE M48 Shell (HE), Supercharge	362 ft-tons	400 ft-tons
	HE M48 Shell (HE), Normal	220 ft-tons	235 ft-tons

Maximum Range (independent of mount)		M2 gun	M3 & M6 guns
	APC M61 Projectile (APCBC/HE-T)	13,600 yards	14,000 yards
	AP M72 Shot (AP-T)	10,200 yards	10,650 yards
	HE M48 Shell (HE), Supercharge	13,300 yards	14,000 yards
	HE M48 Shell (HE), Normal	11,000 yards	11,400 yards
	HC BI M89 Shell, Smoke	approx. 1,500 yards	1,500 yards

Penetration Performance (M2 gun)

Homogeneous Armor at 30 degrees obliquity

Range	500 yards	1,000 yards	1,500 yards	2,000 yards
APC M61	2.4 inches (60mm)	2.2 inches (55mm)	2.0 inches (51mm)	1.8 inches (46mm)
AP M72	2.4 inches (60mm)	2.1 inches (53mm)	1.8 inches (46mm)	1.5 inches (38mm)

Face-Hardened Armor at 30 degrees obliquity

Range	500 yards	1,000 yards	1,500 yards	2,000 yards
APC M61	2.7 inches (69mm)	2.4 inches (60mm)	2.2 inches (55mm)	1.9 inches (48mm)
AP M72	2.3 inches (58mm)	1.8 inches (46mm)	1.3 inches (33mm)	1.0 inches (25mm)

(M3 and M6 guns)

Homogeneous Armor at 30 degrees obliquity

Range	500 yards	1,000 yards	1,500 yards	2,000 yards
APC M61	2.6 inches (66mm)	2.4 inches (60mm)	2.2 inches (55mm)	2.0 inches (50mm)
HVAP T45*	4.6 inches (117mm)	3.8 inches (97mm)	3.1 inches (79mm)	2.5 inches (64mm)
AP M72	3.0 inches (76mm)	2.5 inches (63mm)	2.0 inches (51mm)	1.7 inches (43mm)

Face-Hardened Armor at 30 degrees obliquity

Range	500 yards	1,000 yards	1,500 yards	2,000 yards
APC M61	2.9 inches (74mm)	2.6 inches (67mm)	2.4 inches (60mm)	2.1 inches (54mm)
AP M72	2.6 inches (66mm)	2.1 inches (53mm)	1.6 inches (41mm)	1.3 inches (33mm)

*Experimental only

3 inch Gun M7

Carriage and Mount	Motor Carriages M10 and M10A1 in Mount M5
Length of Chamber (to rifling)	23.15 inches
Length of Rifling	126.85 inches
Length of Chamber (to projectile base)	21.5 inches (square base projectiles)
Travel of Projectile in Bore	128.5 inches (square base projectiles)
Length of Bore	150.0 inches, 50.0 calibers
Depth of Breech Recess	8.10 inches
Length, Muzzle to Rear Face of Breech	158.10 inches, 52.7 calibers
Additional Length, Muzzle Brake, etc.	None
Overall Length	158.10 inches
Diameter of Bore	3.000 inches
Chamber Capacity	205.585 cubic inches (APC M62), 203.50 cubic inches (HE M42A1)
Total Weight	1,990 pounds
Type of Breechblock	Semiautomatic, vertical sliding wedge
Rifling	28 grooves, uniform right-hand twist, one turn in 40 calibers
Ammunition	Fixed
Primer	Percussion

Weight, Complete Round	APC M62 Projectile (APCBC/HE-T)	27.24 pounds
	HVAP M93 Shot (APCR-T)	20.77 pounds
	AP M79 Shot (AP-T)	26.56 pounds
	HE M42A1 Shell (HE)	24.91 pounds
	HC BI M88 Shell, Smoke	15.40 pounds
Weight, Projectile	APC M62 Projectile (APCBC/HE-T)	15.44 pounds
	HVAP M93 Shot (APCR-T)	9.40 pounds
	AP M79 Shot AP-T)	15.00 pounds
	HE M42A1 Shell (HE)	12.87 pounds
	HC BI M88 Shell, Smoke	7.38 pounds
Maximum Powder Pressure	38,000 psi	
Maximum Rate of Fire	15 rounds/minute	
Muzzle Velocity	APC M62 Projectile (APCBC/HE-T)	2,600 ft/sec
	HVAP M93 Shot (APCR-T)	3,400 ft/sec
	AP M79 Shot (AP-T)	2,600 ft/sec
	HE M42A1 Shell (HE)	2,800 ft/sec
	HC BI M88 Shell, Smoke	900 ft/sec
Muzzle Energy of Projectile $KE=\frac{1}{2}MV^2$ Rotational energy is neglected and values are based on long tons (2,240 pounds)	APC M62 Projectile (APCBC/HE-T)	724 ft-tons
	HVAP M93 Shot (APCR-T)	753 ft-tons
	AP M79 Shot (AP-T)	703 ft-tons
	HE M42A1 Shell (HE)	699 ft-tons
Maximum Range (independent of mount)	APC M62 Projectile (APCBC/HE-T)	16,100 yards
	HVAP M93 Shot (APCR-T)	13,100 yards
	AP M79 Shot (AP-T)	12,770 yards
	HE M42A1 Shell (HE)	14,780 yards
	HC BI M88 Shell, Smoke (at 12 degrees elevation)	2,000 yards

Penetration Performance — Homogeneous Armor at 30 degrees obliquity

Range	500 yards	1,000 yards	1,500 yards	2,000 yards
APC M62	3.7 inches (93mm)	3.5 inches (88mm)	3.2 inches (82mm)	3.0 inches (75mm)
HVAP M93	6.2 inches (157mm)	5.3 inches (135mm)	4.6 inches (116mm)	3.9 inches (98mm)
AP M79	4.3 inches (109mm)	3.6 inches (92mm)	3.0 inches (76mm)	2.5 inches (64mm)

76mm Guns M1, M1A1, M1A1C, and M1A2

Carriage and Mount	Medium Tank M4 series in Mount M62, Motor Carriage T72 in Mount T2	
Length of Chamber (to rifling)	22.46 inches	
Length of Rifling	133.54 inches	
Length of Chamber (to projectile base)	20.7 inches (square base projectiles)	
Travel of Projectile in Bore	135.3 inches (square base projectiles)	
Length of Bore	156.00 inches, 52.0 calibers	
Depth of Breech Recess	7.75 inches	
Length, Muzzle to Rear Face of Breech	163.75 inches, 54.6 calibers	
Additional Length, Muzzle Brake, etc.	11.6 inches, Muzzle Brake M2 on M1A1C and M1A2 only	
Overall Length	163.75 inches (M1, M1A1), 175.4 inches (M1A1C, M1A2)	
Diameter of Bore	3.000 inches	
Chamber Capacity	142.6 cubic inches (APC M62), 140.50 cubic inches (HE M42A1)	
Weight, Tube (w/o muzzle brake)	870 pounds (M1), 940 pounds (M1A1)	
Weight, Complete (w/o muzzle brake)	1,141 pounds (M1), 1,206 pounds (M1A1C), 1,231 pounds (M1A2)	
Weight, Muzzle Brake M2	62 pounds	
Total Weight	1,141 pounds (M1), 1,268 pounds (M1A1C), 1,293 pounds (M1A2)	
Type of Breechblock	Semiautomatic sliding wedge. Gun mounted so breechblock slides horizontally in Mount M62	
Rifling	28 grooves, uniform right-hand twist, one turn in 40 calibers (M1, M1A1, M1A1C) or 32 calibers (M1A2)	
Ammunition	Fixed	
Primer	Percussion	
Weight, Complete Round	APC M62 Projectile (APCBC/HE-T)	24.80 pounds
	HVAP M93 Shot (APCR-T)	18.91 pounds
	AP M79 Shot (AP-T)	24.24 pounds
	HE M42A1 Shell (HE)	22.23 pounds
	HC BI M88 Shell, Smoke	13.43 pounds
Weight, Projectile	APC M62 Projectile (APCBC/HE-T)	15.44 pounds
	HVAP M93 Shot (APCR-T)	9.40 pounds
	AP M79 Shot (AP-T)	15.00 pounds
	HE M42A1 Shell (HE)	12.87 pounds
	HC BI M88 Shell, Smoke	7.38 pounds
Maximum Powder Pressure	43,000 psi	
Maximum Rate of Fire	20 rounds/minute	
Muzzle Velocity	APC M62 Projectile (APCBC/HE-T)	2,600 ft/sec
	HVAP M93 Shot (APCR-T)	3,400 ft/sec
	AP M79 Shot (AP-T)	2,600 ft/sec
	HE M42A1 Shell (HE)	2,700 ft/sec
	HC BI M88 Shell, Smoke	900 ft/sec
Muzzle Energy of Projectile, $KE=\frac{1}{2}MV^2$ Rotational energy is neglected and values are based on long tons (2,240 pounds)	APC M62 Projectile (APCBC/HE-T)	724 ft-tons
	HVAP M93 Shot (APCR-T)	753 ft-tons
	AP M79 Shot (AP-T)	703 ft-tons
	HE M42A1 Shell, (HE)	650 ft-tons
Maximum Range (independent of mount)	APC M62 Projectile (APCBC/HE-T)	16,100 yards
	HVAP M93 Shot (APCR-T)	13,100 yards
	AP M79 Shot (AP-T)	12,770 yards
	HE M42A1 Shell (HE)	14,200 yards
	HC BI M88 Shell, Smoke (at 12 degrees elevation)	2,000 yards

Penetration Performance* — Homogeneous Armor at 30 degrees obliquity

Range	500 yards	1,000 yards	1,500 yards	2,000 yards
APC M62	3.7 inches (93mm)	3.5 inches (88mm)	3.2 inches (82mm)	3.0 inches (75mm)
HVAP M93	6.2 inches (157mm)	5.3 inches (135mm)	4.6 inches (116mm)	3.9 inches (98mm)
AP M79	4.3 inches (109mm)	3.6 inches (92mm)	3.0 inches (76mm)	2.5 inches (64mm)

*Penetration values are for the M1A1 gun. A slight increase for APC is obtained with the M1A2 gun at the longer ranges.

17 pounder Mks IV and VII

Carriage and Mount	Cruiser Tanks Sherman IC and VC in Mounting No. 2, Mk I
Length of Chamber (to rifling)	25.21 inches
Length of Rifling	140.24 inches
Length of Chamber (to projectile base)	21.42 inches
Travel of Projectile in Bore	144.03 inches
Length of Bore	165.45 inches, 55.1 calibers
Depth of Breech Recess	9.51 inches
Length, Muzzle to Rear Face of Breech	174.96 inches, 58.3 calibers
Additional Length, Muzzle Brake, etc.	9.1 inches
Overall Length	184.1 inches
Diameter of Bore	3.0 inches
Chamber Capacity	300 cubic inches
Weight, Tube (w/o muzzle brake)	1,121.5 pounds
Weight, Complete (w/o muzzle brake)	1,985 pounds
Weight, Muzzle Brake	47 pounds
Total Weight	2,032 pounds
Type of Breechblock	Semiautomatic, horizontal sliding wedge
Rifling	20 grooves, uniform right-hand twist, one turn in 30 calibers
Ammunition	Fixed
Primer	Percussion

Weight, Complete Round	APCBC Mk VIII T Shot (APCBC-T)	37.5 pounds
	SVDS Shot (APDS-T)	28.4 pounds
	HE Mk I T Shell (HE-T), Full Charge	34.2 pounds
Weight, Projectile	APCBC Mk VIII T Shot (APCBC-T)	17.0 pounds
	SVDS Shot (APDS-T)	7.9 pounds
	HE Mk I T Shell (HE-T)	15.4 pounds
Maximum Powder Pressure estimated	47,000 psi	
Maximum Rate of Fire	10 rounds/minute	
Muzzle Velocity	APCBC Mk VIII T Shot (APCBC-T)	2,900 ft/sec
	SVDS Shot (APDS-T)	3,950 ft/sec
	HE Mk I T Shell (HE-T), Full Charge	2,950 ft/sec
	HE Mk I T Shell (HE-T), Reduced Charge	1,800 ft/sec
Muzzle Energy of Projectile, $KE=\frac{1}{2}MV^2$ Rotational energy is neglected and values are based on long tons (2,240 pounds)	APCBC Mk VIII T shot (APCBC-T)	991 ft-tons
	SVDS Shot (APDS-T)	854 ft-tons
	HE Mk I T Shell (HE-T), Full Charge	929 ft-tons
	HE Mk I T Shell (HE-T), Reduced Charge	346 ft-tons
Maximum Range (independent of mount)	HE Mk I T Shell (HE-T), Full Charge	17,000 yards
Penetration Performance	Homogeneous Armor at 30 degrees obliquity	

Range	500 yards	1,000 yards	1,500 yards	2,000 yards
APCBC Mk VIII T	5.5 inches (140mm)	5.1 inches (130mm)	4.7 inches (120mm)	4.4 inches (111mm)
SVDS	8.2 inches (208mm)	7.6 inches (192mm)	6.9 inches (176mm)	6.3 inches (161mm)

25 pounder C, Mks II and III

Carriage and Mount	Self-Propelled Carriages Sexton I and II in Mounting C, Mks II and III	
Length of Chamber (to rifling)	18.14 inches (Mk II cannon), 18.48 inches (Mk III cannon)	
Length of Rifling	74.235 inches (Mk II cannon), 73.895 inches (Mk III cannon)	
Length of Chamber (to projectile base)	14.47 inches (Mk II cannon), 14.54 inches (Mk III cannon)	
Travel of Projectile in Bore	77.905 inches (Mk II cannon), 77.835 inches (Mk III cannon)	
Length of Bore	92.375 inches, 26.8 calibers	
Depth of Breech Recess	5.1 inches	
Length, Muzzle to Rear Face of Breech	97.47 inches, 28.3 calibers	
Additional Length, Muzzle Brake, etc.	9.25 inches	
Overall Length	106.72 inches	
Diameter of Bore	3.45 inches	
Chamber Capacity	151 cubic inches	
Total Weight (estimated)	1,124 pounds	
Type of Breechblock	Manually operated, vertical sliding wedge	
Rifling	26 grooves, uniform right-hand twist, one turn in 20 calibers	
Ammunition	Separated	
Primer	Percussion	
Weight, Complete Round	AP-T Shot, 3rd Charge	26.0 pounds
	AP-T Shot, Supercharge + Increment	27.1 pounds
	HE Shell, 3rd Charge	31.0 pounds
	HE Shell, Supercharge	31.8 pounds
	BE Shell, Smoke, 3rd Charge	27.9 pounds
Weight, Projectile	AP-T Shot	20.0 pounds
	HE Shell	25.0 pounds
	BE Shell, Smoke	21.9 pounds
Maximum Powder Pressure	34,720 psi (design)	
Maximum Rate of Fire	8 rounds/minute	
Muzzle Velocity	AP-T Shot, 3rd Charge	1,550 ft/sec
	AP-T Shot, Supercharge + Increment	2,000 ft/sec
	HE Shell, 3rd Charge	1,450 ft/sec
	HE Shell, Supercharge	1,700 ft/sec
Muzzle Energy of Projectile, $KE=\frac{1}{2}MV^2$ Rotational energy is neglected and values are based on long tons (2,240 pounds)	AP-T Shot, 3rd Charge	333 ft-tons
	AP-T Shot, Supercharge + Increment	555 ft-tons
	HE Shell, 3rd Charge	364 ft-tons
	HE Shell, Supercharge	501 ft-tons
Maximum Range (independent of mount)	HE Shell, Supercharge	13,400 yards
Penetration Performance	Homogeneous Armor at 30 degrees obliquity	

Range	500 yards	750 yards	1,000 yards
AP-T Shot, 3rd Charge	2.5 inches (63mm)	2.3 inches (58mm)	2.1 inches (54 mm)

90mm Gun M3

Carriage and Mount	Motor Carriage M36 series in Mount M4 (T8), Motor Carriage T53 series. This weapon mounted experimentally on the Medium Tank M4 using the turret from the Medium Tank M26
Length of Chamber (to rifling)	24.8 inches
Length of Rifling	152.4 inches
Length of Chamber (to projectile base)	20.8 inches (boat-tailed projectiles)
Travel of Projectile in Bore	156.4 inches (boat-tailed projectiles)
Length of Bore	177.15 inches, 50.0 calibers
Depth of Breech Recess	9.00 inches
Length, Muzzle to Rear Face of Breech	186.15 inches, 52.5 calibers
Additional Length, Muzzle Brake, etc.	16.0 inches, Muzzle Brake M3 on late production
Overall Length	202.2 inches with muzzle brake
Diameter of Bore	3.543 inches
Chamber Capacity	300 cubic inches
Weight, Complete (w/o muzzle brake)	2,300 pounds
Weight, Muzzle Brake M3	149.5 pounds
Total Weight	2,450 pounds
Type of Breechblock	Semiautomatic, vertical sliding wedge
Rifling	32 grooves, uniform right-hand twist, one turn in 32 calibers
Ammunition	Fixed
Primer	Percussion

Weight, Complete Round	APC M82 Projectile (APCBC/HE-T) early	42.75 pounds
	APC M82 Projectile (APCBC/HE-T) late	43.87 pounds
	HVAP M304 (T30E16) Shot (APCR-T)	37.13 pounds
	AP T33 Shot (APBC-T)	43.82 pounds
	HE M71 Shell (HE)	41.93 pounds
Weight, Projectile	APC M82 Projectile (APCBC/HE-T)	24.11 pounds
	HVAP M304 (T30E16) Shot (APCR-T)	16.80 pounds
	AP T33 Shot (APBC-T)	24.06 pounds
	HE M71 Shell (HE)	23.29 pounds
Maximum Powder Pressure	38,000 psi	
Maximum Rate of Fire	8 rounds/minute	
Muzzle Velocity	APC M82 Projectile (APCBC/HE-T) early	2,650 ft/sec
	APC M82 Projectile (APCBC/HE-T) late	2,800 ft/sec
	HVAP M304 (T30E16) Shot (APCR-T)	3,350 ft/sec
	AP T33 Shot (APBC-T)	2,800 ft/sec
	HE M71 Shell (HE)	2,700 ft/sec
Muzzle Energy of Projectile, $KE=\frac{1}{2}MV^2$ Rotational energy is neglected and values are based on long tons (2,240 pounds)	APC M82 Projectile (APCBC/HE-T) early	1,174 ft-tons
	APC M82 Projectile (APCBC/HE-T) late	1,310 ft-tons
	HVAP M304 (T30E16) Shot (APCR-T)	1,307 ft-tons
	AP T33 Shot (APBC-T)	1,310 ft-tons
	HE M71 Shell (HE)	1,177 ft-tons
Maximum Range (independent of mount)	APC M82 Projectile (APCBC/HE-T) early	20,400 yards
	APC M82 Projectile (APCBC/HE-T) late	21,400 yards
	HVAP M304 (T30E16) Shot (APCR-T)	15,700 yards
	AP T33 Shot (APBC-T)	21,000 yards
	HE M71 Shell (HE)	19,560 yards

Penetration Performance: Homogeneous Armor at 30 degrees obliquity

Range	500 yards	1,000 yards	1,500 yards	2,000 yards
APC M82 early	4.7 inches (120mm)	4.4 inches (112mm)	4.1 inches (104mm)	3.8 inches (96mm)
APC M82 late	5.1 inches (129mm)	4.8 inches (122mm)	4.5 inches (114mm)	4.2 inches (106mm)
HVAP M304 (T30E16)	8.7 inches (221mm)	7.9 inches (199mm)	7.0 inches (176mm)	6.1 inches (156 mm)
AP T33	4.7 inches (119mm)	4.6 inches (117mm)	4.5 inches (114mm)	4.3 inches (109mm)

105mm Howitzers M2A1 and M4

Carriage and Mount	Medium Tank M4A4E1 in Mount T70 (M2A1 howitzer), Medium Tanks M4 and M4A3 in Mount M52 (M4 howitzer), Motor Carriages T32, M7, and M7B1 in Mount M5 (M2A1 howitzer)	
Length of Chamber (to rifling)	15.03 inches	
Length of Rifling	78.02 inches	
Length of Chamber (to projectile base)	11.38 inches (boat-tailed projectiles)	
Travel of Projectile in Bore	81.67 inches (boat-tailed projectiles)	
Length of Bore	93.05 inches, 22.5 calibers	
Depth of Breech Recess	8.30 inches (M2A1 howitzer), 8.25 inches (M4 howitzer)	
Length, Muzzle to Rear Face of Breech	101.35 inches, 24.5 calibers (M2A1 howitzer) 101.30 inches, 24.5 calibers (M4 howitzer)	
Additional Length, Muzzle Brake, etc.	None	
Overall Length	101.35 inches (M2A1 howitzer), 101.30 inches (M4 howitzer)	
Diameter of Bore	4.134 inches	
Chamber Capacity	153.80 cubic inches	
Total Weight	1,080 pounds (M2A1 howitzer), 1,140 pounds (M4 howitzer)	
Type of Breechblock	Manually operated, horizontal sliding wedge	
Rifling	36 grooves, uniform right-hand twist, one turn in 20 calibers	
Ammunition	Semifixed, variable charge except for HEAT M67	
Primer	Percussion	
Weight, Complete Round	HE M1 Shell (HE)	42.07 pounds
	HEAT M67 Shell (HEAT-T)	36.85 pounds
	WP M60 Shell, Smoke	43.77 pounds
	HC BE M84 Shell, Smoke	41.94 pounds
Weight, Projectile	HE M1 Shell (HE)	33.00 pounds
	HEAT M67 Shell (HEAT-T)	29.22 pounds
	WP M60 Shell, Smoke	34.31 pounds
	HC BE M84 Shell, Smoke	32.87 pounds
Maximum Powder Pressure	28,000 psi	
Maximum Rate of Fire	8 rounds/minute	
Muzzle Velocity	HE M1 Shell (HE), maximum charge	1,550 ft/sec
	HEAT M67 Shell (HEAT-T)	1,250 ft/sec
	WP M60 Shell, Smoke, maximum charge	1,550 ft/sec
	HC BE M84 Shell, Smoke, maximum charge	1,550 ft/sec
Muzzle Energy of Projectile, $KE=\frac{1}{2}MV^2$ Rotational energy is neglected and values are based on long tons (2,240 pounds)	HE M1 Shell (HE), maximum charge	555 ft-tons
	HEAT M67 Shell (HEAT-T)	317 ft-tons
Maximum Range (independent of mount)	HE M1 Shell (HE), maximum charge	12,205 yards
	HEAT M67 Shell (HEAT-T)	8,590 yards
	WP M60 Shell, Smoke, maximum charge	12,150 yards
	HC BE M84 Shell, Smoke, maximum charge	12,205 yards
Penetration Performance	Homogeneous Armor at 0 degrees obliquity, HEAT M67, 4.0 inches at any range	

155mm Guns M1917, M1917A1, and M1918M1*

Carriage and Mount	Motor Carriage M12 in Mount M4	
Length of Chamber (to rifling)	40.0 inches	
Length of Rifling	182.0 inches	
Length of Chamber (to projectile base)	37.1 inches (square base projectiles)	
Travel of Projectile in Bore	184.9 inches (square base projectiles)	
Length of Bore	222.0 inches, 36.4 calibers	
Depth of Breech Recess	10.9 inches	
Length, Muzzle to Rear Face of Breech	232.87 inches, 38.2 calibers	
Additional Length, Breech Mechanism	5.0 inches (estimated)	
Overall Length	238 inches (estimated)	
Diameter of Bore	6.102 inches	
Chamber Capacity	1,330 cubic inches (HE M101), 1,394 cubic inches (AP M112B1)	
Total Weight	8,715 pounds	
Type of Breechblock	Single cut interrupted screw, horizontal swing	
Rifling	48 grooves, uniform right-hand twist, one turn in 29.89 calibers	
Ammunition	Separate Loading	
Primer	Percussion	
Weight, Complete Round	AP M112B1 Projectile (APBC/HE), maximum charge	124.75 pounds
	HE M101 Shell (HE), maximum charge	119.48 pounds
	WP M104 Shell, Smoke, maximum charge	122.96 pounds
Weight, Projectile	AP M112B1 Projectile (APBC/HE)	100.00 pounds
	HE M101 Shell (HE)	94.70 pounds
	WP M104 Shell, Smoke	98.18 pounds
Maximum Powder Pressure	31,500 psi	
Maximum Rate of Fire	4 rounds/minute	
Muzzle Velocity	AP M112B1 Projectile (APBC/HE), maximum charge	2,360 ft/sec
	HE M101 Shell (HE), maximum charge	2,410 ft/sec
	WP M104 Shell, Smoke, maximum charge	2,410 ft/sec
Muzzle Energy of Projectile, $KE=\frac{1}{2}MV^2$	AP M112B1 Projectile (APBC/HE), maximum charge	3,861 ft-tons
Rotational energy is neglected and values are based on long tons (2,240 pounds)	HE M101 Shell (HE), maximum charge	3,813 ft-tons
	WP M104 Shell, Smoke, maximum charge	3,953 ft-tons
Maximum Range (independent of mount)	AP M112B1 Projectile (APBC/HE) maximum charge	19,200 yards
	HE M101 Shell (HE), maximum charge	20,100 yards
	WP M104 Shell, Smoke, maximum charge	20,247 yards
Penetration Performance	Homogeneous Armor at 30 degrees obliquity	
Range	500 yards	1,000 yards
AP M112B1	5.0 inches (127mm)	4.7 inches (119mm)
	Face-Hardened Armor at 30 degrees obliquity	
Range	500 yards	1,000 yards
AP M112B1	4.3 inches (109mm)	4.0 inches (102mm)

*The M1918M1 gun is of U.S. manufacture. The M1917 is of French manufacture and when fitted with a U.S. breech ring it is redesignated as the M1917A1

155mm Guns M1, M1A1, and M2

Carriage and Mount	Motor Carriage M40 in Mount M13	
Length of Chamber (to rifling)	45.3 inches	
Length of Rifling	229.5 inches	
Length of Chamber (to projectile base)	38.7 inches (boat-tailed projectiles)	
Travel of Projectile in Bore	236.1 inches (boat-tailed projectiles)	
Length of Bore	274.8 inches, 45.0 calibers	
Depth of Breech Recess	9.6 inches	
Length, Muzzle to Rear Face of Breech	284.4 inches, 46.6 calibers	
Additional Length, Breech Mechanism	6.4 inches	
Overall Length	290.8 inches	
Diameter of Bore	6.102 inches	
Chamber Capacity	1,640 cubic inches (HE M101), 1,691 cubic inches (AP M112B1)	
Total Weight	9,595 pounds	
Type of Breechblock	Stepped thread, interrupted screw, horizontal swing	
Rifling	48 grooves, uniform right-hand twist, one turn in 25 calibers	
Ammunition	Separate Loading	
Primer	Percussion	
Weight, Complete Round	AP M112B1 Projectile (APBC/HE), maximum charge	131.25 pounds
	HE M101 Shell (HE), maximum charge	125.48 pounds
	WP M104 Shell, Smoke, maximum charge	128.96 pounds
Weight, Projectile	AP M112B1 Projectile (APBC/HE)	100.00 pounds
	HE M101 Shell, (HE)	94.70 pounds
	WP M104 Shell, Smoke	98.18 pounds
Maximum Powder Pressure	40,000 psi	
Maximum Rate of Fire	1 round/minute	
Muzzle Velocity	AP M112B1 Projectile (APBC/HE), maximum charge	2,745 ft/sec
	HE M101 Shell (HE), maximum charge	2,800 ft/sec
	WP M104 Shell, Smoke, maximum charge	2,800 ft/sec
Muzzle Energy of Projectile, $KE=\frac{1}{2}MV^2$ Rotational energy is neglected and values are based on long tons (2,240 pounds)	AP M112B1 Projectile (APBC/HE), maximum charge	5,223 ft-tons
	HE M101 Shell (HE), maximum charge	5,147 ft-tons
	WP M104 Shell, Smoke, maximum charge	5,336 ft-tons
Maximum Range (independent of mount)	AP M112B1 Projectile (APBC/HE), maximum charge	24,075 yards
	HE M101 Shell (HE), maximum charge	25,715 yards
	WP M104 Shell, Smoke, maximum charge	25,940 yards

Penetration Performance			
	Homogeneous Armor at 30 degrees obliquity		
Range	500 yards	1,000 yards	
AP M112B1	6.3 inches (160mm)	6.0 inches (152mm)	
	Face-Hardened Armor at 30 degrees obliquity		
Range	500 yards	1,000 yards	
AP M112B1	5.3 inches (135mm)	5.1 inches (130mm)	
	Reinforced Concrete at 0 degrees obliquity		
Range	1,000 yards	5,000 yards	10,000 yards
HE M101 w/CP Fuze M78	6.6 feet	4.6 feet	3.0 feet

8 inch Howitzers M1 and M2

Carriage and Mount	Motor Carriage M43 in Mount M17	
Length of Chamber (to rifling)	35.2 inches	
Length of Rifling	164.8 inches	
Length of Chamber (to projectile base)	26.2 inches (HE M106)	
Travel of Projectile in Bore	173.83 inches (HE M106)	
Length of Bore	200.0 inches, 25.0 calibers	
Depth of Breech Recess	9.6 inches	
Length, Muzzle to Rear Face of Breech	209.59 inches, 26.2 calibers	
Additional Length, Breech Mechanism	6.4 inches	
Overall Length	216.0 inches	
Diameter of Bore	8.00 inches	
Chamber Capacity	1,527 cubic inches	
Total Weight	10,240 pounds	
Type of Breechblock	Stepped thread interrupted screw, horizontal swing	
Rifling	64 grooves, uniform right-hand twist, one turn in 25 calibers	
Ammunition	Separate Loading	
Primer	Percussion	
Weight, Complete Round	HE M106 Shell (HE) with Charge M2	228.19 pounds
	HE Mk1A1 Shell (HE) with Charge M1	213.19 pounds
Weight, Projectile	HE M106 Shell (HE)	200.00 pounds
	HE Mk1A1 Shell (HE)	200.00 pounds
Maximum Powder Pressure	33,000 psi	
Maximum Rate of Fire	1 round/minute	
Muzzle Velocity	HE M106 Shell (HE) with Charge M2	1,950 ft/sec
	HE Mk1A1 Shell (HE) with Charge M1	1,339 ft/sec
Muzzle Energy of Projectile, $KE=\frac{1}{2}MV^2$ Rotational energy is neglected and values are based on long tons (2,240 pounds)	HE M106 Shell (HE) with Charge M2	5,272 ft-tons
Maximum Range (independent of mount)	HE M106 Shell (HE) with Charge M2	18,510 yards
	He Mk1A1 Shell (HE) with Charge M1	11,170 yards
Penetration Performance	Reinforced Concrete at 0 degrees obliquity, HE M106 with CP Fuze M78; 5.5 feet at 1,000 yards, 4.7 feet at 3,000 yards, 4.0 feet at 5,000 yards, 3.2 feet at 10,000 yards, 3.1 feet at 15,000 yards	

REFERENCES AND SELECTED BIBLIOGRAPHY

Books and Manuscripts

Chase, Daniel, "A History of Combat Vehicle Development", unpublished manuscript

Gardiner, Colonel Henry E., Tank Commander", unpublished manuscript

Green, Constance McL., Henry C. Thompson, and Peter C. Roots, "The Ordnance Department: Planning Munitions for War, *The U.S. Army in World War II*, Office of the Chief of Military History, Washington, D.C., 1955

Howe, George F., "The Battle History of the 1st Armored Division", Combat Forces Press, Washington, D.C., 1954

Koyen, Captain Kenneth, "The Fourth Armored Division from the Beach To Bavaria", published 1946

Mayo, Lida, "The Ordnance Department on Beachhead and Battlefront", *The U.S. Army in World War II*, Office of the Chief of Military History, Washington, D.C., 1968

Robinett, Brigadier General Paul McDonald, "Armor Command", published 1948

Rubel, Colonel George Kenneth, "Daredevil Tankers, the Story of the 740th Tank Battalion", published 19 September 1945

Thompson, Harry C. and Lida Mayo, "The Ordnance Department: Procurement and Supply", *The U.S. Army in World War II*, Office of the Chief of Military History, Washington, D.C., 1960

Whiting, Theodore E., Richard H. Crawford, and Lindsley F. Cook, "Statistics: Procurement", *The U.S. Army in World War II*, Office of the Chief of Military History, Washington, D.C., 9 April 1952

Whiting, Theodore E., Carrel I. Todd, and Anne P. Craft, "Statistics: Lend-Lease", *The U.S. Army in World War II*, Office of the Chief of Military History, Washington, D.C., 15 December 1952

————, "Paths of Armor", Albert Love Enterprises, 1950

Reports and Official Documents

"Catalogue of Standard Ordnance Items—Tanks and Automotive Vehicles", Office of the Chief of Ordnance, Washington, D.C., Revised to June 1945

"Final Report on Test of Medium Tank M4A3E2, Project Number P-581", The Armored Board, Fort Knox, Kentucky, 29 December 1944

"Final Report on Test of Medium Tank M4E5, Project Number 343-1", The Armored Board, Fort Knox, Kentucky, 4 December 1943

"Fire Warfare", Office of Scientific Research and Development, National Defense Research Committee, Washington, D.C., 1946

"A Handbook of Ordnance Automotive Engineering—Combat and Tracklaying Vehicles", Aberdeen Proving Ground, Maryland, 1 May 1945

"Instruction Book, Cruiser Tank Ram II", Department of National Defence, Ottawa, Canada, April 1943

"Mine Explorer Mission to ETO U.S. Army, 4 April 1944 to 19 October 1944", Office of the Chief of Ordnance, Washington, D.C., 11 November 1944

"Notes on Materiel, Assault Tank T14", undated

"Notes on Materiel, Medium Tanks T4 and T4E1", Rock Island Arsenal, 1936

"Notes on Materiel, Medium Tank M2 with Supplement for Medium Tank M2A1", Rock Island Arsenal, 1940

"Operator's Manual, 25pr S.P. Tracked, Sexton II", Department of National Defence, Ottawa, Canada, December 1944

"Record of Army Ordnance Research and Development—Tanks", Office of the Chief of Ordnance, Washington, D.C., undated

"Report Number 835, Engineer Armored Vehicle", The Engineer Board, Fort Belvoir, Virginia, 1 July 1944

"Report Number 927, Mine Clearing by Detonation Wave Method", The Engineer Board, Fort Belvoir, Virginia, 27 April 1945

"Report of the Fiscal Year 1944-1945, Research and Development Service" Office of the Chief of Ordnance, Washington, D.C., October 1945

"Report on Modifications of Medium Tank M4 Series, Project Number P-426" The Armored Board, Fort Knox Kentucky, 26 January 1944

"Report on Service Test of Medium Tank M4A1 with 76mm Gun, Project Number P-338", The Armored Board, Fort Knox Kentucky, 5 April 1943

"Report on Test of "E" Vehicle with Special Stowage, Project 557-2", The Armored Board, Fort Knox, Kentucky, 28 June 1945

"Report on Test of Medium Tank M4A4 (105mm Howitzer), Project Number P-343", The Armored Board, Fort Knox Kentucky, 10 March 1943

"Report on Test of Medium Tank M4E6, Project Number P-456", The Armored Board, Fort Knox Kentucky, 13 October 1943

"Service Instruction Book for Sherman III (M4A2) (DD) and Sherman V (M4A4) (DD)", Chilwell Catalogue Number 72/496, March 1944

"Service Instruction Book for the Ordnance, Q.F. 17pr Mks IV and VII, Bomb-Thrower, 2 inch Mks I* and IA*, Mounting 17pr and Browning .300 M.G., No. 2, Mk I fitted to Sherman Tanks", Chilwell Catalogue Number 62/757, June 1944

"Technical Manual TM9-307, 75mm Tank Guns M2 and M3 and Mounts M1, M34, and M34A1", War Department, Washington, D.C. 23 March 1944

"Technical Manual TM9-308, 76mm Guns M1A1C and M1A2 Mounted in Combat Vehicles", War Department, Washington, D.C., September 1947

"Technical Manual TM9-324, 105mm Howitzer M4 (Mounted in Combat Vehicles)", Department of the Army, Washington, D.C., August 1950

"Technical Manual TM9-730C, Medium Tank M3A4", War Department Washington, D.C., 30 November 1942

"Technical Manual TM-731A, Medium Tanks M4 and M4A1", War Department, Washington, D.C., 23 December 1943

"Technical Manual TM9-731AA, Medium Tank M4 (105mm Howitzer) and Medium Tank M4A1 (76mm Gun)", War Department, Washington, D.C., 23 June 1944

"Technical Manual TM9-731B, Medium Tank M4A2", War Department, Washington, D.C. 13 January 1943

"Technical Manual TM9-731E, 105mm Howitzer Motor Carriage M7", War Department, Washington, D.C., 15 August 1944

"Technical Manual TM9-738, Tank Recovery Vehicles M32, M32B1, M32B2, M32B3, and M32B4", War Department, Washington, D.C., 8 December 1943

"Technical Manual TM9-739, Tank Recovery Vehicle T2", War Department, Washington, D.C., 11 August 1943

"Technical Manual TM9-745, 90mm Gun Motor Carriage M36B2", War Department, Washington, D.C., 28 July 1945

"Technical Manual TM9-747, 155mm Gun Motor Carriage M40 and 8 inch Howitzer Motor Carriage M43", War Department, Washington, D.C., September 1947

"Technical Manual TM9-748, 90mm Gun Motor Carriage M36B1", War Department, Washington, D.C., 20 January 1945

"Technical Manual TM9-749, 105mm Howitzer Motor Carriage M7B1", War Department, Washington, D.C., 9 August 1944

"Technical Manual TM9-750, Medium Tanks M3, M3A1, and M3A2", War Department, Washington, D.C., 9 May 1942

"Technical Manual TM9-751, 155mm Gun Motor Carriage M12 and Cargo Carrier M30", War Department, Washington, D.C., 28 January 1944

"Technical Manual TM9-752, 3 inch Gun Motor Carriage M10", War Department, Washington, D.C., 25 November 1943

"Technical Manual TM9-753, Medium Tanks M3A3 and M3A5", War Department, Washington, D.C., 16 September 1942

"Technical Manual TM9-754, Medium Tank M4A4", War Department, Washington, D.C., 21 January 1943

"Technical Manual TM9-756, Medium Tank M4A6", War Department, Washington, D.C., 21 December 1943

"Technical Manual TM9-758, 90mm Gun Motor Carriage T71", War Department, Washington, D.C., 15 April 1944

"Technical Manual TM9-759, Medium Tank M4A3", War Department, Washington, D.C., September 1944

"Technical Manual TM9-1901, Artillery Ammunition", War Department, Washington, D.C., 29 June 1944 and Department of the Army, Washington, D.C., September 1950

"Technical Manual TM9-1907, Ballistic Performance Data of Ammunition", Department of the Army, Washington, D.C., July 1948

INDEX

CPSIA information can be obtained
at www.ICGtesting.com
Printed in the USA
BVHW020242110621
609182BV00004B/60